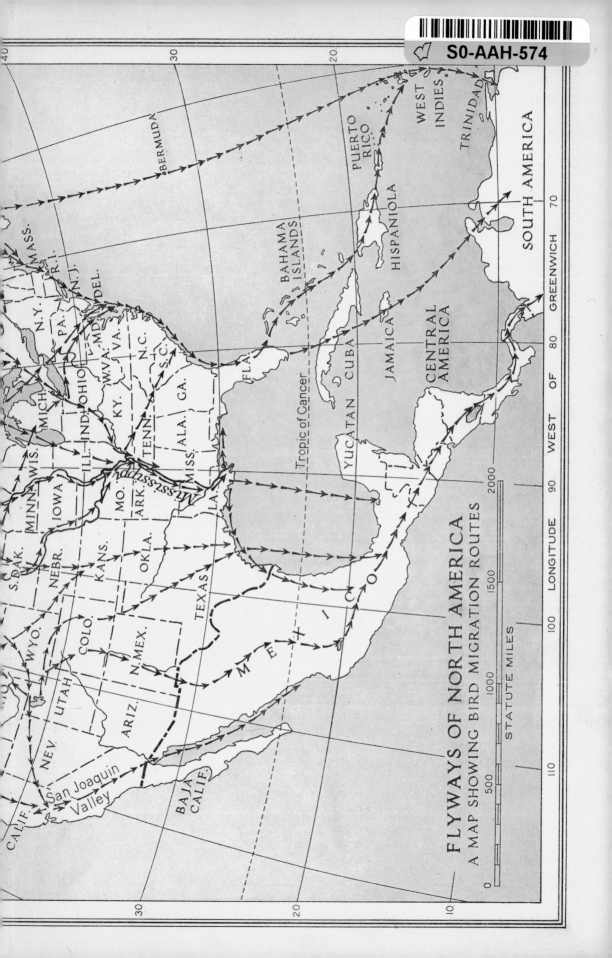

FLYWAYS OF NORTH AMERICA
A MAP SHOWING BIRD MIGRATION ROUTES

THE BOOK OF BIRDS

*The First Work Presenting in Full Color All the Major
Species of the United States and Canada*

EDITED BY

GILBERT GROSVENOR, LL.D., Litt.D., D.Sc.
President, National Geographic Society

and

ALEXANDER WETMORE, Ph.D., D.Sc.
Assistant Secretary of the Smithsonian Institution

With 950 Color Portraits by Major Allan Brooks

VOLUME II

OWLS, GOATSUCKERS, SWIFTS, WOODPECKERS, FLYCATCH-
ERS, CROWS, JAYS, BLACKBIRDS, ORIOLES, CHICKADEES,
CREEPERS, THRUSHES, SWALLOWS, TANAGERS, WRENS,
WARBLERS, HUMMINGBIRDS, FINCHES, AND SPARROWS

Narrative by Arthur A. Allen, M.A., Ph.D., *Professor of Ornithology in Cornell Uni-
versity;* T. Gilbert Pearson, LL.D., *President Emeritus, National Association of Audubon
Societies;* Robert Cushman Murphy, M.A., D.Sc., *Curator of Oceanic Birds, American
Museum of Natural History;* Frederick C. Lincoln, *Senior Biologist in Charge, Distribu-
tion and Migration of Birds, U. S. Biological Survey;* Alexander Wetmore; Gilbert
Grosvenor; Francis H. Herrick, Ph.D., D.Sc.; Henry W. Henshaw, and others.

NATIONAL GEOGRAPHIC SOCIETY
WASHINGTON, D. C.

Table of Contents

Page

Adventures with Sparrows and Juncos—By T. Gilbert Pearson 280

An Unusual Bird Record 298

Astonishing Capacity of Birds' Stomachs 88

Blackbirds and Orioles—By Arthur A. Allen 211
By Some Strange Law of Distribution These Handsome Flutists Are Confined to the New World.

Crow Roosts—By E. R. Kalmbach 120

Crows, Magpies, and Jays—By T. Gilbert Pearson 101
Unusual Intelligence Has Earned a Unique Position for These Common Birds.

Encouraging Birds Around the Home 130

Goatsuckers—By Alexander Wetmore 40

Handsome Flickers and a Rare Cousin—By T. Gilbert Pearson 64

Holidays with Hummingbirds—By Margaret L. Bodine 98

Hummingbirds, Swifts, and Goatsuckers—By Alexander Wetmore 27
Sixteen Species of the Smallest of Feathered Creatures, Peculiar to the New World and Found from Alaska to the Strait of Magellan, Are Pictured with Their Nearest Relatives.

Interesting Recoveries of Banded Birds—By Frederick C. Lincoln 351

Our Greatest Travelers—By Frederick C. Lincoln 301
The Seasonal Movements of Birds Revealed by Birdbanding.

Our State Birds 225

Owls, Shadowy Birds of the Night—By Alexander Wetmore 5
From the Great Horned to the Tiny Screech These Queer Birds Are Subjects of Superstitious Beliefs, But Virtually All Are Friends of Man.

Parrots, Kingfishers, and Flycatchers—By Alexander Wetmore 75
Strange Trogons and Curious Cuckoos are Pictured with These Other Birds of Color, Dash, and Courage.

Random Notes on Tanagers and Finches—By Arthur A. Allen 248

Some Owl Personalities—By Alexander Wetmore 16

Tanagers and Finches—By Arthur A. Allen 235
Their Flashes of Color and Lilting Songs Gladden the Hearts of American Bird Lovers East and West.

Thrashers, Mockingbirds, and Swallows—By T. Gilbert Pearson 168

Thrushes, Sweet-Voiced Favorites—By T. Gilbert Pearson 155
Robins and Bluebirds are Familiar Members of a Famous Musical Family Which Includes the Hermit Thrush and European Nightingale.

Towhees, Sparrows, and Longspurs—By T. Gilbert Pearson 259
These Happy Little Singers Make Merry in Field, Forest, and Hedgerow Throughout North America.

Warblers, Friends of Our Forests—By Henry W. Henshaw and A. A. Allen 179
An Avian Police Force Dressed in Handsome Uniforms and Singing Merrily on Their Beats Keep in Check Insect Malefactors.

Winged Denizens of Woodland, Stream, and Marsh—By Alexander Wetmore 135
Chickadees, Creepers, Nuthatches, and Titmice.

Woodpeckers, Guardians of Our Trees—By T. Gilbert Pearson 51
This Numerous Family, Which Includes Several Species of Flickers and Sapsuckers, Does Much More Good Than Harm in Forests.

Wrens—By Alexander Wetmore 145

Photograph by Frank and John Craighead

A YOUNG FALCONER SUCCEEDS IN TRAINING OWLS AS WELL AS HAWKS

Two fierce great horned owls, eager to be on the wing, are perched on the gloved hands of Frank Craighead, of Washington, D. C. The dangling loop is a leash attached to leather jesses fastened to the legs. Using exactly the same methods they employed in training hawks for falconry, Frank and his twin brother John trained owls as pets and even taught some of their barn owls to fly at mice. But the short, unspectacular flights of the owls lacked the thrill of the lofty spiraling and stooping of the falcons. Also, of course, owls do their best hunting at night when the trainer's eyes cannot follow them. The two young birds shown here were captured along the Potomac in Virginia and later were freed in Rock Creek Park, in the Nation's Capital.

4

THE OWLS, SHADOWY BIRDS OF THE NIGHT

From the Great Horned to the Tiny Screech These Queer Birds Are Subjects of Superstitious Beliefs, But Virtually All Are Friends of Man

By Alexander Wetmore

THE evening air of late February in the Everglades of southern Florida is soft and mild. Delicate scents from unseen blossoms come with the breeze, together with the voices of myriad frogs in incessant but attractive chorus from the marshes. Suddenly, from the moss-festooned live oaks in this peaceful background, comes an outburst of demoniacal laughter, guttural and startling.

Playing the beam of light from an electric torch through the branches, I discover presently two glowing spots of ruby red, reflections from a pair of eyes. As my own eyes adjust themselves to the feeble illumination, I can distinguish dimly the shadowy form of a great barred owl. The hubbub stops immediately, for the bird is puzzled by the spot of light; but as I pass, the owl utters a loud, prolonged, eery *whoo-oo-oo-aw*.

The voices of owls are more familiar than their persons, for most of them are active principally at night. Their presence, unseen but constantly felt, has caused imagination to create fables and superstitions about them in virtually every country.

FABLED BIRDS OF WISDOM AND OF DOOM

The little owl of Europe has long been an emblem of wisdom, and in early years was accepted as a special ward of Pallas Athena of the Greeks. Romans, to whom this goddess became Minerva, did not retain this reverence for the bird, considering it of evil omen and a messenger of bad news. Death was foretold by owls alighting on the housetops, and their calls near by at night aroused fear and foreboding.

The vogue of the owl as an emblem of wisdom is not due to any special intelligence of the bird, but to the conformation of the head, with the two eyes so placed that they look directly ahead like those of man.

As the companion of night-flying witches, or as one of the ingredients in their brews, the owl developed a black and unsavory reputation, attested by many references in the plays of Shakespeare and the works of other writers.

Among American Indians, owls, though feared at times, were in better repute and were the basis of various lively legends. Zuñi tales include stories of one called "gray owl" that lived in a house as a man does. The Pima Indians held that at death the human spirit passed into the body of an owl and, to assist in this transmigration, they gave owl feathers to a dying person.

ELVES AND GIANTS AMONG OWLS

Among the Plains Indians, the Arikara included an owl group as one of their eight mystic societies, and in the sacred rites of this body they used the stuffed skin of an owl with disks of cunningly fitted buffalo horn for eyes. This emblem represented night, the eyes the morning star.

Owls are found throughout the world from the Arctic regions through the continents and to remote islands in the sea. More than three hundred kinds are known, ranging in size from the tiny elf owls, no larger than sparrows, to the powerful horned owls and eagle owls, two feet or more in length.

Scientifically, all owls are included in one order, the Strigiformes, in which two families are recognized, one for the barn owls (Tytonidae) and the other (Strigidae) for all other species.

Regardless of their size, owls are instantly identified by their broad faces with prominent disks of feathers about the eyes, coupled with sharp, curved beaks and claws, and long, fluffy feathers. Their nearest relatives are the whippoorwills, nighthawks, and goatsuckers.

Formerly it was thought that owls were allied to hawks and falcons, but these two groups differ radically in structure. Superficial resemblances are due to the form of the beak and claws, developed from seeking the same kinds of foods.

Most owls are nocturnal and by day sleep in caves, hollow trees, tangles of leaves, or whatever else may offer protection. When they are found by other birds, there is high excitement, jays, cardinals, and the like gathering to scold and chatter at these enemies of the night. Crows, more aggressive, often drive off the largest owls.

The homes of owls are located in hollows of trees, in caverns in rocks, or in stick nests built by hawks, crows, or other birds. Often no nesting material of any kind is used. The eggs are white, occasionally tinted with buff or pale blue, but without markings, and are peculiar in being usually elliptical or nearly round. The young are covered with white down and remain in the nest under care of the parents for a considerable time.

QUICK TO DEFEND THEIR FAMILIES

In defense of their young, owls are often aggressive and swoop at any and all who chance to pass, sometimes with startling effect when the attack is delivered without warning. A friend of mine, climbing to the nest of a great horned owl, was struck so savagely in the back by one of the parents that the strong talons of the bird drew blood through his heavy clothing.

While walking at dusk near a woodland camp in eastern Kansas, I was startled by something that, without warning, struck my bare head. The aggressor was a little screech owl with a family of young near by. At other times owls have knocked off my hat, or at least so unsettled it that my involuntary flinching at the unexpected alarm caused it to fall from my head. In Puerto Rico, country people informed me gravely that a native owl stole the hats of persons who walked the trails at night and carried them off to use them for nests.

All owls have soft plumage composed of long, fluffy feathers. The wings have softened margins, so that in flight the birds move without sound, as if they were shadows. In owls, the lower leg, or tarsus, and upper surfaces of the toes, bare in most birds, are covered with feathers, these being reduced or absent only in a few species that inhabit warm countries. The plumage colors run usually to gray, brown, and buff, with lighter markings of buff and gray. White and black are extensive in some, but brighter colors are rare or absent.

Some of the smaller owls have on the backs of their heads rounded markings resembling eyes. In South America the country people told me these birds were "four eyes" and could see behind as well as ahead.

The eyes of an owl are fixed so immovably in the head that the bird must change the position of the head to alter its line of vision. They are especially large and are adapted for vision where there is little light. As a very small boy, I was told that an owl, sitting on a perch, would follow with its eyes a person moving around and around it, until eventually its neck would be wrung and its head would be twisted off.

Opportunity arose to test out this intriguing theory on a Florida screech owl, perched in a low pine, and I walked around it for some time with its eyes steadily on me. Its head did not fall off, however, and I was completely mystified. It was not until I had reached a somewhat more mature age that, in conducting other experiments of this kind, I detected the quick movement by which the owl snaps its head around rapidly, giving the semblance of continuous motion in one direction.

Though the majority of owls remain hidden in shaded, secluded places by day, there are a few that are abroad by day or by night indifferently. This is true of the snowy owl, which lives in summer through the long Arctic day, and of the burrowing owls of open country of the New World. One of the latter that I had in captivity for some time delighted in resting in the sun, and in broad daylight would detect and watch hawks and other birds flying at such great heights that I could barely see them.

OWLS REGURGITATE AS PELLETS INDIGESTIBLE PARTS OF A VARIED MENU

Owls live mostly on animal food which is captured alive, except that occasionally they feed upon rabbits freshly killed by automobiles along our highways, or upon other carcasses. Mice, rats, and other small mammals are regular prey, as are birds of various species.

The barred owl eats many crayfish and fish, while crabs and fish are staple foods of the fish owls of Africa and India.

Owls, like hawks, tear their prey apart and swallow the pieces entire. During digestion the flesh is assimilated, while bones, fur, feathers, and other indigestible portions are formed into compact pellets, which are regurgitated to leave the stomach empty for another meal. Such pellets accumulate about roosts and, through identi-

Photograph by Ben East

THE BARN OWL MAY BE RECOGNIZED BY ITS HEART-SHAPED FACE

Naturalists have classed barn owls under one family, while all other owls are members of another. This one brooded nearly ninety days over a clutch of ten eggs that failed to hatch. Then, after pushing them from the nest, she laid others and raised a family of four.

fication of the bones contained, give a valuable index to the food of the bird.

The great horned owls and snowy owls are fiercely predatory, killing rabbits, squirrels, and other creatures of good size. The former has been known to capture and eat small owls. In the Dominican Republic I once saw a burrowing owl tearing at the body of a young bird of its own kind which had been killed and thrown aside by some native. Beetles, crickets, other large insects, and the periodically abundant wild mice, form staple foods for many kinds of owls.

BARN OWLS DWELL IN THE HEART OF THE NATION'S CAPITAL

Since the early days of the Smithsonian Institution in Washington, barn owls have inhabited the northwest tower of the Smithsonian building, a secure retreat in the midst of the city. From 1,247 of their regurgitated pellets, picked up on the tower floor, I have taken the skulls and other bones of 1,987 field mice, 656 house mice, 210 rats, 92 sparrows and blackbirds, and 4 frogs.

The usefulness of these birds in the destruction of injurious rodents is evident, but in spite of this all owls are considered vermin by some and are killed by hunters whenever they are seen.

The sins of the larger species, which eat chickens and game, are visited on all their brethren, to the end that, with the hawks, owls have been included in bounties, and hundreds of useful kinds are killed under the mistaken belief that they are injurious. The majority of them should be protected at all times, for the good they do far outweighs any trifling depredations of which they may be guilty.

Great Horned Owl

(Bubo virginianus)

Average Length, Twenty-one to Twenty-three
Inches

Fiercest and most powerful of our common owls, the great horn is the best known of those found in America. It ranges widely and is able to live under many different natural conditions. It is sometimes called the cat owl because of its catlike ears, eyes, shape of head, and appearance when huddled up on its nest.

The great horned owl, except during the nesting season, is solitary and in the main inhabits unsettled areas. In the East and North it frequents dense woodlands of conifers or hardwoods, coming into the open only on its hunting expeditions at night. In arid sections in the West it is found along the cliffs of rocky canyons, or along earth-walled gulches where holes and crannies offer shelter during the day. In the mountains it ranges in open forests where there is little settlement and the birds are not frequently disturbed.

Even in the colder parts of its range this owl nests early in the year. I have taken eggs in Wisconsin the first week in March, during a blizzard, when the weather was so cold that the eggs were frozen before I arrived home. To give approximate dates, in New England this owl may breed in February and March, in Virginia in late January and February, and in Florida in late November and December.

The nest is usually in the deserted domicile of a hawk or crow, sometimes high above the ground, or about cliffs where holes may be occupied. Where such shelters are lacking, the birds have been known to nest on the ground. The eggs usually number two or three, rarely as many as five. One family is reared each season, and both male and female incubate the eggs, which require about four weeks to hatch.

To protect the eggs the parents may line the nest with feathers from their own breasts. When snow falls, brooding bird and nest may be covered completely, but at such times, and during severe cold, the eggs and small young are hovered solicitously. The young, if taken early, make interesting pets and show much affection to their keepers. Their appetites, however, are insatiable and their care is often a problem.

Great horned owls are solicitous parents, protecting their nests most successfully against depredation by other forest creatures, and many are the recorded occasions on which they have struck fearlessly at men who approached their homes. Driven with savage vigor, the claws of this owl can inflict wounds through heavy clothing.

The voice of the great horned owl is a low *whoó whoo whoo whoó whoo whoo,* the first four notes given rapidly and the last two somewhat slowly. One bird of a pair, supposed to be the female, has a deeper voice than the other. The notes carry for long distances, and appeal to ears attuned to Nature.

Besides its characteristic hoot, the great horned owl utters cries resembling the yelping of a dog and the squalling of a cat. Rarer is a loud, piercing scream that is one of the most blood-curdling sounds of the deep woods.

In choice of food the great horned owl is bold and predatory. Any bird or mammal not too large is subject to attack, this owl killing with ease rabbits, hares, woodchucks, and ducks, and occasionally even taking geese and turkeys. Domestic cats are not immune, and the bird regularly kills and eats skunks without seeming to be affected by the odor. I have shot great horns which were so heavily impregnated with this scent that it still remained evident after days of "airing" in the open and years of seclusion in a museum case.

Poultry raisers are this owl's worst enemies. When rabbits, squirrels, mice, and other rodents (its preferred food) are abundant, the great horn seems to leave poultry and game birds alone. But scarcity of its favorite mammal prey turns it to the fowls, wild and domestic. And when it learns that the farmer's fowls are more easily captured, it is likely to forgo wild game almost entirely and concentrate on the barnyard varieties.

If chickens, turkeys, and guinea-fowl are obtainable in any numbers, the great horned owl may turn fastidious and eat only the brains of its prey, or some other choice morsel, leaving most of the flesh untouched.

In the north woods great horned owls have been shot filled with the quills of a porcupine, an animal usually immune to attack. One owl was found in Massachusetts holding a large blacksnake in its talons with the snake wrapped about its body so that the bird was nearly choked. Rats, mice, crayfish, large insects, domestic poultry, and birds of all kinds figure in the diet of this species, which must be rated as destructive.

That great horned owls are not entirely savage, however, is shown by one kept as a pet; year after year it served as foster parent to broods of young chicks, hatching the eggs and caring for the unusual brood assiduously.

In the broad territory it occupies, this owl has developed a number of forms that differ in size and color. These differences are illustrated by the accompanying plate, which shows the ordinary type with dark coloration, and the arctic horned owl of the north, very pale though retaining the darker markings.

As a species, the great horned owl ranges from Tierra del Fuego and the Strait of Magellan north through western and northern South America, Central America, and Mexico to the limit of trees in the far north. North of Mexico ten geographic forms are recognized.

A HIGHWAYMAN OF THE NIGHT AIR LOOKS DOWN ON AN ARCTIC HENCHMAN

One of the fiercest and most powerful of birds, the **Great Horned Owl,** perched on a tree stump, has been called the "tiger of the air," so savage and fearless are its methods. Like the jungle beast, it strikes unheard, its talons dealing death to birds and mammals. Another form is the **Arctic Horned Owl,** shown with daggerlike claws deep in the fur of a snowshoe rabbit, whose peculiar track is seen in the snow at the right. The great horned is a bird of eastern, the arctic horned owl of northern, North America.

Barn Owl

(Tyto alba pratincola)
Average Length, Seventeen Inches

The nest of the barn owl ordinarily is concealed in a hollow tree, cave, or building. The eggs are laid at irregular intervals, so that partly incubated eggs and young are often found together. The nesting season is somewhat variable. No nesting material is used except rubbish that may have accumulated in the cavity chosen for a home.

Barn, or "monkey-faced," owls often do not offer to bite or scratch even when handled. In captivity they are interesting mainly for their peculiar appearance, since they sit quietly by day and are active only by night (see also page 16).

Beneficial everywhere, this species, like other owls, is subject to constant persecution, sad to say. The barn owls eat destructive field mice and rats in large numbers, and in the West add to this diet numerous pocket gophers, a bane to ranchers everywhere. In regurgitated pellets of this owl from California I have identified hundreds of skulls of these destructive mammals. Barn owls also consume large insects, being especially partial to the Jerusalem cricket of the West.

The barn owl is found regularly from northern California, Colorado, Ohio, and Connecticut south to Nicaragua, and occurs casually north into Canada. Related forms are widely spread through temperate parts of the world.

Long-eared Owl

(Asio wilsonianus)
Average Length, Fourteen and One-half Inches

Though formerly abundant, the long-eared owl has suffered at the hands of hunters and bounty systems, so that in many sections of the East it is now rare.

This owl is found during the day hidden in heavy cover, seeking pine and spruce trees where these are available, and the shelter of dense growths of leaves or limbs elsewhere.

In the Middle West I found them in fall and winter in little groups of six or eight that rested near one another. Possibly these were family parties. I have seen them in clumps of willows and in tangled roots beneath the bank of a gully when other cover was not at hand.

Like the screech owl and other small woodland species, the long-eared owl sometimes tries to escape detection by drawing its feathers close against its body and becoming stiffly erect with partly closed eyes, simulating a broken branch or part of a tree trunk. (See page 16.)

These birds breed in nests of sticks placed in trees, often using old abodes of crows or herons, but sometimes building their own. Rarely, they place their nests on cliffs or in holes. Their brood is from three to seven.

The food of this owl is mainly mice and other small mammals, with only an occasional bird. In 225 regurgitated pellets that I examined, I identified remains of 187 mice and only five small birds. The long-eared owl also eats many large beetles, must be considered beneficial, and merits constant protection.

The notes of the long-eared owl include a low, hooting call, peculiar whining notes, and twittering, whistling sounds. They are less common than the calls of the larger owls.

The long-eared owl nests from central British Columbia and southern Quebec to southern California and Virginia. In winter it ranges south to southern Florida and central Mexico. Closely allied forms are found in Europe, northern Asia, and North Africa.

Short-eared Owl

(Asio flammeus flammeus)
Average Length, Thirteen and One-half Inches

More wary than the long-eared owl, the short-eared owl has remained common in spite of the many killed by hunters.

Although it has excellent eyesight by day, it usually hunts by night, flying with soft wings a few feet above the ground and pouncing suddenly on any prey that appears beneath it. I have seen them in winter coursing by moonlight near the highway on the Virginia shore of the Potomac River at Washington, and also flying by day over small areas of waste marshlands completely surrounded by railroad tracks in the suburbs of Chicago.

The nest of this owl is placed on the ground, where from four to nine eggs are laid in a slight depression containing a small amount of nesting material. When caring for their young, the parent owls hunt constantly by day.

The short-eared owl eats mice and other small mammals mainly, with occasional birds. Over open ground, the owls seize their living prey easily without stopping, and carry it to a perch to be eaten.

When cover is heavy, the owls pounce quickly into the grass and may remain on the ground to eat if successful in effecting a capture. Where there is a sudden increase of mice, these owls gather in numbers.

The call is a monotonous hoot, repeated rapidly. Its regular cry is higher in tone than the call of the great horned owl, and the bird also has high-pitched squealing calls. When its nest or young are approached, it often protests by loudly snapping its bill (page 16).

This species is regularly migratory and ranges widely when not nesting. It breeds from northern Alaska and Greenland to California, Kansas, and New Jersey, and in winter is found south to Guatemala. It also ranges in South America to the Falkland Islands, and in Europe, Asia, and northeastern Africa. Related forms are found throughout the world.

LET RATS AND MICE BEWARE THESE OWLS' SHARP TALONS!

When the author analyzed more than a thousand disgorged pellets of a pair of **Barn Owls** (top) nesting in a tower of the Smithsonian Institution, Washington, he discovered that they had consumed 2,853 rodents. Because of its characteristic markings, this bird is known to many as the "monkey-faced owl." It and the **Long-eared Owl** (left), of catlike face, hunt chiefly at night. Inhabitant of marsh and prairie, the **Short-eared Owl** (bottom) is abroad frequently by day. The three represent two families found throughout the United States, the range of the short-eared owl being almost world-wide.

Great Gray Owl
(Scotiaptex nebulosa)
Average Length, Twenty-five to Thirty Inches

Related to the barred owl, which it resembles in smooth, rounded head without feather horns, this species is easily distinguished by larger size, grayer coloration, and light-colored eyes. The great gray owl lives in numbers in heavy forests in the far north and more rarely in the western mountains. It is known to relatively few persons.

Though this species in actual measurements of total length is among the largest of our owls, equaling or exceeding the great horned and snowy owls, its apparent size is due to the long wings and tail and to the length and fluffiness of its plumage in general. As compared to the others, its body is slight and its feet and legs are small and delicate.

In the far north, this owl must be forced to hunt at times by daylight; but it prefers night, and even in the land of the midnight sun it rests secluded in dense shade when not in search of food.

The great gray owl builds in a tree, making its nest of twigs and moss and lining it with feathers or other soft materials. From three to five eggs, slightly smaller than those of the great horned owl, are laid, nesting taking place in the north from April to June.

With its wonderfully thick dress of long, soft feathers which extend to its toes, this owl is immune to cold. Though it comes south in winter into the northern United States, its presence there is casual except during years when its food supply in the North fails.

It lives on mice, rabbits, squirrels, and birds, but, being less powerful than the great horned owl, it necessarily chooses smaller prey. Its long, slender, sharply pointed claws penetrate the thick winter fur and feathers of its victims and hold them without difficulty.

The great gray owl (Scotiaptex nebulosa nebulosa) in America nests from the northern limit of trees south to central California, northern Montana, and central Canada. It comes south in winter as far as Wyoming, Ohio, New York, and New England. The paler Siberian gray owl (Scotiaptex n. barbata) has been found in Alaska. Allied forms range in northern Europe and Asia.

Snowy Owl
(Nyctea nyctea)
Average Length, Twenty-two to Twenty-five Inches

The male of the snowy owl is frequently so nearly pure white that careful search is necessary to discover a few dusky flecks on the concealed margins of the wing feathers. The female, considerably larger than the male, is also white, but the plumage is barred more or less heavily with dusky and slaty brown. The birds are well suited for life in regions of cold, since their feathers are long and abundant and grow in dense, closely set filaments to the tips of the toes. Even the bill is almost concealed amid the feathers of the face (see page 16).

The usual home of the snowy owl is in the far north, where it ranges through the circumpolar regions of both the Old and New Worlds. It lives on the open tundra or on the barren slopes of mountains, and seldom enters regions of extensive forests except in winter.

The food of this owl is composed largely of lemmings, the arctic or varying hares, and, to a less extent, birds and fish.

At intervals of eight to ten years tremendous numbers of the arctic hares, or snowshoe rabbits, die from disease, and the many creatures dependent upon them are left to starve miserably in the cold of the dark winter days. Then the snowy owl spreads its broad wings and glides away southward.

The snowy owl travels without fear over the ocean and has come aboard ships a thousand miles from land. Individuals have even reached the island of Bermuda.

In the northern tundras the snowy owl places its nest on the ground on some low eminence. The eight or ten white eggs, longer and less rounded than those of most owls, are as large as small hen's eggs, and are laid in a slight depression which may be lined with a feather or two and some bits of moss, or may be bare. The eggs are not deposited at intervals of a day or so, as those of most birds are, but are laid irregularly through a considerable period, so that it is usual to find newly hatched young and fresh or partly incubated eggs in the same nest.

The young are covered with white down, which, as in the adults, extends clear to the toes. The task of incubation is said to fall to the female, but the male stands guard near by or seeks food for his mate.

The snowy owl is not nocturnal, since, in its northern haunts where the sun remains above the horizon during midsummer, it must perforce remain active by day. Even where woods are at hand, these birds delight in perching on the ground, preferably on some low hillock where they can look about over open spaces. One that lived for several years in a cage in the National Zoological Park rested usually on the ground, instead of the perch.

The snowy owl nests in the barren grounds from northern Russia to Greenland and Alaska, and in its southern flights spreads south to Japan, Turkistan, and even into northern India. It regularly occurs in the north of Europe and comes casually farther south. During its irregular migrations in the United States it is common in the Northeast on the seaboard and less abundant westward.

MUCH OF THEIR FORAGING IS DONE IN DAYLIGHT

Because true night is shortened or absent in the northern summer range of the **Great Gray** (top), and the **Snowy Owl,** they must perforce hunt for hares, mice, and birds during daylight. Both are known as winter residents in northern United States. Foolish crows have been seen mobbing the supposedly sun-blinded snowy owl, only to meet swift death in a rush of silent wings and unerring claws. The comparatively rare great gray, clothed in fluffy feathers, measures the largest of North American owls, though less powerful than its snowy companion.

Barred Owl
(Strix varia)
Average Length, Twenty Inches

In the eastern half of our country the barred owl is one of the best known of its family, its loud calls being familiar to all who are abroad at night in regions of lowland woods. The bird is large, appearing equal to the great horn, though, as in the case of the great gray owl, a good part of its bulk is due to its long feathers. The head is round, without vestige of ear tufts, and the bird, unlike most of our other owls, has dark-colored eyes. It is solitary except during the nesting season, and then is encountered only in pairs.

In the South barred owls are partial to wooded swamps, and everywhere they are found in the open mainly during their nightly hunt for food. They are loudly vociferous in their calls, these being heard to some extent throughout the year. In spring the variety of their notes is surprising, and on many occasions when sleeping outdoors I have been awakened by their noisy cries.

This owl is frequently mobbed by the small birds of the forest when discovered by day, and at such times it is much disturbed by scolding groups of jays, cardinals, titmice, sparrows, and other species that gather to peep and peer and protest against its presence. Crows speedily put a barred owl to flight to more secluded quarters.

The barred owl nests in hollows in trees, or in old hawk or crow nests, laying from two to four eggs. In Florida it nests as early as December and January, but in the North the date is later, usually March and April. Eggs have been found in Connecticut, however, in February, when the ground was covered with snow and the eggs themselves lay on ice frozen in the nesting cavity. One brood is reared each season. These birds are migratory to some extent, and in fall sometimes are lost in unusual situations, so that at times they are found about tall buildings in cities.

The food of this owl is composed mainly of mice and other small mammals, and includes comparatively few birds. Curiously enough, remains of smaller owls have been found occasionally in stomachs of this species. It also eats frogs, fish, crayfish, and large insects.

The northern barred owl (Strix varia varia) is found from Saskatchewan and Newfoundland to eastern Wyoming, Arkansas, and the mountains of North Carolina. The Florida barred owl (Strix varia alleni), which is slightly smaller and has toes nearly bare of feathers, ranges in the South Atlantic and Gulf States from the coast of North Carolina to eastern Texas. The Texas barred owl (Strix varia helveola), which is paler in color, occurs in south-central Texas. Another form ranges in the highlands of Mexico.

Spotted Owl
(Strix occidentalis)
Average Length, Nineteen Inches

A western cousin of the barred owl, the spotted owl is rightly considered one of our rare and unusual birds. In the Northwest it is found in heavy forests, and in the mountains hides in dense growths of quaking aspens, or in deep, dark canyons. In fall and winter the birds wander from their secluded haunts to some extent. Even so, they are seldom seen, and until recently have been known to few, even among naturalists.

Resembling the barred owl in smooth, round head and dark eyes, this species likewise is chiefly nocturnal, being active in daylight hours principally when it has growing young in its nest. By preference it is abroad at night, coming out by day mainly when driven by necessity to search for food. The mottled colors of the plumage of this owl harmonize completely with sunlight coming through leaves; so that, whether resting motionless on the face of a cliff or against the trunk of a tree, the bird blends with its surroundings and so escapes detection.

The nest of the spotted owl is a structure of sticks lined with bark and other soft materials in the fork of a tree or in a cavity in rocks. One found by Donald Dickey in southern California was located in a hole in the side of a cliff 50 feet above the bottom of a deep canyon. The parent owl, which had two young, was tame and unsuspicious and in no way resented approach, once even alighting in the nest cavity when it was being examined by a man suspended from a rope.

The principal note of the spotted owl is a hooting call, heard most frequently and at its noisiest during the nesting season. The birds also utter several other notes. Only occasionally may they be attracted from their coverts during the day by calls imitating the shrieking of a wounded or frightened bird.

The spotted owl feeds mainly on mice and rats, occasionally taking birds. In New Mexico and California it is recorded as killing many of the abundant wood rats, and a skull of the rare red tree mouse was found in the stomach of one killed in northern California.

One kept in captivity by E. S. Steele was tame and confiding and never refused to take mice, rats, or chipmunks from the hand, though even when hungry it would not accept birds.

Three forms are recognized. The California spotted owl (Strix o. occidentalis) ranges from central California in the Sierras of Mariposa County to northern Baja California. The northern spotted owl (Strix o. caurina), somewhat darker, is found from southern British Columbia to central California, and the Mexican spotted owl (Strix o. lucida), occurs from Colorado and Arizona to central Mexico.

THEIR EERIE HOOTING FRIGHTENS THE TIMID

The weird *whoo-oo* night serenade of the **Northern Barred Owl** (top) may continue until dawn. They frequently respond to imitation of their calls. Inhabitants of dense woods and swamps, they live on mice, fish, crustaceans, insects, and sometimes small birds. Below is the rare **Northern Spotted Owl,** a western cousin. With the barn and flammulated screech owls, these are the only dark-eyed members of the owl families found north of Mexico.

SOME OWL PERSONALITIES

By Alexander Wetmore

WHEN encountered in a barn, hollow tree, or other retreat, the barn owl exhibits mannerisms so grotesque and utters calls so strange that often there is question as to whether it is bird or beast. Frequently letters come to the Smithsonian Institution asking information regarding it, and to most it is known as the "monkey-faced owl" (see page 10).

This owl remains completely secluded by day, coming out at dusk to search for food. In Arizona I have seen them abroad in early twilight, quartering back and forth over the banks of dry washes and mesas, searching for mice and kangaroo rats. After nightfall in the city of Washington I have glimpsed the white breast of one of these birds by the light of street lamps, as it flew over from the Smithsonian towers to raid the sparrow and starling roosts on Pennsylvania Avenue. In southern California as many as fifty have been found roosting together in groves of oaks.

The young crouch, peer, and posture, with nodding heads, in attitudes most strange and unbirdlike, uttering weird calls and hisses that at times resemble the sound of escaping steam. Little wonder that they are objects of surprise to those not acquainted with them!

The barn owl regularly raids the summer roosts of the abundant starlings where these birds gather to spend the night in groves of trees. The capture of a starling or two seems to make little difference to the multitude of its companions, but when the owls remain after the meal and call and chatter, this is too much for starling nerves, and the birds rush out with a roar of wings to circle in the darkness. A few nights of this and they usually remove to other quarters. Those who suffer the annoyance of starling roosts may well wish that barn owls were more numerous.

When the long-eared owl is flying, its broad wings and tail give a deceptive appearance of size, as in reality the body of this species is small and slight, its bulk being composed principally of long, fluffy feathers. In general appearance it resembles the darker forms of the great horned owl, but is decidedly smaller and differs completely in temperament. (See page 10.)

At a camp in northern Wyoming where I was collecting small mammals as specimens for the National Museum, I was troubled by the loss of numerous traps. I was puzzled as to what had become of them until one day I found a nest of young long-eared owls in a low willow near my camp, with my missing traps scattered about it. Evidently the parent owls were not averse to assistance in securing food for a large and constantly hungry family, and as fast as mice were caught they were carried away, traps included, to the nest, where the mice were eaten and the traps discarded.

While most owls are inhabitants of woodlands, the short-eared owl ranges in open country in marshes, prairies, and meadows, where it rests on the ground or on clumps of low vegetation. Walk through its haunts and it rises suddenly, often at a distance of forty or fifty yards, and flies rapidly away, turning its head back over its shoulder to see what has startled it. Sometimes it perches for a moment on a post or low bush. Then its head appears completely round, the tufts of feathers that compose the "horns" being so short as to be seen only near at hand. More often it drops back to the ground, where it is hidden from sight by grass or rushes. (See page 10.)

THE SNOWY OWL

One bleak December day on the beach near Ocean City, Maryland, a large, apparently pure-white bird, of graceful flight, glided past me to perch on the summit of a low sand dune overlooking the ocean. From its size and color, I recognized it instantly as a snowy owl, a winter visitor from the north. It faced the cold wind with gaze directed steadily out across the water, where its attention was attracted by flocks of ducks driving steadily southward. At intervals it turned to look back over the inland dunes, a form of wild beauty against a wintry setting of gray sky, gray water, and yellow, wind-blown sand (see page 12).

As I came near, partly hidden behind a ridge of sand, the owl rose and flew to the south, resting from time to time on the summits of the tallest dunes.

Track walkers along a lonely stretch on one of the principal railroads leading into the city of Washington some years ago were terrified at night by a moving white object that glided noiselessly through the air. It was interpreted as the ghost of a man who had been killed in the vicinity. After several weeks during which this spirit of the night had appeared at intervals, striking terror to the soul of the observer, the apparition was laid most effectively when a large snowy owl was shot from its perch in a tree by a hunter.

In its northern home this owl is regarded at times with dread, as it is fierce in its attacks on those who approach its nest. Some have asked if it can be really a bird. Laplanders are said to consider the flesh of the snowy owl excellent eating. This taste in food may have been shared by men of earlier periods in Europe, as bones of the snowy owl have been found in numbers in the kitchen middens, or refuse heaps, near the caverns and grottoes inhabited by the strange, primitive men of the hunting tribes of Pleistocene times in France.

According to one amusing western story, prairie dogs, burrowing owls, and prairie rattlesnakes live in amity all in the same burrow, each with its own little lateral compartment off the main tunnel leading down from the entrance. The tale is more romantic than probable, as the three are hardly compatible, both rattlesnake and owl being partial to young prairie dogs and possibly also to the flesh of one another. Should all three be found in one prairie dog burrow, this is due to necessity for haste in concealment and not to any preference for one another's company.

Photograph by Willard R. Culver

SILENTLY AWAITING NIGHTFALL—AND A MEAL OF MICE

Daylight finds most owls hidden from sight in dark places—hollows of trees, old woodpecker nests, and other crevices and recesses. This long-eared owl, though resting in an open nest, is sheltered from intense light by thick pine foliage.

A BROWN-EYED WESTERNER ENTERTAINS WINTER VISITORS FROM THE NORTH

Lazy sleepyhead is the **Saw-whet Owl,** clutching a rodent. It often places its nest in an old wood-pecker hole or tree hollow. At night its rasping cry sounds like a saw being filed. Eskimos call **Richardson's Owl** (right) "the blind one," since it may often be caught by hand in daylight. Its musical cry is like water dripping from heights. Good mousers, both birds inhabit northern North America. At the moment they are guests of the little-known **Flammulated Screech Owl** (bottom), whose home is in mountain regions of the West.

Saw-whet Owl

(Cryptoglaux acadica)

Average Length, Eight Inches

This tiny owl takes its name from its curious notes, uttered constantly during the nesting season. They often resemble the sound made by filing a saw, though at times they are more softly modulated.

The saw-whet owl inhabits forests, where it hunts at night. It breeds from April to June, placing its nest in an old woodpecker hole or other tree hollow, or rarely in a cavity among rocks or in the abandoned nests of birds or squirrels. There is sometimes a slight nest lining to protect the eggs, which range from three to seven in number. The birds call regularly from February to April, when some idea of their abundance may be gained. After the nesting season they become quiet and are seldom seen, since they rest quietly by day and are detected only by chance.

This owl feeds on mice and insects, occasionally taking small birds. At irregular intervals considerable numbers of saw-whet owls come south in winter beyond their usual range, probably through shortage of their food supply. On such occasions some are thin and emaciated from lack of food, and the birds often appear in unusual localities. Even when in good condition they are frequently captured by hand, for they are so unsuspicious as to appear stupid. It is even possible at times to stroke them without alarming them.

The saw-whet owl *(Cryptoglaux a. acadica)* nests from southern Alaska, Alberta, and Nova Scotia to California, Arizona, and Mexico, and in the East to the northern United States, coming as far as western Maryland in the mountains. In winter it goes casually as far as Louisiana and Georgia. The Queen Charlotte owl *(Cryptoglaux a. brooksi)*, darker in color, is confined to the Queen Charlotte Islands, British Columbia.

Richardson's Owl

(Cryptoglaux funerea richardsoni)

Average Length, Ten Inches

This relative of the saw-whet owl is a northern bird that nests north of the United States, ranging widely through forested areas from eastern Canada to Alaska. Like the related species, it is rather strictly nocturnal and even in the far north, where daylight in summer is long, it appears sluggish except after dark. The Eskimos, according to Dr. E. W. Nelson, believe that it cannot see by day and call it *tuk-whelinguk*, "the blind one."

It is certain that the birds are tame to a point where they seem stupid, because, when they come in winter to more southern regions where they are in contact with man, they are often caught by hand. One New England lady, seeing a ball of feathers hanging on her clothesline, was astonished to discover that it was a Richardson's owl, alive. When captured, the birds are passive and offer no resistance.

Richardson's owl is an inhabitant of timbered areas, though where large trees are lacking, as in the Yukon Delta in Alaska, it frequents willow thickets. The birds nest in May and June in holes in trees, or in the deserted nests of other birds, laying from four to six eggs. Their food is mice, insects, and small birds, and they come south in winter when a shortage of mice deprives them of this food supply. At such times they are found frequently about farm buildings, often starving.

At intervals they are very common in winter in the woods of Maine and elsewhere in New England, but as yet there is no record of their nesting within United States territory aside from Alaska. The southern invasions are governed by shortages of mice in the north.

Richardson's owl ranges from the tree line in Alaska, Yukon, and Mackenzie to northern British Columbia and Nova Scotia. In winter it is found casually to Oregon, Colorado, and New England, and its bones have been identified in ancient cave deposits in New Mexico. Tengmalm's owl *(Cryptoglaux f. magna)*, a closely related form of eastern Siberia, has been taken on St. Paul Island, Alaska.

Flammulated Screech Owl

(Otus flammeolus)

Average Length, Six and One-half Inches

The flammulated screech owl is nocturnal and is seldom abroad by day. It is found in wooded areas in the western mountains, in Colorado as high as 10,000 feet above the sea.

The nest is usually in an old woodpecker hole, where the eggs, two to four in number, are placed on a few chips, to which there are added sometimes bits of twigs or feathers. The egg of a flicker has been found with those of the owl, indicating that the latter may sometimes preëmpt domiciles in use by other birds. However, the owls do not seem quarrelsome, for occasionally neighboring holes in the tree occupied by them may be in use by bluebirds and other hole-nesting species.

One flammulated screech owl collected by Dr. C. Hart Merriam at the Grand Canyon in Arizona had eaten a scorpion and some beetles. These birds also feed on small mammals.

This screech owl ranges from southern British Columbia and Idaho to Colorado, south through the mountains into Mexico and the highlands of Guatemala.

The spotted screech owl *(Otus trichopsis)*, is somewhat like the ordinary screech owl, but has long bristly tips on the feathers of the face. Like the eastern screech owl, it has two color phases, gray and reddish brown. It is found from the Huachuca and Santa Catalina Mountains of Arizona south into Guatemala.

ONE REVEALS ITSELF IN TREE TOPS, THE OTHER HIDES IN HOLES

Perching high on an old tree stub, the **American Hawk Owl** of Alaskan and Canadian forests awaits the moment to swoop silently down on unsuspecting rodents and birds, while the **Western Burrowing Owl** stays close to its ground hole, feeding on locusts, snakes, grasshoppers, or anything its sharp claws can snatch. Unlike most owls, both see well and hunt regularly in broad daylight. The burrowing owl, inhabiting unforested regions of western North America, will occupy any abandoned hole or perhaps dig its own.

American Hawk Owl
(Surnia ulula caparoch)
Average Length, Sixteen Inches

A long tail and slender body mark the curious hawk owl of the north from all our other species of owls, though comparatively few persons see it, as its range in the main is in the vast forests of Canada and Alaska, where human habitations are widely scattered.

The hawk owl is much more conspicuous than any other forest owl. It rests on the top of a tall dead stub or some other commanding perch, where, in broad daylight, it is entirely in the open.

It has the habit of jerking its tail nervously like a sparrow hawk, a movement that aids in attracting attention. Ability to hunt by day or night is truly an advantage to a species of the north where day is long in summer and night equally extended in winter.

These owls are entirely fearless, and there is no difficulty in approaching them within gunshot. Though seen constantly in the open, they are flushed occasionally from thickets of aspen and willow.

The notes are described as a rolling trill, and when the birds are disturbed about their nests the hawk owls utter chattering calls and other sounds of protest.

Heavily feathered to the tips of its toes, this species is entirely unmindful of cold, so that it remains in the far north throughout the winter, coming south in numbers only in those years when mice, lemmings, and other small mammals are scarce. Even then the hawk owl remains as far north as possible, unlike the snowy owl and other species that pass southward in numbers.

Regardless always of temperature, the hawk owl begins its nesting season in April and early May, even in the high latitude of Great Slave Lake, at a season when ice and snow abound and the weather is still extreme. A nest of twigs is built in a pine or spruce, or, failing this, the eggs are placed on decayed wood on the summit of a broken stub or stump.

Intruders in the home domain are attacked without hesitation, and many naturalists have had hats knocked off by parent owls when climbing to their nests. The birds' sharp claws are a menace, for they can easily gash the skin or put out an eye.

The hawk owl subsists mainly on mice and lemmings. It eats insects in summer and also kills birds the size of a ptarmigan.

The American hawk owl breeds from northwestern Alaska and Hudson Strait south to southern British Columbia and the Ungava region. It winters south into the southern Canadian Provinces, casually across the border in the northern United States.

The Siberian hawk owl has been taken twice in Alaska. Other forms of this bird are found across Siberia and northern Europe.

Burrowing Owl
(Speotyto cunicularia)
Average Length, Ten Inches

During travel through the open plains and desert areas of the West, small owls with long legs and round heads are often seen resting on the ground, perhaps on a little mound of earth.

Approach them, and they watch attentively, bobbing their heads gravely, or crouch as if about to fly. At the last moment, instead of taking wing, they turn tail and dash precipitately into holes in the earth, hitherto unnoticed, and disappear in a most astonishing and unorthodox escape. On other occasions the burrowing owl rests on posts, poles, or low trees, and flies off in usual owl fashion.

These owls regularly use old burrows of prairie dogs and other small mammals as their homes, but when these are not available they dig shelters of their own. The form found on the open prairies of Florida must regularly excavate its own homes, as do the related forms of the West Indian islands, since there are no other burrowing animals of proper size to supply them with domiciles.

The burrowing owl nests in the holes that it inhabits, and its young do not venture far from the burrow opening until they are well able to fly. During the warmer weather these owls subsist largely on insects.

In late summer, in the plains regions, grasshoppers form the bulk of their food, and in locust years the owls eat little else. They also feed on mice, rats, and lizards, and on occasion eat small birds.

One that I kept as a captive was fond of garter snakes, seizing them, pinching them with the bill all along the body, and then swallowing them headfirst. Ordinarily the snake was too long for all of it to be swallowed at once, and the owl stood about for an hour with a few inches of the snake's tail drooping from the corner of its mouth until digestion made room for all inside.

The ordinary call of this little owl is a loud *boo boo boo,* and it has various chattering notes. Though active at night, it is regularly abroad by day, being able to see in bright sunlight without difficulty. My captive bird, by watching intently, often brought to my notice soaring hawks so distant that they were mere specks in the sky.

Throughout the West these interesting birds are known as "billy owls" or "prairie dog owls." The western burrowing owl *(Speotyto cunicularia hypugaea)* is found in the treeless districts of the West from British Columbia and Manitoba south to western Iowa, Louisiana, and Panama. The Florida burrowing owl *(Speotyto c. floridana),* darker in color, ranges in the prairie region of central and southern Florida. Related forms are found in the Bahamas, Hispaniola and other West Indian islands, and in South America.

ALTHOUGH SMALLEST OF THE OWLS, THEY ARE STOUT-HEARTED AND SHREWD

Resting on the pine bough above is the courageous **Rocky Mountain Pygmy,** who will pounce on squirrels or other rodents twice its own size. In Latin America, natives call the **Ferruginous Pygmy** (left) "four eyes," believing the black spots on either side of its neck are eyes and that it sees both in front and behind. Little **Whitney's Elf,** in the tangle of cactus, is the dwarf among owls, being hardly larger than an English sparrow. Wise in the ways of the possum, it feigns death when captured. Southern California to Texas is its habitat.

Pygmy Owl
(Glaucidium gnoma)
Average Length, Seven Inches

With the rapid fall of darkness in deep-walled Oak Creek Canyon in north-central Arizona there came a slow, whistled call, uttered in mournful cadence, from distant shelter near the cliffs. At my imitation of the notes, answer followed quickly, and after two or three repetitions a little pygmy owl alighted in the tree above me to peer down balefully with distended eyes and jerking tail, searching for the intruder that had dared to invade its domain.

Various birds are attracted by this call. On my first experience with it in the Chiricahua Mountains near the Mexican border a screech owl came, leaving me much puzzled for a time as to whether or not this was the owl that produced the strange and unusual note. In daytime, as I stood in deeply shaded gulches, the whistled imitation of the pygmy owl call has brought about me in scolding flocks kinglets, hermit thrushes, warblers, and other small birds, ready to mob the disturber of their rest.

These little owls are sometimes abroad by day, particularly when they have young, and appear to see in bright light without much difficulty. They are, however, normally nocturnal, being thus safe from attack except by larger owls.

Pygmy owls are found in forested country, usually about gulches and canyons, where they nest in old woodpecker holes or similar cavities in trees or stumps. Sitting close to the trunks of pines or other thick-leaved trees, they are practically invisible. The family ordinarily numbers three or four.

Active to some extent by day, they often feed on grasshoppers and other insects which they pounce upon from stumps or low branches. They also eat mice and other small mammals, lizards, frogs, and small birds, the latter including English sparrows. In California these owls have been known to kill pocket gophers, good indication of their strength and prowess, since the mammal is certainly as large and heavy as the owl. They will also strike birds as large as a robin. Superstitious Indians believe that killing a pygmy owl will bring heavy misfortune.

This owl has two color phases, one grayish and one rufescent.

Five forms of the pygmy owl are found in the region from southeastern Alaska, British Columbia, and Wyoming south to Baja California and Arizona. Another form ranges from the highlands of Mexico to Guatemala.

Ferruginous Pygmy Owl
(Glaucidium brasilianum ridgwayi)
Average Length, Six and One-half Inches

This tiny owl, closely related to the ordinary pygmy owl, is widely distributed in tropical America, ranging north barely within the border of the United States. Though small, it is fierce and rapacious. It has been known to attack birds several times its size, tearing at them until they were worn out and at its mercy.

The nest of this owl is placed in old woodpecker holes and similar hollows, where the eggs are laid without nesting material. By day the bird generally hides in thickets, but since it is often abroad to hunt, it is far from being strictly nocturnal.

The black spots on either side of the neck seem to natives in South America to resemble eyes, and owls of this type are known in Spanish as "four eyes," in the belief that they can see both before and behind.

The ferruginous pygmy owl ranges from the lower Rio Grande Valley, Texas, and southern Arizona south to Panama, with allied forms in South America.

Elf Owl
(Micropallas whitneyi)
Average Length, Six Inches

Tiniest of all our owls, no larger than a sparrow, the elf owl is abroad mainly at night, so that it is far more abundant than ordinarily may be supposed. It is found in the Southwest, in the country of the saguaro, or giant cactus. Living in old woodpecker holes in the trunks of this cactus, it is secure from most enemies. These woodpeckers' nests have a tough inner lining of hardened cactus sap and are very permanent.

When captured, elf owls often feign death, lying limp and motionless until chance offers escape, when they dart away instantly to safety. They have been seen also raising one wing and extending it in front of them, so that, hidden behind this shelter, they had no appearance whatever of being a bird. Though confined to the giant cactus belt while breeding, elf owls later may wander afield and appear sometimes in growths of willows or similar trees that offer dense cover.

Eggs are laid in a woodpecker hole without nesting material. Occasionally the owls preëmpt occupied nests, and their eggs have been found mingled with those of the woodpecker, with the owl in possession.

The elf owl feeds almost entirely on insects, principally ants, beetles and grasshoppers, with occasional mice, and in captivity has been known to starve rather than eat birds. In its hunting it seems to be wholly nocturnal.

Whitney's elf owl *(Micropallas whitneyi whitneyi)* ranges from southeastern California and southwestern New Mexico into Sonora. The Texas elf owl *(Micropallas w. idoneus)*, grayer above, is found from the lower Rio Grande to the Valley of Mexico. Sanford's elf owl *(Micropallas w. sanfordi)*, paler gray, is confined to southern Baja California. A related species is restricted to Socorro Island, of the Revilla Gigedo group, west of Mexico.

HOBGOBLIN OF THE DARK IS THE POORLY NAMED SCREECH OWL

A high-pitched quavering note is its nearest approach to a screech, but the uncanny call sometimes stirs the superstitious, who go to fantastic ends to break its "evil spell." Because these small birds destroy harmful mice and insects, they bespeak man's protection. There is no satisfactory explanation as to why the **Eastern Screech Owls** (lower pair) develop the two plumage phases, red and gray. **Kennicott's** (top with young) inhabits northwestern North America.

Screech Owl

(Otus asio)

Average Length, Nine Inches

A tremulous, high-pitched call, quavering in ghostly cadence through the still night air, announces the screech owl, best known of the smaller American owls, since it is found through a broad range. The name is really a misnomer, because the characteristic wailing cry is not at all screechlike.

To some superstitious folk of the South, the note of this bird betokens the approach of death or other trouble if uttered near a house. They call it the shivering owl, a name perhaps of double significance, describing the quality of its note and also its effect on the listener. As a charm to counteract the evil, they turn the left shoe upside down, pull the left trousers pocket inside out, or cast a bit of iron or a handful of salt in the fire—such are the beliefs of those who follow omens.

The ill thus imagined becomes fact and not fancy to the mice and other small creatures that form the food of this rapacious bird. To them the screech owl is indeed a goblin.

A bird of woodland groves and forests, it dwells indifferently in the orchards of New England, the scrub pines of the South, or the scanty cottonwoods that follow the small watercourses in the drier sections of the West. It has prominent "horns" of feathers that project above the head, distinguishing it from any of our other small owls except its cousins, the flammulated and spotted screech owls.

By day the screech owl retires to hollows in trees when these are available, and, failing these, to the densest cover accessible, where it may hide from the eyes of other birds and rest. Holes in the limbs of apple trees provide its favorite refuges from enemies. When it is discovered, there is loud outcry, as jays, cardinals, flickers, titmice, and other small species gather to peer and scold, reviling the one responsible for the destruction of many of their number. Occasionally, when the owl is in an exposed situation, the attack becomes real, and, handicapped by daylight and by force of numbers, the owl may be put to flight.

When pulled out of a nesting place, the screech owl makes a show of resistance, producing crackling sounds with its bill. Dazzled by the sudden light, it will sit bewildered, almost closing its eyes. But, when daylight fades, it comes quickly to alert wakefulness, ear-tufts erect and round eyes staring. The screech owl, like others of its family, seems always to be hungry. Away it speeds on silent wings, bent on the night's hunting, perhaps warning night-prowlers of its presence with an occasional tremulous, wailing call.

Among the screech owls found in the eastern United States there are two distinct color phases, one gray and one reddish brown. These are merely individual variations, for both reddish birds and gray birds are found in the same family of young, regardless of sex. Curiously, the western screech owls do not exhibit these two definite styles in coloration.

Hollows in trees furnish nesting quarters for these little owls, old woodpecker holes being frequently selected. Or the birds may choose holes in hidden corners of outbuildings, or nesting boxes erected for their use. The eggs are laid in the bottom of the hollow without nesting material.

Ordinarily from three to five young constitute a family, but as many as nine have been found. When the young are out of the nest the parents often swoop at the heads of passers-by, snapping their bills threateningly.

The young birds remain under the care of the parents for some time after they leave the nest. When fully grown, the family breaks up, and the individuals then live alone until the following nesting season. Young birds taken from the nest make interesting pets in spite of their inactivity. Adults captured in their hiding places may feign death until there is a chance for escape, sometimes being so passive that it is possible to handle them and pose them at will.

Many screech owls are killed and eaten by larger owls, and probably thus a definite check is maintained on their abundance.

The screech owl feeds extensively on mice of several kinds and on large insects. Moths and beetles are taken in numbers and birds of many sorts are eaten. Crawfish, frogs, spiders, small snakes, snails, scorpions, earthworms, and millepedes in small amount vary the menu, and the birds on the whole are decidedly beneficial.

About country estates the activities of the tree surgeon in filling cavities and removing dead limbs reduce the number of shelters available for small owls, a matter perhaps to the advantage of other birds. Where natural holes are not available, the owls will often use flicker boxes and similar artificial shelters in which to make their homes.

The screech owl ranges from New Brunswick, southern Manitoba, and Sitka, Alaska, into Baja California and northern Mexico. In this vast area are 15 geographic forms, differing in size and color.

The plate presented herewith illustrates two types among these forms. Kennicott's screech owl *(Otus asio kennicotti)*, a large dark form, of the northwest coast from Sitka to the State of Washington, is shown in the upper figure.

The red and the gray phases of plumage in the eastern screech owl *(Otus a. naevius)*, which ranges from New Brunswick, Ontario, and southern Manitoba to the highlands of Georgia and west as far as the eastern part of Oklahoma, are depicted at the bottom.

Photograph by Margaret L. Bodine

GETTING READY TO SERVE A QUICK LUNCH IN APPROVED HUMMINGBIRD STYLE

The female usually perches beside her young when feeding it, but sometimes she serves lunch on the wing, balancing herself on whirring wings as she does so.

Photograph by A. A. Allen

A NEWLY HATCHED RUBY-THROAT AND A RED-LEGGED LOCUST

The swelling on the side of the young bird's neck is its crop distended by a recent injection of nectar from its mother.

HUMMINGBIRDS, SWIFTS, AND GOATSUCKERS

Sixteen Species of the Smallest of Feathered Creatures, Peculiar to the New World and Found from Alaska to the Strait of Magellan, Are Pictured With Their Nearest Relatives

By Alexander Wetmore

THE smallest birds in existence are hummingbirds — the Trochilidae. They are found only in the New World, where they range from the Strait of Magellan to Canada and Alaska, constituting one of the most brilliantly colored and specialized families of birds to be seen in this vast region.

Approximately 488 species of hummingbirds are known, with 150 or more additional subspecies or geographic forms, making a total of more than 600 recognized kinds.

NUMBERS OF SPECIES DECREASE AS THE CLIMATE BECOMES COLDER

The family is most abundant, as regards species, near the Equator, in the Andean region of South America. The Republic of Ecuador has 148 kinds of hummers and Colombia 105 known forms.

In country north and south from these centers of maximum abundance, species become fewer; so that in North America north of Mexico (but including Baja California) only 16 kinds of hummingbirds are found regularly. There are three others which may come casually within these limits.

In the United States hummingbirds are found in greatest variety in the Southwest, only one species, the ruby-throat, ranging east of the Mississippi River.

The mountain meadows of our Southwestern States in midsummer, when their rich assortments of flowers are in bloom, frequently swarm with hummingbirds of a number of species feeding at the blossoms and pursuing one another pugnaciously in pure exuberance of life. It is under such circumstances that these sprightly birds appear at their best, and the bird enthusiast never tires of watching them.

Hummingbirds are most abundant in regions where there are thickets or other woodland interspersed with meadows and openings where the birds may feed and disport themselves in the sunshine. Some kinds are inhabitants of heavy forests, these being found mainly in tropical regions, where certain species have become adapted to life in the dense rain forests.

The emerald hummingbird *(Riccordia swainsonii)* of Haiti and the Dominican Republic lives in the densest of forest growths, where the vegetation drips constantly with water from the daily rains, and comes only occasionally into little openings to feed at flowers. Its deep-green coloration blends with its forest background, so that often the subdued humming of its wings, as it moves among the branches, may be heard for some time before one can distinguish the form of the bird in the somber shadows.

An existence of such a type is in strong contrast to that of the beautiful long-tailed Sappho hummer *(Sappho sapho)* that I found in the Andean foothills of western Argentina, living in open valleys grown with low creosote bush, where the birds were constantly in the open.

THE HUMMER'S PLUMAGE UNDER A MICROSCOPE

The majority of hummers are characterized by glittering reflections from their plumage, and as a general rule the males are more brilliant than the females.

The hues of the plumage are iridescent and are caused by the refraction of light. On close examination of the feather of a bird, it is found to be composed of many fine filaments, which under the microscope are seen to be divided into still finer divisions. In the shining feathers of hummers, there is an abundance of dark pigment in

Photograph by A. A. Allen

THE NEST WITH A SILVER LINING

The newly hatched ruby-throated hummingbird barely half fills the bowl of a teaspoon.

the tiny feather divisions known as bar-bules. The sheath overlying this pigment is either smooth and highly polished or has many minute lines on or under its sur-face. This structure causes a reflection or a refraction of the light, according to the circumstance, making the brilliant hues found in these birds. The colors vary ac-cording to the angle of the light, changing in intensity and in hue as the bird shifts position.

As for form, the variation among hum-mers is truly astonishing. The smallest bird in the world is Helena's hummingbird *(Calypte helenae)* of Cuba, from two and one-fourth to two and one-half inches or a trifle more in length, with the wing only one and one-third inches long or less and the bill less than half an inch long.

This tiny sprite is sometimes called the fairy hummer. In contrast to it, there is the giant hummer of the central and south-ern Andean mountains that is about eight and one-half inches in length and has a wing five inches long. This species is as large in body as a bluebird and is strong and powerful, resembling a large swift in gen-eral appearance.

Variations in details of form are as re-markable as those in size. In one species of hummer, the sword-bearer *(Docimastes ensifera)*, the bill is nearly five inches long, being longer than the rest of the bird. An-other *(Ramphomicron microrhynchum)* has the bill less than a quarter of an inch long.

HUMMERS WITH SICKLE-SHAPED BILLS

Most hummers have straight bills, but there is the sicklebill, in which the bill is curved so that its outline forms one-third of a circle. Such adaptations allow feed-ing in special flowers, the sword-bearer fre-quenting long, trumpet-shaped blossoms, while the sicklebill is partial to certain or-chids, palms, and other peculiar blossoms, where the throat of the flower is curved.

Variations in the form of the tail in this group are equally remarkable. Most spe-cies have the feathers of ordinary length, forming a square or slightly notched tail, but in contrast to these there are the racket-tailed hummers *(Spathura)*, in which the lateral feathers are greatly elongated, with the tip narrowed and then expanded so that it resembles a racket. The long-tailed hum-mers have tails three or four times as long as the body, the longest feathers being seven inches in length.

It is usual for male hummingbirds to have a spot of brilliant iridescent color on the throat. With this there are often peculiar feather developments in the form of crests, or gorgets, that provide increased surface for these areas of brilliant color, and often produce most remarkable and extraordinary appearances.

The nest of a hummingbird is made of soft plant downs, formed into a cup-shaped structure that in most instances is placed firmly on some small twig or branch, sometimes near the ground and sometimes high above it. The outside of this structure usually is covered with bits of bark and moss bound in place with spider web, so that the nest is inconspicuous, resembling merely a knot on a limb. Some species attach their nests to leaves or to the ends of branches, so that they are semipendent.

PUGNACIOUS FEMALES PROTECT PEARLLIKE EGGS

Most of the nests that I have found have come to my notice from the pugnacious attacks of the females, whose repeated darting at birds that came near, or at my head as I passed, gave notice that a nest was somewhere about.

Two white eggs, resembling pearls against their background of plant down, are laid by most species whose nesting habits are known. Occasionally one egg constitutes a set, and rarely three are found, but this is unusual.

Though large in comparison to the size of the parent in the case of the smaller hummers, the eggs are very tiny. Those of the vervain hummer of Haiti, a species that is barely larger than the Helena's hummingbird, the smallest species known, measure less than half an inch long by one-third of an inch in diameter.

That hummingbirds feed on the nectar of flowers is generally known, but the part that nectar plays in their diet is not so great as is popularly believed, since large numbers of tiny flies, bees, beetles, and other insects, as well as spiders, are captured in the flower corollas.

These tiny birds are hungry for meat as well as for sweets. The dozens of stomachs of the various species that I have examined to learn something of their food have been filled with fragments of insects and spiders. After the nutriment has been extracted

from these, the indigestible parts are formed into tiny pellets that are regurgitated to empty the stomach for another meal.

Although flowers are attractive to most hummingbirds, some kinds, particularly forest-inhabiting forms, pay little attention to blossoms, but devote much of their time to gleaning over the moss-covered bark of the trees of their forest haunt searching for animal food.

I have seen others feeding on tiny gnats gathered in whirling clouds in the air. The hummers hung with rapidly vibrating wings, seizing the minute insects one by one in flight and whirling about with the greatest celerity in securing their prey.

In their feeding, hummers, like bees, carry pollen from blossom to blossom and some species are important agents in the fertilization of flowers.

Among popular misconceptions relating to hummingbirds is the belief that they come commonly in the evening—a supposition that is based upon confusion between these birds and the equally large sphinx moths, which hover with rapidly beating wings over beds of petunias and other flowers to probe their cups exactly as hummers do during the day.

The Indians of northern South America still use the feathers and skins of hummingbirds for decorative borders or pendants from bags or other articles, and formerly tens of thousands of the skins of these birds were shipped from South America for millinery ornaments. Happily, the use of wild birds as hat decorations is no longer the fashion or is prohibited by law, so that the birds are not now destroyed in numbers for this purpose.

SWIFTS ARE THE NEAREST RELATIVES OF HUMMINGBIRDS

While it may seem strange to associate hummingbirds and swifts in one order, they are actually close relatives and alike in their wonderful powers of flight. The plumage of both is firm and the feathers are small and compact. The body in both has strong breast muscles, with greater development of the breastbone, to which these muscles are attached, than in most other birds. Both have small feet and long, pointed wings.

The long and narrow bill of the hummingbirds seems strikingly different until we find that when hummingbirds are first hatched their bills are short and flattened, being not widely different from those of

<figure>
Photograph by A. A. Allen

A HALF-GROWN CHIMNEY SWIFT IN ITS COAT OF MAIL

The feathers do not break from the sheaths until the "pin feathers" are practically fully grown.
</figure>

cemented to the side of a small limb, constructed just large enough to hold the single egg.

The typical swifts are plainly colored birds of small or moderate size. Some species have spots or bands of white in the plumage, but the majority are plainly colored in brown, gray, and black.

In general appearance swifts resemble swallows and are frequently confused with that group. The resemblance is entirely superficial. The novice may distinguish the two by the fact that swifts have only ten tail feathers, while all swallows possess twelve.

The typical swifts rest by clinging to the inside of hollow trees or chimneys, the faces of cliffs, or the hanging dead fronds of palms, never perching on twigs or limbs, as do ordinary birds. Their feet are relatively small, but their claws are strong and sharp, so that they can hang on comparatively smooth surfaces or clamber along them without difficulty. Many species can direct all four toes forward to assist in clinging.

swifts. The growth in length of the bill comes almost entirely after the young bird leaves the egg.

Swifts lead a more aërial existence than any of their bird relatives, passing the greater part of the daylight hours in seemingly tireless flight.

The one hundred known species are divided into two families—the tree swifts (Hemiprocnidae) and the typical swifts (Micropodidae). The former are found from India through the Malay region and adjacent islands. They have crested heads, brighter colors, and a softer plumage than the other swifts. They perch frequently on the limbs of trees, like ordinary small birds, and make a peculiar nest of bits of bark

SWIFTS ARE THE SPEED CHAMPIONS OF THE BIRD WORLD

The wings of swifts are long and narrow, and the plumage of the body is close and firm. Members of this family have the most rapid flight known among birds.

Among American forms, the cloud swift, which is nearly as large as a sparrow hawk, is our fastest-flying bird.

In Haiti I found these great swifts circling about the tremendous cliffs of Morne La Selle, where it was exhilarating to a high degree to watch their skill on the wing. One of them was observed to loop the loop without pause in its rapid course, and aviators from the Marine Flying Field at Port-au-Prince told me of having seen these birds circle about their planes when they were traveling at a rate of 85 miles an hour.

Specimens for study and for preservation for the National Museum were obtained only by the expenditure of many cartridges, as the birds crossed the projecting point on which I stood, at the summit of a cliff, at such tremendous speed that they were gone before I could swing my gun to catch their line of flight. Their speed is far more rapid than that of the fastest-flying grouse or duck.

It is not exceptional for swifts to feed and travel at a rate of approximately 70 miles an hour—a speed that can be accelerated to fully 100 miles at pleasure. By means of a stop-watch, E. C. Stuart Baker, in India, has recorded the flight of two species of swifts over a measured course two miles in length, and found that the fastest individuals covered this distance in from 36 to 42 seconds, or at the rate of 171.4 to 200 miles an hour.

The nest of the swifts is peculiar, being ordinarily formed of twigs, bits of bark, and similar material cemented together by the viscous saliva of the bird to form a basket that is fastened by this same saliva to the inside of hollow trees or chimneys, to the branches or leaves of trees, or to the walls of cliffs, caves, or barns. (See nest in illustration on this page.) The eggs are pure white and range in number from one to six, according to the species.

Photograph by Guy A. Bailey

CHIMNEY SWIFTS, WITH A YOUNG BIRD IN ITS NEST

Other young cling with the parent to the wall. The photograph was made by flashlight, in a barn near Syracuse, New York.

The swiftlets (genus *Collocalia*), smallest in their family, have most peculiar nesting habits. Their nests are composed of a mucous secretion from large glands opening into the mouths of the birds. It is this group that produces the edible birds' nests prized among the Chinese for making soup.

The food of swifts, so far as known, consists entirely of insects captured on the wing. In the Tropics swifts consume termites or white ants during their periods of flight. While these birds have short bills, the gape is wide, forming a scoop in which food is seized.

The notes of swifts are chattering, squeaky calls with little musical merit.

Ruby-throated Hummingbird

(Archilochus colubris)

Average Length, Three and Three-quarters Inches

The ruby-throat is the most generally known of its family. A subdued hum, perhaps accompanied by a mouselike squeaking note, attracts attention to these tiny birds working vivaciously about beds of flowers in gardens. The naturalist may come across them in woodland or in fields, where they pass with the direct flight of bees, but with startling rapidity, or stop to feed at jewelweed, thistles, trumpet vines, and other blossoms. (See pages 98-99.)

It is possible to attract hummingbirds about yards and gardens by providing supplies of syrupy sugar water in small bottles suspended from sticks. Miss Althea Sherman has found by experiment that one hummer will consume regularly a teaspoonful of sugar daily.

The nest of the ruby-throat is placed ordinarily in open woodland, on a small limb, at an elevation where it is difficult of access. The female makes her nest and rears the young alone, the male showing no interest.

This species nests from Alberta, central Saskatchewan, and Nova Scotia south to Florida and the Gulf coast, ranging west to North Dakota, central Kansas, and central Texas. In winter it is found from central Florida and Louisiana south through Mexico to Panama.

Costa's Hummingbird

(Calypte costae)

Average Length, Three and One-quarter Inches

Costa's hummers frequent growths of sage and greasewood, other shrubbery, eucalyptus groves, or similar haunts. Ordinarily rather quiet, they become more active and vivacious at the approach of the nesting season.

The display of the male before the female at this season is most curious. He ascends in the air a hundred feet or more, swings down at dizzy speed past his perched mate, passes within a few inches of her, and rises a hundred feet on the opposite side. During this flight he produces a loud, whirring sound that often is the only indication of the display, as the downward speed of the tiny bird is such that the flight is completed before the eye can be directed toward it. At the finish he may dart away in a series of zigzag turns. The male utters a peculiar low whistling call.

In its nesting, Costa's hummer is not so solitary as most of its family, since in favorable locations several nests may be found in a small radius. The nest is less compactly built than that of the ruby-throat and its relatives.

Costa's hummingbird is found in the warmer sections from southern Utah and southern California south through Baja California, Arizona, and New Mexico. It is rare in winter in California, being found at that season in Baja California and northwestern Mexico.

Black-chinned Hummingbird

(Archilochus alexandri)

Average Length, Three and Three-quarters Inches

This species has the general habits and customs of the ruby-throat, of which it is the western counterpart, but from the nature of its range inhabits drier areas. It is common in foothill regions in mountainous sections, where there are flowers to furnish suitable feeding grounds. I have observed them frequently drinking at little brooks where the water trickled over stones. Their needs for water are not always met by dew, as is ordinarily the case in the ruby-throat.

The nest of this species externally is covered with spider web, into which leaves, seed heads, and similar vegetable substances may or may not be woven. Ordinarily nests are placed from four to eight feet from the ground, saddled on small limbs. The eggs, as in other species of the group, are white. Usually there are two, but occasionally three. Two and possibly three broods may be raised in a season.

The female is closely similar in color to the female ruby-throat, but is slightly larger.

This hummer nests from southern British Columbia to northern Baja California, Sonora, and Tamaulipas, ranging east to western Montana and central Texas. It winters in Mexico south to Guerrero and Mexico City.

Anna's Hummingbird

(Calypte anna)

Average Length, Four Inches

This hummingbird, one of the most familiar of the western species of the family, resides in thickly populated areas as well as in the wilder districts. In winter, when flowers are few or absent, it obtains its food of insects and spiders by searching the leaves of trees. It has also been seen feeding on tree sap and the insects attracted by exudations from sapsuckers' punctures in the bark of oaks.

These birds nest from January and February until May and June, usually rearing two families each season. The male at nesting time utters twittering notes that form a pleasant little song. The nests ordinarily are located near water, often on branches overhanging streams. Usually they are built of soft plant downs, but occasionally are formed of dried flowers of eucalyptus. The lining may contain a few feathers or fur.

Though the male is distinct, the female is quite similar to that of Costa's hummer, differing in slightly larger size, darker gray underparts, and narrower outer tail feathers.

Anna's hummingbird is resident in California, mainly west of the Sierra Nevada, ranging south into northwestern Baja California. It is not known to perform regular migrations, but in late summer it has been observed making probably casual visits in parts of Arizona.

WHIRRING WINGS PRODUCE THE HUM WHICH NAMES THESE BIRDS

The alert, vivacious **Ruby-throated Hummingbird** (upper left; male hovering, female perched) is the only hummingbird of the eastern United States. The male **Costa's Hummingbird** (male and female, lower left) of the Southwest makes 100-foot dives through the air to dazzle its mate. Two other westerners are **Anna's Hummingbird** (male and female, lower right), which is equally at home in densely peopled suburbs or wild woodlands of California, and the **Black-chinned Hummingbird** (above, at the right).

Calliope Hummingbird

(Stellula calliope)

Average Length, Three Inches

This species is the smallest bird of the United States. In northwestern Wyoming I found them in June in little valleys, often in swampy sections, where they rested on dead twigs in the tops of alders and other shrubs. Each male objected vigorously to the encroachment of others on his chosen territory, pursuing interlopers with rapid flight and squeaky call notes. Calliope hummers feed about flowers with others of their family.

The mating display flight of the male of this species is less spectacular than that of some of its relatives, the bird swinging in a semicircular path past his mate on the downward sweep, making a loud, metallic sound.

The nest ordinarily is placed in pine trees on or beside cones and closely resembles a dead cone. The mimicry is so exact that nests usually are discovered only when the birds fly about them.

The female has the throat spotted lightly with dusky and the sides washed with brown, otherwise closely resembling the male.

The Calliope hummingbird nests from northern British Columbia, southwestern Alberta and Montana, south through the higher mountains to New Mexico and northwestern Baja California. It is found in winter in Mexico south to Guerrero and Mexico City.

Rufous Hummingbird

(Selasphorus rufus)

Average Length, Three and One-half Inches

This is one of the most spectacular hummingbirds because of the brilliant color of the male and the abundance of the species in its range. At times these birds fairly swarm where thistles, agaves, and other flowers are abundant. Aggressive to a degree and filled with vibrant, nervous energy, they seem never to rest, their feeding grounds being in constant turmoil, as with chattering calls they dash at rivals seeking favored flowers or perches. The males glow in the sun like coals and, seeing them, one overlooks the females.

The male dazzles his mate in a courtship flight in which he swings down from high in the air to pause fleetingly an inch away, and then rises swiftly to repeat the dashing performance. Nests are placed in trees, shrubs, and bushes. The inside is composed of cottony downs and the outside covered with fine moss and shreds of bark.

The rufous hummer nests in Transition and Canadian Zones from latitude 61° north, on the coast of Alaska, to east-central British Columbia and southern Alberta south to Oregon and southwestern Montana. It is abundant in migration through the Rocky Mountain region and winters in southern Mexico.

Broad-tailed Hummingbird

(Selasphorus platycercus platycercus)

Average Length, Four and One-half Inches

The broad-tailed hummer is one of the most abundant hummingbirds of the Rocky Mountain region, where it has wide distribution. In flight the attenuated outer primaries produce a loud, rattling sound which brings the species conspicuously to the attention of visitors.

The broad-tail is preëminently a flower feeder, though it may visit the tree borings of sapsuckers to obtain sap and the insects attracted by this fluid. In its seasonal movements it is governed largely by the flowering of plants, following the changing season from the mountain foothills into the higher parks as summer advances. These hummers come regularly to gardens in towns.

The male has a diving nuptial display resembling that of some of the other hummers, executed with much metallic rattling of the wings.

The majority of nests are placed near the ground, and there is more variation in their appearance than in nests of other species. Two broods, and possibly three, are reared each season, the eggs being two in number.

The broad-tailed hummer nests from southern Idaho, Montana, and southern Wyoming to eastern California, western Nebraska, and western Texas, south to the Valley of Mexico. It is found in winter in Mexico.

Allen's Hummingbird

(Selasphorus alleni)

Average Length, Three and One-third Inches

This species is generally similar to the rufous hummer and is often confused with that species, particularly where the plainly colored female is concerned. The latter is distinguished from its relative by being slightly smaller, with narrower tail feathers.

This species, like the rufous hummer, is more than commonly aggressive among species noted for their pugnacity, and has even been known to drive large hawks to flight.

The male has a display flight somewhat like that of the broad-tail, in which he rises high in the air and then darts down with a loud, metallic sound, produced by the rushing of air through the flight feathers. The species breeds principally in the coastal region of California, and after the nesting season scatters widely before the fall migration carries it southward. The nests are like those of Anna's hummer and may be in trees or in bushes. It is said that two broods are reared each season.

Allen's hummer nests from Humboldt County, California (possibly into Oregon), to Ventura County and the Santa Barbara Islands. It is found in migration in eastern and southern California, Arizona, and Baja California, and winters on the Santa Barbara Islands and probably in northwest Mexico.

LIKE CERTAIN INSECTS, HUMMINGBIRDS HELP TO POLLINATE PLANTS

The **Calliope Hummingbird** (upper left), ranging throughout the Rockies from Canada to Mexico, is the smallest bird in the United States. The **Broad-tailed Hummingbird** (male hovering above its mate, upper right) and the **Rufous** (male and female, lower left), which glows in the sunlight like a burning coal, are two other Rocky Mountain species. Large hawks have been put to flight by the **Allen's Hummingbird** (lower right) of California, which is often confused with the rufous.

Lucifer Hummingbird

(Calothorax lucifer)

Average Length, Three and One-half Inches

This rare and unusual species is apparently a casual visitor from Mexico along our southern border. The first one known within our limits was taken by Mr. Henry W. Henshaw near Camp Bowie, in southern Arizona, on August 7, 1874. It was found, with a host of other hummers, about the flowering spikes of the agave. Subsequently this species has been obtained by the United States Biological Survey in the Chisos Mountains, Texas.

In southern Mexico the Lucifer hummer is common. While it feeds at flowers, it is said also to visit the abundant great spider webs to pick off small insects that have become caught in these nets. The hummer moves circumspectly through the web to avoid being entangled. The larger spiders rush at the bird, which darts to safety instantly.

The beautiful feathers of this species were among those used by the ancient Mexicans to cover feather mantles made in the time of the Montezumas, the gorgeous reflections of the Lucifer hummer being especially decorative.

In a family noted for its aggressiveness, this species is reputed to be more active and pugnacious than most. The nest and eggs are of the usual type found in this group.

Lucifer's hummer is found in Mexico south to Mexico City, Puebla, and Chiapas.

Broad-billed Hummingbird

(Cynanthus latirostris)

Average Length, Three and Three-quarters Inches

This handsome hummer is found in the foothills of the small mountain ranges of southern New Mexico and Arizona. It inhabits arroyos, canyons, and the borders of streams, perching on dead twigs at the tops of bushes or low trees, resting in the sun on cool mornings and in shade in the heat of the day. The light color at the base of the bill, prominent even at some distance, serves to distinguish it.

The broad-bill seems quieter and less active than some of the other species described, and frequently, after aggressive flight, I have seen two combatants perch four or five inches apart for a few seconds, while with raised wings they gave a low, chattering call.

The ordinary flight is accompanied by a subdued humming sound. The birds feed at flowers and also glean small insects and spiders from the under side of branches and leaves.

A nest in the collection in the National Museum, Washington, is made of fine shreds of bark and plant fibers, bits of lichens and similar materials, bound with spider web, the construction coarser than is usual in this family.

This species ranges from the mountains of southern Arizona and southwestern Mexico to the City of Mexico and Guerrero.

Xantus's Hummingbird

(Hylocharis xantusi)

Average Length, Three and One-quarter Inches

This hummer was discovered in 1859 by the naturalist John Xantus de Vesey, who, through arrangement by Spencer F. Baird, then Assistant Secretary of the Smithsonian Institution, had been sent to Baja California as a meteorological observer for the Signal Service. Xantus's hummer is found from the hedges in the towns of the coast region to the live oaks of the highest mountains of the interior.

The courtship display of Xantus's hummer is said to be confined to a flight during which the birds pursue one another through the trees. Though some nests are saddled on limbs, others are hung from several small twigs or leaves at the tip ends of branches. The nests are made of the usual fine materials and soft linings common to the family. Though two eggs are found frequently, in numerous instances nests contain only one egg or one young bird. The eggs vary greatly in shape, ranging from oval to elliptical. Many eggs and young are destroyed by ravens.

The male of Xantus's hummer has a pleasing song, heard often toward nightfall. While not particularly aggressive, these birds guard the nest locality jealously. The female differs from the male in having the entire undersurface brown and in being lighter green above.

This species is restricted to the Cape region of Baja California, ranging north to latitude 29°.

White-eared Hummingbird

(Hylocharis leucotis leucotis)

Average Length, Three and One-quarter Inches

Found in the mountains of southern Arizona, this species is comparatively little known. The first specimen known from the United States was collected by Dr. A. K. Fisher in Fly Park, in the Chiricahua Mountains, in 1894. Since that time it has been found in other mountain ranges in southern Arizona and seems to appear regularly north of the Mexican boundary.

The white line behind the eye is very prominent in life and attracts immediate attention. Watching the hummers in Barfoot Park, in the Chiricahuas one July day, by this mark I singled out a male of this species instantly among myriads of other forms.

In Mexico this hummer is reported to be one of the most common of its family in the highlands, where it feeds principally at blossoms. The nest has been mentioned by one author, but without detailed description. The bird has been reported carrying nesting material in the Huachuca Mountains. An allied race is found in Nicaragua.

This form ranges from the Chiricahua, Huachuca, and Santa Rita Mountains of southeastern Arizona to Guatemala.

Allan Brooks -

TINIEST OF BIRDS, HUMMERS SOMETIMES FLY 500 MILES NONSTOP

Glittering jewels of birdland, hummingbirds are found only in the New World. The **Lucifer Hummingbird** of Mexico (upper left-hand pair, male perched) steals insects from large spiders' webs. The **White-eared Hummingbird** (lower right), which may be singled out by the white line behind the eye, and the **Broad-billed** (upper right) live in Mexico and the Arizona mountains. Ravens eat eggs and young of **Xantus's Hummingbird** (lower left), found only in southern Baja California.

Rieffer's Hummingbird

(Amazilia tzacatl tzacatl)
Average Length, Four Inches

Inclusion of this species in the present list is based on one captured alive at Fort Brown, Texas, in June, 1876, and brought to Dr. James C. Merrill. Hardly had a careful description been taken, when the bird escaped. No other specimens having been obtained, it is believed to have been only a straggler.

In certain areas in Central America this hummer is reported as the most abundant of its kind, ranging from the coast to an altitude of 6,000 feet. It is found in cultivated regions and about houses. Inquisitive and active, it darts about with shrill chirps.

In the lowlands of eastern Nicaragua, Rieffer's hummer has been found placing its nest in trees and shrubbery, but seldom more than six feet above the ground. Many of the nests are coated with moss that continues to grow, so that the small, cuplike structures are handsomely decorated in green.

The female closely resembles the male, but usually has more extensive white markings underneath, a paler gray abdomen, and a less distinct brown streak in front of the eye.

This species ranges regularly from Tamaulipas south through eastern Mexico and Central America to Colombia and Venezuela.

Buff-bellied Hummingbird

(Amazilia yucatanensis chalconota)
Average Length, Four and One-half Inches

The buff-bellied hummer is plainer than our other species. It is found among dense, tangled thickets, where it darts about with ease, coming out frequently into open gardens and among the bushes of pastures. Its shrill notes often advertise its presence.

This hummer barely crosses our borders. In the lower Rio Grande Valley, in Texas, it is common during the summer, arriving from the south about the first of April and remaining until September and October.

These birds usually nest in open woodland and at the borders of chaparral thickets, placing their nests on small, drooping limbs or on the fork of a horizontal twig from three to eight feet from the ground. Their tiny homes are neatly built of shreds of vegetable fiber, covered with bits of dried flowers, lichens, and fragments of bark and lined with thistledown. The two eggs are rather small for the size of the parent. It is believed that two broods may be reared each season.

The buff-bellied hummer has a more restricted range than most of the other members of the species under discussion, being found in a comparatively small area from the lower Rio Grande Valley, in Texas, south into southern Tamaulipas and Nuevo Leon. In winter it has been reported to southern Vera Cruz.

Blue-throated Hummer

(Lampornis clemenciae)
Average Length, Five Inches

The blue-throat is one of the larger forms of its family. It inhabits canyons and mountain valleys, occurring to the tops of the small mountain ranges in the United States, and in the higher mountains of Mexico to elevations of 12,000 feet. Though its flight is swift, it is quieter than some of the smaller species, resting long on low, open perches.

The birds utter sharp, squeaking calls, and the male has a simple song of three or four notes, repeated at short intervals while the singer perches upright with head elevated.

Few nests of this species have been recorded. One, obtained by E. W. Nelson on the volcano of Toluca, was placed on a fork in a small shrub growing on the face of a cliff. In Arizona nests have been found inside small buildings, placed in the crook of a suspended lard pail handle or on a loop of wire. Others are reported built in an old black phœbe's nest, and among ferns.

The Texas blue-throat (Lampornis clemenciae clemenciae) ranges from the Chisos Mountains, in western Texas, south to Michoacan and Oaxaca, in Mexico; and the Arizona bluethroat (Lampornis clemenciae bessophilus) is found in the Santa Catalina, Huachuca, Chiricahua, and Santa Rita Mountains of southern Arizona, the San Luis Mountains of southern New Mexico, and the Sierra Madre of Mexico. The Arizona form has a shorter bill and duller coloration than the Texas bird.

Rivoli Hummingbird

(Eugenes fulgens)
Average Length, Five Inches

In addition to its handsome coloration, the Rivoli hummer is noteworthy for being one of the largest of its family in the United States. It is from four and one-half to more than five inches long, with proportionately heavy body. It is found in open pine forests, where it feeds at flowers. The flight is rapid, but has an apparently less rapid wing motion than that of smaller hummers.

The nest has been found among pines, fifty feet from the ground, saddled on a small limb in a location difficult of access. It is built of plant downs, with an external covering of lichens held in place with spider web, the structure being similar in appearance to that of the ruby-throat but considerably larger.

The first sight of this species is not easily forgotten, for among its small fellows it appears a handsomely colored giant.

The Rivoli hummingbird is found in the mountains of southeastern Arizona and southwestern New Mexico, ranging from 6,000 to 10,000 feet altitude. It occurs through Mexico and Central America to Nicaragua.

HUMAN EYE CAN HARDLY FOLLOW THEIR BULLETLIKE FLIGHT

Bound about with spiders' webs and trimmed with lichens, bark, and moss, the hummer's nest may be mistaken for a knot on a limb. Only a straggler into the United States, **Rieffer's Hummingbird** (upper left) frequents cultivated regions from Mexico to northern South America. "Plain clothes man" of hummers is the **Buff-bellied Hummingbird** (upper right) of northern Mexico. The **Blue-throated** and **Rivoli Hummingbirds** (lower, left and right) are larger members of the family.

THE GOATSUCKERS

By Alexander Wetmore

THE name of goatsucker comes from a superstition of Old World peasants, who hear the calls of these nocturnal birds about their herds at night and believe that they subsist on stolen milk. Nightjar is a name bestowed in England, referring to calls heard from the woodland at night.

When at rest in trees, these curious birds ordinarily perch lengthwise on limbs, so that with their dull coloration they appear to be merely knots or excrescences.

The voices of this family are unusual or even weird and, being heard mainly at night, have been the subject of much superstition. Most of them consist of a rapid repetition of a phrase or a series of notes that may be heard for a considerable distance and in imitation of which many species, as the whippoorwill, pauraque, and chuck-will's-widow, have been given their common names.

Like many other nocturnal creatures, the eyes of goatsuckers shine from reflected light, and one method used in securing specimens is to hunt them at night by the aid of headlights.

While studying the bird life of the Chaco in western Paraguay, I went out one evening equipped with a small electric headlight to ascertain the source of a tremulous call heard from the forest for several evenings. The time was September, spring in the Southern Hemisphere, and the night air soft and warm as I left the house.

I walked along a trail that led toward a deep forest. As I crossed a pasture the eyes of horses glowed clear green in the reflection from my headlight. A screamer called loudly from the edge of a lagoon.

THE JACKLIGHT "SHINES" THE EYES OF THE GOATSUCKERS

The scent of blossoming trees hung heavy in the night air, and as I entered a footpath leading into the depths of a dense forest a jaguar coughed near at hand. My light threw only a small beam that illuminated a tiny circle of branches and leaves.

The tremulous note that I had heard from the tree tops came now near at hand, and suddenly I saw a single spot of deep ruby red a few feet from the ground. The point seemed to be nearly an inch in diameter and appeared and disappeared, apparently as the bird turned its head. It suggested a glowing coal, but had a deeper, more intense light.

Raising my gun so that the sight was visible in the weak ray from the headlight, I took careful aim and fired. In the dead night air the gas from the discharge crowded back in my face and the red spot disappeared. Hastening up, I found a beautiful little goatsucker *(Setopagis parvulus)*, eight or nine inches long, of a kind which I had not seen before and which I was much pleased to add to the valuable bird collection of the U. S. National Museum.

The food of goatsuckers consists principally of insects that the birds capture on the wing. They eat many moths, since these creatures are active at night, and also take almost anything else that flies.

The order of goatsuckers, found throughout the temperate and tropical parts of the earth, includes four families: the frogmouths (Podargidae), the wood nightjars or potoos (Nyctibiidae), the owlet frogmouths (Aegothelidae), and the true goatsuckers (Caprimulgidae).

MOST GOATSUCKERS, ACTIVE ONLY AT NIGHT, ARE SELDOM SEEN BY DAY

Birds of this order are active at night, and, except for the nighthawks and their relatives, are not seen by day except when flushed from their roosting places.

The goatsuckers include about 100 forms of small to medium size. All have soft, fluffy feathers, colored in delicate grays, buffs, and browns, with occasional markings of white. Their wings are long and pointed and their feet small, the claw on the middle toe possessing a comb, or pecten, perhaps of use in cleaning the plumage. The bill is small and weak, but the mouth is enormous, its capacious opening extending back beneath the large eyes.

When the mouth is opened, the outline of the lower portion of the eyeball is visible through the thin membranes lining the roof of the mouth. Years ago some naturalists, believing that these birds had the power of rolling their eyes inward, so that they could look out through the transparent mouth membranes and so direct the capture of their insect food, aroused a highly amusing controversy that continued for some years before it was determined that the eye, instead of being swivel mounted, was really only slightly movable in its socket.

To most persons the whippoorwill is a voice in the night; comparatively few see the bird. Its Latin name *Antrostomus vociferus vociferus* (cave mouth, loud voice) is, therefore, peculiarly appropriate; and the repetition of "vociferous" tells a pat story.

A WHIPPOORWILL SINGS FOR HOURS WITHOUT A PAUSE

The whippoorwill is not only a loud singer; it is a most persistent and tireless one. Indeed if the entire bird population of the country were to conduct a "marathon" singing contest, the mournful bird that urges punishment upon "poor Will" would be among the finalists. Heard near at hand, the notes are rather harsh, but a little distance mellows them to a melodious quality.

There is something plaintively appealing in the whippoorwill's music. At nightfall it steals upon the ear as a fitting accompaniment to the gathering of soft shadows. Not so mournful as the sad tone of the mourning dove, it yet fits perfectly into a pensive mood and to most persons is pleasing.

Concerning the vocal feats of the whippoorwill John Burroughs wrote, "One April morning between three and four o'clock, hearing one strike up near my window, I began counting its calls. My neighbor had told me he had heard one call over two hundred times without a break, which seemed to me a big story. But I have a much bigger one to tell. This bird actually laid upon the back of poor Will one thousand and eighty-eight blows, with only a barely perceptible pause here and there, as if to catch its breath. Then it stopped about half a minute and began again, uttering this time three hundred and ninety calls, when it paused, flew a little further away, took up the tale once more, and continued till I fell asleep."

By day the whippoorwill is exceedingly difficult to find. It often rests upon the ground among fallen leaves with which its plumage blends so perfectly as to tax the eye of an expert to distinguish it. When flushed from cover, it flies swiftly and without a sound, and takes to earth again not far from its original position.

The person who accidentally drives it from its nest will see it flutter along the ground, flapping its wings and gasping as if badly hurt. As soon as it has led the intruder far enough astray to insure the safety of its eggs, it casts off its pretended infirmities, and flits out of sight in the twinkling of an eye.

Many naturalists have described their observations of the curious whippoorwill. One of the best is by the late E. H. Forbush in his *Birds of Massachusetts and Other New England States:* "It is natural to suspect those who move silently in darkness; and birds which, like the owl or the whippoorwill, fly soundlessly by night from place to place and are so concealed by the shades of evening that they are never seen distinctly are likely to be at least misunderstood. Since man became man he has feared the evil that stalks in the dark, but a creature so harmless as the whippoorwill should never be regarded with suspicion or alarm. When one of these birds comes from the woods to alight on the roof-tree or on the door-stone, it should be a welcome visitor even though its plaintive calls may banish sleep for a short time.

MYSTERIOUS WINGS IN THE NIGHT BRUSH A SLEEPER'S HEAD

"Whippoorwills often appear in the evening about country dwellings in pursuit of nocturnal insects, such as moths, beetles and mosquitoes, which are attracted to the buildings by the lights. While I slept unsheltered nightly for a week in the Concord woods, rolled in my blanket, with only a head-net hung to a branch overhead to protect me from mosquitoes, I noticed each morning upon awaking just before daylight that something fluttered softly about my head. The sound was like that produced by a large night-moth, but soon I heard something strike the ground a few feet away, and then a well-known cluck convinced me that my visitor was a whippoorwill. The bird came nightly while I remained in the woods, and each morning before daylight it flew around my head-net until it had caught all the mosquitoes there. Never at any other time have I been able to detect a sound from the wings of a whippoorwill."

SOARING SWIFTS CAN OUTFLY AIRPLANES

In full flight, swifts snap up their insect prey. Familiar to easterners is the **Chimney Swift** (lower left) that attaches its shelflike nest of twigs with salivary "cement" to the inside of chimneys or dark buildings. **Vaux's Swift** (lower right), of western North America, resembles its eastern cousin but nests deep down within tall, hollow stubs. Preëminent in powers of flight is the **White-throated Swift** (upper figure), another westerner. **Black Swifts** (two in center: immature left, adult right) are rare throughout their range in the West.

Black Swift

(Nephoecetes niger borealis)

Average Length, Seven and One-quarter Inches

The black swift is counted as one of our rarer birds throughout much of its range. While in dark coloration it resembles the chimney and Vaux's swifts, it is larger, and may also be told by the longer, narrower wings and the decidedly longer, forked tail. Like all its relatives, it is entirely at home in the air and is usually seen darting and turning high above the earth. Though ordinarily silent, at times it utters loud, chirping calls that may be modified to a rolling twitter. Usually it is found in little flocks.

The nesting of this species remained a mystery until it was found breeding on cliffs above the sea in southern California. The single white egg was placed on a slight depression, on moist sod. In the Yosemite nests have been found on cliffs in mountain gorges, built of fern leaves to form a cup. It is believed that these swifts may nest also in hollow trees.

This form of the black swift is found from southeastern Alaska and southern Colorado to southern Mexico, wintering in its southern range. An allied form occurs in the West Indies, sometimes in flocks of hundreds.

Chimney Swift

(Chaetura pelagica)

Average Length, Five and One-quarter Inches

This species is known to many as the chimney "swallow." In pairs and trios, with rapidly moving wings, these birds pass swiftly overhead, with chirping, twittering notes. This swift once inhabited hollow trees, but with the advent of the white man's houses it began to occupy chimneys, until now, though found occasionally in ice houses or other dark buildings, it seldom lives in tree trunks. It prefers to perch on the inside of a chimney, in a hollow tree, or on a wall, never elsewhere.

The nest is formed of small twigs cemented by a salivary secretion into a semicircular saucer, glued against the side of a chimney or wall. From four to six white eggs are laid. The young leave the nest when partly grown and cling to the wall like the parents.

In fall migration swifts gather at nightfall and wheel in funnel-shaped clouds over chimneys, into which they descend to roost. For many years their winter home was unknown, and when they disappeared in the fall the ignorant believed they had gone into hibernation. Recently, however, they have been recorded as migrants in Haiti, Mexico, and Central America, and it is assumed that they pass the winter somewhere in northern South America.

The chimney swift is found in summer from southern Canada to the Gulf coast, ranging from the Atlantic seaboard west to eastern Texas, Montana, and central Alberta.

White-throated Swift

(Aëronautes saxatilis saxatilis)

Average Length, Six and Three-quarters Inches

The white-throated swift is preëminent in powers of flight among the swifts of the United States. I recall distinctly my amazement at its seemingly incredible speed on my first sight of these birds wheeling over the great abyss of the Grand Canyon. Without seeming effort, they swung back and forth over courses a mile or two in length.

This swift is most common in mountainous regions, where it is found principally in the vicinity of the cliffs on which it nests, but ranges at times in level country. When feeding, it may come near the ground to fly about with ordinary speed, but at other times darts about high overhead, uttering shrill, high-pitched, laughing calls.

White-throated swifts breed in crevices and crannies in cliffs, caves, and old ruins, making their nests of soft vegetable materials and feathers, fastened together by gluelike mouth secretions and fastened by this same cement to the rocks. The eggs are pure white and number four to six in a set. From the rapidity of their flight, these birds have few enemies except the owls and small climbing mammals that capture them at night in their roosts.

This swift is found in summer from south-central British Columbia and southern Alberta to the Black Hills and Baja California; in winter from central California southward.

Vaux's Swift

(Chaetura vauxi)

Average Length, Four and One-quarter Inches

This western species is similar to the chimney swift, from which it differs in slightly smaller size and somewhat paler coloration. It is far less numerous than the chimney swift and in many areas in its range it is found only casually. The flight and general habits of Vaux's swift are also like those of its eastern cousin. It often feeds high in air for long periods, which limits most observations to glimpses of its small, erratically darting form.

In nesting, Vaux's swift still resorts to hollow trees, constructing a shallow saucer of twigs or of pine needles fastened together and glued to the walls of its safe retreat with the salivary secretion. The eggs are four to six in number and are pure white. It usually nests in tall, dead stubs and ordinarily selects those that are hollow throughout their length, descending inside to near the bottom. Nests have sometimes been placed actually below the surrounding ground level.

Vaux's swift nests from southeastern Alaska, central British Columbia, and Montana south to the Santa Cruz Mountains, California, and Nevada. It migrates through Arizona and Baja California to winter in Central America.

DURING THE DAY, GOATSUCKERS PERCH LENGTHWISE ON TREE LIMBS

Members of this family are active at night. They eat no vegetable food, but devour all kinds of insects, from the largest moths and dragon flies to tiniest gnats. Shadows that dart through the fading dusk and the distant call of *chuck-whip-poor-will* may be all we see or hear of the **Eastern Whippoorwill** (male, above). The **Chuck-will's-widow** (male, on the ground) of the Southeast is the largest of its family found within the United States.

Whippoorwill

(Antrostomus vociferus)

Average Length, Nine and Three-quarters Inches

The whippoorwill is a voice of the night, which repeats its name loudly and persistently in the evening and again before dawn. It is often confused with the nighthawk, seen frequently by day, but the two are distinct species. Rarely may whippoorwills be flushed in the thickets in which they sleep during daylight. They rest on the ground or on low limbs, where they always perch lengthwise of the branch. Their mottled coloration is so similar to the background against which they rest that they are not seen until they dart away with noiseless wings.

When heard near at hand, the call is loud and strident, and usually there is a low, harsh note at the beginning, so that the call resembles *chuck-whip-poor-will.*

The birds may call from the ground, but usually perch on posts, on fallen logs, or on limbs of trees. I have known them to fly in to scold with low notes at the apparition of a tent suddenly erected in their usual haunts, and once, while sleeping on the ground in a light rain, I felt one perch on the canvas I had drawn over my head. Their calls are most vociferous in spring and summer.

The food of the whippoorwill is entirely animal, consisting principally of large insects. Occasionally, they may be seen darting up from some open perch to seize passing insects, their food being taken principally on the wing.

The whippoorwill deposits its eggs on a bed of leaves, without other pretense of a nest than the slight hollow sufficient to hold them. The site is secluded and little disturbed and ordinarily is heavily shaded by bushes. The eggs number two, the eastern variety being white blotched and spotted with shades of brown and lilac. The eggs of Stephens's whippoorwill, the western form, are pure white.

When disturbed, the female tumbles about with widely spread mouth, uttering strange whining, hissing sounds, in an endeavor to distract the attention of the intruder and thus protect her brood. The female resembles the male but has the light tips to the outer tail feathers buff instead of white, and the general coloration browner.

The eastern whippoorwill nests from Manitoba, New Brunswick, and Nova Scotia south to northern Louisiana and northwestern South Carolina, and west to eastern North Dakota and eastern Kansas. It is found in winter from South Carolina to Central America.

Stephens's whippoorwill (*Antrostomus vociferus arizonae*) is similar in color, but is larger, with the bristles about the mouth longer and stouter. It is found from southern Arizona, southern New Mexico, and southwestern Texas south through northern Mexico. In winter it ranges south to Guatemala.

Chuck-will's-widow

(Antrostomus carolinensis)

Average Length, Twelve Inches

This is the largest of its family found within our limits, being from ten and one-half to nearly thirteen inches long. The mouth seems enormously broad and capacious when the small size of the bill is considered, and is bordered by long bristles that differ from those of any of our other goatsuckers in having lateral filaments instead of being smooth. The female differs from the male in having the inner webs of the outer tail feathers mottled instead of white or buffy white.

The chuck-will's-widow is another nocturnal species found in densely wooded swamps or on rock-strewn hillsides. During the day it rests on the ground, hides in hollow logs, or perches longitudinally along low limbs near the earth, where it is shaded from the sun. George Shiras, 3d, reports its eyes shine red at night under a jacklight.

At nightfall it flies forth silently for food. Like the whippoorwill, it derives its common name from its reiterated call of *chuck-will's-widow*, the first note being low and the first syllable of the third strongly accented.

The mouth of this bird is fully two inches from corner to corner. More than half of its food is composed of large beetles, among them May beetles, or "June bugs," seemingly harsh and unpalatable fare. Other insects taken include the largest kinds of dragon flies, large moths, locusts, and roaches. Small birds, including warblers, small sparrows, and hummingbirds, have been found occasionally in stomachs of this species.

The chuck-will's-widow makes no nest, placing its two eggs on dry leaves or on the bare ground, in well-drained wooded localities where the nest site will not be flooded by rains. The eggs are handsome, having a ground color varying from rich cream buff to nearly white, marbled and spotted with shades of brown, lavender, and gray.

When a nest is discovered the female tries frantically to draw the intruder away by fluttering and tumbling on the ground as if injured. The mouth is widely opened at such times and the bird presents a most grotesque appearance. Some have claimed that this bird, like the whippoorwill, when disturbed at its nest will move the eggs to another site, carrying them in its capacious mouth. The young, when first hatched, are covered with long down of a peculiar cinnamon-buff shade.

The chuck-will's-widow nests principally in the Lower Austral Zone, in the southeastern United States, from southern Missouri and southeastern Kansas and southern (occasionally central) Maryland south to the Gulf States and central Texas. In winter it is found from Florida to the Greater Antilles, Central America, and Colombia.

THE NIGHTHAWK IS NOT A HAWK AT ALL

Its common name is derived from its long-winged appearance in flight. The **Nighthawk** (male, on the rock) is the most familiar of the goatsuckers because it cruises abroad by day as well as at night. It prefers open country throughout its range from northern Canada to Mexico and the West Indies. Partial to desert areas of the Southwest, the **Texas Nighthawk** (below) is browner and slightly smaller than its more widely known namesake.

Nighthawk
(Chordeiles minor)
Average Length, Ten Inches

In a family whose members are known principally as voices of the night, the nighthawk is the most frequently seen, since, though it shares the nocturnal habits of its relatives, it is also regularly abroad by day. Its common name is given from its hawklike appearance when on the wing, a resemblance that is entirely superficial, since it has no close affinity with the falcons and their relatives.

The female differs from the male principally in the lack of the white bar across the tail. The white mark across the wing is prominent when the bird is in flight.

The nighthawk is largely a bird of the open country, where it rests on the ground, on stones, stumps, and fence posts and at times in trees. In the latter case it always perches lengthwise of the limbs. In wooded country it ranges in the open borders of the forests.

The food of the nighthawk is composed entirely of insects, including almost everything from the largest moths and dragon flies to mosquitoes and tiny gnats. The food is captured entirely on the wing, during intricate aërial evolutions, the prey being gathered in the widely opened mouth.

Collections of small insects by these birds are truly remarkable. Several thousand individuals, including more than 50 species, have been found in the stomach of one nighthawk. Flying ants are eaten in large quantities.

The nighthawk nests on gravel bars, sand spits, in pastures, particularly in rocky soil, and in similar locations, placing its two eggs in the open, in some slight depression, on the bare ground. With the development of modern cities, the birds may nest in safety on the flat, gravel-covered roofs of tall buildings, with the wide sky overhead as a feeding ground—an interesting adaptation to modern civilization. The eggs vary from cream to olive gray, blotched and speckled with blackish brown and lavender (page 50).

In the mating and nesting season the male nighthawk indulges in rapid, erratic flights, which terminate in a thrilling downward plunge at high speed with stiffly set wings. As this rapid course is suddenly checked, the vibration of the air through or against the flight feathers produces a vibrant, roaring sound that may be heard for a considerable distance. Formerly this species, under the name of "bull-bat," was shot for sport, a practice that now is prohibited by law.

The nighthawk ranges from Yukon, Mackenzie, and Newfoundland south into northern Mexico, the Bahama Islands, and the Greater Antilles. In winter it travels into South America. Nine geographic forms, differing in size and color, have been recognized.

Texas Nighthawk
(Chordeiles acutipennis)
Average Length, Nine Inches

This bird resembles the ordinary nighthawk, but is slightly smaller, has the white bar on the wing located nearer the tips of the primaries, and is somewhat browner.

The Texas nighthawk is found in the warmer sections of the Southwest, being especially partial to desert areas. It is most active during early morning and late evening. If disturbed in daytime it flies without confusion, seemingly unaffected by the light. It rests on the ground, or on low branches of mesquite or greasewood, perching always lengthwise of the branches. On the ground, it moves about to some extent, and when disturbed frequently raises the head and neck and moves the body up and down.

Its flight is easy and graceful, but the birds ordinarily remain near the ground. The wing motion is somewhat quicker and less vigorous than in the larger nighthawk.

In courtship the birds pursue one another quickly, the males at times sailing with the wings held stiffly decurved at an angle below the level of the body. Their ordinary call is a mellow, rolling trill. It may be continued for many seconds. The bird utters some whining notes also, but not the booming sound of its larger cousin in courtship.

The two eggs are laid on the open ground, without nesting material, ordinarily where there is not the slightest shelter. The eggs are pale gray to light cream color, minutely marbled and spotted with shades of gray and lilac, with a few bolder markings of slate and brown. Occasionally an egg is found with only a few very minute markings.

Within a day or two after hatching, the young are able to crawl about from place to place, selecting spots where they get some protection from the sun. Both eggs and young are so closely similar to the ground that they are not easily detected, even when their exact location is known.

This species has begun to nest on the flat tops of low adobe houses, thus showing an adaptation to the encroachment of man.

The true Texas nighthawk (Chordeiles acutipennis texensis) nests in the Lower Austral Zone from north-central California, southern Utah, and central Texas south to about latitude 30° in Baja California, and to south-central Mexico. It is found in winter casually in southwestern Arizona and regularly from central Mexico to Panama. A related race, the San Lucas nighthawk (Chordeiles acutipennis inferior), occurs in Baja California from about latitude 30° to the southern extremity of the peninsula. Another form of this species is found in southern Mexico, Guatemala, and Honduras.

PLUMAGE OF SOFT GRAYS, BUFFS, AND BROWNS MATCHES A SEMIARID BACKGROUND

Unless accidentally flushed, **Nuttall's Poorwill** (above) is seldom seen and remains, to most of us, a voice in the night. It frequents dense brush clumps throughout the West and Southwest. The **Merrill's Pauraque** (on the ground), like some of its relatives, takes its name from a characteristic call. In Mexico and the border regions of the Southwest, where it breeds, it shows little fear when the nesting place is approached. Goatsuckers dispense with the bother of nest building, laying their eggs on leaves or on the bare ground.

Poorwill

(Phalaenoptilus nuttalli)

Average Length, Seven and One-half Inches

Like the whippoorwill, the poorwill is often heard but seldom seen. It is nocturnal in habit, resting by day in thick brush, where it is not easily disturbed. Its dark form resembles that of a short-tailed whippoorwill, as with erratic flight it seeks some secure hiding place when flushed.

At times poorwills are found in growths of low forest, but they are more often encountered where dense clumps of brush are scattered over otherwise open ground, as is common in desert and semiarid localities, or in brush-grown, rocky canyons. They rest during the day on the ground, though after dark they may seek higher perches on stones or posts or on low branches. I once saw one by bright moonlight calling from a bush, where it perched crosswise on a small limb, like any ordinary bird. Ordinarily they rest lengthwise of branches.

The call of this species resembles the syllables *poor-will poor-will, poor-will-low*. Near at hand these calls are harsh, but with distance the first two assume a pleasant, somewhat melancholy cadence. The third, often omitted, is harsher. Occasionally, in the nesting season, one may be heard in daytime. The poorwill feeds on insects. Beetles, moths, and various species of the locust group are favorites. When feeding, the birds may course along the ground, or rest in open places, rising in short flights to seize passing insects in their capacious mouths, which are fringed with long bristles. They watch for insects attracted by electric lights, even seizing them against the globes. Hard portions of their food are ejected as pellets after digestion.

The eggs are placed on a patch of gravel, on flat rock exposures, or in slight hollows scratched in the bare earth. They may be in the open or under brush. Two eggs constitute a set. They vary from white to cream, unmarked or with delicate purplish spots. Both birds are said to assist in incubation. When disturbed about the nest, they tumble about and with widely opened mouths make a loud, snakelike hissing sound.

Nuttall's poorwill *(Phalaenoptilus nuttalli nuttalli)* is found from southeastern British Columbia and North Dakota to eastern Kansas, southern Arizona, and eastern California. It winters from California and Texas to central Mexico. The dusky poorwill *(Phalaenoptilus nuttalli californicus)* is found in California west of the Sierra Nevada, south to northwestern Baja California. The desert poorwill *(Phalaenoptilus nuttalli hueyi)* occurs in the valley of the Lower Colorado River. The San Ignacio poorwill ranges in Baja California south of latitude 30°.

Merrill's Pauraque

(Nyctidromus albicollis merrilli)

Average Length, Twelve Inches

This nocturnal species belongs to a tropical group that barely crosses our border in the lower Rio Grande Valley. It is found in dense thickets in wooded lowlands in the winter months, and in the nesting season spreads to sections where the cover of shrubs and trees is more open. It rests during the day on the ground, or on low limbs, where it perches lengthwise of the branch, and is only flushed by chance, when it darts off with rapid, erratic flight. Though sensitive to light, it seems to fly easily when frightened in daytime.

The length of the tarsus, or lower part of the leg, and the strength of the toes in these birds is marked, compared with our other species. Seemingly this would indicate that the bird has greater ability and ease of movement on the ground than its fellows.

The name pauraque is given in imitation of its call. The song is in three syllables and may be written *pau ra kee*. It is uttered in loud, harsh tones and repeated steadily. In addition, it has an explosive note that resembles the call of a turkey.

The pauraque lives on insects that it captures in its large mouth on the wing, watching for its prey from a perch on the top of a bush, on a log, or from an open spot on the ground. Not much is known of its food, except that it eats beetles and moths. One naturalist records that he found the stomach of a pauraque filled with fireflies.

The two eggs are placed on the bare ground, usually near a clump of bushes, with no attempt whatever at nest building. The eggs differ in color from those of other species of this family found in the United States, varying from cream to deep buff, spotted and blotched with varying shades of brown and lilac. Their bold markings are quite distinctive. Occasional eggs are nearly plain, with a few markings that are so fine that they pass unnoticed except on close examination; but this is unusual.

The adult offers little objection when the nest is approached, sitting close until forced to take wing, and then flying only a short distance before settling quietly. The nesting season along the lower Rio Grande begins during the second week in April, reaches its height in May, and ends toward the close of June. It is possible that two broods may be reared each season.

Merrill's pauraque ranges from the Gulf coast of southern Texas and the lower Rio Grande Valley south into Tamaulipas. In winter it is found in Mexico south to Vera Cruz and Puebla. It is a representative of a wide-ranging species distributed through tropical America to Brazil.

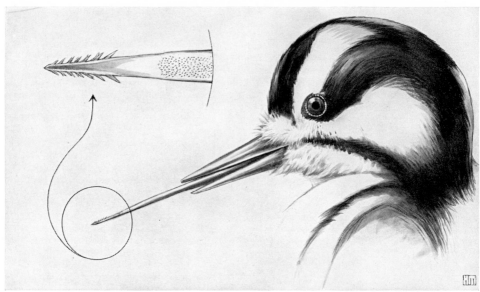

Drawing by Hashime Murayama

A WOODPECKER'S TONGUE IS A FORMIDABLE CONCEALED SPEAR

The free end is armed with spines, so that wood-boring larvæ may be impaled as on a spear, and so be drawn from their hidden tunnels in trunks of trees. This illustration of the hairy wood-pecker shows also the spiny tip as seen from above, enlarged four times. The slender bones that support the greatly elongated tongue slide in a sheath that extends around the back of the head and over the crown.

Photograph by Dr. Frank N. Wilson

A NIGHTHAWK EXAMINES HER NEST AND EGGS

This picture, unusual because the bird's home is difficult to find, was taken on Beaver Island, Lake Michigan (page 47).

WOODPECKERS, GUARDIANS OF OUR TREES

This Numerous Family, Which Includes Several Species of Flickers and Sapsuckers, Does Much More Good Than Harm in Forests

By T. Gilbert Pearson

ONE sunny morning in late autumn, I pushed through a growth of briers and entered a small wood in search of any birds which might be abroad. My footsteps rustled the newly fallen leaves and made a quiet advance impossible, so I sat down on a fallen tree, hoping that soon some kind of bird might come my way.

I had sat there only a minute or two when the sounds of repeated tappings from some near-by point reached my ears. They seemed to come from a decayed tree stub, about 20 feet away. Shifting my position, I could see in the stub a small round hole 12 feet from the ground. Just then a downy woodpecker appeared in the entrance and dropped a billful of small chips. Seeing a man so near, he uttered a sharp note and flew to a tree near by.

Woodpeckers excavate holes in trees for their nests, but, as everyone knows, birds lay their eggs in the spring, and here this little workman was digging a hole late in October. It was to be his winter bedroom, where he could pass the nights, shielded from winds and sleet and safe from the claws of hungry owls that haunt the shadows of the woodlands. One evening a little later I saw him enter the hole, and on another occasion in the twilight I was rude enough to disturb his privacy by tapping on the stub. The unexpected knocking on the wall of his chamber aroused his suspicion and caused him to fly away.

When winter approaches, the downy does not migrate as do so many other birds. Any day, when the weather is not too inclement, he may be found not far away. He is often in company with a number of chickadees that are traveling about among the tree tops. The *yank* of a white-breasted nuthatch announces his presence, and now and then a quiet brown creeper joins the troop, all of them hunting for insect eggs tucked away in crevices of the bark.

The downy is a valuable bird among the orchard trees, where he destroys innumerable insects, their eggs and larvæ. As a rule he is unsuspicious and will come readily to the garden or lawn to procure the suet wired to a limb for winter bird guests.

In rural districts this bird, along with the somewhat larger hairy woodpecker, is generally called sapsucker, and is often shot with the mistaken idea that a noxious bird is being killed. Like every other creature, he has his natural enemies. One day, while watching the activities of various birds in a small strip of woods by a country roadside, I heard the startled alarm notes which birds give when sudden danger breaks upon them.

A jay dashed headlong into a cedar, and a robin, too frightened to fly, stood erect and rigid on a limb. Then a sharp-shinned hawk swept past, seized a downy woodpecker from the side of a tree, and carried away his shrieking victim.

WOODPECKERS EASILY RECOGNIZED

There are few birds that so satisfactorily reveal their family connection as do the woodpeckers. The beginner in bird study may learn that the meadowlark belongs to the family Icteridae, but he may be excused if he does not learn at once that the bobolink, the oriole, and the red-winged blackbird, all strikingly different in habits and color, belong to the same family. He may study the wood thrush, and be surprised to find later that the robin and the bluebird bear to it a close family relationship. But if he becomes thoroughly familiar with the appearance and activities of just one woodpecker, he will thereafter be able to recognize at once any other member of the family Picidae which he may encounter.

Woodpeckers are of wide distribution. They inhabit all the countries of the globe except Madagascar and the Australian

Photograph by George Shiras, 3d   Drawing by Hashime Murayama
THE "BILLWORK" AND THE "FOOTWORK" OF A WOODPECKER

At the left are the workings of a pileated woodpecker on a dead tree near Whitefish Lake, Michigan. The powerful birds use their chisel-like bills to make large, deep cavities in decaying trees and logs in search of larvæ. In the ordinary form, as with the hairy woodpecker shown in the upper figure of the right-hand picture, there are two toes directed forward and two behind, forming a yoke, with the claws curved and sharply pointed. The bird indicated at the side illustrates the position of the feet in climbing. The inner toe is reduced in size, and in the specialized foot of the peculiar three-toed woodpeckers, illustrated in the lower figure, is entirely lost, so that there is only one toe behind. Both feet shown are from the left side and are drawn natural size.

region. More than four hundred species are known, and many geographical forms of these have been described.

In North America the family is represented by 10 genera, classified into 22 species, several of which in turn are divided into subspecies or geographical forms. In all, 64 kinds of woodpeckers are recognized in continental United States, Canada, and Baja California.

Woodpeckers do not possess the stately dignity of the heron, the singing powers of the thrush, or the graceful flight of the swallow. They do not stir the imagination to thoughts of distant lands, as does the wild goose when far overhead we see him leading his flock toward the frozen pole. The woodpeckers are known rather as hard-working, substantial citizens of the bird world, rendering service which could ill be spared.

These birds possess highly specialized equipment for their business of getting a living. They are the only birds in our country that can dig holes in solid trees. As a group they pass most of their days

Photograph by Stanley W. Cosby   Photograph by A. A. Allen

CALIFORNIA WOODPECKERS USE OLD FENCE POSTS AND TELEPHONE POLES
AS STOREHOUSES

The energetic California woodpeckers collect acorns from oaks and wedge them into holes which they have cut for the purpose and in which they are preserved for later use. At times, thousands of acorns are stored in the trunk of a single large tree. Occasionally, the food-storing instinct goes astray and the laboriously made holes are stuffed with pebbles or other inedible objects. At the right a downy woodpecker clings to an apple tree beside the small oval hole which it has made to reach in with its barbed tongue and extract a borer.

pecking decayed trees or stumps for ants or the larvæ of wood-boring beetles.

No other bird leaves behind such striking evidence of its presence. A hundred thousand warblers may migrate through a small region, and many may remain for the summer and rear their young. When they have gone, little sign of their former presence is left behind, but a half dozen woodpeckers in the same community will leave very definite evidence of their occupancy. Numerous holes in dead trees, with here and there an entrance to a nesting cavity, will all bear convincing testimony

that these birds have been in the forests and the orchards of the neighborhood.

Woodpeckers nest in hollows which they dig in trees, and all of them lay white eggs on beds of fine chips at the bottoms of the cavities they fashion.

Their toes usually number four, two of them pointing forward and the others backward. This arrangement enables the birds to grasp firmly the side of a tree, and especially is this the case when they brace themselves with their long, stiff tail feathers.

It was one morning early in spring that I found a mourning cloak butterfly stupefied

THE PILEATED IS SECOND LARGEST OF OUR
WOODPECKERS

In size it ranks next to the great ivory-bill, and, like that
bird, is an inhabitant of the wilder woodlands, and disappears with too much human encroachment on its haunts.
Most birds have strong neck muscles, as the bill must serve
in picking up and carrying comparatively weighty objects,
having in a way the function of the human hand; but in the
woodpeckers the neck muscles are especially developed, as
these birds are engaged constantly in the hard labor of digging in wood with their bills. The steady and continued
motion with which they work is remarkable. Compensa-
tion to absorb the shock of the impact from the repeated
heavy blows of the bill is highly perfected, as otherwise
there would be definite injury to the brain, the eyes, the
ears, and other delicate parts of the head.

with drink. It flew sluggishly from the
side of a tree and sprawled on the ground
not four feet away. With wings distended
it lay as if all ambition for movement had
departed. A moment later I discovered
that at least 20 others were likewise pros-
trate on the ground, and that fully a dozen

were still on the side of the tree.

They were drinking their fill
of sap that flowed from many
small holes which had been drilled
through the bark. A yellow-bellied
sapsucker had been here and I
hoped that it might be found somewhere in the neighborhood. In
five minutes I located it hanging
quietly to the side of another tree,
and all about were little holes from
which oozed sap twinkling in the
sunlight.

The sapsucker is looked upon
with serious disfavor by foresters
and orchardists, some variety of it
being found in nearly every part
of the country. This dislike arises
from its universal custom of pecking holes in live trees. The bird
does this chiefly to get the sap
which flows upward through the
soft cambium lying just beneath
the bast, or inner bark, and it also
eats the cambium and bast. To
get this food the sapsucker drills
holes in rings around the tree or,
at times, in rows on the trunk, or
along a limb.

As the sap collects in the openings, it is consumed by the bird
until the little springs begin to
fail, when another series of holes
is made near the first one. Thus
the work continues, until large
areas of the tree may be covered
with these perforations.

In North Carolina I had opportunity to watch the work performed by a sapsucker on a small
balsam growing on a college campus. The tree had been used by
sapsuckers for some years, and
numerous partly healed scars were
in evidence. I first saw the bird
pecking a fresh hole one day in
autumn. Probably it had just arrived from its northern summer
home. Only a few wells were sunk
through the bark at this time, but
I saw the bird on the tree at intervals throughout the winter.

When spring came and the sap began to
rise, the sapsucker became very busy, and
worked industriously every day until March
29, when the bark showed 671 openings
which had been made since the previous
autumn. As a rule the holes were about
as large around as a lead pencil. Some

were smaller, and others were of much larger size. One that I measured was an inch and a quarter long by three-quarters of an inch wide.

Some of the openings were at a distance of less than a foot from the ground, and they extended upward over much of the surface of the tree for 20 feet or to a point about two-thirds of the way to the top. The branches of the tree began 12 feet from the ground, and three of these contained a sprinkling of sapsucker holes. I kept a watch on this tree and examined it at intervals for the next 15 years. I believe that a sapsucker came here for its food every winter and spring throughout this entire period.

The tree became much swollen, as Nature struggled to overcome the damage done to it by the birds. When it finally died, the diameter of the tree at a height of seven feet was 25 per cent greater than it was seven inches above the ground. There were other trees near by, but this balsam was the only one in the vicinity for which the sapsuckers seemed to care.

SAPSUCKERS LEVY TRIBUTE ON MANY TREES

Elsewhere I have watched sapsuckers feeding on the sap of many kinds of trees, and have seen the holes or swollen rings produced by their drilling. They will take the sap of maple, mountain ash, pear, plum, apple, cherry, oak, peach, spruce, and ironwood trees, and of almost all species of pines, firs, hemlocks, cedars, cypress, or cottonwoods.

In the northern forests, where many sapsuckers pass the summer, numerous birch trees are killed annually by them. In the Northwest, where at times sapsuckers are unusually plentiful, whole apple orchards have been destroyed. Fruit growers, thus losing their source of income, have no love for the birds.

In some trees, such as maples, walnuts, and hickories, their holes often pierce the sapwood beneath the cambium. In the subsequent growth of the trees, these wounds sometimes cause curly or bird's-eye wood well known to lumbermen. More often, however, this exposure of the wood allows insects, fungi, or bacteria to enter. These cause blemishes or decayed areas, which reduce in value the lumber which later may be cut from the tree.

About the rings of holes made by these birds in locusts and sycamores, shoots often

Photograph by A. A. Allen

ALMOST READY TO LEAVE HOME

These young yellow-shafted flickers were raised in the bird house. Unlike most birds, young flickers resemble their fathers instead of their mothers. Note the black mustache on each bird, a mark of the male in grown individuals, as adult female flickers do not possess it.

sprout from adventitious buds, and thus the symmetry of the tree is marred. Not only are hundreds of thousands of trees injured by sapsuckers, but a considerable proportion of those that are attacked die either the same year or subsequently.

These woodpeckers do not confine their attentions wholly to trees. They make their explorations for sap through the bark of large vines like the Virginia creeper, poison ivy, rattan, and trumpet creeper.

In the nesting season they eat ants, flies, beetles, and numerous other insects which are drawn to the springs of sap. Other birds and squirrels come also to drink.

Downy Woodpecker

(Dryobates pubescens)

Average Length, Sixteen and Three-quarters Inches

The downy woodpecker, in its various forms, inhabits most of the timbered country of North America, from Alaska to Florida. Smallest of our woodpeckers, it lives in more or less open woodlands and is a familiar species that comes regularly to orchards, wood lots, parks, and the shade trees of our dooryards.

When approached, instead of flying away it often works around to the other side of the tree or limb up which it may be climbing. Remain quiet for a few minutes and it will peep around to see if you are still there and may then continue its search for food, or, if alarmed, may fly to a near-by tree. It is one of our most useful woodpeckers, eating the larvæ of bark and wood-boring beetles, insect eggs and ants.

Fruit growers should give it complete protection, for many of the most destructive orchard borers are favorite items in its diet. Caterpillars make up a large percentage of its food each year. The downy eats little fruit.

In spring the downy woodpecker mates and chisels out a nest cavity in a dead tree where the wood is not too hard. In this hole from three to six glossy white eggs are laid with no other nesting material than a few chips left from the work of excavation.

The downy is a year-round resident and in winter often keeps company with chickadees and nuthatches. Old nest holes are used as sleeping quarters, but the birds are solitary for most of the year and must therefore often dig winter nests in which to sleep, as there are not enough old nest holes to go around. The location of these and of the nest holes may sometimes be detected by seeing bits of wood lying on the ground near the selected tree.

The ordinary call of the downy is low and rather harsh, but cheerful. This clear *peek, peek* note frequently may be heard as the bird spirals up a tree trunk hunting for grubs and larvæ. In addition it utters a rattling call.

The northern downy woodpecker *(Dryobates pubescens medianus)* ranges from southeastern Alberta to Newfoundland and throughout the country southward to eastern Kansas, Tennessee, and Virginia.

Gairdner's woodpecker *(D. p. gairdneri)*, also illustrated on the plate, is a form of the humid coastal area from southern British Columbia to northern California. It is darker below than the other forms of downy woodpeckers and has little white on the wings. It is found in willows and other timber along the streams and comes also into orchards.

There are four other geographical forms of the downy in addition to the two just mentioned. These differ slightly in size and color, but all are found within the same range.

Hairy Woodpecker

(Dryobates villosus)

Average Length, Nine and One-half Inches

The hairy woodpecker closely resembles the downy in appearance, but is larger, some of its geographical forms being as many as three inches longer than its smaller relative. When in doubt as to which of the two species you are watching, focus your attention on the tail when it is spread, as is often the case when feeding. The outer white tail feathers of the downy bear black spots; those of the hairy lack such markings.

I have never found the hairy as abundant as the downy, though it occupies the same range under the same natural conditions. Furthermore, it is more of a woodland bird and hence is less often seen than is the downy which so frequently comes to the trees about houses.

Hairy woodpeckers are destroyers of insects, many of which are injurious to mankind, and wise is the farmer or fruit grower who never kills them through the mistaken belief that their pecking is detrimental to his trees. Much of the food is composed of wood-boring larvæ that the woodpecker secures by drilling holes into the trunks of trees. The grubs are drawn from their tunnels by means of the extensible barb-tipped tongue, which can reach far beyond the end of the bill and is a remarkable organ. (See p. 50.)

There is no great seasonal variation in the ratio of animal to vegetable food because the borers and most of the seeds the hairy eats are obtainable throughout the year.

The hairy flies strongly in deep undulations and its swift passage among the tangled branches of an evergreen forest is a miracle of split-second timing.

The hairy woodpecker builds its nest in holes cut in tree trunks, often on the underside of limbs. The nests may be found in upland forests, along the borders of swamp lands, in the cottonwood groves of the West, or in the chinaberry trees of southern plantations. From three to five glossy white eggs ordinarily make a set and one brood is the usual number for the season. Fourteen days of incubation are required for the eggs to hatch.

These birds are widespread throughout North America, where ornithologists have recognized no less than 21 local varieties or geographical forms.

Harris's woodpecker *(D. v. harrisi)* is found in the humid coast country of southern British Columbia and northern California. It is rather easily distinguishable from its relatives of the East, for the white spots on the wings are much less noticeable than those of the eastern form, and the feathers of the throat, breast, and belly are brownish instead of white.

WOODPECKERS HELP MOTHER NATURE WITH HER HOUSEKEEPING

By eating injurious insects, their eggs and larvæ, these carpenters of birddom protect fruit trees and woodlots. The **Northern Downy Woodpecker** (male and female, upper left) is a familiar eastern resident. Less abundant and much larger than the downy, though resembling it in appearance and habits, is the **Hairy Woodpecker** (lower left). It prefers lonelier woodlands and is represented by 21 varieties throughout North America. **Gairdner's Woodpecker** (upper right) and **Harris's Woodpecker** (lower right) are Pacific coast variants of the downy and hairy woodpeckers.

Texas Woodpecker

(Dryobates scalaris symplectus)
Average Length, Seven and One-half Inches

This form of the ladder-backed woodpecker is found in southeastern Colorado, central and western Texas, and adjacent Mexico.

Throughout a large portion of Texas it is by far the most abundant woodpecker, and, like the downy of the Northeastern States, is the best-known of its family in the region it chiefly inhabits. It frequents the post-oak and chaparral country, and where trees are scarce it perches in bushes and feeds about the cacti. It is a bird of the lowlands, preferring slopes below five thousand feet, where it may be tracked down by its thin but very persistent note.

It comes into the towns and into parks or yards with trees, there to be seen diligently at work gathering its food. Wood-boring beetle larvæ, caterpillars and ants are its favorite food. Living, as it does, mainly in regions where large trees are absent, one need not be surprised to find its nest within a few feet of the ground. The hole is often excavated under the curve of a limb on an oak or mesquite tree and may even be found in telephone poles or gate posts.

Fifteen forms of this species are known, of which three others occur in the United States and Baja California.

Red-cockaded Woodpecker

(Dryobates borealis)
Average Length, Eight and One-third Inches

This bird is a resident in the yellow-pine country of the South Atlantic and Gulf States, and northward to southeastern Virginia, Tennessee, and southern Missouri.

The large white cheek patch, untraversed by any suggestion of a black stripe, at once identifies it as not being a downy or a hairy woodpecker, both more or less common in the red-cockaded's range. It frequents the tops rather than the lower limbs of trees and, unlike the downy, it avoids human habitations, orchards and shade trees.

This is a bird of the open pine woods, and is rarely seen except among pine trees and seldom alone. All through the winter months I have found them, sometimes four or five, or even six, feeding together.

When feeding they call frequently, in a sharp and strident voice that has a very noticeable carrying power. Often they are seen in the tops of the tallest long-leaf pines, industriously searching for food on the limbs or the terminal twigs. When thus occupied they do not mind hanging head downward if the exigencies of the moment require such a position.

The nest is made in a large living pine tree, the heart of which is more or less decayed. This bird may return year after year to the same nesting tree, although sometimes its nest is stolen by the bigger red-bellied woodpecker. The white eggs number from three to five.

Nuttall's Woodpecker

(Dryobates nuttalli)
Average Length, Seven Inches

Nuttall's woodpecker is found from southern Oregon to Baja California, but occurs only west of the southern Cascades and the Sierra Nevadas. It is about the size of the Texas woodpecker and, except for the little black area on the forepart of the head and the somewhat lighter breast, varies little in appearance from that bird.

It is a noisy, naturally suspicious bird and is very likely to announce its presence upon seeing a visitor approaching the tree which it occupies. It utters a "rattling staccato cry."

This woodpecker nests in dead or in living trees of many varieties, and digs a hole from 3 to 60 feet above the ground. The male helps incubate the four to six white eggs, and is very solicitous about them and the young, which appear after a two weeks' period of incubation. Nuttall's woodpecker is usually found in openly wooded areas or groves, often where trees are of small size.

Arizona Woodpecker

(Dryobates arizonae arizonae)
Average Length, Eight Inches

The Arizona woodpecker ranges throughout the mountains of southeastern Arizona and southwestern New Mexico and across the Mexican border in suitable mountain regions as far south as Durango.

It is a bird of the mountains, being found in foothill areas in rocky canyons or again in more open localities in groves or regions of scattered trees. It is particularly partial to oaks. In summer it is widely spread, but on the approach of winter it leaves the higher altitudes for lower levels. Less common than most species of the family, its habits are not so well known.

It is quiet and inconspicuous, climbing over tree trunks like other small woodpeckers in its search for food. Though it eats many insects, it can thrive well on a diet composed largely of acorns. When hunting food it usually begins near the base of a tree and works up the trunk, along the limbs and even out into the foliage. It picks tiny insects out of pits and crannies in the bark instead of drilling into the wood for them.

Occasionally these birds are found in bands, but more often are encountered alone and are shy and retiring. The nests are placed in holes cut in dead trunks or branches and the white eggs usually number three or four in a set.

An allied form of the species is found in southwestern Mexico.

ALL WOODPECKERS SHARE A STRIKING FAMILY RESEMBLANCE

It's easy to say "That's a woodpecker!" but to tell what kind is another story. The **Texas Woodpecker** (female and male, upper left) gets its name from its abundance in that State. Very similar in appearance is **Nuttall's Woodpecker** (upper right) of the Pacific coast. The **Red-cockaded Woodpecker** (below, at the left) lives in open pine forests of the southeastern United States. Acorns as well as insects form the diet of the shy, mountain-loving **Arizona Woodpecker** (lower right) of the Mexican border.

Sapsucker

(Sphyrapicus varius)

Average Length, Nine Inches

The sapsucker as a species ranges throughout the wooded regions from Alaska to Panama. The yellow-bellied sapsuckers *(Sphyrapicus varius varius)*, a form illustrated on the opposite plate, is the most migratory of all our woodpeckers. In the breeding season it occupies many localities from Alberta east to Cape Breton Island, and south to central Missouri and northern Ohio; also from western Massachusetts to the mountains of North Carolina.

In autumn this bird leaves Canada and spreads over the eastern United States from Iowa and New England southward to the Gulf of Mexico. Some even travel to Cuba, Jamaica, Haiti, Mexico, and as far as Panama. During migrations the male birds have the unusual habit of preceding the females into the new territory.

This is one of the few woodpeckers that eat more vegetable than animal food. As implied by the name, birds of this group are fond of sap. To obtain this, it passes much time in pecking holes through the bark of trees. Often these are small, round punctures, and again the bark is removed in little squares, sometimes half an inch or more across. The holes are made in rows about the trunks or the larger limbs.

When the soft cambium layer of the bark is reached by the industriously working bird, it is eaten as it is picked from the hole. As drops of sap accumulate they are sucked up and the hole is wiped out by the tongue, which is tipped with a little brush instead of the dartlike point that terminates this organ in the typical woodpecker.

Particularly in the southern States, serious damage results from this theft of the sap and the soft inner bark of standing timber, and the birds consequently incur the disapproval of timber growers. These woodpeckers also eat many of the insects attracted by the exuding liquid.

The nests of sapsuckers are dug in living or dead trees and contain four to seven white eggs.

The manner in which the amazingly rapid tattoo beat of the courting sapsucker comes to an end quickly acquaints the experienced ear with the fact that one of these birds is abroad in the land. Sometimes it drums on a dry branch or a hard strip of bark just for fun.

The extremely handsome northern red-breasted sapsucker *(S. v. ruber)*, found in summer from southern Alaska to western Oregon, is illustrated on the plate.

The southern red-breasted sapsucker *(S. v. daggetti)*, a close relative, breeds in the mountain country of California.

Another form, the red-naped sapsucker *(S. v. nuchalis)*, occurs from British Columbia and northeastern California to Wyoming, New Mexico, and west Texas.

Williamson's Sapsucker

(Sphyrapicus thyroideus)

Average Length, Nine and One-half Inches

This handsome species ranges in the western mountains from southern British Columbia and Montana to central Arizona and New Mexico. In winter it migrates south as far as Texas, and northern Baja California and Jalisco, in Mexico. This is the only American four-toed woodpecker that has no red feathers on the head or the nape in either sex.

In the case of most North American woodpeckers, the sexes so closely resemble each other that even when there is a difference in their plumage the careful observer has little difficulty in determining that they are of the same species. The male and the female of Williamson's sapsucker are so dissimilar in appearance that, when the bird was first discovered, for many years they were supposed to be different species.

The female was described by Cassin in 1851 and became known as the brown-headed woodpecker. In 1857 Newberry described the male and believed it to be a distinct form. It was not until 1873 that Henshaw discovered the true relationship of these supposedly separate species.

Like other sapsuckers, this bird pierces the bark of trees for much of its food. However, it prefers the sap of pines and is inclined to neglect the deciduous trees of the regions it inhabits. It enlarges its area of feeding pits steadily, so that on the trunk of a yellow pine these may occupy a square foot or more.

The call note is low and complaining, being somewhat stronger than that of the other sapsuckers. The drum of this sapsucker generally resembles that of the other species, though it is slower and less energetic than that of most others. The nest may be in a dead pine or a living aspen; the white eggs number from four to six. When the female is on the nest, the male frequently stands guard on a nearby branch, and both sexes are highly attentive in caring for their families.

The birds sometimes nest at high altitudes, even to 10,000 feet. The site may be in dense or open woodland and at times the sapsuckers may have hole-nesting wrens and swallows as neighbors in other cavities in the same tree trunk. The young resemble the female when they first leave the nest, the males changing later to the brighter plumage.

Another form, Natalie's sapsucker *(S. t. nataliae)*, breeds in the Rocky Mountain region from Montana to New Mexico.

SAPSUCKERS ARE THE BLACK SHEEP OF THE TREE-BORING TRIBES

Orchardists and foresters frown upon these businesslike drillers that ring favorite trees with myriad tiny holes to drain the life-giving sap. Of a handsome and widely distributed species, none is more striking than the **Red-breasted Sapsucker** (upper left) that breeds from Alaska to Oregon. The **Yellow-bellied Sapsucker** (male above his mate, upper right), of the eastern United States and southern Canada, is the widest ranging of his kind. Unusual among woodpeckers is the clear-cut contrast between male and female plumage, so evident in the **Williamson's Sapsucker** (male and female, below) that frequents pine forests of the western mountains.

White-headed Woodpecker
(Dryobates albolarvatus)
Average Length, Nine Inches

The range of the northern white-headed woodpecker *(D. a. albolarvatus)* extends from Washington through the Cascades and Sierra Nevadas to Kern County, California; also in western Nevada and Idaho. A few have been found across the Canadian line in the Province of British Columbia.

Another geographic form, the southern white-headed woodpecker *(D. a. gravirostris)*, ranges through the mountains of San Gabriel, San Bernardino, San Jacinto, Santa Rosa, and Cuyamaca, in southern California.

This is another of the numerous varieties of woodpeckers that inhabit the States bordering on the Pacific Ocean. Incidentally it is one of the easiest to describe. It is "a black woodpecker with white head and a white wing patch." Its plumage bears no longitudinal bars and no spots. All except three of our North American woodpeckers are characterized by such markings, either in the adult or in the immature stage of plumage. There is a red stripe across the nape of the male, but at a distance this is not distinguishable. The female is without this decorative marking.

This species makes its home among the coniferous trees of the mountains. Pine seeds constitute more than fifty percent of its food. Insects (half of them ants) complete the fare. The bark of the pines is very rough, with cracks and fissures checkering its surface. Furthermore, it consists of many layers, the outer scales of which warp, and thus make fine hiding places for spiders and small insects. To obtain these the woodpecker pries off fragments of bark, using his bill as a crowbar rather than as a pick.

The white-head's exploratory efforts are entertaining as it boldly pokes its head into cavernous gashes in the tree trunks, twisting from side to side—the epitome of thoroughness and industry. But in spite of the routine nature of grub hunting, life among the giant pines appears to be a continuous adventure for this woodpecker. To vary its technique, it may alight upside down on the under side of a limb, or may walk backward down a tree. The birds are a protection to the forests, for in many places their numbers are legion and the quantity of injurious beetles they consume must be truly enormous.

The nest is made either in a dead or a living tree. In California I have watched them visiting their nests that had been dug in the bark of sequoia trees. Since the bark of these ancient forest giants is from one to two feet thick, it serves a useful purpose for the woodpeckers when the season comes to assume their domestic duties. From three to seven white eggs constitute a set.

Arctic Three-toed Woodpecker
(Picoïdes arcticus)
Average Length, Nine and One-half Inches

This species is found somewhat regularly, but never abundantly, except in newly burnt lands, in northern California, Montana, Wyoming, Minnesota, Michigan, New York, Vermont, New Hampshire, and Maine; north to northern Quebec, Mackenzie, and central Alaska.

Here is a bird that loves evergreens. Deciduous trees are not to its liking. Along the northern border of our States and in Canada, when floods or fires kill the coniferous trees, look for the three-toed woodpeckers. From far and near they gather to feed upon the wood-borers that assail the lifeless trees. Very quietly, with only an occasional call, they go about the business of collecting food. Stripping off the bark, they seize the grubs lurking beneath it and explore the burrows of borers.

Not particularly shy, the three-toed is nevertheless hard to approach because of its nervous restlessness. Audubon compared its infrequent shrill cries to "those of some small quadruped suffering great pain."

This bird excavates its nest in either dead or living coniferous trees and four or five white eggs are deposited.

American Three-toed Woodpecker
(Picoïdes tridactylus bacatus)
Average Length, Eight and Three-quarters Inches

This bird ranges from northern Labrador and Mackenzie to our northern tier of States from Minnesota eastward, and is a permanent resident wherever found. It measures from eight to nine and three-quarters inches in length, thus being smaller in size than the species just discussed. The best way to distinguish it, however, is to look for the pattern of numerous bars of white that traverse its back, and to remember that the back of the Arctic three-toed is solid black. The cry of the American three-toed resembles that of his Arctic cousin.

In general habits the two birds are much alike, both feeding largely on an insect diet, but eating also nuts, acorns, wild fruit, and the cambium layer under the bark of trees. This species digs out larvæ of wood-boring beetles and moths all year round, but particularly during the colder months. The nesting habits are like those of the related species.

There are two other geographic forms of *Picoïdes tridactylus* in the United States, the alpine three-toed woodpecker *(P. t. dorsalis)*, ranging from Montana and Wyoming to Arizona and New Mexico, and the Alaska three-toed woodpecker *(P. t. fasciatus)*, which inhabits forests from Oregon and Montana northward to Alaska and western Mackenzie.

LIKE TELEPHONE LINEMEN, FEATHERED WOODCHOPPERS HANG ON BY THEIR FEET

With powerful, curved claws they fasten on limbs to pry and drill for insects. The far-western **White-headed Woodpecker** (upper left), "a black woodpecker with white head and a white wing patch," is one of the easiest to describe. Freaks in a four-toed family are the **American Three-toed** (right center) and the **Arctic Three-toed Woodpecker** (at bottom, male with the yellow cap, female half hidden), both lovers of the evergreen forests of the western mountains, the northern States, and Canada.

HANDSOME FLICKERS AND A RARE COUSIN

By T. Gilbert Pearson

AMONG the woodpeckers the flicker is a bird of distinctive personality, and it attracts universal attention. Undoubtedly it is known to far more people than are the other woodpeckers. Its local names are numerous. "Wilkrissen," the people of Cape Hatteras call it. I have heard it spoken of as the "yucker bird," "golden-winged woodpecker," "high-holder," and "pigeon woodpecker." One very popular name is "yellow-hammer."

The red-headed woodpeckers and others of the family will now and then dart down to a road or to the lawn to capture an insect, or to pick up an acorn, but when the flicker drops to the ground he remains there for some time, often until frightened away. In the woods, the field, or the garden, we may come upon him hopping awkwardly through the grass.

His chief interest at such times is ants, which constitute 50 per cent of his food. He secures them by use of his remarkable tongue, which can be thrust outward two and a half inches or more beyond the end of the bill. His tongue is at all times covered with a sticky saliva, which catches and holds the ants as they rush forward to attack what appears to be a long worm that has crawled across their path or entered their burrow. Prof. F. E. L. Beal counted 5,000 small ants in the stomach of one bird and more than 3,000 each in the stomachs of two others.

THE TONGUE IS A DELICATE AND MOST EFFICIENT ORGAN

This tongue is a very wonderful organ. Behind the mouth it branches, and the two horns pass up the rear of the skull. On top they meet, and close together the two parts run forward and downward over the right eye to the right nostril, which they enter, and extend onward into the base of the bill.

Flickers often associate with robins, and in the northern part of their range they may accumulate in considerable numbers during the time of migration. A few years ago, while inspecting the city park properties of Baltimore in an effort to decide what should be done there to attract wild birds, I found flickers, robins, and purple grackles to be the most common birds. All of these are ground feeders.

In the mating season flickers are very noisy, and their antics, as they dodge about the trees or bow to each other, are most amusing. The female is coy at first, and the male follows her from tree to tree. Then, becoming bolder, he sidles up to her, swinging his head and displaying the beauties of spread wings and tail as he softly calls, *yucker, yucker, yucker*. A rival male appears, and both suitors outdo themselves in prancing, bowing, and generally showing off. They keep up a great fuss and produce a greater variety of sounds than does any other bird of my acquaintance. More than 40 different notes have been recognized.

Like other woodpeckers, these birds feed their young by regurgitation. When the little ones are old enough to come to the mouth of the nesting hole to be fed, this operation may often be observed. The parent puts its bill into the mouth of a nestling, and repeatedly stabs downward in a most alarming manner.

FLICKERS KEEP UP THE EGG SUPPLY

Some flickers have the curious habit of continuing to lay an egg daily if, before the clutch is completed, all the eggs except one are taken. Being careful always to leave one nest egg, Joseph Armfield, of Greensboro, North Carolina, was the cause of one of these birds laying 32 eggs in 35 days. Ordinarily a flicker lays four or five eggs, but Charles L. Phillips writes in *Bird-Lore* of a female that laid 71 eggs in 73 days.

Flickers frequently enter barns, unused schoolhouses, or deserted buildings of various kinds. To get in, they will, if necessary, drill entrance holes through the weatherboarding. In the woods on Roanoke Island, North Carolina, there stood, some years ago, a small wooden church which contained several of their holes that had been made through the weatherboards just under the eaves.

There were four hollow wooden pillars supporting the roof of the veranda, and I found in them no less than 10 holes. The flickers had been at work for some time, for I noticed tin tacked here and there on the pillars where the caretaker had covered old openings. Sometimes these birds cut holes through the sides of ice-houses, throw out some of the hard-packed sawdust, and lay their eggs in the cavities thus formed. In a hundred ways, flickers adapt their habits to their environment, and are one of the marked successes of the woodpecker tribe.

THE THRILL OF SEEING A LIVING IVORY-BILLED WOODPECKER

The supreme moment of my life as a bird student came in May, 1932, when in a great primeval forest in northern Louisiana, I saw, for the first time, a living ivory-billed woodpecker. Many ornithologists have sought this bird during the past 40 years, but few have succeeded in their quest. My own expeditions to discover this rare species began in 1891, when I traversed the lonely stretches of the great Dismal Swamp that lies spread across the boundary line of the States of Virginia and North Carolina.

Trips with the ivory-bill especially in mind have since been made in the swamp lands of several southern States, but all of them ended in disappointment. The opportunity finally came through the kindness of members of the Louisiana State Conservation Commission.

A male bird 21 inches in length had been sent to the Commissioner's office. I was invited to New Orleans to go as the guest of the State in search of any living specimens that might be left in the neighborhood where this one had been shot. With Ernest G. Holt I journeyed south, and a week was passed in search of the birds. We found them, only half a dozen, to be sure, but the satisfaction of seeing even this small number of a species that appears to be on the verge of extinction was great indeed. It is sincerely to be hoped that by means of complete protection the species may be saved and its numbers gradually increased.

The ivory-bill is decidedly larger than the pileated, and this difference in size is very apparent, as we had ample opportunity to observe, when by chance birds of both species fed at the same time on a tall decayed stump within 80 feet of our hiding place. (See page 73.)

The note of the ivory-bill is not so loud as that produced by several kinds of smaller woodpeckers. It might be described as a nasal *kent* repeated continually as the bird feeds. We heard nothing resembling the *pait, pait, pait,* a monosyllable three times repeated, as described by Audubon a hundred years ago and subsequently mentioned by a number of other writers.

Its flight, so far as we observed, is not of the typical bounding woodpecker variety, but is more direct, and reminded me of the movements of a crow or a cormorant.

The birds were found feeding on the dead upper limbs of gum trees, or on decayed stumps and snags. Everywhere the forest was filled with evidences of the work of large woodpeckers, for there was hardly a dead tree that had not been stripped of its bark, and subsequently perforated with numerous holes of various sizes and shapes. How much of this was attributable to the ivory-bills could not be determined, since many pileated woodpeckers were present, and we did not discover any particular difference in the signs left on the trees by the two species.

What caused the disappearance of the ivory-billed woodpecker throughout its former range, from Texas and Illinois to North Carolina and Florida, is a question that may never be answered with entire satisfaction. Many great swamps with large trees still exist where the ivory-bill lived at one time, and where the large pileated is still plentiful. However, it is known that Indians often use the bills as ornaments, and many white people and negroes have killed these birds for food.

LOUISIANA HARBORS THE LAST OF THE IVORY-BILLED WOODPECKERS

In Louisiana we found them not particularly shy, and fully as easy to approach as were the numerous pileated woodpeckers of the territory. Perhaps some unsuspected natural cause has been accountable, in part, for their disappearance—perhaps man alone is to blame.

The Louisiana Department of Conservation has entered heartily into a plan to preserve this little colony of ivory-bills. In future no permits will be issued for collectors to kill them, and a special guard has been employed to range the forest which they inhabit and to protect from gunners these few remaining representatives of a vanishing race. Prof. A. A. Allen has made motion and sound pictures of them.

EVERYBODY KNOWS THE RED-HEAD, THAT CONCEITED RURAL DANDY

Protective legislation cannot destroy the woodpecker's worst enemy—his own bright coat. The nifty **Red-headed Woodpecker** (above, adult right and flying, young bird left) is found in semi-open country throughout most of the United States east of the Rockies. Below, at the left, perches the **California Woodpecker,** of the Pacific coast region, which pounds acorns into neatly excavated holes in tree-trunk "storehouses." The gray-bibbed **Lewis's Woodpecker** (lower right) of the Far West flies directly as a crow, in contrast to the undulating flight of most of his kind.

Red-headed Woodpecker

(Melanerpes erythrocephalus)
Average Length, Nine and One-half Inches

The range of the red-head extends from southeastern British Columbia, Ontario, and New York to New Mexico, central Texas, the Gulf coast, and southern Florida. It is irregularly migratory in the north.

These woodpeckers are very handsome birds and are so conspicuous in their red, white, and bluish-black attire that they are known to nearly everyone throughout much of North America. In many sections of the Eastern, Southern, and Middle Western States they are abundant. One sees them along fence rows, or lines of telephone posts, or clinging to the sides of trees. They come to the lawn, the orchard, the wood lot, or to isolated trees in the fields, preferring at all times open, or semi-open, country. Only the flicker is more commonly seen in the open than the red-head. Often they are very noisy and especially in spring and summer chase one another about.

They feed on acorns and beechnuts, also on a great variety of fruits, and consume large numbers of insects, many of which are harmful to the interests of mankind. Unlike most woodpeckers, they eagerly devour grasshoppers and flies. The red-head, the flicker, and Lewis's woodpecker are the only North American members of the family that regularly feed on the ground. Fortunately their value is recognized, and, with others of their family, they are everywhere protected by State laws.

The nests are made in tall stumps or dead trees. Lacking natural sites, the red-head will readily build in telephone poles, fence posts or holes in outbuildings. The white eggs are usually four or five in number. The young upon leaving the nest appear with a brownish-gray head and neck, and it is not until the molt of the next spring that the red feathers on the head appear. Naturalists visiting this country in colonial days reported the young red-head as a distinct species.

California Woodpecker

(Balanosphyra formicivora bairdi)
Average Length, Nine and One-half Inches

The species to which the California woodpecker belongs *(Balanosphyra formicivora)* is distributed from southern Texas, Arizona, and California south into western Panama. The California woodpecker ranges over much of the Pacific coast region from southern Oregon to southern California.

A few miles from Santa Barbara I came upon an oak tree which California woodpeckers had selected as a storehouse for acorns. The tree was forked and, beginning two feet above the point where the branches separated, and thence upward for more than fifteen feet, the bark was everywhere studded with acorns.

Holes had been pecked and the acorns driven in point first. Every acorn fitted its hole perfectly and had been pounded home by the bill of the bird. So tightly did they fit their cavities that I found it impossible to remove one, except by cutting it with my knife, or by removing some of the surrounding bark. Many thousands have been found in the trunk of a single tree. At times this curious storing habit goes astray and the birds place small stones in the holes instead of nuts. (See p. 178.)

Often when suitable trees are not available, the California woodpecker drills storing holes in corners of houses, church spires or other buildings. Telephone poles and fence posts are also frequently used. A result of this curious habit is much quarreling with squirrels, jays, and other creatures that steal from the acorn caches.

Half the food of this bird consists of acorns. It also eats flies, beetles, and insects picked from the bark of trees, or seized, flycatcher fashion, while on the wing.

California woodpeckers have eyes that are noticeable because they are generally creamy white. The nest is in a hole and the four or five eggs are white. There are four additional geographic forms within our limits.

Lewis's Woodpecker

(Asyndesmus lewis)
Average Length, Eleven Inches

This species ranges from southern British Columbia and Alberta to New Mexico, and from the mountains of California to South Dakota and Kansas.

This remarkable bird was one of the ornithological discoveries made during the exploring expedition to the Northwest by Lewis and Clark in the years 1804-1806.

This bird does not excavate in dead wood for its insect food, but catches it in the air or from the bark and leaves of trees, or descends to the ground for this purpose. It is one of the few woodpeckers that feed freely on the ground, where it seizes crickets, beetles, grasshoppers and other insects. It eats many acorns and some fruit, such as wild strawberries, and now and then cherries, pears, and apples. Like the California woodpecker, this species at times stores acorns.

Most woodpeckers have a bounding flight, but the present species flies as directly as a crow, a peculiarity that distinguishes it at a glance from others of its size. At times the birds are found in bands, their handsome colors flashing in the sunlight.

The bird does very little of the characteristic woodpecker carpentry, seldom digging out its own nesting hole. It seems greatly to prefer to occupy the deserted house of some other member of its tribe. Sometimes it even nests in natural cavities in trees. The white eggs number from five to nine.

THE FAMILIAR "YELLOW-HAMMER" IS A FEATHERED ANTEATER

Ants compose half the diet of the **Yellow-shafted Flicker** (below), which is the State bird of Alabama and one of the dozen best-known birds of the eastern United States. The flicker's spearlike tongue can be thrust out more than two and a half inches beyond the end of the bill and is covered with a sticky saliva to which tiny insects adhere. The **Red-shafted Flicker** (male and female, above) inhabits the great area between the plains States and the Pacific, making itself equally at home in remote regions and on village lawns.

Red-shafted Flicker

(Colaptes cafer)
Average Length, Thirteen Inches

The red-shafted flicker dwells in that vast region lying westward from South Dakota and western Texas and terminating only with the shores of the Pacific Ocean. It is not found in quite all sections of this territory, but in thousands of localities its rolling drumbeat and clamorous calls are known to every boy of the countryside. It is a resident throughout most of the districts in which it is found. In general, it is a trifle larger than the eastern flicker and is found more often in heavily forested regions than its cousin. The flashes of the red feathers which line the wings and the under side of the tail are among the well-known bits of color that catch the eye as one travels through fields and forests or by tree-bordered streams.

Few birds so well adapt themselves to every environment. Not only are they found in regions where man is seldom seen, but they dwell in the towns, and collect ants and other insects on the lawn, the college campus, and in the open sections of parks. Although more or less common in the semi-desert regions in winter, they usually are not found in such places during the heat of summer. They inhabit the mountains to the tree line, being perfectly at home in the higher regions up to altitudes of about 10,000 feet. They are also common in the low, hot valleys and the timbered bottom lands.

As a rule their nesting cavities are dug in dead trees, but sometimes live ones are selected for this purpose. They will use bird boxes, and if they find the entrance hole too small for their liking they will enlarge it to suit their needs. At times they cut holes through the weatherboards of a house and lay their eggs on the horizontal beam beneath the opening. They have also been known to dig burrows for their nests in banks of earth as do bank swallows and kingfishers.

Here and there we find a species of bird that has the habit of beginning to incubate as soon as the first egg is laid. This flicker is one of them. Bendire found a nest in Oregon which, he stated, contained five fresh eggs, two that were pipped, and three newly hatched young. Ten seems to be the greatest number of eggs laid. The clutch ordinarily consists of six or eight.

Four geographical forms of this flicker are recognized. There is not space here to discuss these in detail, and it would be rather pointless to attempt to do so. The distinguishing differences in size and color are so slight that an observer in the field would hardly be able to detect them. Indeed most of them are rather difficult to recognize when the birds are captured and compared in the hand. All are red-shafted flickers.

Yellow-shafted Flicker

(Colaptes auratus)
Average Length, Twelve Inches

Among the dozen best-known birds of eastern United States is the flicker widely known under the name of "yellow-hammer." Its rapidly repeated calls in spring and summer are heard on all sides, whether it be in a forest, orchard, park, or among trees bordering the highway. Where little disturbed and accustomed to see people pass to and fro, this bird loses much of its natural suspicion of man. Hence in towns one may usually approach much closer to a flicker than in the country districts.

Each of its numerous idiosyncrasies has given it a different name. But whether it is called "high-hole," "yarrup," "clape," "yellow-hammer," "wick-up," or just plain "flicker," it is the same friendly neighbor. The flicker is constantly on the move, up and down, in and out, and it makes friends with many kinds of birds, from the lowly English sparrow to the princely members of the hawk family.

Near my home in New York City, there is a college campus containing a few dozen large trees and numerous small trees and shrubs. Two pairs of flickers have made this little grove and the surrounding lawn their home for several years. The past summer I again saw them when the young of the two families had left their nests and were being fed on the ground. They would allow me to come within fifteen or twenty feet before exhibiting any concern at my presence. Occasionally one would pick at the ground in a tentative, inquiring manner, but for the most part they hopped about after their parents, begging for food in fault-finding tones.

One spring I visited frequently the scene of operations of a pair of campus flickers that were engaged in excavating their nest in a dead tree from which the upper two-thirds had been broken. The stub stood on the side of a slope about sixty yards from the Hall of Fame, along the open corridor of which many people wandered daily. Within forty feet of the nesting site was a road over which automobiles and motor trucks roared almost continually. The flickers dug their nest in the side of the tree facing both the road and the Hall of Fame, apparently oblivious to the crowds and the noise, and I am glad to say that in time they successfully brought off their brood.

The farmer and horticulturist should be the flicker's friends, for practically all of the insects it eats are harmful species. (See page 64.)

The northern form of this species *(C. a. luteus)* breeds in Alaska, southern Canada, and south to the Gulf of Mexico and central Texas. The southern form *(C. a. auratus)* breeds from North Carolina and southeastern Kansas to the Gulf and central Texas.

FROM SOUTHERN SWAMPS TO ARID ARIZONA, THE FAMILY COLORS FLY

"Zebra woodpecker" is a nickname for the **Red-bellied Woodpecker** (upper left, male and female) of the eastern United States. Among shady groves in Texas and Mexico may be found the **Golden-fronted Woodpecker** (upper right), a close relative of the red-bellied. Only a reversal of colors on the throat, head, and neck of the **Gilded Flicker** (lower left) differentiates it from the eastern flicker. It shares a southwestern range and a habit of nesting in giant cactuses with the **Gila Woodpecker** (lower right), which loiters around ranch houses, alert for discarded scraps of food.

Red-bellied Woodpecker

(Centurus carolinus)

Average Length, Nine and One-half Inches

This species is confined to eastern United States and lower Ontario. Its northwestern limits are southern South Dakota and southeastern Minnesota.

Among woodlands of deciduous trees in the Southern States the red-bellied woodpecker is a common bird. It is apparently almost as numerous in the pine barrens as among the dense, tangled thickets, or "hammocks," around the ponds and marshes. In the swamp lands bordering some of the rivers in the Carolinas and in Mississippi I have found it so abundant as to outnumber all other kinds of woodpeckers two to one.

They are sometimes called "zebra woodpeckers" or "chads," the latter name evidently derived from one of the common call-notes. Many people merely call them "sapsuckers," as they do the downy and all other small woodpeckers. Although possessed of a certain habitual wariness, they do not hesitate to approach the home of man if they have any special reason for venturing from the forest and are frequently found nesting in thick groves around plantation homesteads.

This bird possesses a strong, musky odor, more pronounced than that of most other woodpeckers. Also this body aroma is of a character different from that of any other bird with which I am acquainted.

The nesting hole is excavated in dead trees. The site is sometimes at considerable distance from the ground. Many years ago I climbed a living long-leaf pine and took a clutch of four red-bellied woodpecker's eggs from a nest that had been made by a red-cockaded woodpecker. The pair of feathered intruders had enlarged the doorway made by the smaller birds.

Golden-fronted Woodpecker

(Centurus aurifrons)

Average Length, Nine and One-half Inches

In the United States we find this bird only in Texas, but it ranges southward to the Valley of Mexico.

In the parks and among the shade trees of San Antonio, Texas, I have found the golden-fronted woodpecker as common as the red-headed woodpecker is in the streets of Gainesville, Florida. In general appearance and in movements, the golden-fronted closely resembles the red-bellied woodpecker, to which it is in fact closely related. It nests in trees, posts, and telephone poles.

In regions where trees are scarce, these woodpeckers cause trouble with their excavations in telephone poles, for each pair often digs two or three holes a year. Yet on the mesquite prairies, they have been known to use one nest several years.

Gilded Flicker

(Colaptes chrysoides)

Average Length, Thirteen Inches

This flicker inhabits southern Arizona, southeastern California, northeastern Baja California, and Sonora.

Take an eastern flicker and transfer the feathers of the throat and top of head and nape, then give him a red malar stripe instead of a black one, and you will have a gilded flicker. I found them very common in all the country around Tucson, Arizona, during the month of November. Especially were they numerous between the town and the mountains lying to the northward, where the giant cactus grows in such profusion. Among the foothills and along the dry stream beds where trees were growing, the bird was often seen, but its favorite haunts were the scattered groves of the tree cactus. They eat its fruit and capture many insects drawn to its flowers. In its trunk many of them build nests and lay their glossy white eggs.

In the late summer and fall, after the nesting season is over, this woodpecker, flocking in saguaro groves, loses much of its shyness.

Three geographical forms are recognized: Mearn's gilded flicker *(C. c. mearnsi)*, the San Fernando flicker *(C. c. brunnescens)*, and the Cape gilded flicker *(C. c. chrysoides)*. This last-named bird inhabits a rather restricted region in Baja California from Cape San Lucas northward for about 425 miles.

Gila Woodpecker

(Centurus uropygialis)

Average Length, Nine Inches

The Gila woodpecker inhabits southeastern California and eastward to southwestern New Mexico; through western Mexico to Jalisco.

This woodpecker often comes to ranch houses and Indian pueblos for scraps of meat, kernels of corn, or other tidbits of food which are to be found in such places. It nests often in the giant cactus trees. When the nesting hole is dug, the juice of the plant exudes, and, upon drying, forms a hard, smooth lining for the entire cavity.

The Gila woodpecker captures the ants, beetles and other insects upon which it largely feeds, among foliage or on the wing. Lizards, cactus fruit, mistletoe and other berries add variety to its diet. It seems to enjoy drumming on dead stubs of cottonwood, sycamore, and mesquite trees.

Three forms of this species are known. They are the Cardón woodpecker *(C. u. cardonensis)*, which ranges throughout the northern half of Baja California; Brewster's woodpecker *(C. u. brewsteri)*, which ranges a limited territory in southern Baja California, and the true Gila woodpecker found commonly throughout the southwestern part of the United States and in Mexico as well.

LARGEST OF ALL OUR WOODPECKERS IS THE RARE IVORY-BILLED

The former range of the **Ivory-billed Woodpecker** (male left, female right, above) included most of the low country of the southeastern United States, but now it is apparently restricted to lonely swamps in Louisiana, Florida, and perhaps a few other southern States. In recent years, this magnificent bird has been shot as a curiosity and this short-sighted policy has brought the species to the verge of extinction. Smaller, but strongly resembling the ivory-billed, is the **Northern Pileated Woodpecker** (male and female, below), found in southern Canada and the northeastern United States.

Pileated Woodpecker

(Ceophloeus pileatus)
Average Length, Seventeen Inches

This bird is found throughout a great part of temperate North America from Mackenzie and Nova Scotia to California and Florida. It is the largest of all the woodpeckers commonly seen in the United States, being almost the size of the common crow, although individuals vary considerably. It is a great black bird with much white flashing conspicuously on the wings as it flies through the heavy forest or swamp lands, which it chiefly inhabits. Sometimes it comes into the outskirts of quiet towns if large forest areas are situated near them.

Pileated woodpeckers eat many ants, especially the carpenter ants which attack trees, beginning their burrows at the base and working upward; also such other insects as they may happen to come upon from time to time. Wild fruit and berries attract them and they are particularly fond of wild cherries. However, they rarely, if ever, disturb cultivated fruit.

Most of the grubs, wood-boring beetles and ants which the pileated woodpecker prefers inhabit dead wood and, in order to extract them, the big bird has developed into a master woodchopper. It is thrilling to watch it attack a dead tree or log with powerful, staccato blows and, in half an hour, blanket the surrounding ground with a thick layer of splinters and chips, some of them as large as a man's hand.

This bird mates in the early spring, and the arduous task of excavating a nest is soon begun. In some of the Southern States, particularly in northern Louisiana, I have noted a great many of their holes in living trees, gums seeming to be the ones generally chosen. Often, apparently the same pair returns to a favorite nesting tree year after year and each season makes a new nest. I have counted as many as four of their holes in one living gum, and once I saw six of them in a dead tree. The nest is excavated to a depth of from one and one-half feet to three feet or more, and the eggs vary from three to five in number.

The pileated woodpecker has been separated into four geographical forms. The northern pileated *(C. p. abieticola)* inhabits Mackenzie, New Brunswick, and Nova Scotia, and southward to Pennsylvania and Indiana; the southern pileated *(C. p. pileatus)* ranges from southeastern Pennsylvania, Illinois, and Oklahoma to northern Florida and central Texas; the Florida pileated *(C. p. floridanus)* is found only in Florida from Orange County southward; the western pileated *(C. p. picinus)* ranges from southern British Columbia into California and Idaho.

Ivory-billed Woodpecker

(Campephilus principalis)
Average Length, Twenty Inches

This magnificent bird is by far the largest of all our woodpeckers, the expanse of its wings measuring from 30 to 33 inches. It is today one of the very rarest birds on the continent, and must be numbered among the birds classed as "nearly extinct." Possibly the names of all living ornithologists who have ever seen one could be counted on the fingers of two hands.

So far as is known, its range was formerly confined to the Southern States. Its territory may be described as extending from southern Illinois and eastern North Carolina southward to eastern Texas and southern Florida. There are, I believe, no records of its ever appearing in the southern mountains.

From nearly all this vast domain it has disappeared. We know of a very limited number in Louisiana, and there still are some in Florida. Possibly a few may still lurk in the larger swamp areas of northeastern Texas, in Arkansas, southern Missouri, and southern Mississippi, although there have been no well-substantiated records of their having actually been seen in any of these States for a number of years.

Like the pileated, this woodpecker has amazing powers as a woodchopper. Great piles of bark and slabs of wood beneath a worm-eaten tree it has attacked attest its energy.

Ivory-bills are said to dig holes for their nests at a great distance from the ground. In all my field experience I have seen only two of these, and I had to take the word of my native guide for the statement that the holes he showed me were made by this species. He undoubtedly knew well the difference between the pileated and the ivory-bill, and went to much inconvenience to take me through an unpleasant section of southwestern Florida to show me the sites where he had seen the birds occupying their nests.

One nest was in the tall stump of what had been a great tree. The hole I judged to be 45 feet from the ground. The other was in a living cypress at an elevation that must have been fully 70 feet in the air. From three to five eggs constitute a set and but one brood is reared each season. The eggs are pure china-white in color and are of such a remarkably glossy surface as to appear enameled.

The ivory-bill is a particularly efficient tree surgeon, for it must consume vast quantities of wood-boring grubs and other injurious insects to sustain its large body.

The reduction in abundance in this species is due most probably to persecution by man, for the species has been shot relentlessly without particular cause except curiosity and a desire for the feathers or beaks. (See page 65.)

Photograph by William L. and Irene Finley
THE ELF OWL SHOWS CONFIDENCE IN A FRIEND

Photograph by Eric J. Hosking
THE HUNTER RETURNS

This flashlight picture of a European barn owl about to enter its nesting hole in a tree with a young rat as food for its young was taken at 11:30 p. m. It was one of several camera studies shown by Eric J. Hosking, F.R.P.S., at the 81st annual exhibition of the Royal Photographic Society.

PARROTS, KINGFISHERS, AND FLYCATCHERS

Strange Trogons and Curious Cuckoos are Pictured with these Other Birds of Color, Dash, and Courage

By Alexander Wetmore

THE place was the Gran Chaco in South America, a vast terrain of marsh-dotted savanna and thorny jungle on the western border of the Paraguay River. The time was September, early spring in the Southern Hemisphere.

As I awakened at dawn in a little grove beside a lagoon, the morning air was so chill that I welcomed the first warm rays of the sun, though I knew that later the heat would be intense. From all sides came the calls and songs of strange birds.

A group of Lengua Indians, employed in cutting trails, squatted before a fire on which something was boiling.

In passing I was careful not to look into the pot, as they might throw out the food for fear my glance had cast a spell on it that would make them ill.

Suddenly I heard a succession of strident calls from behind the trees and stepped out into the open to watch a flock of parrots crossing the sky. They flew with steady wing beats, shrieking in raucous chorus. Though in close flock formation, they were grouped in pairs, male and female flying side by side.

Later in the day I found little flocks of long-tailed parakeets feeding on the hard, insipid fruits of a forest tree, while they clambered through the branches by aid of feet and bill. The ground was strewn with husks, and there was a steady rasping sound as they cut the fruits.

WILD PARROTS IN THE UNITED STATES

As I sat against a tree trunk that afternoon, preparing notes and specimens, hidden parrots called at intervals among the trees. Before sunset small flocks streamed across the sky to some distant roost.

In pioneer days these scenes might have been duplicated in many sections of the eastern United States, as then a bird of this family, the Carolina parakeet, ranged widely from the Gulf coast northward. On frosty mornings flocks of them gathered to feed on cockleburs and other seeds. In summer they penetrated far north into Wisconsin and Ontario.

Subsequently this parakeet became restricted mainly to Florida and it now is nearly extinct.

Another native parrot is found wild in the United States on those rare occasions when the thick-billed parrot comes from northern Mexico into the mountain ranges of southeastern Arizona.

Throughout the world there are nearly 800 different species and subspecies of parrots (family Psittacidae). Although some range into Patagonia, even to frigid Tierra del Fuego, and the kea of New Zealand lives in the interior mountains where winter snows are deep, the large majority inhabit warm parts of the earth.

NO PARROTS NATIVE IN EUROPE

No parrots are native in Europe, or in northern Asia. Their metropolis is in tropical America, Australia, Africa, and the East Indian region.

Though the size and color of the many forms of parrots are diverse, all have a certain family resemblance. The strongly hooked bill, rather heavy body, relatively large head, and peculiar feet, with two toes directed forward and two to the rear, make identification easy.

In most members of the family the head is round, but the cockatoos have large crests in which a spot of color shows when the feathers are thrown forward.

Cockatoos, Amazon parrots, and many other kinds have square-cut, macaws and parakeets long, graduated tails.

Green is a common color in the plumage, and is often variegated with yellow, orange, and red. Although there are a few exceptions, bright coloration is the rule.

The most brilliant members of all the parrot group are found among the lories of Australia and adjacent islands. Red, orange, yellow, blue, and green are mingled in their plumage in bizarre patterns.

In most parrots the tongue is soft and

Photograph by A. A. Allen

AN AVIAN POACHER GETS A CHANCE WHEN "KINGFISH" HAS A SUCKER IN ITS BILL

The belted kingfisher is notoriously jealous of its "fishing rights" along a favorite river. Some call this frequenter of lonely streams an enemy of young trout, but its diet is largely restricted to chubs, minnows, and other shallow-water fish of no value to anglers. An expert high diver, this bird may plunge 50 feet to snap up its prey from the water. The second band across the lower breast identifies this one as a female.

flexible at the tip and is used to hold food while it is cut up by the bill. The tongue in lories has a brushlike fringe at the end that is supposed to assist in extracting nectar from blossoms.

Members of the parrot family range in size from giants to midgets. The great all-blue hyacinthine macaw of Brazil is nearly three feet in length, with a long, pointed tail. The black cockatoo of northern Australia and adjacent islands is perhaps even a larger and heavier bird in body, since it is 32 inches long despite its short square tail.

SOME PARROTS THREE FEET LONG, OTHERS THREE INCHES

What a contrast there is between these huge-billed giants and the tiny pygmy parrots of New Guinea and near-by islands, the smallest of which is barely three inches long!

Probably the best-known members of the family are the Amazon parrots of the New World. Small to medium in size, they have square tails and are green in general color, more or less marked with yellow or red. There are many kinds, of which several are regularly kept in captivity.

MAY LIVE TO BE EIGHTY

The African gray parrot has been known in captivity for hundreds of years, and is the most famous of those species that imitate human speech and other sounds. Some of the Amazon parrots also are excellent mimics and in America are more familiar than the African species. Certain cockatoos also learn to "speak."

Ability in this direction varies with different individuals, some being gifted and some extremely stupid. Parrots learn by hearing often repeated sounds or phrases.

It is not unusual to see one that whistles, barks like a dog, mews like a cat, and repeats various sentences, sometimes so aptly as to make the bird appear more intelligent than it really is.

Curiously enough, this mimicry seems to be developed only in captivity. I have

Photograph by L. W. Brownell

SCRAGGLY BABY KINGFISHERS LINED UP FOR A SUN BATH

Usually hatched on a mass of regurgitated fish bones, these pinfeathered youngsters pass the first days of their lives in a burrow underground. The kingfisher digs a home in a bank, most commonly beside stream or lake.

known many species of Amazon parrots in the wild state, where they are noisy and vociferous, but have never found one with the slightest tendency to imitate familiar forest sounds.

The longevity of parrots is proverbial, and, while sometimes stories of it may be exaggerated, there is no question that some individuals live for many years.

In the National Zoological Park in Washington, D. C., is a sulphur-crested cockatoo called "Dick." He is the only living individual of the animal stock brought to the park from the Smithsonian grounds when the zoo was established in its present location in 1890. At that time this bird was fifteen or twenty years old. Dick in 1937 is in fine feather, and I have been able to see no difference in him during the more than twenty years I have known him.

There are various records of parrots that lived to be eighty and a few accounts, less definitely proved, of birds that reached one hundred years.

On a pleasant May morning in the Cantabrian Mountains of northern Spain I followed a woodland path that led me be-

neath the opening leaves of oaks and chestnuts. Strange notes of unseen birds came from every hand and I strained ears and eyes to identify songsters known previously only from books and museum specimens.

Through all these enticing sounds there came one that I recognized without the slightest difficulty, a steady *koo-koo, koo-koo* that announced the European cuckoo.

Years of familiarity with the striking of cuckoo clocks in my native land left not the slightest doubt of the identity of this note, and I laughed at the exactness of the imitation as I searched for the singer.

PARROTS AND CUCKOOS ARE RELATIVES

Ornithologists consider the cuckoos close relatives of the parrots in spite of their entirely different appearance. More than two hundred forms of cuckoos (family Cuculidae) are known, all being birds of slender form and small or medium size, often with long tails. Though widely distributed, they are commonest in tropical areas.

While most cuckoos live among the branches of trees, some, such as the ani, feed regularly on the ground, forming a

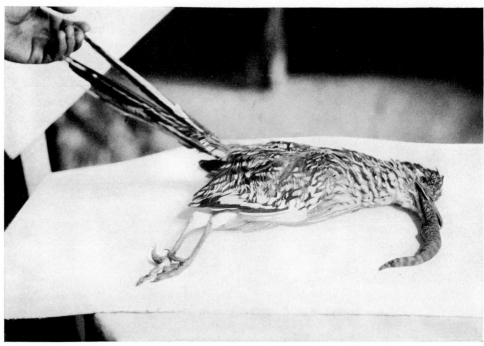

Photograph from F. W. Hoepfner

EVIDENCE THAT A ROAD-RUNNER MAY EAT A RATTLER!

Early one spring a farmer, J. C. Carraway, of Robstown, Texas, was walking in the mesquite brush with some of his dogs when he came upon this bird devouring a snake. His dogs killed the road-runner, which, being encumbered, was unable to run or fly away. The reptile was about fifteen inches long (page 82).

transition to those species like the road-runner that are entirely terrestrial.

The family activities of many of this group are strange and interesting, as among them parasitism in breeding is more widespread than in any other group of birds. The best-known example is the European cuckoo, a species that always places its egg in the nest of some small bird. About fifteen inches in length, this cuckoo has the size and color of a small hawk.

THE CUCKOO AN UNWANTED GUEST OF SMALL NEIGHBORS

In the mating season each female cuckoo has a definite range in which it seeks out the nests of small bird neighbors.

Each cuckoo is believed to parasitize nests of one kind of bird to the exclusion of others, one selecting the meadow pipit, another the hedge sparrow, another one of the wagtails, and so on.

Often the cuckoo removes one egg of the rightful owner to make room for her own, and in all events the young cuckoo when hatched soon gets rid of its nestmates.

With an instinct that is almost gruesome, the parasite, still too young to have its eyes open or to hold itself erect, works and squirms its body beneath those of its companions, gets them on its back, and then with awkward but certain movements heaves them over the edge of the nest.

One by one the rightful babies are thrown out until the cuckoo remains in solitary possession, so that it may profit by all the food brought by small but attentive foster parents, who through all this ghastly procedure never seem to understand that they are being duped.

The young cuckoo grows apace, until beside its small attendants it appears truly monstrous before it finally leaves their care.

While the cuckoo is larger than the species that it ordinarily chooses to parasitize, its egg is small. Thus it may not offer too great a contrast to those of the foster parent and so cause sufficient alarm to bring about desertion of the nest. Furthermore, individual cuckoos become specialized for the parasitism of particular kinds of birds, and have developed a modified color in their eggs to agree with those of the host.

In England the common cuckoo has an egg that matches fairly well in color those of the wagtails and pipits. In other parts of Europe some cuckoos produce bluish eggs like those of the European redstart. Even more striking color resemblances are found among the eggs of cuckoos in India.

In contrast to this bizarre parasitism, many species of cuckoos build nests and care for their own young. This is the case with the familiar yellow-billed and black-billed cuckoos of the United States.

Some observers say that these two are occasionally parasitic on each other, but this is not their regular custom.

One hot April day in Haiti I came slowly down the slopes of a mountain, interested in the abundant gray robins, lizard-cuckoos, strange flycatchers, and other birds that were seen at every turn. Suddenly a brilliant green bird marked with red beneath alighted on a branch in front of me to utter a strange nasal, cooing call that had puzzled me before but which I now knew was the note of a trogon. An instant later the bird had retreated to the tree tops where I saw only its silhouette, dark against the sky.

The trogons (family Trogonidae) include more than sixty forms. Three species inhabit Africa, and sixteen are found in India and adjacent regions. The remainder live in the warmer parts of the New World, one coming as far north as southern Arizona.

Nearly all are birds of lovely plumage, the most resplendent being the quetzal *(Pharomacrus mocinno)* of Central America. One of the largest of its family, this handsome bird has metallic-green plumage above, red underparts, a compressed crest, and long, flowing upper tail coverts that fall in a sweeping curve more than two feet below the tail.

The quetzal to the Aztecs was the emblem of Quetzalcoatl, God of the Air, and as such was sacred, its plumes being reserved for the chiefs. It is today the national bird of Guatemala, being shown on the coat of arms of the country and also on stamps and money.

STRANGE HABITS OF SOME KINGFISHERS

Our common belted kingfisher is so associated with water and a diet of fish that it is startling to learn that many of the family have other habits. I recall distinctly my own surprise in northern Argentina when a tiny green-backed kingfisher, no larger than a sparrow, flew out to seize a passing insect on the wing.

True enough, this mite of a bird came later to fish for minnows in a lagoon, but wherever I encountered it afterward I had the feeling that it was always likely to do some strange and unusual thing.

The kingfishers (family Alcedinidae) have almost world-wide distribution and number more than 200 forms.

The kingfisher of Europe *(Alcedo atthis),* whose flashing colors I have seen along the Thames in England, is only seven inches long. Above, it is bright blue, and below, it is colored rusty red.

THE LAUGHING JACKASS A LAND BIRD

The kookaburra, or laughing jackass, of Australia is a large kingfisher that lives on dry land far from water. At intervals it opens its huge bill to utter a loud, rolling call from which it derives its common name. It is one of the famous birds of the island continent, widely known, and often displayed in zoos.

Many other kinds of kingfishers live in forests or on dry land, where they feed on insects, lizards, and other animal foods.

The tyrant flycatchers (Tyrannidae) are one of the families of birds confined entirely to the New World. More than six hundred kinds are known to science, some of them of beautiful color and striking form, but many so obscure that they are known to few ornithologists. They are most abundant in the Tropics, but range widely, except in regions of extreme cold. Most flycatchers are birds of thickets and woodlands.

The majority are small birds that feed on insects which they capture expertly on the wing. They have developed broad, flat bills and a fringe of hairlike bristles about the sides of the mouth that assist in entrapping their moving food. Their bodies are slender, and their feet small.

A number have greatly elongated tails, and many sport concealed spots of color in the feathers of the crown which they display at times with a surprise effect that is highly pleasing.

The most ornamental in this respect are the royal flycatchers of tropical America, which have a conspicuous crest of red, tipped with steely blue, that is spread like a fan, much larger than the head, to form a truly resplendent ornament.

Carolina Parakeet

(Conuropsis carolinensis)

Average Length, Twelve and One-half Inches

The Carolina parakeet, like the vanished passenger pigeon and great auk, has disappeared with increasing settlement in our country, until now it is nearly extinct.

When the southeastern and central United States was first explored, the parakeet was abundant in many localities. Travelers, attracted by its flocking habit and brilliant colors, made frequent mention of "parrots" in their writings. But none recorded the habits of this bird in detail, so that now what information we have must be pieced together from scattered sources.

Although most common apparently in the Gulf States, the parakeet ranged widely toward the north even during seasons of cold. Captain John Smith wrote of Virginia that "in winter there are great plenty of Parrats," and the birds were also recorded from Maryland.

Their decrease began early. Audubon in 1832 said the parakeet was lessening in numbers, and by 1900 few remained in Florida, where they were once abundant. Dr. Frank M. Chapman saw two small flocks in April, 1904, near Lake Okeechobee, and casual report of them came from residents in that area until 1920.

For years the bird was considered extinct, but recently there has been persistent claim that a few remain in certain remote swamps of South Carolina. At this writing (April, 1936) the number left is not known, but we may hope that this interesting species may not be lost to us as a living bird.

According to available accounts, this parakeet in earlier years ranged in noisy flocks wherever food was plentiful. Normally the birds fed on seeds of cypress, pine, and thistle, and also on cockleburs and sandburs, the rough hulls of which were shelled easily by strong bills. At night the flocks gathered in hollow trees, where they clung suspended by feet and bills.

The parakeet was hunted for food and sport at an early day. Indians used its plumes for ornament, and early white settlers found its flesh good to eat.

With the planting of grain and orchards the birds became destructive to crops, and thousands were killed by farmers. Parakeets were said to be especially bad in apple orchards, since they cut up the fruit to get the seeds, sometimes stripping the trees completely. In Florida hundreds were trapped to become cage birds and thousands more were killed. Under these circumstances the birds rapidly decreased.

The Carolina parakeet nested in hollow trees, where it deposited pure-white eggs on whatever rubbish was accumulated in the cavity. Somewhat uncertain reports indicate that from three to five eggs constituted a set. It has been recorded on hearsay that the birds made nests on the horizontal limbs of cypress trees, but it seems certain that this statement is erroneous.

The Carolina parakeet proper *(Conuropsis carolinensis carolinensis)* formerly ranged from Florida and Alabama north to Maryland, and was found casually in Pennsylvania and New York. A western race, slightly duller in color, the Louisiana parakeet *(Conuropsis carolinensis ludovicianus)*, was found from Louisiana and Mississippi to Ohio, Wisconsin, and Nebraska.

Thick-billed Parrot

(Rhynchopsitta pachyrhyncha)

Average Length, Sixteen and One-half Inches

In the Chiricahua Mountains of southeastern Arizona, at intervals of several years, flocks of large parrots may be found feeding on the seeds concealed in pine cones. They are not regular residents of Arizona but visitors from the mountains of northern Mexico.

Bills and feathers become smeared with pitch, but the food is rich and attractive, and the birds linger in the pines until all this food is gone. Cold does not trouble them, and they may remain through the ice and snow of winter, feeding on acorns when the crop of pine cones has been harvested.

The birds are found in flocks and range widely, passing at times to other mountains near by. After a few months they disappear.

The proper home of this fine bird is in the mountain ranges bordering the Mexican tableland, where it lives in large flocks among the pines. The huge imperial woodpecker of that area is a friendly neighbor, since its old nesting holes, cut in dead or living pines to a depth of one and one-half to two feet, furnish the parrots with shelters for brooding.

From one to three eggs are deposited on the fine bits of wood in the bottom of these cavities, often late in the season, as is attested by the fact that small young have been found in October. Since the parrots range from 4,000 to 10,000 feet altitude, the nights then are cold and the young parrots must undergo some hardship.

The last large invasion of these parrots in the United States occurred in July, 1917, and the birds remained in the pine forests of the Southwest until the following March, feeding as is their wont on seeds which their strong bills broke out of pine cones. Their occasional appearance is believed to be due to some lack in the food supply in their proper home.

The thick-billed parrot is found normally in the mountains of northern and central Mexico. In the United States, it has been found not only in the Chiricahua Mountains, but in the Dragoon, Galiuro, and Graham mountains in Arizona.

FLOCKS OF BRILLIANT PARAKEETS ONCE ROAMED THE SOUTH

The green-yellow-and-orange **Carolina Parakeet** (upper) ranged from Florida to Virginia and westward in the early years of the Nation; some even wandered north to New York and Wisconsin. Many were shot because they ate fruit, and now they are nearly extinct, but a few may remain in remote southern swamps. The bird uses one strong foot in the manner of a hand for grasping food, while it clings to a branch with the other. The larger **Thick-billed Parrot** (lower) sometimes appears in southeastern Arizona in quest of pine seeds, which it digs from tough cones with its powerful beak.

Smooth-billed Ani

(Crotophaga ani)

Average Length, Twelve and One-half Inches

The curious ani is of only casual occurrence within the United States, but in the larger West Indian islands it is common.

In a Puerto Rican pasture I first saw these black, long-tailed birds on the ground, feeding on insects disturbed by cattle.

As I drew near, the anis began to call querulously and then flew in straggling procession across the field to perch in a tree. There they crowded so closely that they touched one another, their long tails and narrow, high-arched beaks giving them an odd appearance.

Always sociable, anis often build a bulky community nest of sticks in a tree. In this several females lay, and as many as 20 eggs may be found together. The habit is not a characteristic of all without exception, however, for I have found one pair building their home apart. The eggs are clear blue, covered with raised white lines of a chalky deposit.

The smooth-billed ani is resident from the West Indies and Yucatán south into central South America. It has been found rarely in Louisiana and Florida and casually elsewhere.

Road-runner

(Geococcyx califorianus)

Average Length, Twenty-two Inches

Walking along a sandy trail in southern Arizona, I noticed a curious track shaped like a crude X, made obviously by a foot with two toes that pointed forward and two backward. The imprints were spaced in long strides that indicated a creature of fair size and were so balanced that it was difficult to say which way the animal was traveling until I noticed that the forward-pointing toes were more deeply impressed in the loose soil.

A slight movement under a bush some distance ahead announced the maker of the curious marks, and upon closer approach I saw the long bill, the crested head with a spot of brilliant red on the side, and the elongated tail of a road-runner.

Finding that it was discovered, the bird started off at a rapid run and almost at once was out of sight.

This strange cuckoo is so entirely terrestrial that ordinarily it prefers to run and hide rather than take to its wings, though when under the necessity it flies with ease.

In the days of horse travel, road-runners delighted to appear in the trail ahead of wagon, stagecoach, or other equipage and to run easily with heads low and tails straight behind, readily keeping in front of the horses. Finally, tired of the game, they would dash aside and suddenly elevate tails and crests. The light eyes and strange attitude at such times gave the birds a grotesque appearance.

It seemed almost that they were poking fun at the carriages they had outdistanced.

Since the coming of the automobile these birds have abandoned their former practice of running ahead of moving vehicles. The approach of a motor car sends them scuttling off the road and into the desert growth. Evidently they have adapted themselves to modern conditions.

The road-runner is primarily an animal feeder, preferring lizards and large insects, which it seizes with its strong bill most expertly. It is not above taking an occasional young bird from the families of its neighbors, but the damage that it does in this direction is considered slight.

Many tales are current of the enmity of the road-runner for the rattlesnake. According to these stories, the astute bird builds a hedge of thorn-covered cactus pads about a coiled rattlesnake, even one of the largest size, to preclude all possibility of escape, and teases the reptile until it leaves the security of its coils; the snake is then dispatched by blows from the sharp bill.

It is to be feared that these stories are more intriguing than true, though it is certain that the road-runner will kill and eat small snakes of any kind (page 78).

The nest of the road-runner is built of sticks, with a lining of feathers, snakeskin, bark, and other soft materials. It is placed in bushes or low trees; sometimes in cactus plants. It holds usually from four to nine white or buffy-white eggs, but as many as twelve have been found in one nest.

The road-runner is found from northern California and western Kansas south into central Mexico.

Groove-billed Ani

(Crotophaga sulcirostris)

Average Length, Thirteen Inches

Except for the smaller bill with distinctly impressed lines or grooves along its sides, this bird is a double of the smooth-billed ani.

It has been widely believed for centuries that anis extract many ticks from the skins of the domestic animals around which they feed in small flocks. But actually much of the credit for this belongs to the equally black grackles that range with them.

Long and slender, anis are slow and direct in flight, alternately beating their small wings and sailing. In a strong wind they are almost helpless.

The groove-billed ani's eggs and gregarious nesting habits are similar to those of its smooth-billed relative. It is resident from the lower Rio Grande Valley in Texas to Peru and British Guiana. A local form of this interesting species, the San Lucas ani *(Crotophaga s. pallidula),* is of paler coloring. It is found in the southern region of Baja California.

STRANGE ANIS AND SWIFT ROAD-RUNNER ARE CLOSE COUSINS

All are members of the cuckoo clan, although they bear little resemblance to their relatives except for the long tail. The **Smooth-billed Ani** (upper left) and the **Groove-billed Ani** (right) are subtropical birds which barely come within the borders of the United States. Like cowbirds, they are often seen around cattle and feed on parasitic insects. The **Road-runner,** holding a lizard, is a ground cuckoo which rivals a horse in fleetness.

Coppery-tailed Trogon

(Trogon ambiguus ambiguus)

Average Length, Eleven and One-half Inches

An exotic species that comes across the southwestern border of the United States, the coppery-tailed trogon, though discovered here fifty years ago, still remains little known.

It has been found most often in the Huachuca and Santa Catalina Mountains of Arizona, where it lives among the pines and oaks of remote canyons, and is known also from the San Luis Mountains, New Mexico, and the lower Rio Grande Valley in Texas. On the wing the birds resemble pigeons.

Trogons are usually solitary. It is unusual to find more than a pair together. The bird illustrated on the accompanying plate is a male. In the female the head and back are brown and the red of the underparts is much reduced.

Though formerly rare, these trogons in recent years have become common in the hot canyons of the Santa Catalina Mountains, and a dozen may be found here in a day at the proper season.

It nests in cavities of trees. The three or four eggs are dull white in color.

This trogon ranges from southern Arizona and southern Texas to Guerrero and Tepic. An allied form is found in the Tres Marias Islands.

Black-billed Cuckoo

(Coccyzus erythropthalmus)

Average Length, Eleven and Three-quarters Inches

On a warm September day, as I crossed a field on the slopes of Whitetop Mountain in the Blue Ridge Mountains of Virginia, a black-billed cuckoo flew from a thicket to a tree.

Walking up slowly, I had to look for several minutes before I made out the bird's slender form as it perched motionless, concealed by branches and leaves. With its slim body and long tail it seemed a part of the branches.

The clucking notes of others came from near-by slopes and a little farther on we saw one feeding a young bird just from the nest, though the summer season was ended and most birds had long ago completed their nesting.

The calls of the two cuckoos are alike in tone and utterance and are distinguished only by those expert in such matters.

The nest is built of sticks and rootlets lined with softer materials, usually at an elevation of less than ten feet and, rarely, on the ground itself. The eggs are plain blue and number from two to six, or, rarely, as many as eight.

The well-grown young of both our cuckoos in the nest present a most curious appearance. The pinfeathers grow rapidly, but the sheath surrounding them remains unbroken, so the birds appear to be covered with quills instead of feathers. Only just before the birds leave the nest do the quills finally open so that soft feathers clothe the body.

The black-billed cuckoo is easily distinguished from its yellow-billed companion by dark bill, smaller white spots in the tail, and less amount of chestnut in the wings. It ranges farther north than the yellow-bill and is especially common in New England.

It does abundant good by devouring great quantities of caterpillars, its favorite food, particularly the "tent" variety that does such heavy damage to fruit trees. Bushy hillsides bordered by wet meadows, and shrubbery along water courses are its chosen haunts.

The black-billed cuckoo nests from southeast Alberta and Nova Scotia to Kansas, and in the mountains to north Georgia. It winters in South America from Colombia to Peru.

Yellow-billed Cuckoo

(Coccyzus americanus)

Average Length, Twelve and One-quarter Inches

A series of grating notes, half harsh and half resonant, following one another in definite arrangement—that is the yellow-billed cuckoo.

Watch closely among the leaves and presently you may see a slender bird with long, white-spotted tail, and, as it turns its head, a distinct flash of orange yellow from the lower half of the bill.

Any farmer will tell you that the voice of the "rain crow" prophesies a downpour. This belief I do not challenge, since the cuckoo calls most frequently when rain is common.

Like its black-billed cousin, this cuckoo feeds on the hairy caterpillars that live in webs in shade and fruit trees and strip adjacent branches of fresh-grown leaves.

I have often found the inner walls of the stomachs of this and other cuckoos of similar habits so filled with spiny hairs from caterpillars that they seemed to be lined with fur. No harm comes from this and at intervals the stomach lining is shed in pieces, leaving the cavity smooth and clean.

The yellow-billed cuckoo builds a loosely constructed nest of twigs with a small cavity in which it places from two to six (rarely eight) pale-blue eggs, larger and lighter hued than those of the black-billed cuckoo.

Although the eggs of black-billed and yellow-billed cuckoos have been reported occasionally in the nests of other birds, I believe neither can be considered parasitic.

The yellow-billed cuckoo (Coccyzus americanus americanus) nests from North Dakota and New Brunswick to northeastern Mexico and Florida. In winter it is found from Venezuela to Uruguay.

The California cuckoo (Coccyzus a. occidentalis), which is slightly larger and paler, is found from British Columbia and Colorado to Baja California and western Texas. It is supposed to winter in South America.

AMERICAN CUCKOOS ARE WHOLLY UNLIKE THE BIRD OF THE CUCKOO CLOCK

Instead of a cheery *cuckoo,* their "song" is an unmusical succession of chucks and clucks. Here the **Black-billed Cuckoo** eats caterpillars while the **Yellow-billed Cuckoo** utters a guttural note. In contrast to the European cuckoo, which lays its eggs in the nests of other birds, they normally hatch and rear their own young. The **Coppery-tailed Trogon,** of red breast, lives along the Mexican border, and is a relative of the gorgeous quetzal, worshiped by the Maya and Aztecs.

Texas Kingfisher

(Chloroceryle americana septentrionalis)
Average Length, Seven and One-quarter Inches

Along any small stream in southern Texas one may encounter a bird that is obviously a kingfisher and yet no larger in body than a bluebird.

Its strong, heavy bill, its position as it rests on a perch, and its mannerisms are unmistakably those of its larger, more common cousin. But its small size gives the bird certain liberties, as it may dart out at any moment, like a flycatcher, to snap at some flying insect. In the next instant the bird is intent on minnows and other small creatures in the water. It prefers small clear streams to the larger rivers with silt-laden currents.

The Texas kingfisher burrows in a perpendicular sand bank, sometimes in company with bank swallows, to make a nest chamber two feet or so from the entrance. In this it places five or six clear-white eggs.

The call is a low clicking note, given with a twitch of the tail and a jerk of the body.

This kingfisher ranges from southern Texas south into Mexico as far as Yucatán. It is also found in southern Arizona. Several closely allied forms are spread through tropical America as far as northern Argentina.

Belted Kingfisher

(Megaceryle alcyon)
Average Length, Eleven Inches

While a land bird in the sense that it is not truly aquatic, the kingfisher finds water essential for its life, as from ponds and streams it obtains most of its food. Though more common on fresh water, it ranges also along the ocean and brackish inlets in both summer and winter.

A high-pitched rattling call and a flash of gray-blue and white announce the presence of this bird, flying ahead as we follow any winding stream in summer. At intervals it perches on posts or limbs, usually over the water, when its crest of feathers and heavy bill make its head seem so large as to be almost unwieldy. Although handsome and full of character, the kingfisher is a top-heavy looking bird, with the size of its head out of all proportion to that of its body.

It is a solitary creature, rarely being seen in company with even one other of its kind, except, of course, in the mating and nesting season. Its "profession" of fisherman compels a sedentary life, which is proved by the fact that it is almost always seen flying away from its perch upon being interrupted at its watchful, contemplative duties. Its sudden, flashing flight, accompanied by the characteristic rattle, only accentuates its usual silent guardianship of its territory. Bendire says the bird usually may be seen "watching for its prey as a cat does for a mouse."

The kingfisher watches intently as small fish swim below it, and then plunges suddenly, head foremost, into the water, where its heavy bill serves as an efficient instrument to seize its slippery prey. Often it hovers in the air, remaining stationary with rapidly beating wings, until fish break below.

Small fish are, of course, its principal food, but crustacea, frogs, lizards, beetles, grasshoppers, and crickets may be added to the diet or substituted when small fry and minnows are lacking. Tiny fish are swallowed head first without delay. Larger ones are beaten vigorously against a branch or stone until they are quiet enough to handle. The bones of fish and the hard parts of crabs and other food are formed into pellets that are regurgitated when digestion is complete. The food is almost entirely animal, though the kingfisher has been seen eating sour gum berries and wild cherries.

In Haiti and Puerto Rico, and elsewhere in the West Indies, I have seen the kingfisher in its winter home not only feeding on fishes but also watching for small crabs that walked on the mud of mangrove swamps.

A kingfisher's home consists of a tunnel driven into the perpendicular face of an earthen bank. Cut banks above streams and lakes are natural locations, but kingfishers use also the walls of railroad cuts and other excavations, sometimes those distant from water.

The burrow extends from 4 to 15 feet or more, with an enlargement at the end. Here, on a mass of regurgitated fish bones, rest from five to eight pure-white eggs. Banks chosen for the nesting tunnels must be compact enough not to collapse. Clay, damp sand, or sand mixed with gravel are preferred. The tunnels may be straight or have angle bends. One unvarying fact is that the nest chamber itself is always slightly higher than the tunnel entrance. The nesting burrow is excavated by the heavy bill, the loosened earth being scraped and scratched out to the entrance by means of the feet, to fall to the ground below. Occupied burrows always show a double track made by the feet of the birds as they shuffle in and out. The incubating kingfisher is not to be trifled with, as many who have unearthed its nests could testify. In defense of eggs or young, the birds can inflict severe bites with their sharp-edged bills.

The eastern belted kingfisher *(Megaceryle alcyon alcyon)* breeds from Mackenzie and southern Labrador to the southern border of the United States and west to the Rocky Mountains. In winter it goes into the West Indies and northern South America. The western belted kingfisher *(Megaceryle a. caurina),* somewhat larger, is found from northern Alaska through the Rocky Mountain region, in winter going into northern Mexico.

KINGFISHERS CAN PLUNGE 50 FEET OR MORE AND SNATCH A SWIMMING MINNOW

Familiar citizens of most of the United States are the **Belted Kingfishers** (lower), which jealously guard their fishing preserves against poaching rivals. Poised on beating wings, the male is about to dive and seize a small fish in his long, sharp bill, while the perched female sounds the characteristic rattling call. Among the small **Texas Kingfishers** (upper) styles are reversed, and the male, not his mate, wears the rufous breast adornment. Both kinds nest in burrows in banks, usually not far from a pond or stream.

ASTONISHING CAPACITY OF BIRDS' STOMACHS

FIELD observations of the food habits of birds serve a useful purpose, but they are rarely accurate enough to be fully reliable. The presence of certain birds in a corn or wheat field or in an orchard is by no means proof, as is too often assumed, that they are devastating the grain or fruit. They may have been attracted by insects which, unknown to the farmer or orchardist, are fast ruining his crop. Hence it has been found necessary to examine the stomachs and crops of birds to ascertain what and how much they eat.

The Biological Survey has in this way examined upward of 112,000 birds. Most of these have been obtained within the last 50 years from scientific collectors, for our birds are too useful to be sacrificed when such action can possibly be avoided, even for the sake of obtaining data upon which to base legislation for their protection.

A BIRD EATS PRODIGIOUSLY

It is interesting to observe that hungry birds—and birds are hungry most of the time—are not content to fill their stomachs with insects or seeds. Many, after the stomach is stuffed until it will hold no more, continue to eat till the crop or gullet also is crammed. Often when the stomach is opened and the contents heaped up, the pile is two or three times as large as the full stomach.

Birds may truly be said to have healthy appetites. To show the astonishing capacity of birds' stomachs and to reveal the extent to which man is indebted to birds for the destruction of noxious insects, the following facts are given:

A tree swallow's stomach was found to contain 40 entire chinch bugs and fragments of many others, besides 10 other species of insects. A bank swallow in Texas devoured 68 cotton boll weevils, one of the worst insect pests that ever invaded the United States; and 35 cliff swallows had taken an average of 18 boll weevils each. Two stomachs of pine siskins from Hayward, Calif., contained 1,900 black olive scales and 300 plant lice. A killdeer's stomach taken in November in Texas contained more than 300 mosquito larvae.

A flicker's stomach held 28 white grubs. A nighthawk's stomach collected in Kentucky contained 34 May beetles, the adult form of white grubs. Another nighthawk, from New York, had eaten 24 clover-leaf weevils and 375 ants. Still another nighthawk had eaten 340 grasshoppers, 52 bugs, 3 beetles, 2 wasps, and a spider. A boat-tailed grackle from Texas had eaten at one meal about 100 cotton bollworms, besides a few other insects. The crop of a ring-necked pheasant from Washington contained 8,000 seeds of chickweed and a dandelion head. More than 72,000 seeds have been found in a single duck stomach taken in Louisiana in February.

The various groups of birds differ so much in habits that they feed upon practically all groups of insects; hardly an agricultural pest escapes their attacks. The alfalfa weevil has 45 different bird enemies; the army worm, 43; billbugs, 67; cotton boll weevil, 66; brown-tail moth, 31; chestnut weevils, 64; chinch bug, 24; clover-root borers, 85; clover weevil, 25; codling moth, 36; cotton worm, 41; cutworms, 98; forest tent caterpillar, 32; gipsy moth, 46; horse-flies, 49; leaf-hoppers, 120; orchard tent caterpillar, 43; potato beetle, 25; rice weevil, 21; seventeen-year locust, 38; twelve-spotted cucumber beetle, 28; white grubs, 67; and wireworms, 168.

In feeding on insect pests not only do birds take a great variety but they frequently destroy very large numbers. Often more than a hundred individuals are devoured at a meal, and in the case of small insects sometimes several thousand. On a 200-acre farm in North Carolina it was found that birds were destroying a million green bugs, or wheat aphids, daily.[*]

As many as 100 grasshoppers have been found in the stomach of a Swainson's hawk, representing a single meal; and in the retreat of a pair of barn owls have been found more than 3,000 skulls, 97 per cent of which were of mammals, the bulk consisting of field mice, house mice, and common rats.

Nearly half a bushel of the remains of pocket gophers—animals which are very destructive in certain parts of the United States—was found near a nest of this species. The notable increase of noxious

[*] Consult "Community Bird Refuges," by W. L. McAtee, U. S. Department of Agriculture, Farmers' Bulletin 1239.

rodents during the last few years in certain parts of the United States and the consequent damage to crops are due in no small part to the diminished number of birds of prey which formerly materially aided in keeping down their numbers.

BIRDS SAVE MANY CROPS

Entomologists have estimated that insects yearly cause a loss of upward of $700,000,000 to the agricultural interests of the United States. Were it not for our birds the loss would be very much greater, and without their aid successful agriculture in many places might be impossible.

While it may be said that most of our birds are useful, there are only a few of them that are always and everywhere useful and that never do harm.

To the extent that birds destroy useful parasitic insects, they are harmful; but the good they do by the destruction of injurious insects far outweighs the harm.

It may be said, too, that of the birds usually classed as noxious there are very few that do not possess redeeming traits. Thus the crow is mischievous in spring and sorely taxes the farmer's patience and ingenuity to prevent him from pulling up the newly planted corn. Moreover, the crow destroys the eggs and young of useful insectivorous and game birds. On the other hand, he eats many insects, especially white grubs and cutworms, and destroys many meadow mice; so that in much (although not in all) of the region he inhabits the crow must be considered more useful than harmful.

Most of the hawks and owls even—birds that have received so bad a name that the farmer's boy and the sportsman are ever on the alert to kill them—are very useful because they destroy vast numbers of insects and harmful rodents.

Birds occupy a unique position among the enemies of insects, since their powers of flight enable them at short notice to gather at points where there are abnormal insect outbreaks. An unusual abundance of grasshoppers, for instance, in a given locality soon attracts the birds from a wide area, and as a rule their visits cease only when there are no grasshoppers left.

So also a marked increase in the number of small rodents in a given neighborhood speedily attracts the attention of hawks and owls, which, by reason of their voracious appetites, destroy great numbers of the swarming foe.

One of the most useful groups of native birds is the sparrow family. While some of the tribe wear gay suits of many hues, most of the sparrows are clad in modest brown tints, and, since they pass much of the time in grass and weeds, are commonly overlooked.

Unobtrusive as they are, they lay the farmer under a heavy debt of gratitude by their food habits, since their chosen fare consists largely of the seeds of weeds. Selecting a typical member of the group, the tree sparrow, for instance, one-fourth ounce of weed seed a day is a conservative estimate of the food of an adult.

On this basis, in a large agricultural State like Iowa, tree sparrows annually eat approximately 875 tons of weed seeds. Only the farmer, upon whose shoulders falls the heavy burden of freeing his land of noxious weeds, can realize what this vast consumption of weed seeds means in the saving and cost of labor.

POLICEMEN OF THE AIR

Some idea of the money value of this group of birds to the country may be gained from the statement that the total value of the farm crops in the United States in 1935 reached the amazing sum of $5,914,174,000. If we estimate that the total consumption of weed seeds by the combined members of the sparrow family resulted in a saving of only 1 per cent of the crops—not a violent assumption—the sum saved to farmers by these birds in 1935 was $59,141,740.

A knowledge of his bird friends and enemies, therefore, is doubly important to the farmer and orchardist in order that he may protect the kinds that earn protection by their services and may drive away or destroy the others. At present many kinds of useful birds need direct intervention in their behalf as never before.

The encroachments of civilization on timbered tracts and the methods of modern intensive cultivation by destroying or restricting breeding grounds of birds tend to diminish their ranks. The number of insect pests, on the other hand, is all the time increasing through importations from abroad and by migration from adjoining territories.

Every effort, therefore, should be made to augment the numbers of our useful birds by protecting them from their enemies, by providing nesting facilities, and by furnishing them food in times of stress.

SWIFT, COURAGEOUS KINGBIRDS ROUT HAWKS AND LUMBERING CROWS

In the distance a doughty little warrior is winning such an aerial battle, pursuing closely and sometimes actually riding on its much larger foeman's back. All four of the birds with the orange-red crowns are **Kingbirds**—the **Eastern** in flight, the **Arkansas,** or **Western,** just below it, **Cassin's** (left), a far-westerner, and **Couch's** (bottom), which nests in southern Texas. Like the Southwest's aptly named **Scissor-tailed Flycatcher** (top), which shares their courage, they all live mainly on insects caught on the wing.

Scissor-tailed Flycatcher
(Muscivora forficata)
Average Length, Thirteen and One-half Inches

At a distance the scissor-tail, called locally "bird of paradise," is remarkable mainly for its slender outline. But near at hand its soft colors arouse admiration. It is a bird of the open prairies, where bushes and scattered trees afford observation perches from which to watch for its insect food. Like the kingbirds it harries crows, hawks, and other birds.

In spring the scissor-tail darts across the sky excitedly in a zigzag, aerial dance accompanied by harsh, chattering notes, a veritable explosion of color and sound combined. Its nest is a compact cup of twigs, weeds, and grass, lined with softer materials, placed in small trees, often in mesquites. It contains from four to six white or creamy eggs, spotted boldly with brown and lavender.

The scissor-tail nests from southern Nebraska to Texas and passes the winter from southern Mexico to Panama. Individuals have been found casually, probably storm-driven, at many points outside this range.

Cassin's Kingbird
(Tyrannus vociferans)
Average Length, Nine Inches

At sunset of a June day at Burford Lake, New Mexico, birds were active everywhere in the cool evening air. Amid the songs of rock wrens, mockingbirds, and western robins, I heard suddenly an excited medley of odd calls and saw a Cassin's kingbird dart out from the top of a dead tree in an erratic sky dance. The air was filled with the explosive sound of its notes.

Both here and later in the Chiricahua Mountains of southeastern Arizona, I found the Cassin's kingbirds nesting, sometimes in trees on open hillsides and sometimes in oaks standing beside ranchhouses. The nests are bulky and the eggs like those of the eastern kingbird, though often less heavily spotted.

Cassin's kingbird nests from central California and central Montana south into Mexico. In winter it ranges to Guatemala.

Couch's Kingbird
(Tyrannus melancholicus couchi)
Average Length, Nine and One-half Inches

In the lower Rio Grande Valley is found this kingbird, distinguished from others of similar pattern by somewhat darker color.

The nest often contains Spanish moss. The three or four eggs are marked by a creamy pink ground color, though the spottings are similar to those of other kingbird eggs.

Couch's kingbird ranges from southern Texas into Mexico, while related forms are distributed widely in tropical America.

The gray kingbird (Tyrannus dominicensis dominicensis), a distinct species, is regularly seen along the southeastern coast from southern South Carolina into Florida in summer. It ranges through the West Indies and along the shores of the Caribbean Sea.

Eastern Kingbird
(Tyrannus tyrannus)
Average Length, Eight and One-half Inches

The kingbird always arouses admiration for its alert bearing and fearless harrying of birds much larger than itself.

Let a crow pass near its chosen territory, and the kingbird circles out at once with incisive cries and quickly beating wings to rise above the black intruder and dart at it savagely. The swooping and diving with which the crow attempts to elude its small tormentor show that these attacks are not play.

Frequently I have seen a kingbird alight on the larger bird's back while it pecked and pulled at its feathers.

Kingbirds often build their compact, softly lined nests above water, placing them openly on overhanging branches. They nest frequently in orchards and in roadside trees, always with disregard for the protection ordinarily sought by other birds of their size. The nest contains three or four eggs, rarely five, white or creamy, spotted boldly with brown and bluish gray.

Kingbirds feed mainly on insects, in late summer eating such small wild fruits as chokecherries. They are entirely beneficial, being favorites with most farmers because they harry crows and hawks from chicken yards.

They nest from southern British Columbia and Nova Scotia to Texas and Florida; and winter from Mexico to northern South America.

Arkansas Kingbird
(Tyrannus verticalis)
Average Length, Nine Inches

Like others of its clan, this kingbird is active and aggressive.

Its nest in bushes or trees is made of weed stems and twigs, lined with softer fibers and feathers. The three to five eggs resemble those of the eastern kingbird.

In the last 60 years the Arkansas kingbird has extended its range steadily eastward until now it occupies wide areas from Minnesota southward where in earlier days it was not known. In the Great Plains area it is found with the eastern bird and it replaces that species in the Far West.

The birds nest from southern British Columbia and Manitoba to northern Baja California and Texas and thence eastward, having been found recently as far as northern Ohio. They winter from western Mexico to Nicaragua and occur casually in the East.

FLYCATCHERS ARE VALUABLE ALLIES IN THE ETERNAL WAR AGAINST INSECTS

Fortunate is the farmer whose orchards or groves shelter the **Great Crested Flycatcher** (upper left), for it eats prodigious numbers of weevils, beetles, and other crop destroyers. This bird has the mystifying habit of weaving a snake's skin into its nest. Its four companions are westerners. The **Ash-throated Flycatcher** (upper right) lives in the Far West, the **Olivaceous** and **Sulphur-bellied Flycatchers** (center, left and right) in the mountains of Arizona, and the large **Derby Flycatcher** (bottom) in the lower Rio Grande Valley.

Great Crested Flycatcher
(Myiarchus crinitus)
Average Length, Nine Inches

Enter any woodland in the eastern United States in summer, walk quietly, and listen to the low sounds that come from ground and tree-top. On dead limbs pointing skyward, half hidden by green foliage, soon there will appear a slender figure with reddish-brown tail, yellow underparts, and gray breast.

With crest raised the great crested flycatcher rests, darting out at intervals for passing insects and giving his ringing call.

In a hollow in a tree trunk near by, this interesting bird has placed its nest, lining the cavity with soft materials to receive from four to eight eggs. These are creamy white, most strikingly marked with lines and blotches of brown and lavender, many of the markings running lengthwise and as firmly scrawled as if laid on with a pen. In these modern times the great crest sometimes nests in birdhouses.

Almost invariably the shed skin of a snake is woven into the nest material; or an entire skin is wound about the upper part of the nest, perhaps for protection or decoration.

True to the habits of its family, the great crest is a pugnacious enemy of all birds that intrude on what it considers its personal rights. Often in the nesting season it may be seen or heard hustling marauding jays through the tree-tops with loudly snapping bill and sharp outcries. It has even whipped starlings.

The northern crested flycatcher (Myiarchus crinitus boreus) nests from Manitoba and Nova Scotia to Texas and South Carolina, and winters from Mexico to Colombia. The southern crested flycatcher (Myiarchus crinitus crinitus), with larger bill and more greenish back, is found from southern South Carolina through the peninsula of Florida.

Olivaceous Flycatcher
(Myiarchus tuberculifer olivascens)
Average Length, Seven and One-quarter Inches

In the brush-grown canyons of the mountains of southern New Mexico and Arizona this small cousin of the great crested flycatcher is fairly common.

Derby Flycatcher
(Pitangus sulphuratus derbianus)
Average Length, Ten and One-half Inches

Though the Derby flycatcher comes into the lower Rio Grande Valley, it is essentially a bird of Latin America. There, in a variety of forms differing only slightly in color and size, it has wide distribution. Among travelers in the American Tropics, it is one of the best known of the small birds.

My first view of this species was in the hills above Rio de Janeiro, where I saw it against a soul-satisfying background of mountain, harbor, and city. It was one of the first of the birds I have come to know in South America. A few days later I heard its querulous calls from the eucalyptus trees in a public park in Montevideo, and still later found it common on the pampas near Buenos Aires and northward into Paraguay.

In mating display these birds stand erect and bend their heads to expose flaring crests, while the partly extended wings flutter rapidly and loud, cracking sounds are made by the snapping bills. The nest is a large structure of twigs, with domed top and side entrance. The creamy eggs are spotted with brown.

These flycatchers eat insects, small lizards, little frogs, and some fish or minnows.

The true Derby flycatcher occurs from the lower Rio Grande Valley in Texas to Panama. Allied races are widely distributed in Central and South America.

Ash-throated Flycatcher
(Myiarchus cinerascens)
Average Length, Eight and One-quarter Inches

In the arid Southwest this bird replaces the great crested flycatcher of the East. Heat and sun are so much a part of its life that, even in desert areas where there is little shade, it seems as much at home as among the oaks and other trees of the lower slopes of the mountains.

Like its eastern cousin, this bird nests in holes, occasionally occupying the domed nests of the cactus wren. In the desert it has been found incubating in iron pipes exposed to the seemingly unendurable heat of the sun.

Fragments of snake and lizard skin are sometimes used for nest decoration, but this is not so general a custom as with the eastern bird. The eggs, which number from three to six, are similar to those of the great crest, but ordinarily have finer markings.

The typical ash-throated flycatcher is found from Washington and Colorado to northern Baja California and Tamaulipas.

Sulphur-bellied Flycatcher
(Myiodynastes luteiventris swarthi)
Average Length, Eight Inches

In the Chiricahua Mountains, Arizona, among the gnarled trunks of sycamores in Pinery Canyon, I heard an emphatic note that drew my eyes to the yellow breast of a sulphur-bellied flycatcher perched on a dead limb.

A friend pointed out the nest of the flycatcher in a hollow limb. For days I devoted much time to watching this interesting bird.

For a nest it lines a small cavity in a tree trunk with leaves and other soft materials, on which it places three or four cream-colored eggs, marked with brown and purple.

The sulphur-bellied flycatcher nests in southern Arizona mountains. It migrates to Central America, probably to South America.

MILLIONS OF PESTS ARE DESTROYED BY THESE WINGED FLYTRAPS

Small, pert, and energetic, the **Least Flycatcher** (upper left) often dashes down to the grass in pursuit of its insect prey. Less well known are the **Alder Flycatcher** (upper right) of similar color but different note, the **Buff-breasted Flycatcher** (center left) of southwestern mountains, and the shy, retiring **Yellow-bellied Flycatcher** (center right). The **Eastern Phoebe** (lower right), a near neighbor of man, catches insects with an audible snap of its bill and animatedly speaks its name. **Say's Phoebe** (lower left) and the handsome **Black Phoebe** (lower center) are western kinsmen.

Least Flycatcher

(Empidonax minimus)

Average Length, Five and One-quarter Inches

In summer the least flycatcher calls steadily its name, *che-bec*. The bird is found in orchards, at the edges of woodlands, and in thickets. It often comes to dooryards.

The nest is a compact cup of shredded bark, plant fibers, down, and spiderweb placed in a tree fork from 8 to 30 feet from the ground. From three to six spotless, creamy eggs are laid.

Least flycatchers nest from Mackenzie and Quebec to Oklahoma and the mountains of North Carolina, and winter from northeastern Mexico to Panama.

The Acadian flycatcher *(Empidonax virescens)*, found from Massachusetts and Nebraska to the Gulf States, is larger and broader billed.

Buff-breasted Flycatcher

(Empidonax fulvifrons pygmaeus)

Average Length, Five Inches

Among pines and oaks of the southwestern mountains this little flycatcher is found in summer. It is among the least known of its group. Its nest is of soft materials fastened to a branch by cobweb. The three or four buffy-white eggs are without spots. Its range is only from southern Arizona and New Mexico into Mexico.

Say's Phoebe

(Sayornis saya)

Average Length, Seven Inches

Say's phoebe is a common resident of arid regions in the West. Its nest, placed under a bridge, against a building, in a cave or tunnel, or against the side of an arroyo, is made of vegetable fibers and hair, held together with spiderwebs. It holds four or five white eggs, sometimes with a few flecks of brown. Say's phoebe is found from central Alaska to Baja California and central Kansas.

Black Phoebe

(Sayornis nigricans)

Average Length, Six and One-half Inches

In California I have found black phoebes about bridges and along irrigation ditches, in city parks and yards, and about ranchhouses. Like the eastern phoebe they are hardy and may remain all winter in sheltered localities.

In spring the male rises with tremulous wings 40 or 50 feet to sing unmusically. A little later a nest will be made of fibered mud pellets, lined with wool and feathers, and placed under eaves, against a bank, or at an abandoned tunnel mouth. This holds from three to six white eggs, sometimes plain and sometimes slightly dotted with reddish brown.

The black phoebe is found from Oregon and Utah to Baja California and Chiapas.

Eastern Phoebe

(Sayornis phoebe)

Average Length, Seven Inches

When I was a small boy the "pewee" that nested under the bridge was one of the first birds that I came to know. Later I dutifully learned to call it the phoebe in accordance with the dictum of my first bird book.

In spring the phoebe comes to the borders of little watercourses soon after the ice disappears, and on sunny days calls cheerfully as with twitching tail it watches for dancing gnats and other early insects. During cold storms it retires to willows and other shelter.

It is among the earliest of our smaller birds to nest, making a bulky cup of moss and other vegetable fibers mixed with mud, with a lining of soft materials. This is placed under a porch, against a rock ledge, or in the erect root base of a fallen tree. The three to six white eggs rarely show small spots of brown.

This species is found from Mackenzie and Nova Scotia to eastern New Mexico and Georgia. In winter it ranges from Virginia south to the Gulf States and Mexico.

Alder Flycatcher

(Empidonax trailli)

Average Length, Six Inches

The alder flycatcher comes when summer is at hand. Ordinarily it is observed merely as an elusive gray form that darts up out of low, dense cover to seize an insect in the air. Usually the compact nest is placed from two to four feet from the ground in a thicket. It contains two to four creamy or pinkish eggs spotted with brown.

These flycatchers are found from Alaska and Newfoundland southward to Colorado and West Virginia, in winter going into the Tropics.

Yellow-bellied Flycatcher

(Empidonax flaviventris)

Average Length, Five and Two-thirds Inches

Among eastern flycatchers of its group this species is the easiest to identify, since its yellow breast marks it instantly. In spring it is one of the last of the migrants, not arriving until leaves are grown. Low perches in shaded woodlands are its favorite haunts, and it ordinarily conceals its nest in heavy moss on the ground, or against a bank or stump. The four or five eggs are white spotted with brown.

In fall the yellow-bellied flycatcher is even more richly colored than in spring. It nests in the north from northern British Columbia and Newfoundland to central Alberta and northern Pennsylvania, and winters from southern Mexico to Panama.

The western flycatcher *(Empidonax d. difficilis)* ranges from Alaska and South Dakota to California and western Texas, with a relative, the San Lucas, in Baja California.

MOST FLYCATCHERS ARE NEAT IN APPEARANCE, BUT ONE IS GAUDY

Compared to his relatives, the vivid **Vermilion Flycatcher** of the Mexican borderland (upper right with his mate) is like a scarlet tanager in a flock of sparrows. His flaming color flashes over a flooded river as he darts after insects, but his lady, perched beneath, is somberly clad. Two other southwesterners are the **Beardless** (upper left) and **Coues's Flycatchers** (lower right). The **Olive-sided Flycatcher** (lower left) breeds in coniferous forests and winters in South America. The **Eastern** and **Western Wood Pewees** (left center) likewise migrate to tropic jungles.

Beardless Flycatcher

(Camptostoma imberbe)
Average Length, Six Inches

In a family of birds of fairly orthodox habits, so far as North America is concerned, the beardless flycatcher is truly an anomaly.

First, it lacks the long bristles about the base of the bill that assist the ordinary flycatchers in capturing prey. Second, it hops about among the smaller twigs, sometimes actively like a warbler and sometimes slowly and deliberately like a vireo. Its song is a cheerful, twittering ditty.

The nest is a ball of fibers placed at the base of a palm leaf, often near the ground. Two eggs are a set; they are white, spotted with brown about the larger end.

The beardless flycatcher enters the United States in southern Arizona and in the lower Rio Grande Valley, Texas. Southward it is found to Guatemala and Costa Rica.

Eastern Wood Pewee

(Myiochanes virens)
Average Length, Six and One-half Inches

A dull colored, inconspicuous bird of the woods, the wood pewee is often a disembodied voice that comes from a singer unseen. Its note is pleasing, if plaintive, a soft *pee-a-wee*. Passing insects provide it with food that it takes expertly from the air.

The nest is a felted cup so covered with lichens that it seems a part of the limb. The three or four eggs are creamy white, with brown spots around the large end.

This bird is found from southern Manitoba and Nova Scotia to Texas and Florida. It winters from Nicaragua to Peru.

Olive-sided Flycatcher

(Nuttallornis mesoleucus)
Average Length, Seven and One-half Inches

This is a solitary bird, ordinarily found perched in the top of some tall tree where it has a clear view. On its breeding grounds in the north and in the western mountains it frequents pine and spruce forests.

Larger than our other flycatchers excepting the kingbirds, it is known instantly by the heavy gray band on either side and by the cottony fluff of white feathers that shows above the wing on the lower back.

The nest is a shallow cup of moss, pine needles, or other vegetable fibers, sometimes low, and sometimes far from the ground. The three or four pinkish or cream-colored eggs are heavily blotched with brown. The old birds are pugnacious in defense of their nests. The food consists mainly of insects taken in air, and in summer a little wild fruit.

The olive-sided flycatcher nests in the great coniferous forests of the north, from central Alaska across to Quebec, ranging south in the mountains to northern Baja California, western Texas, and North Carolina. It winters from Colombia to Peru.

Vermilion Flycatcher

(Pyrocephalus rubinus mexicanus)
Average Length, Six Inches

On a hot summer morning in southern Arizona I saw a vermilion flycatcher rise above the bushes with slowly flapping wings.

Its brilliant colors seemed to reflect the coming heat of the day as it hung like a giant moth 50 feet above the ground. Truly, this lovely creature merits its Spanish name of *brasita de fuego*, "little coal of fire."

This beautiful bird is found in arid regions, often along dry watercourses. The nest is a frail cup of twigs and plant fibers lined with feathers, wool, and down, placed in trees. The two or three eggs are buff, boldly marked with brown and lavender.

Vermilion flycatchers are found from southeastern California, southwestern Utah, and southern Texas to Baja California and southern Mexico.

Western Wood Pewee

(Myiochanes richardsoni)
Average Length, Six and One-half Inches

A counterpart of the eastern bird in size and appearance, except for a slightly darker breast and duller lower mandible, the western wood pewee is chiefly distinguished by its voice. This is a low, double-noted *pee-er*, a whistled call given more quickly and without the cadence of the longer song of its eastern kinsman.

The western wood pewee is a bird of groves along streams and hillsides, of mountain canyons, and of open mountain forests. It is widely distributed and at times is common.

The nest, located on a tree limb, is deeper and more strongly built than that of the eastern bird. The eggs of the two are similar.

The western wood pewee (*Myiochanes richardsoni richardsoni*) breeds from central Alaska and Manitoba to northern Baja California and Tamaulipas. A related race is found in lower Baja California.

Coues's Flycatcher

(Myiochanes pertinax pallidiventris)
Average Length, Seven and Three-quarters Inches

On the summit of the Chiricahua Mountains of Arizona, I saw these flycatchers perched on dead branches in the tops of the tallest pines, from which they sallied for insects.

The nest is a compact cup placed on a tree limb, often at some height. The eggs, usually three, are creamy buff spotted with brown and lilac, often in a wreath about the larger end.

Coues's flycatcher ranges in the mountains from central Arizona and southwestern New Mexico south into Nayarit, Mexico.

HOLIDAYS WITH HUMMINGBIRDS

By Margaret L. Bodine

THE porch of our summer home in Maine is only 11 by 13 feet, quite in proportion to the hummingbirds which spend so many satisfying hours there. It is a second-story affair, bounded on two sides by the walls of the cottage, which is built on a bank. A clematis vine grows there in profusion, and on the wide railings are flower-boxes, which first made this nook known to our winged visitors. However, the flowers are not the secret of the porch's attraction for them, but miniature bottles, about two inches long, covered with some bright-hued material and filled with sugared water.

These bottles are fastened among the blossoms and are speedily discovered by the hummingbirds. Once found, there are few daylight hours from the middle of June till September when at least one is not there. Sometimes as many as eight rubies are feasting at a time.

On the day after our arrival at our summer home last year we put the little bottles out, and in less than ten minutes the first hummer came, drank, and perched.

HUMMINGBIRDS HAVE "TELEVISION"

The hummingbird's powers of vision are marvelous. One of the little mites, which we discovered for the first time with field glasses, sat on a branch of a tree several hundred feet from the porch, watched us from there when we filled the bottles, and was at the tip of the medicine dropper, which was used for this purpose, before we were through. This happened very often, and, as much of her time was spent on the same twig of this bough, we felt that her nest was probably near by. But the tree was a very tall one and it was not possible for us to prove it.

Doubtless what seems to be curiosity in hummingbirds is in many cases a search for food, which consists largely of insects caught in the air and of the nectar sucked from flowers. The tongues of these birds are long and tubular, and they extract the honey easily from such blossoms as the honeysuckle and the trumpet vine. They dine on many other favorites, such as the bee balm, larkspur, phlox, gladiolus, rose, and clematis.

The hummers investigate all bright objects on the porch: a red film box; one's purple sweater, in which the long bill is poked vigorously; they poise in front of the camera's lens or close to one's face, apparently studying it; or peer into each seed-cup of the birds' merry-go-round.

The merry-go-round is a successful device invented to circumvent the red squirrel, which stole the seed from an ordinary hanging tray that was provided for other varieties of feathered guests.

One day there was a male purple finch in our black birch tree close by the porch, brilliant raspberry-colored in the sun, which was shining brightly on him. A young hummer, evidently mistaking the finch for a sweet flower, darted at him and gave him repeated jabs. The finch, appearing much bored, moved from spot to spot and finally flew away.

Hummers are among the most fearless of all birds, despite their size, and are quite able to hold their own in the avian world, where they are treated with wholesome respect. They will attack hawks, eagles, and crows, and I have a firm conviction that if conflicts were to occur between a hummingbird and the great blue heron, which sometimes comes to our near-by harbor, the vanquished one would never be the hummer.

Observation of these small birds during the past five summers does not lead us to the conclusion that they exemplify the Christian virtue of meekness to any marked degree. For temper, pure and simple, they surely have no equal. One of our hummer visitors apparently was frequently thrown into a violent rage by the approach of another. With tail wide spread, the white-edged tail feathers giving the effect of a petticoat showing beneath a skirt, and fairly shrieking, it would dart at the newcomer, striking with its rapierlike bill.

Some days there are hours when one couple will be fighting in the air, sailing close together, then suddenly separating, dashing at each other and striking with terrific force. We hear the sound of bill striking bill, or the thud of body against body, and are always fearful of finding a dead bird below.

Such battles may account for the small dark marks which we see on the necks and breasts of some of the birds. After each duel the victor invariably returns to the exact spot which it had left, breast heaving, but with triumph written on every feather, an illustration for a "Winged Victory."

There have been several red-letter days in our hummingbird summers. One of these was early in August, when there seemed to be a veritable swarm of birds on the porch. There was a constant buzzing, creaking, and squeaking, as our "boarders" darted across the porch to drive others from their perches. We watched spellbound. It was difficult to count them and we could not be sure that there were more than eight at any one time, though the number seemed much greater.

THE HUMMINGBIRD FAMILY LIFE

Another day worthy of remembrance was that on which the first baby hummingbird was brought to the porch. It was the most diminutive ball of feathers we had ever seen and was discovered clinging tight to the clematis vine. Soon we found its twin being fed by the male ruby-throat in the birch tree, though it is often stated that the father forgets all family cares after the nest is completed.

The nest itself is very beautiful. It is an inch or less in diameter and the same in depth, and is lined with milkweed and plant down. Usually the tiny structure is saddled to the limb of a tree and fastened securely with cobwebs.

The little ones grew unbelievably fast and came often to the porch, though for some time they were unable to drink from the bottles. The mother fed them, and the first time we saw her do it we were quite ready to notify the Society for the Prevention of Cruelty to Children. The baby crouched flat on the perch squeaking as if in distress, and the bird hovering over it seemed to be stabbing it to death.

We thought an alien infant was being persecuted by one of our birds until we discovered that the little one was being fed by regurgitation, the predigested food being pumped into its stomach by its mother. Often the baby would cling upside down to the perch with bill wide open, begging to be fed.

One baby bird with a yellowish tinge on throat and breast spent much time on a porch perch making its toilet, going carefully over each feather, preening and licking it with bill and tongue. Often one sees the very long tongue, which is stuck in and out with great swiftness.

Several times a hummer has perched quite calmly on a friend's extended finger, once running its tongue lightly along where sweetened water had been placed—the most gentle touch imaginable.

One summer, for some inexplicable reason, no adult male hummingbird was seen on the porch, although there were the usual females and immature males. We missed seeing the gorgeous red throats, but that was our most peaceful summer, with many photographic opportunities. The following and each succeeding summer we have had several males, who have appropriated the porch as a private club and have driven away with much fierceness all females and young birds. They have guarded the premises either from a perch on the porch or from a near-by tree and allowed no other hummers to touch the sweetened water, whether or not they themselves wanted to drink.

A mother bird will allow one of her children to perch with her, but woe betide the intruder who attempts to share her resting place. It is an amusing and ludicrous sight to watch the parent bird take her stand on a perch and protect it against all interlopers. She herself will drink and permit her children to do so, but flies into a fury at the approach of others, spreading her tail and wings wide, darting at them violently and looking so formidable that only the bravest would dare try to stay near her for long.

BANDED HUMMINGBIRDS RETURN TO SUMMER HOME

An enthusiastic bird lover is a summer neighbor of ours. She lives at a near-by inn, where she has a unique third-story bird window, a feeding and banding station combined. There she has performed the extremely delicate operation of putting microscopic bands on a number of hummingbirds, and has succeeded in getting several back and checking them up as "returns," indicating that hummers are constant to a locality.

The game of attracting the hummingbirds has proved a most rewarding one, and the attempt to catch these diminutive creatures with lens and shutter on a photographic plate is an alluring pastime.

Photograph courtesy U. S. Biological Survey

FREE LUNCH FOR A FEATHERED FRIEND

A Florida jay at Sebring, Florida, takes food from the hand of the late Dr. E. W. Nelson, former chief of the U. S. Biological Survey and a contributor to THE NATIONAL GEOGRAPHIC MAGAZINE.

Photograph by George Shiras, 3d

EVEN A STUFFED OWL MAKES HIM SEE RED

One of the chief delights of a group of Florida blue jays is to locate some sleepy old owl and worry him. This one, attacking a stuffed bird, is puzzled at the victim's unconcern (page 110).

CROWS, MAGPIES, AND JAYS

Unusual Intelligence Has Earned a Unique Position for These Common Birds

By T. Gilbert Pearson

WHILE driving along an unfre-quented road in the semidesert country of southern Oregon, I noticed at a distance two large birds ap-parently engaged in some kind of game. They would fly almost together, then one would dive and quickly mount aloft. Twice he alighted on the ground, but only to rise at once. As we approached, they sepa-rated, one perching on the post of a barbed-wire fence. When we were within 80 yards, one flew to a distant post. For half a mile he thus preceded us with short flights.

This bird was carrying something in his beak. My companion fired his revolver, and the bird dropped an object which proved to be the dried leg bone of a jack rabbit. We had come upon a pair of ravens at a time when they were in one of their playful moods. Sometimes a dozen or more may be seen maneuvering about one an-other, nose-diving, volplaning, or tumbling about in mimic combats. For the time all dignity is forgotten and the solemn birds present a performance entirely out of keep-ing with what is generally regarded as their usual habits of life.

THE RAVEN IN FOLKLORE

Tradition emphasizes the idea that the raven is a dour and somber bird. The shadow of his sable wings falling across the path of a bride foretells disaster. He is sinister and mysterious, and his coarse croakings through the centuries have been thought prophetic and portentous of evil.

His remarkable sagacity has caused many to believe that he possesses attributes of a divine nature, while others think that his uncanny shrewdness is derived directly from the Evil One. Odin, the chief god of the Norsemen, was attended by two ravens, who whispered advice in his ears. It was the raven that Noah first sent forth from the Ark. To Elijah, hiding by the brook Cherith, the ravens brought food. In Wales the legendary hero, Owein, was accom-panied by an army of ravens that guarded him from harm. In Ireland, Cú Chulainn had the constant service of two magic ravens to warn him of the coming of his foes. The Greeks were not unmindful of the raven's power.

Tradition is back of the ravens kept in the Tower of London; there is meaning in the raven forms carved on the totem poles of Alaska.

THE PILGRIMS WARRED ON THE RAVEN

In the world are many thousands of spe-cies of birds to which the people pay scant attention. But wherever the raven is found, the inhabitants are aware of his presence, and tell of his weird powers as they gather about the campfire or sit in council in the igloo, the hogan, or the mountain cabin.

Our raven is merely one of the geographi-cal forms of the ravens inhabiting many parts of the Northern Hemisphere.

The Pilgrim Fathers found him in Mas-sachusetts, but he soon fell into evil repute, for it was discovered he would attack and kill the newborn lambs and sickly sheep. So the people made war upon him, and to-day ravens do not build their nests within the boundaries of that State.

The bird is not uncommon in Maine, especially near the sea, where he is a scourge to some of the bird colonies of that rocky coast. On the island of No Mans Land, near the fishing village of Matinicus, Maine, a pair of ravens has lived for years in a nest in a sturdy evergreen tree. How long ago it was built I was not able to learn, but it is a very substantial structure. Year after year it has been repaired by the ad-dition of a few new sticks, a little fresh wool, a few billfuls of seaweed, and small roots.

Defying the fierce gales which in winter sweep over these icy seas, the eyrie stands secure, and every season has seen it occu-pied by young ravens.

On this rocky island, safe from the ordi-nary enemies of birds which haunt the neighboring mainland, many thousands of

Photograph by A. A. Allen

YOUNG CROWS ARE MOSTLY APPETITE

This is the welcome home which awaits Jim Crow or his spouse when they return to the nest with dinner. They are faithful parents and work hard to keep their youngsters' voracious hunger appeased.

herring gulls assemble in summer. Their eggs, as well as the young, are constantly eaten by the ravens, and a continuous warfare goes on between the two species.

On a sagebrush slope in northern Nevada I found a raven feeding upon a sage hen, and in a little opening in a Utah forest I came upon three ravens and a turkey vulture eating the body of a young mule deer. Probably in neither case were the ravens responsible for the death of the creatures upon which they were feasting.

It makes no difference to the raven how long an animal has been dead; he seems to relish carrion just as much as he enjoys the flesh of recently killed animals. Groups of ravens gather every day in summer about the refuse heaps back of the hotels in Yellowstone National Park and pick over the garbage in company with the bears. Often you may find one or more waiting expectantly on the posts of a certain corral in Glacier National Park.

Just north of the Grand Canyon, in northern Arizona, lies the Kaibab Plateau, with its famous deer herd attracting visitors from afar. Here, when the deer were

accustomed to gather in the afternoon, I noticed that ravens were frequently present. In August, 1924, I counted more than 60 at one time. They would sail out from over the forest and gradually descend to the short grass, there to walk sedately about and feed upon the numerous grasshoppers of the valley.

PARENT RAVENS STAY TOGETHER AFTER THE YOUNG DEPART

Very rarely one sees so many ravens together. Usually they are found only in family groups, composed of the parents and their offspring. When the young have attained the necessary age and experience to shift for themselves, they wander off, but their elders remain together even until the snow begins to melt and the call comes to repair again the old nest.

Although sometimes ravens use trees as nesting sites, their usual selection is a high, beetling cliff. Here, often hundreds of feet above the sea, or above the floor of some inland valley, protected by projecting rock above, the nest is built in a niche of the wall. Such situations are

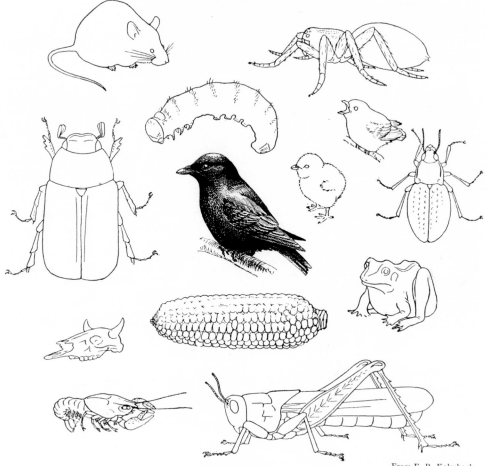

WHAT IT TAKES TO RAISE A CROW

From E. R. Kalmbach

The nesting crow requires about 10 ounces of food per day, or about 13⅛ pounds for its nesting life of three weeks. At the end of that time it will weigh about a pound. During this period it will have eaten two and a quarter times its own weight of May beetles. The grasshoppers it has eaten would, if combined, form a mammoth insect about twice the size of the bird. Wild birds and poultry would each form a mass about a fifth of the crow's weight and corn about one and one-half times its mass. Here are pictured a fully fledged young crow and its principal food items. These include small mammals, spiders, caterpillars, May beetles, poultry, wild birds, miscellaneous beetles, carrion, corn, amphibians, crustaceans, and grasshoppers. These are all drawn to a scale that approximately represents the aggregate mass of the different items consumed during the nesting life, compared with the bird that ate them. No less than 656 different items have been identified in the food of the crow.

exceedingly difficult to approach and the birds cannot readily be disturbed save by air attack.

The cranny chosen for a nesting site may be of any shape, and often must be well filled in order to make a substantial structure of proper size and shape. The nests of many birds show little variety in their form or in the character of the materials used. This is not the case with the ravens, for their practical imagination permits them to adapt their nests to almost any kind of opening in the rock, and to use a wide variety of objects in its construction.

A few of the materials that have been noted as component parts of the nest are: sticks, twigs, cow-ribs, rope ends, ragged canvas, fragments of cloth of various kinds, moss, seaweed, roots of many sizes, hay, cow dung, clusters of hair from the carcasses of deer, horses, cows, and coyotes, and strips of hide and shredded bark.

That the raven's wit sometimes fails him is illustrated in an account by a California

Photograph by George Shiras, 3d

A CANADA JAY INVESTIGATING A HAUNCH OF VENISON

Meat is his favorite food and the sound of a hunter's gun seems to attract rather than to frighten him, for he has learned to associate that sound with meat.

The raven mates for life and a pair uses the same nest season after season. These birds are extremely devoted to their young and to each other. Their domestic lives, therefore, are very regular, well ordered, and much more formal than those of the average bird.

The family Corvidae in America includes two subfamilies. One is the jays and magpies; the other, ravens, crows, piñon jays, and nutcrackers. It is represented in North America by 17 species and 22 subspecies, or varieties.

KINDS NUMBER 41

If to these be added two European species, the rook *(Corvus frugilegus frugilegus)* and the hooded crow *(Corvus cornix cornix)*, which h a v e been recorded a s accidental wanderers of the Old World to Greenland, we find a total of 41 kinds of the Corvidae which have been accredited to this continent north of Mexico.

South America is the only continent where there are no native crows. Africa has a black-and-white species and Asia one whose black feathers are interspersed with markings of gray and brown. In Europe some of the family representatives are rooks, jackdaws, and carrion crows. The first named congregate in vast numbers to roost, and this practice has given us the name "rookery," which in the United States is applied to any numerous assemblage of birds in trees.

In the Piedmont country of North Carolina I came upon a little girl weeping beside the road. The mother, with red and toil-worn hands, was caressing her child and trying to comfort her. Dismounting, I led

ornithologist, who for some time watched a pair carrying sticks to a certain point on a cliff.

He says: "Investigation disclosed an astonishing condition of affairs. The daffy birds had been trying to lodge the foundations of a nest in a small sloping crevice where any sort of lodgment was practically impossible. As a result, every stick had fallen until a pile 6 feet in diameter and not less than 2 feet high lay at the bottom of the cliff—two hundred pounds' weight of wood and not a mud-sill to the good yet! And about 40 feet along, under the same cliff, was another stick pile, evidently the accumulation of the preceding season."

my horse nearer and learned that the outburst of grief was caused by a crow which had just killed and carried away the last of five newly hatched chickens, the pets of the distressed child.

It was no use telling these people that the crow is not really so black as he is painted, that he eats many grubs and beetles, and does much good about the farm. They lived with him throughout the year and found their contacts with him too intimate and disturbing. Crows had stolen their hens' eggs repeatedly and now had acquired a taste for young chickens.

Crows pecked holes in their melons; pulled up sprouting corn, and robbed the nests of birds which the family liked to have about the home. In fact, they were so destructive that the father had devised every means he could think of to rid the place of their presence.

The opinion which this family held about crows is entertained generally by farmers. In almost every community where the crow appears in numbers, the inhabitants view his presence with apprehension and dislike. From the early settlement by Europeans, every man's hand has been against him. Scarecrows erected in ten thousand fields and poisoned grain scattered about have had little effect.

No town or city ordinance and no State or Federal law protects the crow. Bounties have been offered for his head. Neighborhood campaigns for destruction of crow nests and "shoots" at their roosting colonies have been organized often.

Despite this widespread, continuous, and almost universal campaign for its destruc-

Photograph by A. A. Allen

YOUNG CROWS TAME EASILY AND MAKE INTERESTING PETS

All three of these desperate-looking plotters are at work hatching some mischief and Jimmie Crow is probably in the thick of it (see text, page 107).

tion, the crow has steadily increased and yearly his numbers are becoming greater. In the bird world the crow is one great American success.

Personally I am very fond of the crow. He is such a shrewd fellow and so tremendously successful in the struggle of life that I cannot but admire him. His caw on a frosty morning reaches my ears from across the fields and I know there is life abroad in the land. He is the one bird I am pretty sure to see when the snow is deep and the sleet glistens on the trees. Sometimes I have seen him on an ice cake riding down the Hudson. Apparently he has a lofty scorn for bad weather and kindred difficulties.

Photograph from Dr. Spencer R. Atkinson

"PUCK-OF-THE-WOODS" HAS SOME FRIENDS AND MANY ENEMIES

The California jay is an impertinent creature, who seems to enjoy mischief-making. He destroys millions of other birds' eggs every year and takes keen delight in pecking cats' tails.

Photograph by Guy A. Bailey

MRS. BLUE JAY MAKES A DEVOTED MOTHER

Usually she and her mate build a new nest each year, using twigs and small branches broken from the trees. Although generally noisy, the female is quiet and cautious while brooding.

Photograph by A. A. Allen

CROWS AT A WATER HOLE IN ITHACA, NEW YORK

The crow comes close to being the "great American bird," for it is likely that a thousand people know him personally for every one who ever saw a live eagle. He has waged a successful battle for existence, and there are probably more of his clan here now than there were when the Pilgrims came. Henry Ward Beecher once remarked that if men wore feathers and wings, very few of them would be clever enough to be crows.

In summer I find him tearing rotten logs to pieces and turning over bark and sticks, and I see numbers of crows swarming in flocks over the newly plowed fields looking for grubs. I enjoy the sight of a crow, but I am a bird lover and therefore not an unbiased observer. Furthermore, I have no chickens, no melon patches, not even a cornfield, for him to raid.

YOUNG CROWS MAKE AMUSING PETS

Young crows make interesting pets. They are voracious eaters and require much food to keep them in a contented frame of mind, but they pay for their keep by performing many curious antics and by their amusing attempts to imitate the words and voices of the people about them.

They are fond of collecting and hiding bright trinkets of many kinds. A broken bit of china, a dry chicken bone, the cap from a ginger-ale bottle, a small block of painted wood, a glossy beetle, and pebbles of various hues are objects which may take their fancy. They have been known to carry away thimbles, small scissors, and pipes. Sometimes their treasures are hoarded in a hidden nook, or they may be buried here and there about the yard or in the garden. They are often forgotten, but sometimes are exhumed and transferred to some other favorite hiding place.

Crows often accumulate in large numbers. Hundreds of thousands have been known to assemble in some favorite roost. At times a flock will gather and engage in

A FLORIDA BLUE JAY AND PROOF OF HIS IDENTITY

This subspecies is somewhat smaller and grayer and has narrower white tips to the feathers than the northern form. Although not a shy bird and quite at home in city streets, he does not tame as readily as his neighbor, the Florida jay.

vociferous cawing. They make seemingly useless short flights, shift their positions on the limbs, or move from one perch or tree to another, all the time keeping up a most animated series of calls pitched in many different keys (page 120).

Some observers claim that crows talk. It certainly is true that their various notes are understood by their fellows, who at once react as the emergency requires. These so-called "crow conventions" are most amusing and would probably be extremely interesting if we could know what they were all about. Some observers claim that they hold trials over the conduct of some of their members. There is little evidence,

however, that anything of this kind takes place.

The nearest opportunity I ever had of being a witness to any of their activities suggesting condemnation proceedings against one of their kind occurred one winter evening while I was watching scattered flocks of hundreds of crows coming to their roost.

Suddenly I became aware of an unusual commotion among a group of eight. One evidently was in great disfavor with the others, for with angry and excited cawings they were striking at him most vigorously. The strength of the persecuted bird was all but spent when I first sighted him,

Photograph by Frank and John Craighead

HUNGRY MOUTHS GAPE EAGERLY FOR FOOD

After a perilous climb two boy naturalists obtained this close-up of a raven home on a cliff. These hungry young birds had to wait for their meal until their parents made sure the camera was harmless. The nest was made of large sticks and lined with horse hair.

and when, a moment later, the fleeing one sustained a particularly vicious onslaught, he began to fall. He did not descend gradually, like a bird injured on the wing, but plunged downward like a falling rock for 100 feet or more, into the top of a large pine tree and, bounding from limb to limb, struck the ground only a few yards from me. When I picked him up he was dead and badly battered.

THE AMERICAN MAGPIE

In the western part of our country is found the black-billed magpie, very closely related to the magpies of Europe and Asia. In some of the States it is a numerous spe-

cies, and because of its large size, striking contrasts of plumage, and extremely vociferous habits, it is one of the outstanding birds which cannot readily be overlooked, even by the most casual observer.

This is another representative of the family Corvidae which is unpopular with several groups of people. Cattlemen tell you that he attacks weak or injured stock, and that by pecking the scars made by the branding irons on calves or colts he prevents the wounds from healing.

All observers agree that the magpies are a scourge to many birds, and that nests are constantly raided by them. Mourning doves, meadow larks, and other birds nesting on or near the ground are especially subject to raids. The eggs and young of swallows are dainties which parent magpies delight to gather for their young. Of course, they eat crickets and grasshoppers as well. A mouse is not safe if a magpie discovers it away from cover.

Ground squirrels are killed by them, and magpies have been known to wait long and patiently for one of these rodents to emerge from its hole, when it is pounced upon and dispatched with blows from the powerful bill.

I have seen flocks of magpies in Alaska, Colorado, and elsewhere engaged in hunting systematically every bush and tree as they progressed. From the way they peeped and peered and investigated, they were unquestionably searching for eggs and young birds. At a distance I could keep track of the onward movement of the marauding band by the cries of alarm and distress raised by the smaller feathered inhabitants of the underbrush.

THE BLUE JAY IS A HANDSOME, NOISY SWAGGERER

It would be difficult to find a more noisy bird than our beautiful blue jay, and when a family group takes up its habitation in the trees about a dwelling, the occupants are kept fully aware of the fact that this bird is in the neighborhood. His note at dawn has been compared to a shout.

These jays have a great variety of calls and often imitate the notes and cries of other birds. Their imitation of the call of the red-shouldered hawk is so nearly perfect as often to deceive the bird student.

Their vocal performances are at their best when an owl is discovered. Shrill screams call together all the jays of the neighborhood. With flashings of blue and white feathers, they arrive and at once plunge into the fray. Abuse is poured out on the sleepy owl, who desires nothing so much as to be left alone. Growing bolder, the jays approach within a few feet of their traditional enemy and shriek anathemas at him in the most outrageous language known to the hardiest members of a blue-jay mob. This fuss and din may continue for half an hour before the owl is driven away.

Jays are silent, however, when about their nest during the period of its construction; also while the eggs are being incubated and when the young are being fed. I have never seen a jay go directly to its nest. Once I watched a mother perch 21 times before she reached her eggs and settled upon them. Her approach and departure are accomplished with extreme stealth and caution.

The nest is usually placed in the crotch of a limb some 10 to 30 feet from the ground. I have found nests in old pear trees at an elevation of only six feet, and again in pine trees many times that distance from the earth. The nest is composed of dead twigs, usually broken from the trees for the purpose. Rootlets for a lining are much used. The eggs are drab-colored, with brownish spots, and number from four to six. Seventeen days are usually required for them to hatch.

Like most other members of his tribe, this jay bears the reputation of being a plunderer of the nests of other birds. Evidences of this habit I have rarely seen, although for many years I have been on the watch for them. Once I saw a hungry jay try to strike down a junco feeding on the snow, and again I saw one seize and kill a young English sparrow just out of the nest. Twice I have seen them taking eggs from a robin's nest.

Blue jays eat insects of several kinds and acorns and beech mast are staple articles of diet. When such food is scarce jays will migrate considerable distances in search of it.

CULTIVATION OF OAK TREES BROUGHT JAYS TO FLORIDA

Fifty years ago little settlements began to spring up in the pine-woods country of central Florida. Jays were not very common there at that time. The settlers planted water oaks for shade, and as these and other deciduous trees developed, the character of the bird life began to change. Crested flycatchers, chuck-will's-widows, cardinals, and wrens, hitherto but little known in that immediate neighborhood, began to come about the houses. Inland towns today have bountiful acorn crops, and blue jays are abundant.

Blue jays are very engaging birds. You may suspect them of taking the eggs from the robin or yellow warbler's nest which you have been watching; you may object to their cries and shouts, but the blue jay is the dashing, handsome rake of the

Photograph by William L. and Irene Finley

CLARK'S NUTCRACKER INHABITS THE HIGH MOUNTAINS OF THE WEST

This avian mountaineer has a harsh, grating voice. One note, which he seems to use when at play, closely resembles the scream of a mountain lion. He is hardy and a good fighter; he has been known to tackle a golden eagle. His powerful claws and beak also serve him well for extracting seeds from pine and other cones.

village, and no one, however prejudiced, can deny its engaging qualities.

In a vast evergreen forest in the mountains of Montana I was awakened one morning by a sound that was entirely new to me. A guttural, grating, rattling note, difficult to describe, yet easy to remember, was issuing from some point near by.

Cautiously raising the flap of my sleeping bag, I discovered the author of the sounds. On a low limb of a tree sat a stocky gray bird at least a foot in length. His wings were glossy black with a dash of white. He was peering at his companion standing on the ground by the log where we had eaten our supper the evening before.

This was my first acquaintance with the "big camp robber," or Clark's crow, and the meeting was just as I would have had it— a perfectly natural environment and a visit staged in a manner wholly characteristic of this little-known bird.

It is encounters of this sort that give piquant interest to the study of birds. I have pleasant memories of many such chance meetings in the course of many years of wandering in out-of-the-way places.

Once when I was in Colorado I saw a sight to delight the heart of the naturalist. It was a demonstration of the remarkable air mastery of the Clark's nutcracker.

CLARK'S NUTCRACKER IS AN AMAZING "STUNT FLYER"

High up on the slopes of Pikes Peak a Clark's nutcracker dashed from a stunted conifer in pursuit of another. Straight out from the mountain they flew. Four hundred yards or more away, they turned to the misty valley far beneath and plunged downward, volplaning, banking, flying with flapping wings, but always descending until, perhaps 2,000 feet below, they were lost to my view.

Diving flights from such dizzy heights meant nothing to them. In the wilderness the Clark's nutcracker is as adventurous as was the great explorer of the Northwest who first discovered it to science and whose name it bears. Nothing terrifies this pioneer of the wilderness (see illustration above).

Northern Raven

(Corvus corax principalis)

Average Length, Twenty-four Inches

The raven looks like a large crow. Although it appears to be about twice the size of its smaller relative, as a matter of fact it is not. The common crow is from 17 to 21 inches long from bill tip to tail tip. Ravens vary from 21½ to 26½ inches. The raven is always heavier, the head and beak are stouter, the feathers on the throat are pointed and not rounded, and the cry is a deep-voiced croak unmistakably different from any note which a crow can produce. It is a bird of the mountains, of rocky cliffs by the sea, of barren mesas, of deserts, and of uncut forest lands.

It has retreated before the advance of man. Its food is the offal or carcasses of animals, fish, and crabs gathered by the sea, insects, eggs, and helpless young birds of any species.

The raven feeds its young for a time by regurgitation. It is said to attack the eagle, if necessary, to protect them. The parents stay with the young, feeding them, guarding them, and teaching them throughout the summer, long after they have left the nest.

The northern raven is found from the Arctic Ocean southward to the northern tier of States and in the Alleghenies to Georgia.

The American raven *(C. c. sinuatus)* is a subspecies occurring from British Columbia, Montana, and North Dakota southward to Nicaragua.

The white-necked raven *(C. cryptoleucus)*, the white seen only if the neck feathers are raised, since it is found only at the base of the feathers, lives in the desert region of western United States and Mexico, from Arizona, New Mexico, and central Texas southward. Of a size midway between the common crow and the northern raven, it is often seen perched on telephone poles in towns.

Eastern Crow

(Corvus brachyrhynchos brachyrhynchos)

Average Length, Nineteen Inches

The common crow of much of eastern North America is one of the best-known birds in this country and in many regions it is abundant.

In the autumn, in some sections, crows congregate in large numbers to roost in a favorite grove, and here come together nightly for many weeks. In the morning they spread out over a great area of country in search of food. Long before sundown they begin to return from all directions, continuing to arrive singly or in small groups until dark. Many thousands thus assemble in a single roost.

They are very cunning and know to a nicety the range of a gun. In the woods and fields it is only by accident, or by the exercise of careful strategy, that a man may approach this bird close enough to kill it.

A story has long been current that a crow will talk only if its tongue is split. This cruel practice is neither necessary nor desirable.

Crows make their nests in trees, usually in March, April, or May. Four to six eggs are laid. They are greenish blue, thickly covered with markings of various shades of brown.

This is one of the species divided by ornithologists into several geographic forms. There is little difference in the appearance of the forms; and their general feeding, resting, and roosting habits show only the variations due to natural surroundings.

The northern boundary of the breeding range of the eastern crow is from Newfoundland and through Quebec to Manitoba. From here it spreads in a southward and southeastward direction through the States to Maryland, the northern part of the Gulf States, and northern Texas.

In addition to the widely distributed eastern crow, this group includes four other forms.

The southern crow *(C. b. paulus)* appears from the lower Potomac and Ohio valleys south to southern Georgia and eastern Texas.

The Florida crow *(C. b. pascuus)* breeds throughout most of the peninsula of Florida.

The western crow *(C. b. hesperis)* occurs from British Columbia and Saskatchewan to New Mexico and northern Baja California.

The northwestern crow *(C. b. caurinus)* is limited to a narrow strip of country from Kodiak Island and Kukak Bay, Alaska, to Puget Sound, Washington.

Fish Crow

(Corvus ossifragus)

Average Length, Sixteen Inches

While skirting a salt marsh on the Virginia coast one June day, I noticed an eggshell on the carpet of pine needles. Near by was another, and still another; in fact, I soon found the remains of at least two dozen eggs of the clapper rail, which inhabited the neighboring marsh in large numbers. The eggs must have been carried to a certain large limb, where they had been eaten and the shells dropped to the ground. While I rested one of the marauders of the marsh appeared. He was a fish crow and he carried an egg in his beak. The devastation wrought by these piratical birds among nests of other species is a serious menace in many places along the Atlantic coast.

Fish crows eat principally crabs, fish, and such other animal food as they can find along the coast and neighboring rivers and lakes. They range from Massachusetts southward to Florida, and thence along the Gulf coast to eastern Texas. One may find them inland, especially in the southern States. The bird is smaller than the common crow and measures about 16 inches in length. Its usual cry is a nasal, reedy *caw*, which resembles the note of the young of the larger species.

THE PORTENTOUS RAVEN SHARES UNUSUAL CUNNING WITH THE COMMON CROW

Gloomy guardian of seaside cliffs, high mountain slopes, and lonely forests throughout northeastern North America is the **Northern Raven** (upper picture). The survival and increase of the familiar **Eastern Crow** (pecking at the fish head), in spite of determined efforts in many sections to destroy it, is a tribute to the raucous bird's adaptability and wit. Ranging along the coasts from New England to Texas, the smaller **Fish Crow** (scolding on the rock) lives largely on fish and other sea creatures, though, like its ubiquitous cousin, it also relishes the eggs of other birds.

American Magpie
(Pica pica hudsonia)
Average Length, Twenty Inches

In 1927, under the direction of the State authorities of Montana, 25,269 magpies were killed and 18,071 of their eggs were destroyed. Nothing, perhaps, can more forcefully illustrate the popular dislike for this bird throughout the range country of the West.

Despite the constant warfare on the handsome black-billed magpies, their numbers seem not to decrease, except locally and then only for a time. When enemies become weary of the seemingly hopeless task of exterminating them, the birds are soon abundant again.

The reason for the rural westerner's dislike is that the magpie persistently destroys the eggs and young of wild birds, and hunters deplore the destruction of game birds by any wild creature which they class as "vermin." Magpies kill young chickens and eat hen's eggs when they can find them. They will gather about a sickly sheep or cow, or the newborn young of either, and kill it by their pecking. They attack newly branded stock and freshly sheared sheep.

Over the greater part of their range the birds appear only in moderate numbers. They are great scavengers, and with the ravens, and in some regions with the vultures, they help to rid the countryside of offensive carcasses. They clean up scraps of meat and offal about places where stock is butchered. They flock about Indian villages or encampments where little effort is made by men to dispose of offensive refuse. Magpies eat grasshoppers that consume the grass, which is scanty enough in many regions. They destroy countless weevils, caterpillars, and grubs and some kill noxious rodents.

The magpie, therefore, is not wholly bad. It is a comfort to one interested in the conservation of all wild life to reflect that its range is so great over vast, thinly settled sections and its fecundity so pronounced that we may expect this striking species to live and prosper for years to come.

The magpie is a very noisy bird and is continually chattering about something. Mr. Henshaw, speaking of the flexibility and the range of its voice, said that it runs "from a guttural chuckle to the softest whistle." The bird is imitative, and here and there magpie pets learn to imitate the human voice in a highly entertaining manner.

The nest is a bulky, domed affair of twigs, built in trees. It contains a mud cup lined with rootlets. Mrs. Bailey speaks of certain old nests which "were much in demand for roof-trees by English sparrows, and to a less degree by house finches."

This species ranges from Alaska and Manitoba to New Mexico.

Yellow-billed Magpie
(Pica nuttalli)
Average Length, Seventeen Inches

The yellow-billed magpie may represent a dying, ancient race. Since scientific interest has been directed toward its habits and distribution, its range has become more restricted. There are reports that 50 or 60 years ago it was common in many places close to the coast, where the observer would now look for it in vain. It inhabits only the interior of California west of the Sierra Nevada, chiefly in the Sacramento and San Joaquin valleys.

It haunts stock ranches, because food to its liking is usually plentiful in such places. When cattle and sheep are butchered, the refuse attracts magpies. They gather about any dead animal. They feed also on grasshoppers, worms, and grubs, and, of course, always look for a reasonable supply of eggs.

The nest is a bulky, roughly rounded structure of twigs. In this is built a deep cup of mud or cow dung. The lining is of rootlets, pine needles, dry grass, shreds of cottonwood bark, and sometimes horsehair. Egress is through two opposite passageways in the side, each permitting swift exit if danger threatens.

These rude cradles for the young are often placed in oak trees from 10 to 60 feet above the ground. Sycamores, willows, and cottonwoods are some of the other trees chosen for nesting purposes. Small colonies of these magpies are sometimes seen, but more often a single pair is found in some out-of-the-way corner. The nest may be cunningly hidden among clumps of mistletoe or be placed where it can be seen from a considerable distance.

These birds become attached to a locality and will return year after year to build their nests near the domicile used the previous spring. Often a pair will make use of the same tree and at times even build the new nest on top of an old one.

The five to seven yellowish or olive eggs are covered with spots of brown or grayish olive.

The yellow-billed magpie is a little smaller than the American, or black-billed magpie, but the difference in size is very slight. The birds look exactly alike, except that one has a black beak and the other has a yellow one and also a bit of yellow skin back of the eye.

The difference in the distribution of these two species constitutes one of the amazing and unexplained problems of ornithology. Closely related subspecies of the black-billed form are found in northern Africa, Spain, northern Europe, northern Asia, China, and western North America. The species occurs over the greater part of the Northern Hemisphere. On the other hand, the yellow-billed magpie is confined to less than half of California. Why one is so restricted and the other so widely distributed is a problem for evolutionists.

CHATTERING MAGPIES ARE COLORFUL SCAMPS

Ranchmen pay for the destruction of the **American Magpie** (upper picture) of western North America because it eats eggs and young of wild birds and poultry, and attacks and often kills young sheep and cattle. Yet magpies do much good by clearing the countryside of carrion and offal and by devouring countless harmful caterpillars, grubs, and insects. The slightly smaller **Yellow-billed Magpie** (below) is confined to the interior of California, principally in the Sacramento and San Joaquin Valleys.

Northern Blue Jay

(Cyanocitta cristata cristata)

Average Length, Eleven and Three-quarters Inches

The blue jay is one of the best-known birds in central and eastern North America.

One of the outstanding characteristics of this dashing, handsome bird is his propensity to make a noise. He shrieks singly and in chorus. He shouts at hawks, owls, cats, and snakes, or screams only for the pleasure of hearing himself make a hair-raising din. His shoutings fill the woodlands of southern Canada and of the eastern United States. Only in the nesting season, when the safety of his eggs and young demand vocal restraint, can he be considered a quiet bird.

The bird is abundant, but has its natural enemies. Scattered clusters of blue feathers here and there in the woods testify to the capture of one by some hawk or owl. Sometimes these feathers appear later among the nesting material used by birds whose eggs and young the blue jay has been known to eat.

Blue jays are devoted to their nests and young and show unusual boldness in defending them. Sometimes one will sit on the nest until actually touched by the hand of the intruder. With its mate it will make a great outcry and will often come within a few feet of the person who threatens its nest.

After the young have left the nest and acquired strength in flight, the family groups forage vociferously about the country. Two or three families will often unite and go trooping along from one grove to another, crossing, a few at a time, the open areas. As autumn approaches, they may move for many miles in quest of more ample supplies of beechnuts or acorns. Some of them stay throughout the winter in the North, but many pass the colder months in southern States.

The Florida blue jay *(C. c. florincola)* is a little smaller, the white tips of the feathers are narrower, and the back is slightly grayer. It is found in the South Atlantic and Gulf States from the coast of North Carolina to northern Florida and westward to Louisiana.

Semple's blue jay *(C. c. semplei)* was described to science in 1928 from specimens taken at Coconut Grove, Florida. Its range is central and southern Florida.

Steller's Jay

(Cyanocitta stelleri)

Average Length, Thirteen Inches

Principally in the mountains, but also at times at lower elevations over the vast sweep of country from Alaska to Central America, this brilliant, long-crested, blue-bodied jay is found. Scientists know it in different places by separate names, but to the casual observer little, if any, difference in habits, form, or color can be detected wherever it is seen.

Steller's jay is common in many localities and is well known to the inhabitants of the country. Singly or in small groups, it comes to the back yard searching for something to eat. Such visits may be looked for especially in winter, when snow covers its food provided for by the forest. It eats insects, vegetables, nuts, eggs, and young birds. At times it robs the California woodpecker and its kin of their store of acorns.

Often the nests are built in firs, saplings being preferred to the larger, taller trees. Nests 60 feet from the ground have been found, but this is unusual. Often they are not more than 5 or 10 feet from the earth. In their construction, twigs are used for the foundation and the outer supports.

Into the basket thus constructed, 8 or 10 inches across, is sunk a deep cup, lined generally with grass or moss. Then the hollow is well plastered with mud, and this in turn is lined with rootlets or pine needles. Now and then the hair of deer or cattle is used to make a soft bed for the three to five spotted eggs which are to come. The eggs are about 1¼ inches long and the greenish-blue ground pattern is sprinkled with dots and spots of brown and lavender. Incubation requires 16 days.

Steller's jay inhabits the Pacific coast country, from the Alaska Peninsula to the State of Washington, including Vancouver and most of the other coastal islands. It is usually resident throughout the year, wherever it is found.

Five other varieties of this group of jays, very similar to it, but possessing sufficiently small differences to justify ornithologists in accrediting them with subspecific status, are found in North America north of Mexico.

The Queen Charlotte jay *(C. s. carlottae)* inhabits the Queen Charlotte Islands, British Columbia.

The coast jay *(C. s. carbonacea)* ranges along the Pacific coast of Oregon to the Santa Lucia Mountains of California and certain small areas to the eastward.

The blue-fronted jay *(C. s. frontalis)* inhabits the high and the medium elevations of the Sierra Nevada, from Mount Shasta southward to San Diego County, California; also, it is found on inner coastal ranges of that State.

The black-headed jay *(C. s. annectens)* lives in boreal and transition areas of the Rocky Mountains from British Columbia south to eastern Oregon, Idaho, and Wyoming. It has been known to wander to Utah and Nebraska.

The long-crested jay *(C. s. diademata)* also likes the moderate and the high altitudes. It is found in the Rocky Mountains from Utah and Wyoming southward into Sonora, Zacatecas, Jalisco, and Nayarit, Mexico.

BEAUTY, BRAINS, AND HIGH SPIRITS WIN FRIENDS FOR FEATHERED VANDALS

The **Northern Blue Jay** (above) seeks the spotlight, proclaiming its handsome presence with a variety of energetic shrieks, calls, and imitative warblings. During the breeding season it maintains strict silence when in the vicinity of the nest, for it is a cautious and devoted parent. Beechnuts, acorns, insects and, on occasion, the eggs and young of other birds compose the diet of the common eastern jay as well as of the **Steller's Jay** (below), whose brilliant coat and loud squalling enliven the solemn evergreen forests of the Northwest.

Florida Jay

(Aphelocoma coerulescens)

Average Length, Eleven and One-half Inches

Forty-three years ago a water oak stood just back of the blacksmith shop, in the village of Archer, Florida. Here for several hours one day a strange bird sat on its topmost twig and called in a harsh, inquiring voice. I had never seen nor heard such a bird, and the impression it made was lasting. Later I learned that it was a Florida jay, and that it was at the extreme northern limit of its range. Not one of them has ever been noted in that neighborhood since that single wanderer made its brief visit.

This jay is very local in its occurrence. It is not found in the extensive pinelands, the heavy growths of hardwood about the lakes, or in the numerous swamps, prairies, and marshes that dot the State. It dwells only where there are dense growths of scrub oak, or of other shrubby bushes, or in the pine areas immediately adjoining these places. Such regions are scattered over about half of the Florida Peninsula.

A short distance outside of Leesburg, Florida, I came upon a sandy area covered with bushes from four to six feet high. This looked like Florida jay country, and although I had seen no bird of this species in all that section, I began a search and within 10 minutes found four. They were feeding on the ground by the side of one of the overgrown cement sidewalks laid down by an optimistic real-estate company. The birds seemed rather tame. They merely flew from bush to bush and watched quietly, as if waiting for me to leave.

Where one of these slender jays is found, there are almost sure to be others, for they live in small colony groups. Among the low dunes close to the ocean, not far from New Smyrna, I once counted 14 in a few minutes.

They are not so noisy as the blue jays, nor have I ever heard them engage in any wide variety of "songs" and calls.

In low oaks these jays nest, making of twigs and rootlets the cradle for their young, and they lay three or four olive-green, black-spotted eggs.

The bird is found in many places in the immediate vicinity of the Atlantic coast, from St. Augustine to Rockdale, south of Miami. Along the Gulf coast it occurs from about the mouth of the Suwannee River southward to Naples. Inland it occupies territory northward from Naples to Palatka and the Orange Lake country.

Woodhouse's Jay

(Aphelocoma californica woodhousei)

Average Length, Twelve Inches

Adjoining the eastern line of the territory occupied by the California jay, we enter the country of the magnificent Woodhouse's jay.

It dwells in the foothills and on the mountains to elevations of 5,000 to 8,000 feet, although in winter it often descends to lower altitudes.

In scrub-oak trees, junipers, and nut-producing pines common throughout most of its range, it builds its nest of twigs, weed stalks, rootlets, and horsehair. For a tree-loving bird, the situations chosen are unusually low, the nests often being not more than two or three feet from the ground. These jays are clamorous birds and certainly make no effort to keep their presence a secret, except in the nesting season, when stealth and caution are their habits.

They live on a wide variety of food. Insects of different kinds are taken, fruits are eaten, and nuts and acorns form a staple article of diet. They are detested by all the small birds of the region, which know well that in spring they are constantly hunting for their eggs and their nestlings.

A collector of scientific specimens, who placed some phœbe eggs on the ground within a few feet of his camp, complained that one of these jays purloined them all while his back was turned on the precious collection for only a few minutes.

The Woodhouse's jay is found in locations suitable to its habits of life, from southeastern Oregon and southern Wyoming southward to southwestern Texas and westward to southeastern California. It is one of the group of the species *californica,* forms of which are distributed over much of western and southwestern United States. All are so similar in appearance that few people can distinguish between them.

Two of these, the California and the Woodhouse's jays, have been mentioned. Five others are recognized by ornithologists.

The long-tailed jay *(A. c. immanis)* is found in the valleys and along the mountain slopes from the Washington border southward between the Cascades and Coast Ranges, and in the Sacramento and San Joaquin valleys of California.

The Nicasio jay *(A. c. oocleptica)* has its homeland in the coast region of California, from San Francisco Bay northward to Humboldt Bay.

Belding's jay *(A. c. obscura)* is a Mexican bird found in the northwestern section of Baja California southward to latitude 30°. It occurs for the most part in the hills and mountains.

Xantus's jay *(A. c. hypoleuca)* is another form inhabiting a region to the southward of our border, viz., the cape region of Baja California and from there on northward to latitude 29°.

The Texas jay *(A. c. texana)* ranges in central and central-western Texas, from Kerr and Edwards counties to the Davis Mountains.

FLASHING FEATHERS BLEND COLORS OF SKY AND CLOUDS

Scrub oak thickets, dense shrubbery, and the borders of pine woods in the Florida Peninsula are the home of the **Florida Jay** (upper picture), which is easily approached though wary. Small colonies of this jay have been found among sand dunes close to the ocean shore. When interrupted at feeding, it pours out a flood of harsh, vituperative screams. The favorite haunts of the clamorous **Woodhouse's Jay** (below) are groves of oaks, junipers, and pines throughout the rugged uplands between the Rockies and the Sierras.

CROW ROOSTS

By E. R. Kalmbach

THE nightly roosts of birds, where thousands, tens of thousands, or even hundreds of thousands of individuals may gather for mutual protection against enemies or the elements, for good fellowship, or for any other reason, offer to the ornithologist a most fertile field for study of the mass activities of birds.

In the vicinity of these roosts are multiplied manyfold those tendencies for good or harm that may be inherent with the species involved. As a result, not infrequently some minor tendency for harm, more or less inconsequential under normal conditions, may become outstandingly injurious when thus intensified by a great concentration of numbers. Likewise, there are reasons for believing that increased benefits, often less easily discerned, may also result under certain conditions.

BIG ROOSTS CAUSE CONCERN AMONG CONSERVATIONISTS

Although many species of North American birds exhibit a certain communal instinct by gathering at nightly roosts, those most noteworthy from the standpoint of numbers involved and close contact with human affairs include such economically important forms as purple martins, robins, starlings, blackbirds, English sparrows, magpies, white-necked ravens, and crows.

In these days of emphasis on conservation of game and other wild life, crows and their roosts, where they congregate sometimes by the hundreds of thousands, are subjects of much comment and concern.

Crows are more or less clannish throughout the year with the exception of the relatively short breeding season. Their love for each other's company varies, however, with the seasons. It manifests itself as soon as the young are on the wing. At that time small parties of five to eight, family groups, may be found searching for grasshoppers and other insects in hayfields and meadows. These may be joined by other families and together roam the countryside in flocks of 20 or more during July and August. Non-breeding birds, of which there are always a few in every nesting area, may add to the numbers.

During late August and September these rather foot-loose nomads begin to manifest the first signs of that gregarious nature that later in the year leads to the habitation of the enormous winter roosts. Nightly gatherings of a few score birds may be found at points in their general breeding range. These early roosts, as a rule, are temporary and unstable institutions that may be abandoned after only a night or two of occupancy. In the prairie Provinces of Canada, as well as in our own Northern States, these ephemeral roosts represent little more than nightly pauses in the incipient process of migration that will eventually bring the bulk of the breeding crows of the North American Continent into several rather circumscribed areas in this country.

In the course of this southward drift of the crow population there are times and places along our northern border when the movement becomes a veritable exodus.

Not only has this shift to the winter roost area long been a matter of record through observations on the moving flocks, but, in more recent years, the banding of crows both at their winter roosts and on their breeding grounds has afforded incontrovertible evidence of its existence. Crows that were banded while they occupied populous winter roosts in Oklahoma and Kansas have been recovered in spring or summer in southern Saskatchewan and Alberta. Conversely, nesting crows banded in Canada have been shot as adults in the United States in winter.

MODERN CONDITIONS ARE FAVORABLE TO INCREASE OF CROWS

Although the bulk of the Canada-breeding crows dwell in the southern portion of the Provinces where they enjoy the advantages accruing from association with agriculture, some go farther north and settle down wherever local clearings give them a vestige of their favorite habitat. Most of even these northerly nesters leave central Canada in winter for roosts in the United States. Along the mild northwest coast, however, one may encounter many wintering crows in Canadian territory.

The large and more stable winter roosts do not acquire conspicuous size until October. It is then that the large conclaves so prevalent in Kansas, Oklahoma, and Missouri, as well as those in the East and in the Northwest, take on the aspects of corvine metropolises with daily commuters by the tens of thousands traveling by air to and from distant feeding grounds. A certain increase in the size and number of roosts may occur in November and by December and January the birds have settled down to a daily routine that marks the peak of the seasonal roosting activity.

Then the struggle for corvine existence is most acute. Not only do the elements offer a bold and severe challenge to the resourcefulness and ruggedness of these sable wanderers, but at times disease runs rampant and gaunt starvation may enter the picture.

CROWS FACE MANY ENEMIES

During these bleak winter nights that avian arch-enemy of the crow, the great horned owl, may wreak vengeance for the tormenting it has suffered through many a daylight hour, and, of course, man also takes a toll with guns, and in recent years even with dynamite bombs.

Roosts located as far south as Kansas and Oklahoma often show a noticeable decrease in size by the middle of February and by the first of March the bulk of the birds again are on their way to northern breeding grounds. En route they often form temporary roosts for a week or more. In effect the spring migration and dispersal of the birds is a process almost the reverse of their southern drift in the fall.

There is little question that the general distribution of North American crows has changed markedly during the last half century and even in the last two or three decades there is evidence of either a shifting of population or of increases and decreases induced by environmental changes.

Ornithological literature formerly dwelt at length on enormous roosts and great winter populations in areas where crows now are only moderately abundant. Although there still are sizable roosts in the Middle Atlantic States, one does not hear of conclaves such as the Arlington, Virginia, roost as it existed in the 90's; or the "Arbutus" roost near Baltimore about the same time, where, it was believed, a fifth to a fourth of a million birds sojourned nightly. Some accounts accredited earlier roosts, such as the one on Reedy Island in the Delaware River during Alexander Wilson's time, with even greater populations.

On the whole there seems to be a lessening, certainly not an increase, in the number of crows frequenting winter roosts in the Atlantic Coast States. In the midwestern States of Indiana, Ohio, and areas contiguous thereto there were formerly and still are roosts of considerable size. The general vicinity of the junction of the Ohio and Mississippi rivers likewise has long been an area of large roosts. Somewhat to the west of this nucleus is a region, embracing central Kansas and Oklahoma, that, from the viewpoint of sheer density of crow population as indicated by the size and numbers of roosts, surpasses any other section of equal area on this continent.

In our Northwest, in Idaho, eastern Oregon, and along the lower Columbia River are other roosts composed of birds that breed in or to the north of that region.

The reason for the quite evident increase of wintering crows in the Central Plains States during the past two decades lies apparently at both ends of the crow's seasonal drift. Most of these birds migrate far enough south to avoid deep snows and extraordinarily low temperatures and at the same time enter an area given largely to the raising of grain sorghums. The shocked grain and the waste kernels of this crop left in the field after harvest present a veritable banquet table for wintering crows, a food supply that was non-existent at the early settlement of this region.

CAUSES OF CROWS' INCREASE

At the northern end of the seasonal drift of these crows environmental changes favorable to the species also have taken place. The crow is partial to agricultural areas and thrives best in such environments, provided it also can find ample security and nesting facilities. These it has acquired in increasing measure during recent decades in the prairie Provinces of Canada north to the very edge of agriculture.

With every added acre of Canadian "bush" that has been cleared and planted to small grains the crow's well-being in the north country has been aided. Thus it is that both in their Canadian summer home and their winter range in this country crows of the plains area have been favored. The increase in their numbers is only a logical result of kindness by nature and man.

INQUISITIVE AND QUARRELSOME, JAYS ARE NEVER LONG OUT OF TROUBLE

Hawks, rattlesnakes, foxes, and refuse heaps are attacked with equal bluster and gusto. Only in the lower Rio Grande Valley does the gorgeous **Green Jay** (above) enter the United States. When humans intrude in their haunts among scrub and open forest, these jays suddenly appear in screaming flocks, look over the newcomers, and disappear as abruptly as they came. The **Arizona Jay** (lower), of northern Mexico and southern Arizona and New Mexico, plants trees by the simple method of storing acorns and forgetting where they are.

Green Jay

(Xanthoura luxuosa glaucescens)
Average Length, Eleven and One-half Inches

In a region of bushy thickets in south Texas a bird suddenly appeared with a twig held in its beak and gazed intently at me. Its size, form and every movement revealed the characteristics of a jay, and its colors showed that it was the little-known green jay. When it flew, I followed, for not many bird students had seen the nest of this species.

It led me for more than half a mile, alighting frequently and appearing to make no special effort to keep out of sight, although I am sure it was aware of my movements. At length it flew into a bushy tree, still carrying the twig. When I came close it departed, but without the twig. In the tree I discovered a nest—an old one with no signs of any repairs being in progress. I have often wondered if that jay did not deliberately deceive and outwit me.

Mr. Ludlow Griscom writes:

"The green jay prefers a relatively dry climate and is most abundant in thick patches of scrub or in dry open gallery forest where there is considerable bushy undergrowth. It is rare or absent in Mexico in the humid rain forests near the coast. In southern Texas it is particularly fond of the dense patches of evergreen scrub which line the *resacas,* depressions filled with standing water in the prairie which formerly served as one of the mouths of the Rio Grande.

"In spite of living in such dense and impenetrable tangles, the green jay is not a difficult bird to observe, because its habits are characteristic of practically all jays throughout the world. It is bold, impertinent, and full of curiosity, and is highly social or gregarious, except in the breeding season. The birds go about, consequently, in small flocks of eight to fifteen individuals, and approach of their haunts by man is almost certain to bring them out to look at him.

"They have a great variety of harsh screaming notes, varied with a medley of caws, toots, and whistles, and for a few minutes noisily hover about the intruder from a discreet distance and then melt silently away into the bush and are seldom seen again unless deliberately followed up. Farther south they wander through the more open forests, and in Yucatán I often suddenly found myself surrounded by a screaming flock where a moment before the forest had seemed silent and empty.

"In spite of its gorgeous coloring, the green jay is surprisingly inconspicuous in its haunts. The green upper parts are not easily seen against the background of the forest, and the golden yellow merges surprisingly well with the dapple-yellow light of open glades."

Very little has been written about the green jay's food or general habits, but it is known to occur within the limits of the United States only in the valley of the Rio Grande below Laredo, Texas.

In Mexico it is a common bird in the States of Tamaulipas and Nuevo Leon. Closely allied forms are found farther south, two of these within the limits of Mexico. The natives call it *pájaro verde*—green bird.

Arizona Jay

(Aphelocoma sieberi arizonae)
Average Length, Twelve and One-quarter Inches

Early in November, 1913, as we ascended the Santa Catalina Mountains north of Tucson, Arizona, my guide kept me in the saddle all day except for a brief rest at noon. We had crossed many miles of arid plains with cacti on every hand. Then we had climbed until late afternoon, when by a little rill we prepared for the night.

A headache, induced by the long ride in a beating, bright sunlight, caused me to spread my sleeping bag in the shade of one of the scrub oaks which dotted the ridges. I had not been resting long when a jarring, querulous note sounded from the limbs above, and there, only a few yards distant, was a pair of Arizona jays. Three others quickly appeared, and for some time they engaged in a critical examination of our duffel and of my recumbent form.

The next day I saw others; so, evidently, they were common in the oak belt. After entering the pine woods of the upper mountain slopes, we saw no more of them.

The nest of this jay is made usually in scrub oaks, at a height of from 10 to 15 feet from the ground. It is a rather untidy, loosely constructed affair of twigs and rootlets. When horsehair can be found, this also is employed. As a rule, the eggs are four or five in number, although six, or even seven, have been found in some nests. They are light greenish blue and are the only jay eggs in America which are not decorated with dots or spots.

The food of the Arizona jay consists of insects, acorns, wild fruit, and many kinds of seeds and nuts. The birds bury many acorns which later grow into trees.

It was in December, 1873, that Robert Ridgway described this bird from specimens taken in Pima County, Arizona. Its eggs were not discovered by a naturalist until 1876. It is one of the western jays having a clearly marked and extensive range. Since Ridgway's publication concerning it, the bird has been found by students in several regions. Its breeding range covers the upper Austral Zone of southern Arizona, southern New Mexico, and parts of Chihuahua and Sonora.

Couch's jay *(A. s. couchi)*, a form of the Arizona jay, occurs in the "Chisos Mountains, central-western Texas, to southern Nuevo Leon and northern Coahuila."

SOCIABLE COUSINS INHABIT UPLAND PINE GROVES IN THE WEST

   The **Piñon Jay,** or "blue crow" (above), prefers semiarid ridges and valleys where junipers and live oaks are interspersed among the piñons. Its noisy flocks seem to "roll" across the landscape as the birds behind fly over those feeding on the ground ahead. Grasshoppers, crickets, grubs, and pine nuts are dietary staples for **Clark's Nutcracker** (lower picture), which plays along the tree line in summer where sheep herders and campers find it only less bold than the native jays.

Piñon Jay

(Cyanocephalus cyanocephalus)
Average Length, Eleven Inches

In the Far West, at 5,000- to 8,000-foot altitudes, where sagebrush ridges and valleys are decorated with scattering juniper and piñon, you may come upon a foraging party of "blue crows," which the books refer to as piñon jays. They are short, stumpy birds, somewhat different in form from the typical jay.

Piñon jays are always sociable. To feed, they often gather in flocks of hundreds. When thus assembled, those in the rear continually rise and fly over their companions in front. In a kind of flattened, hooplike formation the flock goes rolling across the country. An advancing company may be heard long before the birds come into view. Their notes are of many kinds. About the nest they are low and soft, soothing and reassuring. A single harsh, guttural, rasping call sounds as the birds fly about the trees. Also there are many squeaks, clucks and chatters strongly suggesting the eastern blue jay.

Because of the wild, unsettled country usually inhabited by piñon jays, and of the fact that they are erratic in their movements, and more or less local in their distribution, comparatively few bird students have observed their nesting habits. Mrs. Florence Merriam Bailey writes of them:

"In 1913, west of the Rio Grande, on the San Mateo and Gila River Forest Reserves, Mr. Ligon found piñon jays constant residents, wintering in flocks, nesting in colonies, roosting in thick tall pines, generally on canyons, and meriting the name of 'the most noisy bird in the Southwest.' He says they nest generally from March 1 to 31, in gray live oaks among the piñons, though occasionally in piñons.

"On February 10, 1913, he noted that the birds showed 'nesting inclinations, flying two and three together.' On February 17, while the ground was still half covered with snow, on the southwest side of Black Mountain in the Datil Forest, at about 7,500 feet, he found one nest nearly complete and others under construction. There were more than 50 birds in pairs and flocks mingling and scattering and flying about noisily.

"On March 3, he returned to the colony and found nests in almost all the scrub oaks of sufficient size, but never more than one in a tree. One, half completed, was in a juniper. Nearly all contained four eggs, but one had five."

Piñon jays breed chiefly in piñon and juniper belts in the mountains, from central Washington, Idaho, and central Montana to northern Baja California, Arizona, southern New Mexico and western Texas, and from the Sierra-Cascade ranges to the eastern base of the Rockies and northwestern Nebraska.

Clark's Nutcracker

(Nucifraga columbiana)
Average Length, Twelve and One-half Inches

Wandering miners, herders who drive their sheep to the higher grazing grounds in the Western States, guides who conduct hunting or fishing parties up to the great plateaus and about the shoulders of the towering mountains, all will give you bits of conflicting information concerning the habits of the Clark's nutcracker.

From such men of the open you will hear much that, with patience, you can readily observe for yourself, for these large gray- and black-winged inhabitants of the wilderness will come to your very tent door. They rarely become so bold as the jays of the neighborhood, and they will not take so many liberties with your belongings. However, they will come for food, and can be studied at leisure.

The nutcrackers make a very pretty picture, walking sedately about, much after the manner of crows. Now and then they may be seen chasing insects like domestic hens, for they are almost as much at home on the ground as in the trees. They consume great numbers of grasshoppers and of the large, wingless crickets of the mountains. At times they chase butterflies, catching them on the wing.

They also cling to the sides of tree trunks and peck in the bark for grubs, as do the woodpeckers. They raid the cones of the pine trees for seeds and feed on piñon nuts, which constitute a staple and very important article of their diet.

The nutcrackers are birds of the mountain heights and in summer delight to play along the tree line. In many places they gather in the fir belt for purposes of nesting.

Wheelock says of them: "Their nests were all rather bulky, composed first of a platform of twigs, each one nearly a foot in length, so interlaced that to pull one was to disarrange the mass. Upon this, and held in place by the twigs at the sides, was the nest—a soft warm hemisphere of fine strips of bark, matted with grasses and pine needles until it was almost like felt. This is stiffened, bound, and made firmer by coarse strips of bark around the outside, these also binding it to the twigs and helping hold it to the limb. So firmly is the whole put together and fastened to the branch that no storm can move it from its foundations."

The birds breed early in the year, when there is little travel in the heavy snows of the upper ranges; consequently their nests are rarely seen. Egg-laying begins in February or March. Incubation requires 18 days.

Their breeding range extends from southern Alaska, southwestern Alberta, and western South Dakota south to the high mountains of Baja California, Arizona, and New Mexico.

"CAMP ROBBERS" OF THE JAY TRIBE LOOK LIKE OVERGROWN CHICKADEES

Coniferous forests from Labrador to British Columbia and from Maine and Minnesota to the northern limit of trees provide a spacious habitat for the **Canada Jay** (upper plate). Quite unafraid of man, "Whiskey Jack" will steal any food or small object left unguarded for a moment and will boldly intrude in an occupied tent or cabin. This strange bird nests when winter still grips the land and may incubate in a temperature far below zero. The equally fearless and very similar **Oregon Jay** (lower) inhabits evergreen forests of the Pacific coast.

Canada Jay

(Perisoreus canadensis)

Average Length, Eleven and One-half Inches

One winter day in the Adirondacks I followed a bear trail which wandered through the snow among the ridges flanking a forested mountain. Wearied at length, I brushed the snow from a log and sat down to enjoy the sandwich I had brought from camp. The forest was very still, and not one living creature had I seen or heard since leaving camp. The only evidence of animal life was that bear spoor and some deer tracks I had crossed.

Then suddenly two birds appeared less than 60 feet away. Not a foot in length, they were gray in color, with some white and a little black in the plumage. Quietly they looked down from the limbs upon me—or perhaps upon my fast-disappearing sandwich. Now and then one changed his position to come a little nearer. They exhibited no alarm, but rather a mild curiosity, mingled with restrained eagerness. Not a sound did they utter. I left some of the bread and a little meat as a token of my appreciation of their visit. I had seen at close range my first Canada jays.

In later years I was to see them in their more northern summer home. About logging camps, or wherever man tarries in the wilderness, they make their appearance. I know of no other bird so bold. One will light on a low limb and watch the meat frying in the pan. He will drop down and seize a piece of bacon, raw or cooked. He will snatch a cracker from the box inside the tent. He will peck at the fresh meat hung up to cool.

It is well to be careful of the articles you leave lying about, for "Whiskey Jack" is the famous "camp robber" of the North. He will carry off your matches, your pencil, your cigarette, or your piece of chewing tobacco, although what he wants with such things I cannot guess. He will peck to pieces your candles or soap and carry away in chunks the fish you catch. He visits the trap line and takes the bait. He is aware of the presence of hunters and comes at the sound of the gun, knowing that when a moose or a deer is killed great feasting is in store. However, he does eat insects and, now and then, a mouse.

The Canada jay breeds from the limit of conifers, from Labrador to British Columbia, and southward to northern Minnesota, and to Maine. Its nests, placed in trees, are composed of twigs, plant fibers, bark, moss and other soft materials. The bird lays from three to five brownish spotted eggs.

The Rocky Mountain jay (P. c. capitalis) is very similar to P. c. canadensis. It breeds in the mountains from British Columbia to South Dakota and New Mexico.

The Alaska jay (P. c. fumifrons) inhabits virtually all the wooded parts of Alaska except the southeastern coastal district.

Oregon Jay

(Perisoreus obscurus)

Average Length, Ten and One-half Inches

The Oregon jay and the Canada jay have certain marked resemblances in figure and color. Their bills are short, and they remind one more of overgrown chickadees than of the jays with which most people are familiar. Also, they lack some of the sleek, smart appearance of the typical jays.

Major Bendire wrote that on the summit of the Blue Mountains in Oregon he saw these birds at an altitude of 6,500 feet. He said, "I heard several whistles in a large pine close by, and these were answered from other directions. Shortly after I saw one of these birds in a little fir a few feet from where I was eating my lunch. I threw him some scraps of bread and meat, and he was by no means slow in accepting the invitation to help himself. A few minutes later three others made their appearance and fed among our party with the utmost unconcern and almost allowed themselves to be touched."

Mr. A. W. Anthony records, "While dressing deer in the thick timber, I have been almost covered with jays flying down from the neighborhood trees. They would settle on my back, head, or shoulders, tugging and pulling at each loose sleeve of my coat. At such times their only note is a low, plaintive cry."

All campers in this country know these jays, for they constantly come about the camps looking for food. "Camp robber" and "venison bird" are names often applied to them. Although only about the size of the robin, they are also called "meat hawk" by some people.

The nests are built in evergreens. They are sufficiently substantial to stand the wear and tear of domestic occupancy, and so serve their purpose well. The spotted eggs are a little more than an inch long.

The species is an inhabitant of the coastal area from southwestern British Columbia and western Washington to Mendocino County, California. The species obscurus is now recognized as composed of two subspecies, the Oregon jay and the gray jay (P. o. griseus).

Since their ranges join and the two subspecies look so much alike, the student may have difficulty in determining which bird he is observing, unless he informs himself carefully as to the exact range of each. The gray jay is found from southwestern British Columbia, south-central Washington, and Oregon through the Cascade Mountains to California. The jays of this species seen in the fir regions of the Warner Mountains and on Mount Shasta, for example, are gray jays. Those inhabiting many of the heavy redwood forests are Oregon jays.

In general habits and activities, they may be considered as one bird. Early ornithologists regarded them all as the Oregon jay.

CALIFORNIA CLAIMS A RUTHLESS RAVAGER AND AN ISLAND PRINCE

Most observers condemn the **California Jay** (above) not only for robbing nests of small birds but also for pulling up sprouting crops and for its continuous harsh shouting. This handsome swaggerer ranges throughout coastal California from San Francisco Bay to Mexico. The less obtrusive **Santa Cruz Jay** (lower plate) is found only on the island of the same name in the Santa Barbara group, where it is the commonest bird. Its eggs are laid in bulky nests placed not far above the ground in trees or bushes.

California Jay

(Aphelocoma californica californica)

Average Length, Eleven and Three-quarters Inches

The "blue jay" of California is quite different in appearance from the bird of the Central and Eastern States that bears that name. The blue is a different shade, there are no conspicuous white patches on the wings, and the bird has no crest on its head. He is one of the noisiest birds in California and is thoroughly disliked by a considerable portion of the people. But he is vigorous, alert, bold, prying, and at times startling in his shouts.

Some of his food habits have brought him into disrepute, for undoubtedly he is an agency of considerable destruction to the small birds of the country. However, this loss seems to have been balanced, for when a bird's eggs or its young are taken it will invariably lay again.

Mr. Mailliard, California ornithologist, relates: "I remember one spring when a patch of about an acre and a half was sown with a mixture of peas and oats, and the peas were pulled up as fast as sprouted, by the jays, so that the crop consisted of oats alone . . . I shot more than 40 one afternoon, and a good many more on succeeding days, but they soon became so wary that it was impossible to get another shot after one was killed—and still the crop was destroyed."

It has remained for a woman, Irene Grosvenor Wheelock, to present one of the most scathing denunciations recorded of this jay. In part she says: "He is one of the greatest trials a bird-lover must encounter, and I know no reason why the law should protect him to the destruction of our beloved birds of song and beauty. Were he of benefit to the farmer or to the fruit grower, no word of dispraise would I offer; but he not only robs them, but also destroys annually hundreds of feathered creatures which, living upon harmful insects, would be of great assistance in preserving the crops. No hawk is more destructive to small birds than he is. Ruthlessly he robs every nest in his vicinity that is left unguarded long enough for him to carry off the eggs or young. Not content with this he pulls down and breaks up the nest itself. Usually he prefers the newly hatched babies to the raw albumen, and waits for the incubation to be finished. I have seen him sneaking around the nest of a pewee day after day until the eggs hatched, when he at once made a breakfast on the nestlings—in this case, calmly disregarding the cries of the poor little mother. . . . About the farms he is even a greater pest, eating the eggs and occasionally killing the newly hatched chicks."

The California jay ranges the coast region of California from San Francisco Bay to Mexico and to the eastern base of the Coast Ranges. The other forms of this species are discussed under "Woodhouse's jay." (See p. 118.)

Santa Cruz Jay

(Aphelocoma insularis)

Average Length, Twelve Inches

There is only one of the Santa Barbara Island group on which any jay is found. This is the island of Santa Cruz, and since the jay which lives here is found nowhere else in the world, it has been named quite appropriately the Santa Cruz jay.

The island, which is some 22 miles long, lies in the Pacific Ocean 20 miles or a little more from the coast of Ventura County, California. Although the region is rock, abundant soil is available, and trees, shrubs, and gardens thrive. The jay is unquestionably the most common bird to be found there.

Few species have such a restricted range within which every individual of its tribe is confined. The Santa Cruz jays have done well in their island home, and are larger than their relatives in Ventura and Santa Barbara Counties, near by. The length of the Santa Cruz jay is more than 13 inches, thus exceeding by an inch or two the measurement of its mainland cousin, the noisy and none too popular *A. californica.*

Bulky nests are built among the limbs of trees or bushes only a few yards from the ground, and the three to five lightly spotted eggs are deposited in March or in April.

This bird was first discovered to science in June, 1875, by the naturalist H. W. Henshaw. Since then other scientific men have visited Santa Cruz for the specific purpose of making its acquaintance. W. L. Dawson wrote of it:

"This gem of the islands belongs to him by unquestioned title, and he has no need to defend his claim by frantic protest or scurrilous abuse.

"This demure quality shows itself to best advantage when his nest is threatened, for it is then, if ever, that a bird's soul is tried. Yet I have passed an hour beside a nest of jay babies with never a word of protest from the closely attendant parents, beyond a mellow and almost inaudible *choop choop*—this and the sound of pecking on tree limbs. But this jay is capable of vigorous expression, and the variety and suggestive affinity of its note are worth considering.

"There is first, the Aphelocomine scolding cry of common use, but this is fuller, rounder, and much less than harsh. Then there is a *djay, djay* note which distinctly recalls that of *Cyanocitta stelleri.* Lastly this note is so modified and accelerated as to simulate the *rickety rack rack* or *shack, shack, shack, shack* of the magpies. I know the magpie's voice well, but I have leaped to my feet and reached for the glasses at this *jack, jack* call before realizing that there are no magpies on Santa Cruz Island."

In common with other jays, this bird is known to eat nuts, insects, and eggs.

ENCOURAGING BIRDS AROUND THE HOME

FROM very ancient times birds have appealed to the interest and imagination of mankind. They have furnished themes for innumerable poets, have appeared in many guises in primitive religions, and by their flight inspired the predictions of the soothsayers of old. Even in these modern and prosaic times birds increasingly interest mankind, and the last decade has witnessed a marked strengthening of the sentiment toward them.

The present interest is direct and personal, and to-day hundreds of thousands of men and women throughout the country, old as well as young, are employing much of their leisure in familiarizing themselves with the birds of their respective localities. The student, in following birds afield, in observing their habits, and listening to their songs, comes into close touch and sympathy with Nature and adds new zest to life—a zest, be it noted, which enriches without harm to any creature.

BIRDS ARE FARMERS' EFFICIENT ALLIES

While birds appeal to the regard and interest of man from the esthetic side as no other creatures do, it is no doubt true that of late years interest in birds has been greatly stimulated by the discovery that they possess an economic value.

The study of the economic side of bird life and of the relations of birds to the farmer and horticulturist has been greatly stimulated in the United States by Federal aid and supervision. In no other country in the world have the activities of birds been so carefully investigated with reference to their practical bearing.

Under the Biological Survey of the Department of Agriculture, for instance, is a corps of trained men, who study the food of birds by careful examination of the stomachs of specimens killed for scientific purposes. The information thus gained is supplemented by observation in the field, and the result is a large amount of invaluable data illustrative of the economic relations of many kinds of birds (see pages 88-89).

A large and increasing number of private citizens are making bird preserves on their lands; many not only prevent the destruction of wild life on their forested estates, but go much farther, and endeavor in several ways to increase the number of their bird tenants.

Efforts to protect birds on a smaller scale and to attract them about dwellings, with a view to their close companionship, are worthy of all praise, and such efforts should be even more common in this country than they are at present, particularly since the means involve little trouble or expense.

The presence of trees and shrubbery near the house is of itself an open invitation to birds which they are eager to accept, particularly if the shrubbery is not too closely pruned. Birds like thick vines and tangles, in the recesses of which they feel safe from their many enemies. Suet, nuts, and other bird foods, if exposed in conspicuous places, can usually be depended on to attract birds in winter, and often save many lives, especially when snow covers the ground.

Species which are not berry eaters, like the woodpeckers, nuthatches, creepers, and chickadees, can be made winter residents of many gardens, even in the North, by putting out at convenient places a supply of suet, of which they and many other birds are very fond, even in summer. Hedges and thickets about the farm are important to furnish nesting sites and shelter both from the elements and from predatory enemies.

Few are aware of the difficulty often experienced by birds in obtaining water for drinking and bathing. A constant supply in all seasons near the house will materially aid in attracting birds to the neighborhood and in keeping them there, at least till the time of migration. Shallow trays or basins of wood, metal or cement admirably serve the purpose, especially since birds delight to bathe in them.

By supplying artificial nest boxes, the bird lover may increase the number of birds around farms and orchards, where their services are most needed. The average boy, if provided with a few tools, is quite equal to the task of making acceptable boxes for martins, swallows, bluebirds, wrens, woodpeckers, titmice, and other species, which are far from fastidious as to the appearance of the box intended for them.

Since the modern movements for bird study and protection have been in progress, the number of people furnishing homes for

Photograph by Newton V. Blakeslee

CRUMBS ON THE LEDGE INVITE A CARDINAL TO "COME TO THE WINDOW"

These flaming dandies of the trees cheer the homes of many bird enthusiasts in Washington, D. C., where they are friendly visitors to the feeding places.

the birds has increased immensely in every quarter of the United States and Canada. Their hospitality has been accepted by almost every kind of bird whose original home can be imitated by man.

The roll of species in the United States known to have nested in bird boxes or on supporting devices built for them now includes 48 names, as follows:*

Mountain bluebird, Western bluebird, eastern bluebird, robin.

Chestnut-backed chickadee, mountain chickadee, Carolina chickadee, black-capped chickadee, plain titmouse, tufted titmouse, red-breasted nuthatch, white-breasted nuthatch, brown creeper.

House wren, Bewick's wren, Carolina wren, mockingbird, brown thrasher.

Violet-green swallow, tree swallow, barn swallow, cliff swallow, purple martin.

Song sparrow, English sparrow, house finch, purple grackle, Bullock's oriole, orchard oriole, starling, phoebe, ash-throated

* Consult E. R. Kalmbach, Senior Biologist, Farmers' Bulletin No. 1456, U. S. Department of Agriculture.

flycatcher, crested flycatcher, Arkansas kingbird.

Red - shafted flicker, yellow - shafted flicker, golden-fronted woodpecker, red-headed woodpecker, downy woodpecker, hairy woodpecker.

Screech owl, saw-whet owl, barn owl, sparrow hawk.

Mourning dove, wood duck, American goldeneye, hooded merganser.

Supplying water, nest boxes, and winter food goes far toward making a bird haven, but it is important also to supplement the summer food. This can best be done by planting fruit-bearing shrubs and trees. Shrubs and trees are essential elements of park composition, but according to the judgment of bird lovers better choice is distinctly possible than that often made.

The guiding principle in park planning should be beauty, but it should not be a temporary or one-seasonal beauty. Shrubs and trees which produce colored fruits and retain them for long periods are preferable to plants whose chief decorative contribution is a short burst of bloom. Such shrubs

Preference of birds among fruit-bearing shrubs and trees[1]

Common name	Scientific name	Number of species of birds known to eat the fruit [2]	Kinds of birds among those desirable to attract that are most fond of the fruit [3]
Juniper; redcedar.....	Juniperus.......	39	Yellow-shafted flicker, European starling, evening grosbeak, pine grosbeak, purple finch, cedar waxwing, myrtle warbler, mockingbird, robin, eastern bluebird.
Greenbrier..........	Smilax........	39	Cardinal, mockingbird, brown thrasher, catbird, hermit thrush, robin.
Bayberry............	Myrica........	73	Bobwhite, downy woodpecker, yellow-shafted flicker, eastern phoebe, European starling, meadowlark, chewink, tree swallow, white-eyed vireo, myrtle warbler, brown thrasher, catbird, Carolina wren, black-capped chickadee, hermit thrush, eastern bluebird.
Hackberry..........	Celtis..........	40	Yellow-bellied sapsucker, yellow-shafted flicker, starling, cardinal, cedar waxwing, mockingbird, brown thrasher, eastern bluebird.
Mulberry...........	Morus........	52	Yellow-billed cuckoo, red-headed woodpecker, red-bellied woodpecker, downy woodpecker, kingbird, starling, Baltimore oriole, orchard oriole, cardinal, purple finch, scarlet tanager, cedar waxwing, red-eyed vireo, yellow warbler, mockingbird, catbird, wood thrush, robin.
Pokeberry...........	Phytolacca.....	49	Mourning dove, yellow-shafted flicker, kingbird, starling, cardinal, mockingbird, catbird, hermit thrush, gray-cheeked thrush, olive-backed thrush, robin, eastern bluebird.
Spicebush...........	Benzoin........	17	Kingbird, red-eyed vireo, wood thrush, veery.
Sassafras............	Sassafras.......	18	Bobwhite, kingbird, red-eyed vireo, catbird, veery, robin.
Strawberry..........	Fragaria........	46	Chewink, catbird, brown thrasher, wood thrush, robin.
Raspberry; blackberry.	Rubus.........	118	Ruffed grouse, bobwhite, red-headed woodpecker, yellow-shafted flicker, kingbird, European starling, Baltimore oriole, orchard oriole, pine grosbeak, song sparrow, fox sparrow, white-throated sparrow, chewink, California towhee, spurred towhee, cardinal, rose-breasted grosbeak, black-headed grosbeak, cedar waxwing, red-eyed vireo, mockingbird, catbird, brown thrasher, tufted titmouse, wren-tit, olive-backed thrush, wood thrush, robin, eastern bluebird.
Rose..............	Rosa..........	25	Ruffed grouse, sharp-tailed grouse, prairie chicken, bobwhite.
Mountain-ash........	Sorbus.........	14	Red-headed woodpecker, Baltimore oriole, evening grosbeak, pine grosbeak, cedar waxwing, Bohemian waxwing, catbird, brown thrasher, robin.
Chokeberry..........	Aronia.........	13	Meadowlark, brown thrasher.
Hawthorn, or red haw.	Crataegus......	33	Ruffed grouse, pine grosbeak, purple finch, robin.
Dwarf apples.........	Malus..........	([4])	Ruffed grouse, ringneck pheasant, red crossbill, pine grosbeak, purple finch, cedar waxwing, mockingbird, robin.
Shadblow, or Juneberry.	Amelanchier....	40	Yellow-shafted flicker, Baltimore oriole, cedar waxwing, catbird, hermit thrush, veery, robin.
Wild cherry..........	Prunus.........	74	Ruffed grouse, bobwhite, mourning dove, red-headed woodpecker, yellow-shafted flicker, kingbird, European starling, Bullock's oriole, Baltimore oriole, orchard oriole, evening grosbeak, purple finch, rose-breasted grosbeak, black-headed grosbeak, Louisiana tanager, red-eyed vireo, cedar waxwing, mockingbird, catbird, brown thrasher, olive-backed thrush, wood thrush, robin, eastern bluebird.
Sumac [5]..............	Rhus [5]........	93	Ruffed grouse, bobwhite, valley quail, downy woodpecker, red-bellied woodpecker, red-shafted flicker, yellow-shafted flicker, phoebe, European starling, goldfinch, golden-crowned sparrow, chewink, white-eyed vireo, Audubon's warbler, mockingbird, catbird, California thrasher, brown thrasher, Carolina wren, black-capped chickadee, Carolina chickadee, wren-tit, hermit thrush, robin, eastern bluebird.

[1] Barberries (Berberis), buckthorn (Rhamnus), and gooseberries and currants (Ribes) are omitted because they serve as alternate hosts of rusts attacking wheat, oats, and white pine, respectively.
[2] When 10 or more.
[3] Included on the basis of field observation or because fruit was found in 10 or more stomachs.
[4] Thirty-eight kinds of birds are known to feed on apples of various sorts, but it is not known just how many seek the small-fruited flowering apples, which are the best to plant for birds.
[5] Only nonpoisonous species of sumac are considered.

are handsomer at all times after flowering and are particularly valuable in winter when every bit of color in the landscape is precious.

A number of railroad companies have already made considerable effort to beautify their right of ways and station grounds. In some places the roads are paralleled for many miles by hedges, and the land on either side of the tracks is covered by beautiful turf. Hedges, shrubbery, and flower beds are common about the stations. If this planting could be directed in part, at least, toward attracting birds, it would be very effective and great good would be done.

The attractiveness of community parkings, including those of cities and villages as well as of rural areas, may well be enhanced by the presence of an abundance of birds. This can be effected without in any way detracting from the utility of

Preference of birds among fruit-bearing shrubs and trees

Common name	Scientific name	Number of species of birds known to eat the fruit [2]	Kinds of birds among those desirable to attract that are most fond of the fruit [3]
Peppertree	Schinus	11	Cedar waxwing, phainopepla, hermit thrush, varied thrush, robin.
Holly	Ilex	45	Ruffed grouse, bobwhite, valley quail, yellow-bellied sapsucker, yellow-shafted flicker, cedar waxwing, mockingbird, catbird, brown thrasher, hermit thrush, robin, eastern bluebird.
Supplejack	Berchemia	13	Mockingbird, robin.
Wild grape	Vitis	77	Ruffed grouse, bobwhite, pileated woodpecker, red-bellied woodpecker, red-shafted flicker, yellow-shafted flicker, kingbird, European starling, cardinal, cedar waxwing, mockingbird, catbird, brown thrasher, wood thrush, veery, robin, western bluebird, eastern bluebird.
Virginia creeper	Parthenocissus	39	Red-headed woodpecker, red-bellied woodpecker, yellow-bellied sapsucker, yellow-shafted flicker, European starling, evening grosbeak, purple finch, scarlet tanager, red-eyed vireo, mockingbird, brown thrasher, tufted titmouse, hermit thrush, olive-backed thrush, gray-cheeked thrush, robin, eastern bluebird.
Buffaloberry	Lepargyrea	16	Sharp-tailed grouse, pine grosbeak.
Silverberry, Russian-olive, etc.	Elaeagnus	(6)	Sharp-tailed grouse, prairie chicken, cedar waxwing, catbird, robin.
Wild-sarsaparilla	Aralia	14	Bobwhite, robin.
Dogwood	Cornus	86	Ruffed grouse, bobwhite, downy woodpecker, yellow-shafted flicker, red-shafted flicker, kingbird, European starling, evening grosbeak, pine grosbeak, purple finch, white-throated sparrow, song sparrow, cardinal, cedar waxwing, warbling vireo, red-eyed vireo, mockingbird, catbird, brown thrasher, hermit thrush, olive-backed thrush, gray-cheeked thrush, wood thrush, robin, eastern bluebird.
Tupelo, or sour gum	Nyssa	36	Yellow-shafted flicker, European starling, purple finch, cedar waxwing, gray-cheeked thrush, olive-backed thrush, robin.
Crowberry	Empetrum	16	Pine grosbeak, snowflake.
Bearberry	Arctostaphylos	16	Ruffed grouse, dusky grouse, valley quail, mountain quail, fox sparrow, wren-tit.
Huckleberry	Gaylussacia	35	Pine grosbeak, chewink, robin.
Blueberry	Vaccinium	67	Ruffed grouse, valley quail, kingbird, orchard oriole, pine grosbeak, chewink, cedar waxwing, catbird, brown thrasher, black-capped chickadee, tufted titmouse, hermit thrush, robin, eastern bluebird.
Beautyberry, or Mexican mulberry.	Callicarpa	10	Mockingbird, brown thrasher.
Partridgeberry	Mitchella	10	Ruffed grouse.
Elder	Sambucus	106	Valley quail, red-headed woodpecker, yellow-shafted flicker, eastern kingbird, Arkansas kingbird, black phoebe, European starling, California towhee, white-crowned sparrow, rose-breasted grosbeak, black-headed grosbeak, phainopepla, red-eyed vireo, mockingbird, catbird, brown thrasher, California thrasher, wren-tit, olive-backed thrush, robin, western bluebird, eastern bluebird.
Snowberry	Symphoricarpos	25	Sharp-tailed grouse, evening grosbeak, pine grosbeak, varied thrush.
Blackhaw	Viburnum	28	Ruffed grouse, yellow-billed cuckoo, yellow-shafted flicker, European starling, purple finch, rose-breasted grosbeak, cedar waxwing, catbird, brown thrasher, robin, eastern bluebird.
Honeysuckle	Lonicera	15	Bobwhite, pine grosbeak, white-throated sparrow, catbird, brown thrasher, hermit thrush, robin.

[6] Data given are based entirely on field observations; total number of birds eating the various species of Elaeagnus unknown.

these reservations for their leading purposes. Making community parkings safe for birds is the first step; they must actually be havens of refuge. In this connection may be cited the admirable law of the State of Oregon that provides that all incorporated towns and cities and all public parks and school grounds in the State shall be, without additional local or general legislation, bird and game sanctuaries.

Picnic grounds, golf courses, and parks may be improved as places of public gatherings, recreation, and education by increasing their bird population. Moreover, the alterations that improve a park as a bird haven may, and should, themselves be made to add to its attractiveness.

The table on pages 132-133 sets forth the kinds of fruit-bearing shrubs and trees that attract birds.*

* Consult W. L. McAtee, Farmers' Bulletin 1239, U. S. Department of Agriculture.

A VERDIN HANGS IN TITMOUSE FASHION TO FEED ITS YOUNG

Eagerness without crowding obtains its reward.   The nest built in a cat's-claw branch is typical.

Photographs by William L. Finley and H. T. Bohlman

THE PARENT CHICKADEE IS A GOOD PROVIDER

Perhaps the youngster receiving the tidbit is the envy of his fellows.   The one behind him looks
disappointed at waiting, or possibly he "has a rather tough worm in his little inside."

WINGED DENIZENS OF WOODLAND, STREAM, AND MARSH

By Alexander Wetmore

THE path through the river woods was hidden by leaves that came drifting slowly down through the cool October air. For a space there was quiet except for the rustling underfoot, and then a low bird call, *chick-a-dee-dee-dee,* announced a little gray and white bird with black crown and black throat, swinging back downward at the tip of a slender twig while it searched in the roll of a curling leaf for hidden insects.

Other chickadees came quickly through the branches, flitting from perch to perch, and soon the little birds were all about me, calling softly to maintain contact in a loosely organized flock.

As I watched them, a scratching sound brought to attention another gray and white bird with a blackish crown, of slightly larger size, that came headforemost down a tree trunk, examining crevices in the bark for food. This was the white-breasted nuthatch. An instant later a brown creeper and some tufted titmice came into view, accompanied by a tiny ruby-crowned kinglet, easily told by its quickly flitting wings.

The little group of birds moved rapidly through the trees, convoyed by the chickadees, and in a moment had passed beyond my view, their low notes lost in the rattling of the leaves.

CHICKADEES AND TITMICE ARE RELATIVES OF THE CROWS AND JAYS

Through much of the year these little companies of woodland birds are a regular feature of our bird life. The nucleus of the mixed flock, which may contain a dozen species or more, is the group of chickadees which has its regular range and does not depart far from its limits. The nuthatches and the downy woodpecker or two that accompany the bands also ordinarily do not migrate. In late summer and fall small migrants of similar habit of life, vireos and some of the warblers, tarry briefly in the company and then pass on.

The observant bird lover soon learns to follow up the notes of the chickadees to see what other interesting species may be in their company.

The family of titmice (Paridae) to which the chickadees belong is widespread in the world, its more than 200 forms being all of small or tiny dimensions. Representatives of the group are found everywhere on the large continents of the world except in South America. They are also lacking in the Pacific islands. In spite of small size, they include some of the hardiest of our birds, chickadees ranging to the limits of forest growth in the far North, where they may remain throughout the coldest winters. The family is nearly related to the much larger crows and jays.

Although titmice are common in North America, in western Europe more varieties are found.

A BIRD LOVER'S PARADISE FOUND IN NORTHERN SPAIN

Walking out one pleasant May morning in the foothills of the Cantabrian Mountains, in northern Spain, I came to a little valley with a grove of gnarled and twisted trees bordering an orchard and a meadow. A small gray and white bird that was feeding through the tips of the branches proved to be a marsh titmouse, closely similar to our black-capped chickadee.

This was interesting, but a moment later I was more delighted to catch a glimpse of the delicately tinted back of the blue titmouse. There followed soon after a view of the greater titmouse, a noisy species as large as a small sparrow, strikingly marked with yellow, blue, and black.

In the same woodland I found the small gray, crested titmouse and an occasional long-tailed tit, with tiny body, greatly elongated tail, and a wash of pink along the sides.

In all, I saw five species of this family in a comparatively short space of time. Against a background of snow-capped mountains, cloud-dotted blue sky, and the clear green of spring vegetation, meeting with these birds, all new to me in life, was a very pleasant experience.

Tufted Titmouse
(Baeolophus bicolor)
Average Length, Six Inches

In a family of gentle, friendly birds the tufted titmouse seems more active and aggressive than others, an appearance heightened by the jaunty tilt of its erect crest.

The tufted titmouse, the "tomtit" of the South, is one of those sympathetic birds that come at any disturbance to peer with raised crest and scolding notes that attract all other small birds in the neighborhood. In winter a screech owl or a cat, or in summer a snake, is certain to rouse their ire, though in their vituperation of the enemy they take good care to keep out of danger's reach. Usually the tufted titmouse's crest is erect and sharp, but when the bird is frightened or busy the tuft is often held flat.

This is one of the species that are sure to be attracted by "squeaking," a kissing sound made by placing the lips against the fingers, used by bird students to draw birds from cover so that they may be seen. A friend once had a tomtit become so exasperated and agitated at this call that the bird clung to the side of his trousers to reach over and nip his hand with its bill.

It is not at all shy and is therefore easily approached for study. It frequents groves and woodlands and is social, so that several are found in company except during the nesting season. It comes fearlessly to feeding shelves in our yards, returning daily and scolding with saucy calls when food is not ready.

In spring this titmouse has a clear double-noted whistle of *peter peter peter* that rings through the treetops and is continued through the nesting season. At first the song is very pleasant to hear, but, when repeated monotonously hour after hour, it may become tiresome. Its ordinary calls are harsh and chattering.

The nesting season extends from April to June, one brood being reared. The homes are located in hollows in trees, sometimes in bird boxes, which are filled with dead leaves and other rubbish, in which is placed the nest of moss and leaves lined with soft substances. The eggs number from five to eight, being white or cream color spotted with reddish brown. They are carefully covered over when the bird leaves the nest. The nesting holes of summer are frequently used for roosting in winter, because titmice do not migrate as the seasons change. Small feeding flocks may be seen throughout the winter.

This titmouse feeds on insects, nuts, and starchy seeds of many kinds and is one of our beneficial species.

It ranges from Nebraska, Ohio, and New Jersey to central Texas and southern Florida. In recent years it has extended its territory into Wisconsin and Michigan.

Black-crested Titmouse
(Baeolophus atricristatus)
Average Length, Five and One-half Inches

This handsome bird is distinguished from the tufted titmouse by the black color of the crest, which attracts the eye instantly. Of limited range, this species has been studied by comparatively few naturalists.

In fall and winter it is fond of pecans and starchy seeds of various kinds, which are held in one foot against a branch and are broken open by sharp blows of the bill.

The scolding calls of this titmouse are like those of the eastern form, and it also has a whistled song like that bird. Its five or six chestnut-spotted white eggs are laid in a well-lined nest in a hole or crack in a tree trunk.

The black-crested titmouse *(Baeolophus atricristatus atricristatus)* is found from the Rio Grande Valley in Texas south into eastern Mexico as far as northern Vera Cruz. Sennett's titmouse *(B. a. sennetti)* which is slightly larger and has clearer gray plumage ranges in central Texas east to the Brazos River.

Bridled Titmouse
(Baeolophus wollweberi annexus)
Average Length, Four and Three-quarters Inches

The notes and songs of the bridled titmouse have a general resemblance to those of the more widely known chickadees, but are higher in pitch, the call notes at times suggesting those of kinglets.

Flocks of twenty-five or more are common, except in the nesting season. Quieter than most titmice, it has a decided preference for oak trees. The softly lined nest is placed in natural tree cavities, often near the ground.

It is found from the mountains of southwestern New Mexico and southern Arizona south into Sonora and Chihuahua.

Plain Titmouse
(Baeolophus inornatus)
Average Length, Five and One-quarter Inches

The vivacious plain titmouse lives in open groves and thickets, finding the oaks of mountain slopes particularly suited to its needs.

In the foothills of the Greenhorn Mountains in California I found them tame and unsuspicious, while in junipers of the San Francisco Mountain region they were at times shy and wary. Their calls are like those of other crested titmice, but recognizably individual.

The plain titmouse nests in holes, sometimes occupying bird boxes, making a warmly felted nest of soft materials. The six to eight eggs are plain white, occasionally with a few small spots of brown.

Six geographic forms, differing slightly in size and color, are recognized, the species ranging from Oregon and southwest Wyoming to southern Baja California and west Texas.

THE SAUCY TITMOUSE PLAYS MANY A PRANK

Snatching hairs from a man's head for nest lining is not too bold a trick for the **Tufted Titmouse,** or "tomtit," of the southern and middle States (upper left). Its crest, raised or lowered, is a barometer of its mood. No less pert are the Southwest's handsome **Black-crested** and **Bridled Titmice** (upper right and lower left), and a cousin from Pacific regions, the **Plain Titmouse** (lower right).

Black-capped Chickadee

(Penthestes atricapillus)
Average Length, Five and One-quarter Inches

Named from its clearly enunciated call note, the gentle little chickadee is a welcome friend wherever it is known. Among the birds that come to the food spread to attract them about our homes, this is the most trusting and the least pugnacious, feeding in amity with its kind and giving way without argument to bullies of all sizes and descriptions, returning unobtrusively when the way is clear.

In addition to its ordinary calls, with the approach of spring the chickadee whistles a plaintive song in a high-pitched tone, and has another harsher effort.

The nest is excavated in the soft wood of a partly decayed dead limb or tree trunk, the cavity being of good size, or the birds utilize openings already prepared. The hole is lined with soft materials to form a nest that contains from five to eight white eggs closely spotted with light reddish brown. One or two broods are reared each season, nesting coming in early spring.

While the chickadee is perfectly nonchalant about alighting on a twig or branch upside down, it lacks the right kind of feet and tail to climb up or down on a perpendicular trunk or limb like the woodpeckers and nuthatches.

The chickadee is among our most beneficial birds and fortunately is a species that can hold its own about the homes of man. More than half its diet is composed of insects of various kinds, among them the hated snout beetles, or weevils. Larvæ, chrysalids and moth eggs are also eaten, and among the latter those of the tent-caterpillar moths are important.

Four forms of the black-capped chickadee are found from central Quebec, Nova Scotia, and northern Alaska, south to New Jersey, Kansas, northern New Mexico, and northwestern California. The closely related Carolina chickadee *(Penthestes carolinensis)*, with similar habits, which is only slightly smaller and duller in color, has three forms that extend from central New Jersey and Missouri to the Gulf coast and Florida.

Mountain Chickadee

(Penthestes gambeli)
Average Length, Five and One-half Inches

This mountain inhabitant of the Western States is distinguished by lines of white on either side of the crown. Although differing slightly from its eastern relative in coloration, it is very similar in habits and general appearance. It is found among the pines and spruces of the higher slopes, but in fall it wanders to some extent and may then be seen in willows and cottonwoods along valley streams.

The calls of the mountain chickadee are closely similar to those of the blackcap species, but are uttered in a slightly slower, drawling tone, so that the notes of the two may be distinguished by a practiced ear. This cheerful chatter is one of the commonest bird notes in the forests of the Sierra Nevada.

It usually nests in an old woodpecker hole and the female's snakelike hissings may keep marauding squirrels at a safe distance.

Six forms of the mountain chickadee are known in the region from northern British Columbia and Montana to northern Baja California and western Texas.

The Mexican chickadee *(Penthestes sclateri eidos)*, colored like the blackcap but with more black on the chest and the sides gray instead of buffy, occurs from the mountains of southern Arizona into Mexico.

Chestnut-backed Chickadee

(Penthestes rufescens)
Average Length, Four and Three-quarters Inches

The chestnut-backed chickadee inhabits the depths of somber forests in whose shades it is entirely inconspicuous. Growths of redwood are a favorite haunt and the bird is one that lives in large part remote from human settlements, although it is found in considerable numbers in open woods along quiet roads and trails and shows no fear when man invades its favorite solitudes. High up in conifers it briskly hunts for insects.

J. H. Bowles describes the habit of the incubating bird of fluttering up with a loud hiss when the dark nest cavity is examined, a startlingly unexpected performance.

Three forms of the chestnut-backed chickadee have been described, ranging in the Pacific coast region from Prince William Sound, Alaska, to near Monterey Bay, California, and east to western Montana.

Hudsonian Chickadee

(Penthestes hudsonicus)
Average Length, Five and One-half Inches

Occasionally along the northern border of the United States a sprightly, active little chickadee appears that has the cap brown instead of black and the markings of the flanks brighter. It is always sure to bring a thrill to the heart of the bird student, for its appearance here is rather infrequent. This is the Hudsonian chickadee, a species especially partial to coniferous trees.

The true Hudsonian chickadee *(Penthestes hudsonicus hudsonicus)* nests from the Kobuk Valley, Alaska, and northern Manitoba south to Ontario and northern Michigan. Its relative, the Acadian chickadee *(Penthestes h. littoralis)*, is smaller and slightly browner. It breeds from Labrador to Nova Scotia, Maine, Vermont, and the Adirondack Mountains of New York, and is found casually in winter from New England to New Jersey.

A HAPPY-GO-LUCKY LITTLE LEADER IS THE CHICKADEE

This optimist greets winter with all the zest of a boy with a new sled. Other small birds follow trustfully as it flits about, consuming countless insects and calling its own name in a voice which Burroughs described as "full of unspeakable tenderness and fidelity." Unlike the familiar **Black-capped Chickadee** (upper left) and the West's **Mountain** (upper right) and **Chestnut-backed Chickadees** (lower right), the **Hudsonian Chickadee** (lower left) sports a "brown derby."

Bush-tit

(Psaltriparus minimus)

Average Length, Four and One-quarter Inches

In a family of birds which are small in size the bush-tit is the tiniest of all, being only slightly larger in body than the ordinary hummingbirds. Bush-tits are found in regions of oaks, piñons, or junipers, usually in hilly or mountainous country. They range in small flocks that feed among the leaves and smaller branches, maintaining a loose group formation through soft calls constantly repeated. They are active birds, clambering about or swinging from leaves or twigs, seldom resting for any length of time. Their gray coloration merges with the gray-green leaves among which they feed, and they would be hard to see if they were not constantly moving.

In March and April the flocks break up into pairs for breeding. The nest is a pendent structure swung from slender twigs, with a small entrance at one side near the top. It is constructed of such soft material as moss, plant downs, and spider web compactly woven together, and measures from 8 to 11 inches in length by 3 or 4 inches in diameter. It holds from five to eight white eggs. Two broods may be reared in a season.

Six forms of the bush-tit are recognized. Lloyd's bush-tit *(Psaltriparus m. lloydi)* is distinguished by the dark markings of the side of the head.

Bush-tits as a species range from British Columbia and western Wyoming to western Texas and Baja California.

Verdin

(Auriparus flaviceps)

Average Length, Four and One-quarter Inches

A true desert dweller, the tiny verdin seemingly is indifferent to heat and must not feel thirst, since it often lives in areas far from any regular water supply. Enter its haunts, and it scolds with chattering notes, and hops about in some thorny shrub.

The nest of the verdin is so placed among the spiny branches of some bush that it is inaccessible without severe lacerations to any exploring hand reaching toward it. Within this safe protection is a lining of leaves and stems felted together with spider web and lined thickly with feathers. The four or five eggs are bluish or greenish white marked with reddish brown.

The old nests, or new ones made for the purpose, serve as warm roosts during the cold nights of the desert winter. The birds are pugnacious and peck viciously at an intruding finger in their warm quarters.

The common verdin *(Auriparus flaviceps flaviceps)* is found in sunny areas of desert growth from southern California and southwestern Utah to southern Texas and Mexico.

Brown Creeper

(Certhia familiaris)

Average Length, Five and One-half Inches

To be inconspicuous seems to be the aim of this curious bird, in which effort it is aided by its softly colored, streaked plumage. The brown creeper passes its days in climbing actively with long claws and bracing tail up the rough bark of trees. The birds feed on tiny insects and insect eggs hidden in crevices of bark, drag them out with their slenderly curved bills, and eat them while climbing.

They seem nearsighted, their small eyes obscured by markings. Their vision, however, is equal to that of any of their companion birds. They can detect insect eggs or a spider an inch away and at the same time recognize enemies or a desirable hunting spot at a hundred yards—truly remarkable accommodation.

The call notes are thin and high-pitched and the birds also utter a warbling song somewhat like the wren's. The nest, placed ordinarily behind a loose flake of bark, is made of twigs, bark, and moss, lined with softer stuff. The five to nine white eggs are brown spotted.

Five forms of the brown creeper are found in North America north of Mexico. They nest in northern or mountain forests and spread widely in migration.

Creepers are found nearly everywhere in the warmer continental areas with the exception of South America and New Zealand.

The majority of the nearly 50 forms of creepers (family Certhiidae) resemble our common brown creeper rather closely, being small, slender birds with brownish-streaked backs and white underparts.

Wren-tit

(Chamaea fasciata)

Average Length, Six and One-half Inches

The wren-tit belongs to the only family of birds peculiar to North America, the Chamaeidae. It lives in growths of chaparral and lowland thickets, where its presence is announced by its staccato, insistent notes.

The birds climb actively about, appearing like wrens, but with more ease and dignity of movement. They make short flights across little openings with quickly tilting flight and pumping tails, but do not fly far. The light-colored eye is a striking feature.

The nest is a cup of grasses, weed stems, and similar materials, lined with horsehair and hidden in some thicket only a few feet from the ground. The eggs, three to five in number, are pale green without markings. Wren-tits feed on insects and on wild fruits.

Five forms of this bird are recognized, varying in depth of color and size. They range from the Columbia River in Oregon south through California into Baja California. These birds do not make regular migrations.

THE CHICKADEE'S TINIEST COUSINS LIVE IN THE WEST

The bustling, businesslike **Bush-tits** (upper left) are a little smaller than a man's thumb, but they build elaborate bird mansions of moss, fibers, lichens, and feathers. The dark-cheeked midget is a **Lloyd's Bush-tit.** A happy little desert dweller is the **Verdin** (upper right). Below are the monotonously busy **Brown Creeper** (left), and the **Wren-tit** (right), which is of a distinct Pacific coast family, resembling both titmouse and wren.

White-breasted Nuthatch
(Sitta carolinensis)
Average Length, Five and Three-quarters Inches

The white-breasted nuthatch is often a friendly visitor to dooryards, where it comes to feeding shelves for nut meats, sunflower seeds, and suet. It may even nest where bird boxes covered with bark are provided. These birds divide into pairs in late summer as soon as grown, and male and female remain together through the fall and winter.

Nuthatches are related to titmice and creepers, differing in their long, straight bills and short tails, which they do not use as braces in climbing. They depend entirely upon their strong feet to cling to surfaces.

About 60 kinds of nuthatches are known, representatives of the family being widely distributed except in South America and Central America and the central and southern parts of Africa. Some of the tropical forms of the Old World are brightly colored.

Most nuthatches nest in holes in trees, building warmly felted nests of feathers, hair, and soft vegetable materials in which they place their brown-spotted eggs. Some of the foreign species use mud to close the cavity except for the small entrance hole. The rock nuthatch, which ranges from Greece to Persia, makes a cone-shaped nest entirely of mud, placing it against a rock. The usual softly felted nest is built inside this structure.

The nuthatch climbs incessantly and is noted for its ability in running head downward on tree trunks, in this differing from all our other tree-climbing birds. The ordinary call is a low *yank yank* like that of no other bird. In early spring it whistles pleasantly.

Nuthatches eat insects, spiders, insect eggs, and similar fare. They are also partial to starchy seeds and nuts, which they wedge into some suitable crevice in a dead limb or the rough bark of a tree. With blows of the bill they then split them open to get the food. From this habit comes the name "nuthatch."

Nuthatches also store seeds and small nuts by wedging them into cracks and crevices, so that they may preserve a supply for periods when food is less abundant. At my feeding shelf in a suburb of Washington the nuthatches work busily all day carrying off sunflower seeds and hiding them under shingles and in the stucco walls of near-by houses, regardless of the fact that the supply is renewed daily. Probably most of this food is eaten by other birds, and the labor goes for nothing.

In the West nuthatches feed extensively on the sweet-meated nuts of the piñon pine. In many regions they eat the meat of acorns. Hard-shelled nuts are also eaten.

Eight geographic forms of this nuthatch are recognized, ranging from British Columbia, Alberta, and Quebec to Florida, southern Mexico, and Baja California.

Brown-headed Nuthatch
(Sitta pusilla)
Average Length, Four and One-half Inches

These nuthatches are found principally in open forests of pine, sometimes low down near the ground and again in the summits of the tallest pines. They travel in little flocks, being social except during the nesting season.

They often scold vociferously at intruders from some high perch. If really alarmed, they hide by remaining motionless against the bark that they match so closely in color.

The brown-headed nuthatch digs a nest hole in a dead stub or stump, a telephone pole, or a fence post. In the South the birds are earnestly at work on nest cavities in February.

The true brown-headed nuthatch is found from eastern Arkansas and southern Delaware to the Gulf coast and eastern Texas. The gray-headed nuthatch, a paler race, ranges in Florida.

Pygmy Nuthatch
(Sitta pygmaea)
Average Length, Four and One-quarter Inches

The pygmy nuthatch, except in the breeding season, is often seen in flocks of 40, 50, or even 100. These travel actively through the pine forests, calling constantly with chattering notes and scolding vigorously at any disturbance. They like especially open growths of yellow pine in western mountains.

Except when freshly grown, the feathers of the breast are often worn by rubbing against rough surfaces and often the birds become smeared with sticky pine pitch.

Three forms of this nuthatch are recognized at present in the region from southern British Columbia and northern Idaho south into Baja California and southern Mexico.

Red-breasted Nuthatch
(Sitta canadensis)
Average Length, Four and One-half Inches

The redbreast has the usual nuthatch customs of searching for food over the trunks of trees and also flies out to capture insects in the air, an infrequent habit in the other species.

The nest is excavated in some dead stub or limb, being sometimes 10 or 12 inches deep. Occasionally the birds will occupy bird boxes. They usually smear pitch about the entrance to the nest, a habit for which no explanation has been offered. The eggs, from four to eight, are white, spotted with reddish brown.

The call of this species is high-pitched and nasal, like the sound of a penny trumpet. Near Washington the birds are always common when Virginia pines produce abundant seed.

The red-breasted nuthatch breeds from Nova Scotia, Quebec, and Alaska south in the mountains to North Carolina, California, and New Mexico. In migration it reaches the Gulf coast and northern Florida.

THE NUTHATCH IS A TOPSY-TURVY BIRD

Up or down trees it runs, often clinging to the bark upside down. The habit of opening nuts with its sharp bill, to vary an insect menu, won for it the common name. Most familiar to bird lovers is the **White-breasted Nuthatch** (lower left, female and male). Above are the **Brown-headed** (left) and **Pygmy Nuthatches** (right). The **Red-breasted Nuthatch** (center) ranges south in numbers from Canada and the Northern States in years when pine seeds are abundant.

Photograph by William L. Finley and H. T. Bohlman

TWO HUNGRY WRENS HAVE BUT A SINGLE THOUGHT

The stick is not at all like their mother, but the worms look entirely familiar.

Photograph by William L. and Irene Finley

A WATER OUZEL POSES ON A ROCK IN A MOUNTAIN TORRENT

It is a creature of the "white water" and the wilderness, a spirit of the spray.

THE WRENS

By Alexander Wetmore

THOUGH the eagle has been recognized as the king of birds, the same title is given in many languages to the tiny wren. According to the ancient fable, the birds decided to choose for their ruler the one with the strongest pinions, that would enable it to rise highest from the earth. In the competition the great eagle mounted steadily upward until he had outdistanced all the others. As the other birds were about to acclaim him king, from his back came a burst of song from the wren, which had concealed itself among the eagle's feathers. Having been borne so far aloft without labor, while all the other birds, including the eagle, were tired out, the wren easily won the test of flight.

"JENNY WREN" IN THE RÔLE OF A GOSSIP

The wren of popular fancy and fable is the species of western Europe, which is closely allied to the winter wren of North America. Early settlers in our country, familiar with the common birds in their Old World home, recognized the relationship of this bird to the bird we know as the house wren and bestowed on it the familiar name of their former residence. The "jenny wren" thus was transplanted to America in name if not in fact, and the appellation has persisted, the bird being widely known.

Among the Cherokee Indians the wren was considered a busybody who slipped about learning everyone's business and reporting it to the birds' council. When a baby was born the wren brought the news. If it was a boy the birds were sorrowful, since they knew that as the boy grew he would become a hunter who would destroy birds. If it was a girl, they were glad, since they would be able later to feed in the leavings from her food grinder.

The wrens (family Troglodytidae) include more than 250 forms, being most abundant in tropical America but ranging into colder regions in Alaska, Labrador, and Patagonia. A few species are found in Europe and the temperate parts of Asia.

The various species of wrens vary from small to medium in size. They have the tail short or abbreviated, the wings rounded, the plumage soft and fluffy, and the bill slender and curved. Gray or brown is their prevailing color. They are most nearly allied to the mockingbirds and thrashers.

Wrens as a whole present traits of timidity, curiosity, and aggressiveness in somewhat anomalous combination. As a rule, they inhabit thickets, vines, weeds, and other dense growths where they may have secure hiding places. From these shelters they appear to chatter at intruders or to sing, but at any alarm they dash back to cover. One group, the marsh wrens, inhabits rush-grown swamps and marshy growths of grasses and sedges. Representatives of this section of the family range widely through North America, going far north into Canada, and in South America they penetrate into Patagonia and the highlands of the Andes.

The dense vegetation of the Tropics is particularly favorable to wrens, and here the birds are found in abundance, particularly in Mexico and Central America. One branch of the family, including the rock wrens and cañon wrens, has become adapted for life about cliffs, rock exposures, and stony ground in general. Here they utilize crevices and crannies among the rocks and scanty growths of bushes for cover. The cactus wrens are inhabitants of the thorny thickets of cactuses in arid regions.

THE CAÑON WREN'S SONG IS BELL-LIKE

As songsters, wrens rank high among their kindred. Descend the steep trails that lead into the Grand Canyon of the Colorado River in Arizona, and if your ears are attuned to the notes of birds you may hear from the cliffs above or below a clear, whistled song with notes that descend the musical scale in a measured cadence. This comes from the cañon wren, whose attractive song expresses in sound the wild and untamed freedom of the tremendous gorge.

The bubbling music of the house wren, with its notes tumbling from the vibrating throat of the songster, and the clear, ringing song of the Carolina wren are other examples of the music of this highly gifted family. Even the chattering efforts of the marsh wren and the staccato notes of the rock wrens, while less musical, are pleasing.

WRENS ENLIVEN THE SOLITUDES

These shy members of a numerous clan are westerners, except the rather widely distributed **Carolina Wren** (upper right) found in southern woodlands. Like the **Cañon Wren** (lower right), it floods its haunts with song. The **Rock Wren** (lower left) paves the entrance to its crevice nest with chips of stone, and the overgrown-appearing **Cactus Wren** (upper left) builds amid thorns.

Carolina Wren

(Thryothorus ludovicianus)

Average Length, Five and One-half Inches

The Carolina wren lives in brushy growths, being found in heavy woods where there is suitable cover. If frightened, it will usually hide in high, thick shrubbery but will readily seek cover behind logs, rocks or ground plants if necessary. It is sedentary without definite migrations, though before and after the breeding season it may wander in search of congenial haunts. Throughout the year it remains in pairs that travel about together.

Like others of its family, this wren is a ball of energy—active, nervous, voluble and curious. It is full of song and its voice is clear, sweet and strong, but lacks the irrepressible, bubbling ecstasy of the house wren. The words *tea-kettle, tea-kettle* have been used to express one of its phrases. Some of its notes resemble those of other birds, a characteristic that has won it the name of "mocking wren" in some places.

In the South it wins favor by its habit of destroying the boll weevil.

The nest is a large structure of grasses, weed stems, and similar rubbish, lined with feathers, fur, and soft vegetable matter. It may be placed in holes in trees, beneath banks, or in accumulations of brushwood. Sometimes it is found in nooks about buildings or in bird houses. The four to six eggs are white or buff spotted with reddish brown.

The Carolina wren ranges from Nebraska and Connecticut to northern Florida and the Gulf coast. The darker Florida wren *(Thryothorus l. miamensis)* is found through Florida.

Cañon Wren

(Catherpes mexicanus)

Average Length, Five and One-half Inches

True to its name, this handsome songster is found about cliffs and rock ledges in cañons, gulches, and steep-walled mountain valleys, usually, but not always, in the vicinity of water. Though it may appear about ranch buildings, it is more abundant in wild areas.

In its native mountain fastnesses, this wren may be picked out against the rocky background by the white, twitching spot of its throat when its head is thrown back in song. Its exuberant melody, which drops down the scale for seven notes and ends with an upward flourish, is rhapsodic and vibrant. The strains are as sunny and free as the tremendous gorges it inhabits. The often repeated tune also has unusual carrying power and, at a distance of a quarter of a mile, there is no blurring or loss of clarity.

Three forms of the cañon wren are found resident from southern British Columbia, Washington, Idaho, and northern Colorado to Baja California and northern Mexico.

Rock Wren

(Salpinctes obsoletus)

Average Length, Five and Three-quarters Inches

In crossing the arid wastes of open mountain slope, mesa, or arroyo in the West, a harshly metallic note may draw attention to a grayish-brown bird that, with tilting body, appears on a stone. This is the rock wren.

Barren granite or lava uplands of the West are enlivened with this bird's saucy bob and shy friendliness. Travelers in dry regions welcome the pert little desert dweller as the sea-weary voyager greets the soaring birds that appear to herald the ship's approach to land.

Its song, a harsh *kra-wee, kra-wee, kra-wee,* first slow and then faster, is a droll and mechanical tinkling but in keeping with the rocky, elemental landscape. The rock wren nests in crevices among rocks and stumps or about buildings. The cavity selected is filled with weeds and grass stems with a softly lined cup for the eggs. These number six to eight, and are white spotted with brown. Frequently bits of stone are laid as a pavement at the nest entrance.

The rock wren *(Salpinctes o. obsoletus)* breeds from southern British Columbia and central Saskatchewan to Baja California and northern Mexico. It winters in the southern part of the breeding range and in Mexico.

Cactus Wren

(Heleodytes brunneicapillus)

Average Length, Five Inches

The cactus wren is one of the characteristic birds of our southwestern deserts. Though normally living in cactus and mesquite thickets and other dense growths, with the coming of our civilization it often has found congenial shelter in palms and shrubbery in towns. The white markings of the long tail are very conspicuous when the bird is in flight.

The nest is a bundle of twigs, thorns and grasses lined with feathers, and this is one of the wrens that often build nests that are not used. These so-called "cock nests" are thought to be built by the industrious male while the female is incubating, perhaps as a means of using up excess energy. Some observers think the extra nests are built as a protective measure, the several unused ones confusing an enemy hunting for the bird's real home.

The cactus wren does not live up to the popular conception of a wren, for it is large and long-tailed, and its harsh, monotonous *chut, chut* bears no resemblance to the typical sweet, bubbling song of its more musical relatives. Four fifths of its food is insects, most of them injurious species.

The cactus wren sings constantly, if rather unmelodiously, throughout the year. The species ranges from the southern part of California, Utah, and Texas south into Mexico.

IN THE WRENS NATURE NEARLY ACHIEVES PERPETUAL MOTION

They seem forever bobbing, bowing, and ludicrously flirting their tail feathers. Singing, they quiver with melody. Less familiar than the bubbling music of the **Eastern** and **Western House Wrens** (upper, left and right) is the "wild, sweet, rhythmical cadence" of the tiny **Winter Wren** (lower left) and the clear song of the **Bewick's Wren** (lower right).

House Wren

(Troglodytes aëdon)
Average Length, Five Inches

The house wren is found from the roadside tangles of honeysuckle along eastern roadways to the quaking aspen groves of our western mountains. Adaptable to changing conditions, it enjoys the shrubbery of our gardens, where it makes itself thoroughly at home exploring flower beds, porches, and the edges of lawns for its food of insects and spiders.

The bird comes without hesitation to the humblest of bird houses. Wrens have been known to build in a tin can, in the brain case of a horse skull hung in a tree, in the pocket of a coat, and in other unusual locations.

A male house wren arriving in a neighborhood proceeds industriously to fill all available cavities with twigs and sticks. When a mate appears, one of the preëmpted sites is selected and a nest lining of softer materials is added to contain the eggs. These range from four to nine in number and are white, thickly spotted with reddish brown and lilac. Two or three broods may be reared in a season. On occasion a male has been known to take two mates in rapid succession and thus to rear two families almost simultaneously.

Although the house wren is an attractive, vivacious little midget, its presence is not always an unmixed blessing for its bird neighbors. On occasion it slips slyly into their nests and with its sharply pointed bill proceeds to puncture the eggs and so destroy them.

The house wren has been the subject of prolonged and detailed study, particularly during the nesting season, by Mr. S. Prentiss Baldwin and his assistants on a country estate at Gates Mills, near Cleveland, Ohio. By means of numbered bands of aluminum Mr. Baldwin has marked the abundant house wrens, so that it has been possible to keep record of many of their activities as individuals. Dozens of nesting boxes have been placed for them, and the work has been extended from year to year until it has covered a wide scope.

It has been popular belief that many birds mate for life and return each year to rear their young in the same neighborhood. With the house wren, however, this proves far from the case. It has been found that though one pair may remain mated for a summer, often they mate with different birds on succeeding years and also change mates frequently for second and third broods of the same season.

The eastern house wren *(Troglodytes a. aëdon)* is found from Michigan, southern Quebec, and New Brunswick to Virginia, North Carolina, and Kentucky. It winters from the Southeastern States to Texas and Tamaulipas. The western house wren *(Troglodytes a. parkmani)* ranges from southern British Columbia and northern Wisconsin south to northern Baja California, southern Arizona, western Texas, and southwestern Kentucky, being casual in Florida and Illinois. It winters from California and Texas to Mexico.

Winter Wren

(Nannus hiemalis)
Average Length, Four Inches

The winter wren, with short tail held at an entirely absurd angle over the back, is seen ordinarily as it bobs up and down nervously on a low perch for an instant before disappearing behind some log, stump, or other cover.

Its song is a beautifully modulated warble of sweet and pleasing tones. Fortunate, indeed, is the bird enthusiast when he may hear this song during migration or, better still, hear it regularly on the breeding grounds.

Two forms of the winter wren breed from the forests of Canada south to the northern United States. In migration they travel south throughout the country. In addition there are seven resident forms in Alaska.

Bewick's Wren

(Thryomanes bewicki)
Average Length, Five Inches

This species suggests the house wren, from which it is easily distinguished by the long tail, with its contrasted light and dark markings, and the prominent light line over the eye. Bewick's wren lives in thickets, tangles of vines, growths of weeds, and similar cover, in which at times it is difficult to discover, so closely does it keep concealed. It is widely adaptable, since it ranges in both arid and humid regions.

The call notes of this wren are harsh, as is usual in the family. The song is beautifully modulated and striking, being given in loud, clear tones that advertise for a long distance the presence of the bird. It is uttered from a more or less elevated perch where the bird rests like a thrasher with hanging tail.

This wren nests in cavities ranging from a hole in a stump to a tin can, the pocket of an old coat, or a pair of overalls hung in a barn. The structure is composed of twigs, weed stems, grass, and rootlets, lined with softer materials. The eggs range from four to seven, occasionally more, and are white, spotted with reddish brown and lilac.

Most of the insects which make up 95 per cent of the food of the Bewick's wren are destructive species.

Seventeen forms of this wren are recognized at present, all but three of which are found in the United States and Baja California. The birds range widely from the North Central States and southern British Columbia southward, being casual in the northeastern section.

THE DIPPER CAN "FLY" UNDER WATER

The curious, wrenlike western **Dipper** (lower), also called the water ouzel, when submerged and hunting aquatic insects or small fish, propels itself with its wings or walks on the bottom. **Long-** and **Short-billed Marsh Wrens** (upper, left and right) build dummy nests which make it difficult for enemies to find the right one. The short-billed form often creeps through grass and sedge like a mouse.

Dipper

(Cinclus mexicanus unicolor)

Average Length, Seven and Three-quarters Inches

The dipper, or water ouzel, finds its chosen haunt about the swift waters of mountain streams, its main requirements being that the water be clear, cold, and unpolluted. Cascades and waterfalls are attractive to it. Though it is usually found along rivers and creeks of fair size, it lives occasionally along little brooks so heavily overhung with bushes that the water is screened from view.

In appearance this curious bird resembles a large wren, for it has a heavy body, large feet, and a short tail, usually carried at an angle above the back.

Follow the streams that form the haunts of the dipper, wading if the current is not too rough and turbulent, and you will soon hear a sharp call that attracts the eye to a gray bird bobbing up and down on some stone. It may walk calmly into the water of shallow pools to pick up aquatic larvæ beneath three feet of water, remaining beneath the surface for half a minute to bob up finally and swim ashore like a little duck; or it may clamber down a bowlder in midstream into the swiftest water to emerge a little later either up- or downstream, apparently unmindful of the current.

The ouzel's secret in this seemingly miraculous under-water progression is in its understanding of the physical laws that govern currents. Through them the bird takes advantage of eddies and projecting stones and logs, in whose shelter it finds quietly moving water.

The plumage is heavy and the ouzel has an abundant coat of under down that acts as a waterproof covering to keep it dry. It flies beneath the surface as readily as in the air and may progress in this manner for 15 or 20 feet.

Added to these lively and interesting habits, the bird has a clear, ringing song that is pleasing and attractive. The ouzel lives through the winter along its chosen streams so long as they are not entirely closed by ice, zero weather not affecting its singing or its diving.

In its food the ouzel eats aquatic insects and larvæ, and small fish.

The nest of the dipper is built of moss, rootlets, and other vegetation, usually placed on a ledge or among roots, where it is kept moist by the beating spray of cascades and waterfalls. The pure-white eggs number from three to five.

The dipper ranges from Alaska to western Alberta, southern California, and southern New Mexico. It has been found accidentally in South Dakota and Nebraska.

The dippers (family Cinclidae) are among the most peculiar of the great order of perching birds. In affinities the group seems near the thrushes and also shows some indication of relationship to the wrens. About 30 forms are known, ranging in Asia and Europe and from the mountains of western North America south through Central America to Argentina. All are closely similar in general form and appearance, though those of the Old World have young with spotted plumage like young thrushes, while in the forms of America the young are plain.

Long-billed Marsh Wren

(Telmatodytes palustris)

Average Length, Five Inches

Enter almost any cattail marsh and you will be greeted by clicking notes resembling the sound made by striking pebbles together. Watch and there will appear a tiny, long-billed bird that clings to the rushes with rapidly bobbing body and tail drawn forward so far over its back that the free end almost seems to touch the head. This is the long-billed marsh wren, its name almost longer than the bird.

The nest is a ball of rush stems and other vegetable matter, lined with plant downs, soft fibers and feathers, with an opening in one side near the top barely large enough to admit one's finger. Not content with one nest, the bird builds several in close proximity, one being finally selected to house the eggs. The rapidity with which the nests may be constructed is truly remarkable, the bird working with a nervous activity that enables it to tug into place masses of vegetation that seem impossibly heavy for it. The eggs number from five to ten and vary from pale brown to dark chocolate, sometimes spotted with darker.

Nine geographic forms are recognized, ranging from New England and Canada to California, the Gulf coast, and Florida. In migration, marsh wrens are found south into Mexico.

Short-billed Marsh Wren

(Cistothorus stellaris)

Average Length, Four Inches

This species prefers wet meadows, where it lives in rank growths of grass and sedges. It is more shy than its relative and few persons become familiar with it.

This wren also delights in constructing dummy nests that are unused and it is often difficult to find those that are actually occupied. The nests are balls of grass and weed stems, each with a small hole in one side, suspended in the tops of grass and sedges. The four to ten eggs are pure white.

Like the long-billed marsh wren, it lives on insects of various kinds and spiders.

This wren nests from southeastern Saskatchewan, southern Ontario, and southern Maine to eastern Kansas and southern Maryland. It winters from southern Illinois and southern New Jersey to Florida and the Gulf coast. It has been found accidentally in Colorado and Wyoming.

BRIGHT CROWNS HAVE EARNED FOR THE KINGLETS THEIR ROYAL NAME

The male **Ruby-crowned Kinglet** (upper left), of sweet song, displays a brilliant head-patch, to charm the unadorned female below. In the **Golden-crowned Kinglet** (upper right, male above, female below) the lord has no such monopoly of color. Perched on twigs below are southern and western relatives of the kinglets, the gnatcatchers. Left to right are the **Blue-gray** and the **Black-tailed Gnatcatchers** (males) and the **Plumbeous Gnatcatcher** (male above, female below). Males often sing their faint but melodious songs while taking their turn on the eggs.

Ruby-crowned Kinglet

(Corthylio calendula)

Average Length, Four and One-quarter Inches

The ruby-crowned kinglet and the golden-crown are among the smallest of the perching birds. They are seen principally in the migration periods or in winter, when they are widely distributed. In the nesting season they retire to mountain areas or forests.

The ruby-crowned kinglet is solitary in habit, associating with others of its kind only when thrown with them during migration flights or when food is abundant.

The song is a rapidly uttered warble with surprising clarity and beauty of tone and a volume astonishing in so small a bird.

Four forms of this kinglet are recognized, ranging from northwestern Alaska and northern Canada southward. In migration they are found throughout the United States and southward into Central America.

Golden-crowned Kinglet

(Regulus satrapa)

Average Length, Four Inches

This kinglet is more social than the ruby-crown, several often being found together in winter. Attention is often drawn to it by its notes, which are so high in pitch that many persons cannot detect them. The song also is high-pitched, ending in a series of warbles.

Both kinglets feed on insects and spiders which they glean expertly from leaves and twigs. Although tiny, the golden-crown can endure considerable cold and does not migrate so far south as the related species.

The globular nest of the golden-crown is suspended in the twigs of a pine or other coniferous tree. It is made of green moss, soft bark, and rootlets, covered with lichens and lined with feathers. The eggs number from eight to ten and are whitish or cream color, spotted with pale brown and lavender.

The eastern golden-crown *(Regulus satrapa satrapa)* nests from central Alberta and southern Quebec to Minnesota, Massachusetts, and the Appalachian Mountains of North Carolina. It winters from Iowa and New Brunswick to Florida and Tamaulipas. The western golden-crown *(Regulus s. olivaceus)*, smaller and brighter, nests from Kodiak Island and the Kenai Peninsula, Alaska, to southern California and New Mexico. It winters from Alaska to the highlands of Mexico.

The ruby-crown is peculiar to North America, but a number of species allied to the golden-crowned kinglet are found in Europe, Asia, and northern Africa. The two best known of the foreign species are the goldcrest *(Regulus regulus)* and the firecrest *(Regulus ignicapillus)*, which, like the American species, derive their names from the brilliant spot of red or orange found in the crown in males.

Blue-gray Gnatcatcher

(Polioptila caerulea)

Average Length, Four and One-half Inches

Gnatcatchers as a group are active and vivacious little birds that move rapidly through the branches, jerking their long tails and drooping their wings in a jaunty, debonair manner. They live in woodlands, sometimes in open groves or thickets, where their small size and soft notes render them inconspicuous.

The song of the gnatcatcher is remarkably pleasing and attractive, but so low that it carries only a few yards to human ears.

The nest of the gnatcatcher is a beautiful cup saddled on a limb, often in a pine tree. Large for the size of the bird, it is made of plant downs, shreds of bark, and soft fibers of several kinds, with the exterior decorated with lichens, so that it resembles a knot on the limb on which it rests. The four or five eggs are greenish white, spotted with reddish brown.

Three forms of this gnatcatcher are found nesting in the area from southern New Jersey, Ontario, Nebraska, and northern California south to the Gulf coast and Mexico. The birds winter in Mexico, Cuba, and the Bahamas, and have been seen often in New England.

Plumbeous and Black-tailed Gnatcatchers

Average Length, Four and One-half Inches

The black-tailed gnatcatchers *(Polioptila melanura californica)* inhabit southern California and northern Baja California.

The plumbeous gnatcatcher *(Polioptila melanura melanura)* is found from southeastern California, southern Nevada, southern Arizona, and the Rio Grande Valley south into Mexico.

About 20 forms of gnatcatchers are known, ranging from the United States south into Argentina. All are tiny-bodied birds with long, slender tails and narrow black bills. The plumage is softly tinted in gray and white, sometimes with markings of black about the head.

The family of true warblers (Sylviidae) to which these birds belong, contains about 600 species, displaying even more variety in color and form than the wood warblers of the New World. Most are insect-feeding forms that live in thickets of shrubbery and open forests, but there are also species specialized for life in marshes and green meadows.

The curious tailor-birds *(Orthotomus)* of India, Ceylon, and Burma are members of this family. These birds make remarkable nests by fastening together the edges of a large leaf or several small ones to form a cornucopia that contains the nest.

In performing this curious feat, the bird punctures the margin of the leaf with its sharp bill, fastens one end of a bit of vegetable floss through the opening from the inside, and then attaches the other end to the opposite side.

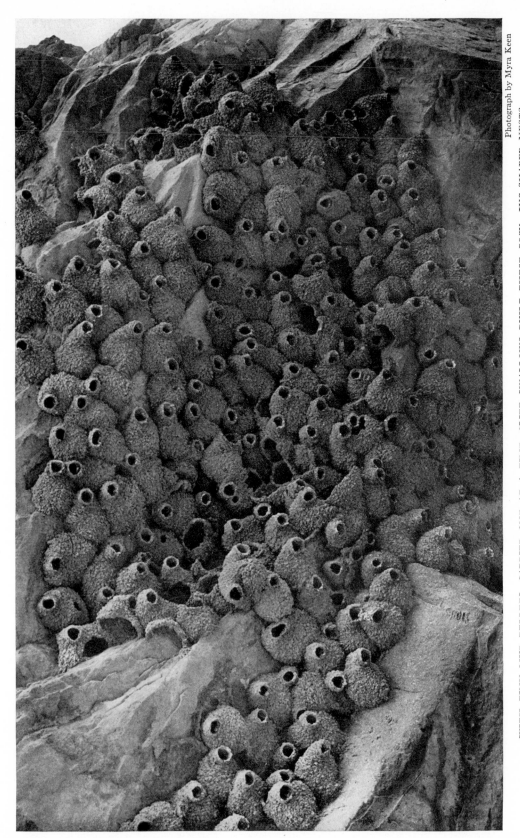

Photograph by Myra Keen

WITH TINY MUD PELLETS, CARRIED ONE AT A TIME, CLIFF SWALLOWS BUILT THESE COZY, JUG-SHAPED NESTS

Some of the occupants are peeping out. Clever architects, they make the entrances only large enough to admit the owners, and point the holes downward to keep out rain. This colony has utilized a shallow cave near Colorado Springs. In the East the birds often settle under eaves, thus earning the name eave swallows.

THRUSHES, SWEET-VOICED FAVORITES

Robins and Bluebirds are Familiar Members of a Famous Musical Family Which Includes the Hermit Thrush and European Nightingale

By T. Gilbert Pearson

AT four o'clock one afternoon in January, 1931, a group of men stood on a low hillside in the southern United States and watched robins as they came in countless flocks to roost in a far-stretching titi thicket below them.

It was a stimulating sight, for as the day waned the number of birds increased to amazing proportions. In every direction the sky was filled with streaming clouds of robins, all converging toward the swamp. Tens of thousands were arriving every minute, and the flight continued until dark.

"A noise very much like the sound of the surf was made by the birds' wings when they settled down to roost," wrote one observer.

The men on the hillside were joined by others until, when darkness fell, about two hundred were assembled. The company now moved from its point of observation and surrounded a large area of trees and low bushes where myriads of sleepy robins were crowded on limbs and twigs.

With torches and flashlights, the men pushed their way into the thicket, and, with sticks and stout clublike branches of trees, began to beat from their perches the light-blinded and bewildered birds. Many were killed, others injured, and still others captured unhurt to be put to death by the pressure of a ruthless thumb and consigned to the sacks the men carried.

GAME WARDENS FIND OUT WHO KILLED COCK ROBIN

Such massacres had been going on at this Alabama winter roost for robins for some time, undisturbed. But suddenly a cry arose, a cry taken up and passed from man to man throughout the fifty-acre swamp. It was a new sound in a Crenshaw County robin roost: "Game Wardens!"

Guiltily the men worked their way out of the titi bushes and began to hurry away in all directions. There were only two

wardens, but they succeeded in stopping 42 of the robin killers. The majority of those arrested had thrown away their sacks of birds, but from the few captured the wardens dumped 375 dead robins, which were confiscated and given to the local poorhouses and to a hospital, to be cooked for the inmates.

It has not been very many years since there were no robin protection laws in the Southern States. In fact, for a long time after the settlement of what is now the United States the robin was regarded as a game bird that might be killed at any time of year and in any manner.

MASSACHUSETTS TAKES THE LEAD

The first State to pass a law for the protection of the robin was Massachusetts, which in 1818 made it a misdemeanor to kill robins during a period of four months and four days each year. After July 4, however, and until March 1 of the following year, this early law provided, they might be taken at any time.

Virginia was the first State south of the Potomac River to prohibit the killing of robins. After two years of strenuous effort by the Audubon Association, a petition with 10,000 signatures was presented to the State Legislature and a law was passed on March 1, 1912.

Widely in the United States and Canada, the robin is the best-known and most popular of all wild birds, and its arrival in spring is hailed with joy. Its song at dawn is the first note of the day to millions of ears.

But over vast areas of the Southland robins are known only as winter residents. They neither probe the lawns for worms nor sing in the gardens. In scattered flocks they frequent the open pine woods or run about on the ground where the wire grass has been recently burned. They come about plantation houses and negro cabins,

Photograph by A. A. Allen

A FAMILIAR SILHOUETTE

The barn swallow is well known to many farmers, for it likes to nest inside barns and other farm buildings.

and feed on the half-dried berries hanging in clusters from the China trees.

At this season robins grow fat and are easy to secure, so to many a southern boy comes the temptation to shoot a string of them to take home for his mother to cook in a stew or robin pie.

It may surprise some old friends of the robin to learn that the redbreast belongs to the family of thrushes. But students of anatomy, who have a gift for studying feathers, dissecting muscles, and measuring bones, long ago agreed that in many cases birds of quite different sizes and colors may in reality be very closely related.

Furthermore, if it is true that from the embryo to the adult stage an animal recapitulates the history of its race, we may feel ourselves to be witnesses of one stage in the robin's evolution when we see the young ones just out of the nest with their breasts spotted in true thrush fashion.

COLONISTS FOUND A "BLUE ROBIN"

This characteristic of the young is shared by another cherished bird companion—the bluebird—which also is a member of the illustrious and musical family of thrushes.

The English people who first settled in Massachusetts found coming about their gardens a little bird which in size, form, and movements reminded them of the "Cock Robin" that the sparrow claimed to have killed with his bow and arrow.

There was one very noticeable difference, however. Whereas the English robin has an olive-brown back, this bird wore a mantle of blue. So the newcomers named it "blue robin." Today we call it bluebird.

We have three distinct species in North America—the eastern, the mountain, and the western bluebirds. The eastern, or common, bluebird occupies most of the country from the Rocky Mountains to Labrador and Florida. Like our robin, it inhabits cities and open farmland country, orchards and woodlots, and keeps away, generally, from dense forests.

Its song is pleasing, its demeanor gentle, and its coloring so attractive that almost everyone enjoys having it near. Hundreds of thousands of nesting boxes have been erected for its accommodation and that of its friends.

THREE WIVES IN A SINGLE SEASON

The first box I put up for bluebirds, nailed to a white-oak tree in the yard, soon contained four blue eggs, and incubation began promptly. But one night calamity came in the form of a neighbor's cat, which crept into the yard, climbed the tree, and thrust a long arm into the box entrance. Dawn disclosed the feathers of the female bluebird scattered about the lawn.

When the male discovered that his mate was not in the box, he began to call loudly for her return, and his anxiety increased with the passing hours. He was very unhappy; in fact, the whole day was ruined for him.

But the very next morning another female came to console him. Evidently the two reached an understanding, for about 11 o'clock we saw her go into the nesting box to look things over.

As a precaution, this time I suspended the box from the limb with a foot of wire, after first removing the ill-fated first wife's eggs and the nesting material.

A new nest was at once begun; eggs were laid and the female began to sit. But once again trouble came. The cat climbed the tree, got onto that swinging box somehow, and pulled the bird from the eggs. Fresh bluebird feathers with chewed wing tips were found in the grass the next morning.

Now the male had still greater cause for lamentation than before, if we may judge by the fact that 11 days elapsed before he could find a third mate. Two things remain to be told: first, that the cat suddenly died and, second, that five young bluebirds were raised in the yard that spring.

The nest is always made in a cavity—in a bird box if there is one handy; if not, a hole in an old apple tree or in a fence post appears to be just as acceptable. One spring, while on a motor trip, I found at least a dozen bluebird nests in mail boxes fastened to posts along the country roads.

Nesting cavities made by woodpeckers are generally abandoned after one season's occupancy, and these attract bluebirds. Holes made by redheaded woodpeckers I have found to be particularly to their liking. The entrances are sufficiently large to admit a bluebird's body, but are small enough to keep out a sparrow hawk or a screech owl, and this is an important consideration in localities where these birds of prey are numerous. The flicker's nesting hole is accessible to either of these enemies, and this may be the reason it is rarely used by bluebirds.

Woodpeckers lay their eggs on fine chips of wood which are left in the hole when it is being constructed, but such a simple arrangement does not suit the bluebirds. Before laying their eggs, they line the bottom of the cavity with an ample supply of dry grasses.

Photograph by S. A. Grimes

GROCERIES FOR THE FAMILY DINNER

Grasshoppers are a favorite "course" on the eastern bluebird's menu. The nest cavity is a "used" one. A hairy woodpecker built it in Florida, then moved on, leaving an apartment for other dwellers. Imitation woodpecker's holes, drilled in logs by bird lovers, often attract bluebirds and other feathered guests.

COUSINS OF THE NIGHTINGALE

In North America there are 17 species and exactly the same number of subspecies of the family of thrushes (Turdidae) to which the robin and the bluebird belong. All of them are singing birds, and the exquisite flutelike notes of the thrushes are the most beautiful of all the sounds that come from the avian chorus. The European nightingale, immortalized by poets, is a thrush, and, on this side of the Atlantic, Nature offers few if any sweeter songs than the vesper music of the hermit thrush.

Along the north rim of the Grand Canyon in Arizona stretches for many miles a high plateau known as the Kaibab. It is clothed with a coniferous forest and is inhabited by perhaps the most famous wild deer herd in America. The region is a Government game preserve, and, when overbrowsing threatened to bring starvation to the tens of thousands of deer roaming

Photograph Courtesy National Association of Audubon Societies

PURPLE MARTINS TAKE TO A VILLAGE OF HOLLOW GOURDS

These birds like to nest in cavities, which they line with weeds, straw, rags, or any other material at hand. In the West, where gourds or man-made boxes are not often available, they find homes in hollows of trees, in cliffs, or even between rocks.

liquid notes were repeated over and over again. These men in their daily lives deal with the problems of wild life and forest preservation in their most practical aspects. No one could call them sentimentalists, yet for a few minutes they seemed completely under the spell of those enchanting notes.

One summer my tent stood in a white-pine grove beside a lake in the Adirondacks. One evening, after we had cooked and eaten our supper, we sat on the lake shore and listened to the song of a hermit thrush, coming with great clearness across the water from the farther shore, a quarter of a mile away.

The little boys from the city, exasperatingly indifferent to many of the sights and sounds of the forest, seemed really interested in the song of this bird. I fondly dreamed that this, the most gifted of all our sylvan musicians, might awaken in them some interest which would in time lead them to become students of ornithology. But maybe they were only tired and sleepy when they sat so still during the vesper service of that wonderful songster of the wilderness.

the forest, some two dozen men representing conservation organizations, natural history societies, and Federal agencies were assembled to see what could be done about it.

One day these men were clustered about some shrubbery which they were examining.

"Listen!" said one of them suddenly.

The clarion notes of a hermit thrush were quivering in the air.

Until the song was finished everyone stood gazing toward the unseen singer, while its

WOODLANDS RING WITH FLUTELIKE MUSIC

Only the favored few may hear the hermit, a true dweller of the deep woods. But far more familiar is the song of the wood thrush. In spring the groves and woodlands from South Dakota to the Atlantic coast ring with its unhurried musical *ee-o-lee*. At dawn its call brings cheer to the new day. In the evening it soothes like a benediction.

In the strains of the wood thrush some bird lovers have noted resemblances to a part of Faust's appeal to Marguerite in Gounod's opera. Others have found suggestions of musical phrases from Weber and Handel.

Along watercourses, where trees are tall and where ferns and skunk cabbages grow, the wood thrush loves to sing. "Swamp robin" is one of the names by which it is known. While much more shy and retiring than the robin, the wood thrush, like it, nevertheless comes to well-shaded parks and to the outskirts of towns and cities where large trees have been left standing. It is an inhabitant of deciduous woods, usually stopping short at the edge of evergreen forests.

The nest is often made in a three-forked upright shoot of a sturdy sapling. Again, it may be saddled on some horizontal bough, with its sides supported by two or more twigs, or may rest in

Photograph by A. A. Allen

BANK SWALLOWS MANEUVER LIKE TINY COMBAT PLANES

They eat their dinners on the wing, swooping and diving to catch flying insects. Bank swallows are so called because they excavate tunnel-like homes by burrowing two or three feet into the side of a sand bank or gravel bed.

grapevines growing thickly over some stalwart bush. A little mud or vegetable mold of decayed forest trees usually gives form to the interior of the nest and, when dried, adds to its firmness. Large dead leaves are much used and, now and then, scraps of paper are employed.

Once I saw a photograph of a wood thrush's nest from which plainly protruded the end of a five-dollar bank note.

The wood thrush is not one of the earliest birds to engage in nest-building.

In New York City studies were made of the time when birds begin to nest in that region. They showed that the first bird to begin egg-laying was the great horned owl, on February 28, and the last was the goldfinch, on June 20. The wood thrush, fifty-second on the list, was ready to begin the incubation of its eggs on May 17, or 27 days later than the first robins.

Since the incubation of robins' eggs is complete in 14 days, and since the young remain in the nest only two weeks, it may very well be that on the day a wood thrush begins to incubate she will hear the anxious call notes of her robin neighbor, whose young have just left the nest.

Robin

(Turdus migratorius)
Average Length, Ten Inches

This red-breasted, handsome member of the thrush family is in many respects America's outstanding bird citizen. In numbers it is impressive, in personality more so. To the North it comes as a herald of spring.

Deep woods are not to the robin's liking, and the clearing of forests has caused it to increase greatly in numbers.

To be sure, cherry raisers in New Jersey and strawberry growers in Florida cry out against the robin's love for fruit, and obtain State and Federal permits to shoot the marauders. Yet among Americans as a whole the robin is a cherished friend.

The robin's song is often heard before a rain, in the early morning and evening, and during the nesting season at almost any hour of the day. A cheerful warble made up of ascending and descending phrases, it sounds as if the singer were breathlessly repeating *cheerily cheerily cheerily cheerily*, with the syllables rather badly slurred. Other familiar utterances include loud calls of distress and alarm raised when a prowling cat threatens the young, a fighting cry, and a *tut-tut* note delivered with a bob of the tail as the robin flies up into a tree.

Soon after their early morning concert robins are seen on the lawn, busily hunting earthworms. Brisk and businesslike, they stop suddenly, erect and motionless, then pounce upon their slippery prey. They also eat quantities of noxious insects.

A good home-maker, the robin builds a workmanlike nest which may be found at almost any distance from the ground about houses or in trees. It is a thick bowl of mud held together with blades of grass, reinforced with leaves and weed stalks, and lined with soft grasses. In shaping the mud shell, the mother bird uses her breast, turning around and around. The eggs are so striking that they have given their name to a color.

The robin has many natural enemies— snakes, jays, crows, hawks, owls, and others. In an aspen grove on a sagebrush-covered mountainside in Utah, I found a robin's nest about three feet from the ground. In it a wren was busying itself making small punctures in the blue eggs.

Robins make their nests and rear their young as far north as the tree limits of Alaska and Labrador. In winter the more northern birds move to the Central and especially the Southern States; but some safely winter in the North, even in cold, snowy central and western New York State, living in swamps, thickets, or gullies and feeding on wild berries.

Five varieties are recognized—the eastern robin *(T. m. migratorius)*; southern robin *(T. m. achrusterus)*; northwestern robin *(T.*

m. caurinus); western robin *(T. m. propinquus)*; and San Lucas robin *(T. m. confinis)*. Their songs are very similar and their food and nesting habits vary only to the extent that might naturally be expected of a species inhabiting such a wide variety of regions.

American robins have been introduced into England and have become established there.

Townsend's Solitaire

(Myadestes townsendi)
Average Length, Eight and Three-quarters Inches

A tuneful resident of the Far West is this gray bird with its white eye rings and white outer tail feathers that flash when it darts about. As its name indicates, it is a shy lover of lonely places. It makes its home along steep mountain slopes and gorges from Alaska to Mexico and eastward to the Black Hills.

The solitaire is about the size of the catbird, which it somewhat resembles. It weighs about one and a half ounces.

Although undoubtedly allied to the thrushes and possessing some of their habits, particularly that of running on the ground and stopping suddenly like a robin, the solitaire also reminds one of a flycatcher. When it darts after a passing insect and promptly returns to its lookout perch, its movements suggest kinship to the phoebe.

A gifted singer, it pours forth its notes in the clear mountain air with a gushing spontaneity that suggests the mockingbird.

Its food, during the warm part of the year, consists mainly of insects. In winter it resorts to wild berries growing on vines or on deciduous and coniferous trees.

Many of these birds winter south of their summer range, although some remain as far north as British Columbia.

Varied Thrush

(Ixoreus naevius)
Average Length, Nine and One-half Inches

In the Puget Sound region of Washington one may hear the banded robin, known as the varied thrush, singing its single, long-drawn note in the autumn when other birds have lapsed into silence.

In summer the varied thrush inhabits chiefly heavily forested regions where fogs are frequent and the foliage is often dripping. It breeds along the Pacific from northern Alaska to northern California, and winters from southern Alaska to southern California.

The nest, built in sturdy saplings or trees of medium height, is composed of twigs, grasses, and moss. The greenish eggs, three and sometimes four, are sparingly decorated with spots of varying shades of brown.

The birds feed upon insects, worms, berries, and mast, all of which are generally gathered from the ground. In winter they may gather in flocks of thousands.

PERKY BUSYBODY OF OUR LAWNS IS THE ROBIN

Millions know the note of the sociable red-breasted **Robin** (lower, young right), a true thrush, whose bright waistcoat is a cheerful contrast to the first green buds of the year. This beloved harbinger of spring, now generally protected, formerly was killed by the thousands as a game bird. The eastern variety is pictured here. A highland dweller is the sweet-voiced **Townsend's Solitaire** (upper left), distinguished by white eye rings and light markings on wings and tail feathers. Misty woodlands are the haunts of the **Varied Thrush** (upper right, with young), another western relative of the robin.

Wood Thrush
(Hylocichla mustelina)
Average Length, Eight and One-quarter Inches

Some of the thrushes are difficult for the bird student to name with certainty, but the wood thrush stands out as a conspicuous exception. Its breast and sides are thickly sprinkled with round black spots, instead of the short bars or stripes of the other thrushes.

Furthermore, this is a large thrush, although smaller than a robin. It is a little more than eight inches long and has a wingspread of 13 inches, being thus about two inches shorter than a robin and three inches smaller as measured from tip to tip of the wings.

These birds nest from South Dakota and Maine to eastern Texas and northern Florida. In the District of Columbia they appear shortly after the middle of April, filling the parks with their music. After rearing their young, they depart southward in October.

Olive-backed Thrush
(Hylocichla ustulata swainsoni)
Average Length, Seven and One-quarter Inches

This little traveler is one of the few species whose journeys twice a year extend over much of the length of the two Americas. In the extremity of its range it makes a round-trip pilgrimage of more than 17,000 miles.

The majority of people who look for the olive-backed thrush see it only as a migrant. In spring in the New York region we expect it to appear during the second week of May and to depart by the last of the month. At that time it is returning from its winter sojourn in southern Mexico or perhaps even as far south as Argentina.

In autumn I look again for the migrating olive-backs near my home and usually find some of them between the middle of September and the fifteenth of October.

This thrush breeds from Alaska and Newfoundland to northern California and New York, and in the mountains to West Virginia.

In the Pacific coast country from Alaska to southern California this form is replaced by a subspecies called the russet-backed thrush (H. u. ustulata).

Gray-cheeked Thrush
(Hylocichla minima aliciae)
Average Length, Seven and One-half Inches

So closely does this species resemble the olive-backed thrush that only a most experienced observer may be expected to tell members of the two groups apart, when perchance they both appear in the shrubbery of the lawn or garden in the course of their seasonal visits. The slightly more pronounced eye-ring of the olive-back is the mark by which a beginner in bird study may most readily distinguish it from its gray-cheeked relative.

The breeding range of the gray-cheeked thrush is a narrow strip of country just below the northern tree limit, extending from Labrador to Alaska and northeastern Siberia. Bicknell's thrush (H. m. minima), a smaller relative, nests from Nova Scotia to western Massachusetts. (See page 182.)

Hermit Thrush
(Hylocichla guttata)
Average Length, Seven and One-half Inches

If you come upon a thrush which has a tail noticeably browner than the rest of its plumage, mark it well, for you have seen the famous hermit thrush.

A true hermit, the sweetest singer among all the thrushes dwells in deep and somewhat swampy woods and seems eager to elude the notice of humans who may, perchance, invade its solitudes. Because of the marvelous quality of its music it has been called "American nightingale."

In summer the hermit thrush inhabits much of North America from central Alaska to California and in the East from southern Quebec to the mountains of Virginia. It is divided into seven subspecies.

Veery
(Hylocichla fuscescens fuscescens)
Average Length, Seven and One-half Inches

There is great charm in the silvery notes of the veery. The song begins strongly and diminishes in volume as it proceeds. It has the peculiar effect of a continuous flow of melody whirling rapidly downward along some invisible spiral cord. This song is given at all times of day, but it is especially noticeable in the early morning and late evening.

One summer, finding myself in a region where veeries were singing all about the camp, I determined to find a nest—a task of no mean difficulty. After three days of fruitless search, I telegraphed a friend who knew the bird well, and asked for help.

"Nest on or near the ground," he replied.

I already knew this much from the bird books. What I wanted to know was in what kind of places I should look.

After two weeks of daily search I found a nest with four young, but not entirely through my own efforts. It was pointed out to me by a red-eyed vireo. She led me to it by her querulous notes as she sat on a low limb overhead, shouting anathemas at the four youthful heads that were raised repeatedly in the hope of being fed. The nest was on the ground.

The veery breeds from Michigan and Quebec to the mountains of northern Georgia and in winter travels to Colombia, British Guiana, or Brazil. The willow thrush (H. f. salicicola), a darker form, ranges from British Columbia and Wisconsin to northern New Mexico, in winter going to South America.

THEIR SONG REPERTOIRE IS AS VARIED AS THEIR DRESS IS DRAB

With drop-shaped spots of brownish-black, the discreet **Wood Thrush** (center) is the handsomest of the clan. Its delightful trill suggests certain refrains of classic composers. One student estimated that an **Olive-backed Thrush** (upper left) sang 4,360 times daily during its spring concert. The somber **Gray-cheeked Thrush** (upper right) sings endlessly in the short far-northern summer. The ascending song of the elusive **Hermit Thrush** (lower left) is heard in northern or mountain forests. In eastern woodlands the shy **Veery**, carrying a grub for its young beside it, whistles a resonant note.

Eastern Bluebird

(Sialia sialis sialis)

Average Length, Seven Inches

Perhaps no other feathered resident has a firmer hold upon human affections than the gentle, lovable bluebird.

Its arrival from the South is made known by a delicate, purling warble with a wistful refrain that seems to say, "Dear, dear, think of it, think of it." Soft and low comes the two-syllabled answer of the female.

They are even better prophets of spring than the robins, for far fewer bluebirds winter in the North. After passing the summer in the Northern States and the south-central and eastern Provinces of Canada, most of them spend the winter in the States below the Potomac and the Ohio Rivers. At this season they are scattered all over the region and are readily seen. One cold day last year I counted 22 of them at one time.

When a bitter cold storm sweeps the country several bluebirds may seek shelter for the night in the same cavity of a tree. In 1895, when sleet covered much of the South for many days and greatly reduced the bluebird population of our country, I knew of eight dead ones that were removed from a single woodpecker's nesting hole.

In their conjugal relations bluebirds are devoted, as befits a bird which has come to be a symbol of happiness.

From a purely practical standpoint it is highly desirable to attract bluebirds to the garden and orchard. Throughout the summer they may be seen killing cutworms whenever they can find them. Caterpillars of many varieties also are in danger when the gentle bluebird is in the neighborhood. It helps, too, when outbreaks of cankerworms occur. During the year a fourth of the bluebird's food consists of grasshoppers. In autumn and winter various wild berries are eaten. A subspecies, the azure bluebird, is found from southern Arizona to Vera Cruz, Mexico.

Western Bluebird

(Sialia mexicana)

Average Length, Six and Three-quarters Inches

Unlike the eastern bluebird, this beautiful species is no singer. Its few twitterings are in no way comparable to the sweet warble of its relative.

Like the eastern species, however, the western form often raises two or more broods in a season. There is an authentic record of a pair building six nests one year, in each of which six eggs were laid. This unusual happening, however, was brought about by the egg-collecting habits of an oölogist who systematically robbed the birds.

In the United States there are two varieties of this bluebird. The better-known type (S.

m. occidentalis) breeds from British Columbia to western Montana and south through California. It winters in the southern parts of its range and in Baja California. The other variety is the chestnut-backed bluebird (S. m. bairdi), which is known to occur in summer from Utah and central Texas southward to Durango and Zacatecas.

Mountain Bluebird

(Sialia currucoides)

Average Length, Seven and One-quarter Inches

Late one afternoon a number of us gladly dismounted from our horses by the side of the Snake River where it goes rushing on its way through western Wyoming. The unstrapping of saddle- and pack-horses had begun when, looking up along the rough trail by which we had descended from Two Ocean Pass, I caught sight of a bird that flew to the side of a dead tree and disappeared.

With blankets scattered about and my tepee not yet erected, I deserted camp and soon found a pair of mountain bluebirds carrying food into an old woodpecker hole. I stayed and watched that nest until sundown. The plumage of the male was a most exquisite cerulean and reminiscent of certain shades seen in the waters of the bay of Nassau, or in the Blue Grotto of Capri.

As I watched him flying about, I found myself pitying certain eastern bird lovers who were not there to thrill at the sight of the gentle and amazingly colored bird of this faraway wilderness. The mountain bluebird breeds from southern Yukon Territory and North Dakota to the Mexican border.

Catbird

(Dumetella carolinensis)

Average Length, Nine Inches

The catbird is one of the most common and best-known feathered inhabitants of southern Canada and the United States. Except for a black crown and chestnut under-tail coverts, it is slate-colored both above and below.

Because of its inconspicuous coloring and slinking habits, the catbird is far more often heard than seen. Its plaintive *mew* is uttered in the shrubbery of the lawn, the vines in the gardens, and the thickets in fields and along fence rows. Its song is rich, varied, and prolonged, and usually is produced when the performer is well hidden in thick foliage.

Besides being a very entertaining bird to have about the premises, the catbird is also a valuable one, destroying numbers of injurious insects. Its taste for domestic fruit is pronounced, as strawberry raisers attest.

The catbird's bulky nest is concealed in vines or thick bushes. It is composed of twigs, leaves, rootlets, and often fragments of soft bark stripped from cedar trees. The eggs, usually four in number, are dark green.

BRILLIANTLY ATTIRED BLUEBIRDS ANNOUNCE SPRING'S ARRIVAL

In gay costume the **Eastern Bluebird** (upper group, male, young, and female) follows the robin north to "pipe in" warm weather. Devoted "family man," the bluebird often lodges in a box placed among fruit trees by the wise orchardist who knows his feathered guests will feed on injurious insects. The **Western Bluebird,** perched outside its home, with the female about to carry in grass for the nest, is marked by reddish back as well as breast. The striking cerulean blue of the **Mountain Bluebird** (center right, female right) is seen in the West. The slinking of the drab **Catbird** (below) through thickets is even more feline than its "mew."

Mockingbird

(Mimus polyglottos)

Average Length, Ten and One-half Inches

Few birds devote so much of their time to song as does the mockingbird. I have noted individuals which, it seemed to me, would literally have sung all day had they not deemed it necessary to pause frequently to chase away other birds that came too near to suit them. They did relatively little food hunting.

Furthermore, they sang for half the night, especially when the moon was shining. They had tales of love to tell, and, like the Ancient Mariner, they had to speak right on. Mockingbirds sing not only in spring but in summer and even on pleasant winter days. No other bird pours forth such a torrent of notes.

If asked to choose my favorite bird, I should name offhand the mockingbird, for I hold many memories of his glorious song in Chevy Chase, Atlanta, New Orleans, Pasadena, and a thousand rural districts.

These expert mimics are dependable danger alarms for other birds, warning them of danger's approach by sounding sharp alarm notes. Full of curiosity, they are much in evidence in our southeastern city gardens, lawns and parks where they seem to take a great interest in "the passing show." Thickets and hedges are their favorite nesting sites and in such places, usually within ten feet of the ground, the structure of twigs and weed stalks lined with rootlets, moss and cotton is built. Their pale bluish-green eggs, four to six in number, are freckled with red-brown spots.

Mockingbirds are not migratory; any wanderings by individuals are of short duration and, of course, are made in quest of a more readily acquired food supply.

The eastern mockingbird ranges from Iowa and Maryland to Florida and eastern Texas; western mockingbirds *(M. p. leucopterus)* are found from central California and western Kansas to Vera Cruz and Cape San Lucas.

Sage Thrasher

(Oreoscoptes montanus)

Average Length, Eight and One-half Inches

It has been my good fortune to meet the sage thrasher now and then in its summer home in the sagebrush country of the West, and one December day I found it in the chaparral of south Texas.

Several miles north of the Enchanted Mesa of New Mexico the pueblo of Laguna has basked in the sunshine for centuries. From the adobe buildings a path worn deep in the rock leads to a water hole of uncertain attractiveness. There, where moccasined feet have long trodden, I first saw the sage thrasher.

With elevated tail it ran along the ground, pausing at intervals to raise its wings in mockingbird fashion. But for its spotted breast it might have passed for a mockingbird, so closely did its form and movements resemble those of that famous songster. It is a gifted musician and its impassioned singing is heard in spring over high reaches in the Far West.

For food the sage thrasher depends chiefly on insects, but it does not hesitate to visit gardens in search of berries or grapes.

The nest is placed in low bushes and the four or five green eggs are covered with large brown blotches.

The summer home of the sage thrasher extends from British Columbia to central California and eastward to the border of Nebraska. It winters from southern California and central Texas southward through northern Mexico.

Curve-billed Thrasher

(Toxostoma curvirostre)

Average Length, Eleven Inches

The curve-billed thrasher and its two associated subspecies, Palmer's thrasher *(T. c. palmeri)* and the Brownsville thrasher *(T. c. oberholseri)*, inhabit the warmer arid regions of southern Texas, New Mexico, Arizona, and northern Mexico. They are all birds of the sagebrush, cactus, and mesquite countries.

Brown Thrasher

(Toxostoma rufum)

Average Length, Eleven and One-half Inches

This is the "merry brown thrush" of our childhood books. But it is not a thrush. It is too brown; its tail is too long; and its eyes are bright yellow and not dark brown. It is a famous singer and by many is regarded as a close second to the mockingbird.

The name "thrasher" probably derives from its habit of emphasizing its joy or anger with strong, twitching movements of the strikingly long tail. It is possessed of extraordinary courage in defense of its nest and young and will boldly fly at the head of an intruder.

Wherever trees are intermingled with shrubbery, especially if vines or briar tangles are present, there is a good chance of finding the brown thrasher. It prefers dry uplands to swamps or the borders of ponds and streams.

The brown thrasher usually appears in the Northern States and southern Canada from the sixth to the fifteenth of April and departs in October for its winter home in the southeastern States and Texas. Throughout much of its range it is abundant, and, since it has a voracious appetite and provides well for its brood, the insects it destroys are countless. It consumes ants, thousand-legs, beetles, grasshoppers, and no end of caterpillars. It also feeds to an extent on grain, fruit, and berries. The bulky nest with its spotted eggs is hidden in thick vines or bushes.

The brown thrasher is found from Alberta and Maine to Louisiana and Florida. It winters from Missouri and North Carolina south.

A VERSATILE MIMIC IS THE MOCKINGBIRD

The wheelbarrow's squeak, the rooster's crow, the postman's whistle—all are within the vocal range of the **Mockingbird** (upper right and flying). No less brave than talented, it attacks other birds, cats, dogs, and even men who molest its nest. The **Sage Thrasher** (upper left), songster of western mesas and plains, also is gifted in song but is heard less often than its mimicking cousin. In the Southwest lives the **Curve-billed Thrasher** (lower left). Often incorrectly called a thrush is the **Brown Thrasher** (lower right), an accomplished singer.

THRASHERS, MOCKINGBIRDS, AND SWALLOWS

By T. Gilbert Pearson

LIKE the thrushes, the members of the family Mimidae, or thrashers and mockingbirds, are gifted singers. This distinctly American group is composed of more than 60 species, of which 11 species and three subspecies are found in the United States. They include such favorite vocalists as the catbird, the brown thrasher, and the world-famous mockingbird.

The rollicksome outpouring of the mockingbird's song constitutes one of the most amazing vocal performances in the bird world. In my opinion, it and the hermit thrush are unquestionably the two outstanding songbirds of the Western Hemisphere.

Mockingbirds are especially abundant in the South Atlantic States, where at times one may hear the voices of half a dozen singing at once.

When the hermit thrush feels the impulse to sing, it mounts to some limb, and, as a rule, remains stationary while it devotes its entire attention to the business in hand. The mockingbird takes its singing much less seriously. It may begin its song on the top of a tree, a fence post, or a chimney, but is easily diverted if it notices something of interest on the lawn or if a neighboring mockingbird invades the particular area to which it has laid claim. After inspecting the object which had looked palatable or chasing its rival a short distance, it returns to its perch, often resuming its song while still on the wing.

There is infinite variety in the mockingbird's singing. The long-tailed black-white-and-gray minstrel produces an astonishing series of notes, some of these but rarely, others repeated over and over again, and all coming with such easy abandon that at times one may wonder if the bird is actually conscious that it is singing.

Sometimes it rises for many feet, and with dangling legs drops again to its perch without interrupting the song that flows forth unceasingly. At times it will sing in tree or brush, hopping from limb to limb.

The mockingbird's scientific name, *Mimus polyglottos,* meaning "mimic of many tongues," is a correct characterization of numerous individuals. I have heard them give with precision the mewing cry of a catbird and the plaintive, staccato nesting call of a sparrow hawk. Almost any bird of the neighborhood may be mimicked in such a way as to deceive the unaccustomed ear.

Especially famous is the singing of these birds on quiet, moonlight nights, when they utter tones which, it would seem, could come only from the spirit land. What would a Florida orange grove be, even in full blossom, without the roundelay of a mockingbird?

Brown thrashers sing much as do the mockingbirds, although the music comes less spontaneously and lacks a certain power of appeal. In a land where the mockingbird was not found, the brown thrasher might well assume the role of the Caruso of the region, but not otherwise.

SWALLOWS OF A FEATHER FLOCK TOGETHER

Swallows are useful and gentle little birds that twitter rather than sing, and many of them prefer to spend much of their time flying about near the homes of men. They are gregarious in habits, large numbers often being found associated together. They feed wholly upon insects which they capture while on the wing.

Thirteen species of the swallow family (Hirundinidae), with five additional subspecies, have been recorded in our country.

The purple martin is the largest member of the group, and, although it is eight inches in length and has a wingspread of almost 16 inches, it would take nearly a dozen of them to weigh one pound!

In spring and summer purple martins inhabit much of North America and are abundant especially in the Southeastern States. They may be attracted easily by erecting a pole hung with a number of gourds or topped by a many-roomed bird box.

Any farmer will tell you that martins will keep hawks away from the chickens. This belief is entirely accurate, for martins defend their homes courageously and will drive hawks or crows from the neighborhood.

Before the coming of the white man purple martins must have used hollow trees as nesting places, a habit to which they still revert on occasion. In a wooded park at Devils Lake, North Dakota, and again near a railway station in eastern Texas, I found small colonies using a large, partly dead tree, the decayed wood of which had been tunneled in a haphazard manner by woodpeckers.

In the pine and palmetto woods twenty miles south of Fort Myers, Florida, I dismounted from my horse at noon one day for lunch. While the guide fried the bacon I examined six pine trees which appeared to have been killed by a single stroke of lightning. Five of them contained holes originally made by flickers. One of these was occupied by a Florida grackle's nest and three others were inhabited by purple martins.

Two martins were carrying straw up to the fifth hole, but as often as they came they were met at the entrance by an array of daggerlike bills. In a few days the young flickers would depart, so in the end the hole may have become the abode of the persistent home-seeking martins.

MARTINS SEEK ODD PLACES FOR NESTS

In Bismarck, North Dakota, I found martins nesting under the eaves of a building on the busiest corner of the town, and in Seattle I watched them carrying nest material to holes left in the side of a recently constructed warehouse. Once I discovered a pair feeding their young in the hood of one of the electric arc lamps at that time lighting the thoroughfares of Plant City, Florida.

Immediately after the close of the nesting season martins assemble in flocks and often establish their roosts in towns, where their numbers, increasing daily, grow into huge proportions. They frequently become a public nuisance as difficult to cope with as the starlings.

Many people living in Atlanta can recall the great martin roosts in the trees bordering one of the residential streets. For several weeks every summer they were a decided annoyance to inhabitants of the neighborhood and to those who had occasion to pass along the street at night. In 1926 two policemen one evening shot into the dense mass of the roosting birds and killed more than four hundred of them, but despite this onslaught the rest remained.

For some years there was such a roost in a grove in Greensboro, North Carolina. One evening I went to the top of a tall building and watched the great hosts arriving for more than an hour. My estimate was 200,000 birds and this I believe to be conservative. They did not leave the neighborhood until late summer, but by the time the trees in the grove had lost their leaves, I knew the martins were in their winter home somewhere in the wilds of Brazil.

NAMES APPLIED TO SOME SWALLOWS SEEM MISNOMERS

Several of the swallow family apparently have been named because of the particular nesting environment which is supposed to be peculiar to each; for example, bank swallows nest in sand banks. But the name of the bird is not always descriptive of the place where its nest is found, and this fact sometimes causes confusion in the minds of inexperienced observers.

The saying, "What's in a name?" seems peculiarly appropriate in a discussion of the several kinds of swallows; but there the names are and there is nothing that the earnest teacher can do about them.

Once I went for a bird walk with Mrs. Pearson in a region that was new to us. As we passed an unused summer cottage some swallows flew from the wide veranda. I pointed out two nests on a joist and said that they were made by barn swallows.

"But this is a house, not a barn," she objected.

"Well," I said, "that's what they are—barn swallows' nests."

A little later we stood watching a row of mud nests stuck to the weatherboarding under the eaves of a barn.

"This is a colony of cliff swallows," I told her.

"Cliff swallows?" she repeated doubtfully.

It so happened that the next day we visited an island in the near-by lake. Along the cliffs on one side there were many cracks and clefts in and out of which birds were passing.

"What kind are they?" she asked.

"Tree swallows," I replied.

"Oh," she said hopelessly, "so barn swallows nest in houses, cliff swallows nest in barns, and tree swallows nest in cliffs!"

PLUMAGE OF WESTERN THRASHERS IS PALE, AS IF FADED BY HOT SUNS

Dwellers of valleys and deserts, these sweet-voiced birds live close to the ground. In fact, **Leconte's Thrasher** (lower right) trusts as much to its strong, long legs as to its wings to escape danger. It can easily keep ahead of a trotting horse. The under-tail coverts, or crissal region, conspicuous with a daub of chestnut, gave the **Crissal Thrasher** (lower left) its name. Shy **Bendire's Thrasher,** singing above, builds its nest in brush or cactus. The **California Thrasher** (upper right) is an expert at probing in the earth with its long, curved bill to capture insects.

Leconte's Thrasher

(Toxostoma lecontei lecontei)
Average Length, Ten and Three-quarters Inches

This bird and its subspecies, the desert thrasher *(T. l. arenicola)*, are very light gray and their colors blend so perfectly with the sands over which they race that when quiet for a moment they are practically invisible. The intolerable heat of the deserts they frequent is no deterrent to these energetic thrashers which are active even in temperatures as high as 120 or 130 degrees. Except for a brief rest in the partial shade of scrawny desert plants during the hottest part of the day, these birds dash about from bush to bush, frequently bursting into ecstatic song. Of course, they are most voluble in the comparative cool of morning and the silence of evening.

Not only are they very swift runners, but they also can dodge with startling suddenness and are adepts at vanishing from sight completely even in the sparsest cover.

They are past masters in the art of skulking through the cactus and creosote bushes and avoiding detection. When flying they usually rise only a few inches from the ground. Men on horseback, trying to run them down, have found it difficult to get them to rise in the air and fly away like other birds. In their efforts to escape, the thrashers prefer the speed of their legs and their ability to dodge behind bushes.

The nest is often placed in the cholla cactus, the long spines and easily detached joints of which provide a most effective defense against marauding animals.

Leconte's thrasher may be found in desert growths of southeastern California, southern Nevada, and Utah; also in Arizona and northern Baja California.

Crissal Thrasher

(Toxostoma dorsale dorsale)
Average Length, Twelve Inches

From Utah to Baja California and from southeastern California to western Texas is the homeland of the crissal thrasher, which favors juniper- and mesquite-clad canyon slopes of the Southwest. More often than other desert thrashers it is found in thick brush. Its rich song is heard most frequently in spring and fall when food is abundant.

This is an exceedingly shy bird. Field observers often have great difficulty in seeing one while it is singing, for if the songster glimpses an approaching intruder it dives instantly to cover and is not readily found again. If, by good fortune, one finds a crissal at close range, it may be identified by the light-yellow eyes, which are not possessed by any of the other thrashers of the same locality, and by the long, curved bill and whitish throat.

The crissal should be sought in the mesquite thickets bordering streams and arroyos.

The nest is made of thorny twigs and lined with grasses, and is usually placed in a thorn bush. This bulky affair, like the nests of some of this thrasher's relatives, is easily seen at some distance, which may prove that the bird frequents wilder regions where enemies which can recognize its nest are rare intruders. The three or four plain eggs are light green.

Bendire's Thrasher

(Toxostoma bendirei)
Average Length, Ten Inches

The various long-billed thrashers of the semi-arid deserts of the Southwestern States are very much alike in color. All are pale brownish-gray or drab as if bleached by the rays of the sun.

In deserts from southeastern California to southwestern New Mexico, one discovers the summer home of Bendire's thrasher. The bird also ranges across the border into northern Sonora. It is largely confined to the flat central part of southern Arizona. Small for a thrasher and rather rare, it pours out its fine song very infrequently and utters its *tirup, tirup* call only when frightened.

The nest is small and well-made. The usual twigs and grasses are carefully lined with soft vegetable materials, wool or feathers. In this basket are laid three or four greenish-white eggs, spotted with reddish-brown.

Observers are often confused by the similarity between this bird and the Palmer's thrasher. But the smaller size, the smaller, neater nest, smaller eggs and shorter bill are aids in identifying Bendire's thrasher.

California Thrasher

(Toxostoma redivivum redivivum)
Average Length, Twelve and One-quarter Inches

This bird's song resembles in many respects that of the mockingbird. It is delivered from the topmost bough of some tree or tall bush. Such a position when singing seems a little odd, since at all other times the bird keeps close to the earth and is usually well hidden from view in the chaparral. It likes to run along the ground and when alarmed will often seek safety by this means.

It ventures from cover now and then in search of food, often spading up the ground with its bill as it looks for worms or grubs. Seeds and insects of many kinds are taken. The three or four spotted eggs are laid in a nest of interlaced sticks and twigs, lined with grass, rootlets, and strips of bark. Usually it is well hidden in a bush or thicket.

A stout-hearted defender of its nest, the bird will even attack intruding humans, and its long, sharp bill is an adroitly handled, dangerous weapon.

The California thrasher ranges west of the Sierras, from Monterey into Baja California.

STRONG-WINGED SWALLOWS SNATCH THEIR MEALS FROM A TABLE OF AIR

Wasps, flies, and beetles, many of them crop destroyers, are targets of the swooping, triangular-billed **Purple Martins** (upper group, male left, female right, young male flying). Largest of the swallow tribe, these aerial acrobats, which often drive off crows and hawks, are always welcomed by farmers, who erect for them many-roomed apartment boxes in poultry yards. The **Cliff Swallow** (flying below) is a cliff dweller in the West, but in the East it builds mud nests under barn eaves. The **Barn Swallow** (right) nests inside on the rafters.

Purple Martin
(Progne subis)
Average Length, Eight Inches

Purple martins are sociable birds with a fondness for the company of their own kind, and where nesting sites for several pairs are available a colony is soon established. They prefer to live about the homes of man, and in most communities gladly accept the hospitality of those who put up nesting boxes.

Sometimes boxes with 100 or 200 apartments are erected for their use. They will accept also hollowed-out gourds suspended from crossbars nailed to a pole. Before the white man came to the New World, the Indian hung gourds from poles to tempt martins to his villages. In unsettled regions they will nest in cliffs or in hollows of trees. Not long ago more than 300 were estimated to be breeding among the bowlder piles on Spirit Lake, Minnesota.

Although breeding as far north as the southern tier of Canadian Provinces and even Alaska, they are most abundant in the Southern States. In the construction of nests, weeds and straw are used, as well as other vegetation, feathers, and even rags. Often mud is employed.

I have examined nests, the linings of which were composed wholly of the dead, smooth leaves of the live oak, which sometimes covered the eggs when the gourds containing them were tossed about in the summer wind. In some sections two or more broods are raised in a year.

The birds are very noisy about their nests, and the sweet twittering carol adds much to the avian chorus about the homes of planters and innumerable negro cabins in the pine-woods country.

Poultry raisers, and farmers generally, encourage martins to nest on their premises because they attack and drive away hawks and crows that intrude in the vicinity. The cheerful sociability and industry of the martins are so much a part of the rural "scene," particularly in the South, that these handsome and useful birds have become the symbol of country pleasures to many people.

The illegal shooting of martins for sport during their migrations in certain of the southern States has cut seriously into the ranks of the birds, although now more rigorous steps are taken to prevent the slaughter.

Almost the entire diet of the martin is composed of flying insects and most of these are harmful species. Malarial and yellow fever mosquitoes are among those destroyed. The eight species of this genus of the swallow family are all found in America.

Martins are among the long-distance travelers of the bird world; for they pass the winter in Brazil, thousands of miles from their breeding grounds.

Northern Cliff Swallow
(Petrochelidon albifrons albifrons)
Average Length, Six Inches

Cliff swallows arrive in the District of Columbia about April 10, in Minnesota between April 13 and May 6, and at the northern limits along the edge of the Arctic still later.

Typically swallowlike, they breed in colonies. Their nests are made of little mud pellets, carried one at a time. Many of the nests are so walled about that only an opening large enough to admit the bird is left. Sometimes a bottlelike neck forms the doorway.

The side of a building, well up under the edge of an overhanging roof, is a favorite nesting place. For this reason the birds are often known as "eave swallows."

Although found locally all over most of North America, except Florida and the Rio Grande Valley, they are much more numerous in some regions. In the Central States, for some obscure reason, their numbers have much diminished during the last 20 years. In Maine they are common, especially along the coast. There I once observed under the eaves of one building 100 nests, all apparently occupied.

In the summer of 1930, I took an extensive motor trip on Cape Breton Island, Nova Scotia. The young of both cliff and barn swallows were out of the nests, and in great numbers were perching on the telephone wires by nearly every farmhouse. In 1927 I counted more than 200 of their nests under an overhanging cliff in Utah.

In early September the birds begin their migration, passing through Florida and Central America to Brazil and Argentina.

Barn Swallow
(Hirundo erythrogaster)
Average Length, Seven Inches

Late in April, 1924, as a steamer on which I was a passenger pushed its way northward through the Strait of Yucatán, I saw a large flock of barn swallows. For perhaps an hour they circled about the ship, alighting on the rigging and twittering cheerfully. Northward bound, they were far out of sight of land.

These little flyers, like many other birds, possess an amazing endurance that enables them to seek their summer abodes somewhere in all that vast area between Alabama and the Arctic shores of northwestern Alaska.

All the swallows are brilliant flyers, but the barn swallows surpass their cousins in variety, ease and grace of flight. They are usually seen skimming over the fields, almost grazing the ground in an erratic, zigzag course. During the breeding season, they are generally more widely distributed than other swallows.

The nest is made of mud with grass or straw and is lined with feathers and fine grasses. Beams or the walls of buildings are now used almost exclusively as nesting sites.

MEMBERS OF THE SWALLOW FAMILY DIFFER WIDELY IN HOME TASTES

On the wing are **Bank** and **Rough-winged Swallows,** often confused, but readily distinguished by the dark band across the white breast of the former. Both nest in river banks or other earth walls where they may be neighbors of the phoebe and kingfisher. Dead stumps and rotted trees are the usual homes of the **Tree Swallow** (upper right). In western North America the trim **Violet-green Swallow** (upper left) has been known to occupy a man-made house, padding it with feathers snatched in flight from a bird-lover's fingers.

Bank Swallow

(Riparia riparia riparia)
Average Length, Five and One-quarter Inches

Like most of the swallows, this one seems to feel that it must have a cavity in which to build its nests, and since usually there is none available to suit its needs, it proceeds to make its own. With bill and feet it excavates a horizontal burrow two or three feet long in the side of a sand bank or gravel bed. The extremity of the hole is enlarged and lined with dead grasses on which the five pure white eggs are laid. The birds breed in colonies, and often the entrances to their burrows are only a foot or two apart.

They get along on the best of terms with the kingfishers, which also tunnel out nests in banks. In fact, these swallows often build in the same banks with the rattling, crested fishermen and even, on occasion, use the kingfishers' tunnels to get to their own nests.

Few birds have such a wide and varied geographical range as does the bank swallow. It is found in many countries of Europe, Asia, and northern Africa. In England I photographed one breeding place in the side of a sand pit that contained more than 140 nests. In America breeding communities of these birds are to be found from Alaska to southern California on the west, and to northern Quebec and central Alabama on the east. They do not, like the eave and barn swallows, seek human companionship.

Tree Swallow

(Iridoprocne bicolor)
Average Length, Six Inches

One day last winter while I was driving with a native Georgian through the pinelands of the southern part of his State, he pointed to a flock of fifty or more birds circling and fluttering over a shallow woodland pond.

"We call them 'cold weather birds,'" he told me, "because they come about such places in winter when a cold day comes."

The birds were tree swallows, easily identified by their blue-black backs with glints of lustrous green and their pure white breasts.

In summer this species inhabits almost the whole of northern and central North America. It breeds from Virginia, Arkansas, Colorado, and central California northward almost to the tree limits on the borders of the Arctic regions. In winter it may be found in North Carolina, Texas, central California, much of Mexico, Cuba, and Honduras.

Tree swallows are among the earliest migrants to arrive in the spring and some of the last to leave in the fall. During the nesting season they do not gather in colonies like some other swallows, but from July to late October, after breeding is over, they collect in enormous flocks and feed in the marshes.

On the outer sand banks of the Cape Hatteras region, and northward along the coast, are many dead trees that have been left standing after being killed by the big sand dunes which bury the timber for a time and then pass onward. Here, in April, I have watched tree swallows alighting, peering into holes, and giving every manifestation of seeking nesting cavities. Yet it was too early for them to breed, and not one of their nests has ever been reported from that part of the country.

The natural places for tree swallows to nest are cavities in rocky cliffs and in trees, but many are now accustomed to the use of bird boxes erected by kindly human hands. My friend, the late William Brewster, once showed me the nest of a pair of these swallows, built in a tin can erected on a pole in the yard of his farm on the Concord River in Massachusetts. The birds had suffered misfortune, for the summer sun had so heated the tin that the young were thereby killed.

The tree swallow's song is no more than a series of chattering notes. Winged insects make up the bulk of its food, but in winter or on migrations various kinds of berries are also eaten.

Violet-green Swallow

(Tachycineta thalassina lepida)
Average Length, Five and One-half Inches

One of the many charming birds inhabiting the greater part of western North America is the dainty violet-green swallow.

It is happy in the wilderness, but also finds safety and contentment about human habitations. I have watched it in wild regions of Alaska, darting about cliffs in the mountains of California, skimming over Lake Washington at Seattle, and fluttering about gardens in the outskirts of Oregon cities. Its varied colors, sprightliness, and cheerful twitterings make it a most welcome bird neighbor.

Its nest of feathers, and sometimes grasses, is built in hollows. Cracks and small openings of various shapes along the faces of cliffs are often utilized, although more often the birds may be found occupying holes in trees, especially the abandoned nests of woodpeckers. Violet-green swallows are frequently seen around farmyards because feathers are usually abundant there, and they have been known to snatch feathers from a man's fingers. The eggs, four or five as a rule, are white.

Being insectivorous, like our other swallows, this bird must retire southward before frost has cleared the air of those multitudes of insects upon which it lives. Thus the violet-greens, after passing the summer in their favorite localities between the Yukon River on the north, South Dakota and Nebraska on the east, and the Mexican border on the south, all fly away to Mexico and Central America for their annual sojourn under tropical skies.

LARKS AND PIPITS FIND THEIR FEET AS USEFUL AS THEIR WINGS

The only pipits north of the Rio Grande are **Sprague's Pipit** (upper left, male) and the **American Pipit** (upper pair, fall phase left, spring right), which run in fields and meadows in search of food. Soaring skyward, Sprague's pipit sings a sustained melody. Then, breaking off suddenly, it folds its wings and plunges headlong downward. Just before striking the ground, it spreads its wings and alights like a feather. The **Pallid** or **Arctic Horned Lark** (male left) and the **Prairie Horned Lark** (lower group, female and young left, male right), also dwellers on open land, bear distinguishing tufts of black feathers on the head.

Sprague's Pipit
(Anthus spraguei)
Average Length, Six and One-quarter Inches

Sprague's pipit likes the Great Plains, from Saskatchewan River to western Montana and North Dakota. It winters from southern Louisiana and Texas to central Mexico.

This soaring songster is often called the Missouri or prairie skylark, because, like the English skylark, it sings while high on the wing. Like other pipits, it lives on the ground and walks and runs like a starling. Its flocks prefer open fields, pastures or roadsides. On the ground they are hard to see, for their coloration merges perfectly with the background.

The pipit's song during the mating season is sweet and, although not loud, carries far.

American Pipit
(Anthus spinoletta rubescens)
Average Length, Six and One-third Inches

The family of wagtails and pipits (Motacillidae) includes one hundred or more species distributed widely in five continents. They are small ground birds, rather nondescript in general appearance. Over much of the United States the pipit is seen as a migrant, or, in the South, as a winter visitor.

Sometimes three or four may be seen together, but as a rule they come in flocks often of many scores. They feed on the ground and walk instead of hop.

Not long ago, by the Cooper River in South Carolina, I watched several running about on the damp ground of a rice field from which the water had just been withdrawn. Once I saw them feed like sandpipers on a sandy shore of Shackleford Banks near Cape Lookout.

Late in winter, when plowing begins in the fields of Virginia, Georgia, Tennessee, or elsewhere south of the Potomac and Ohio Rivers, you may expect to see flocks of these birds descend to the newly broken ground. In flight they undulate through the air, but at times have a drifting, uncertain, butterfly manner of movement different from that of other birds. They breed from the Arctic Zone throughout northern and central Canada, and along the higher mountains to New Mexico. Their winter range extends from the central tier of States through the Gulf region, the Southwest, and Mexico to Central America. Therefore, they are seen most commonly in the United States in spring and fall.

While I was serving as a member of President Hoover's Yellowstone Boundary Commission, our party one day made the long climb from the upper Yellowstone River to the high ranges to the westward. Where the trail crossed the Continental Divide a wide undulating plain lay before us. Here, well above timber-line, I suddenly realized that I was looking at a pipit flying with food in its mouth.

I quickly turned my horse in pursuit of the bird.

It is amazing how exasperating a bird can be sometimes. It simply would not go to its nest, and after watching it walking about and alighting on nearly all the bowlders over two or three acres of ground, I was forced to give up the best chance that I may ever have to find the cradle and young of this little bird of the high altitudes. Many have said that the nest is built on the ground. I wished to prove the fact for myself.

While preferring wet, boggy ground, they may be found in autumn and winter in comparatively dry plowed or stubble fields and uplands. At intervals, while on the wing, these birds utter a clear, faint *dee-dee, dee-dee*.

In the song season the pipit soars high in the air, like the famous skylark of Europe, and when its music has been poured forth the singer descends with direct flight.

Horned Lark
(Otocoris alpestris)
Average Length, Seven and Three-quarters Inches

The larks (Alaudidae) constitute a very numerous family, 225 species and subspecies being recognized in the science of ornithology. Two species are found in North America. One is the skylark of Europe, which has been introduced and is now breeding on Vancouver Island, British Columbia. Our other member of this family is the horned lark, which is divided into no less than 16 subspecies. This bird is readily identified by the black tufts, above and behind each eye, which, when erected, look like horns.

The meadowlark, easily distinguished by its much larger size, distinctly yellow breast, and the absence of the black, hornlike tufts of feathers, belongs to a different family.

Horned larks breed in suitable places throughout Canada and the United States, except the South Atlantic and Gulf States. Primarily ground-dwellers, they frequent open country. Except that the male prairie horned lark has a yellow throat, there is such little difference in the plumage of these numerous birds that only by comparison of them in the hand can their characteristics be distinguished.

Horned larks begin to breed in February or March as soon as patches of bare ground appear through the melting snow. Many eggs are frozen and new sets must be laid.

A little later the young may be seen crouching in the nest with bills pointed toward the cold wind. The nest is a slight hollow of dried cow manure. The three or four eggs are finely speckled.

The males begin singing in February or sometimes even in January. Often they mount in circling flight until out of view.

Photograph by Wright M. Pierce

THIS YELLOW PINE IS A CALIFORNIA WOODPECKER'S STORE HOUSE

Though the bark is scored by thousands of pits drilled to store acorns for winter food, the tree is well rid of injurious insects and worms. It seems incredible that birds could produce such an over-all pattern of lace-work in tough material, but Nature has fitted the avian workers with perfect tools for the task (see page 67).

WARBLERS, FRIENDS OF OUR FORESTS

An Avian Police Force Dressed in Handsome Uniforms and Singing Merrily on Their Beats Keep in Check Insect Malefactors

By Henry W. Henshaw and A. A. Allen

AT EVERY stage of their growth, from the seed to the adult tree, our forest, shade, and orchard trees are subject to the attacks of hordes of in sect enemies, which, if unchecked, would soon utterly destroy them.

What the loss of our forest and shade trees would mean to us can better be imagined than described. Wood enters into so many products that it is difficult to think of civilized man without it, while the fruits of our orchards also are of the greatest importance. Aside from the economic loss, how barren the world would seem shorn of our forests and shade trees!

Fortunately, the insect foes of trees are not without their own persistent enemies, and among them are many species of birds whose equipment and habits specially fit them to deal with insects and whose entire lives are spent in pursuit of them. Many insects at one or another stage of their existence burrow deeply into the bark or even into the living wood of trees, and so are quite safe from ordinary bird enemies. Woodpeckers, however, being among the most highly specialized of birds, are wonderfully equipped to dig into wood and to expose and destroy these hidden foes.

Certain insects that largely confine their attacks to the smaller branches and terminal twigs are preyed upon by nuthatches, creepers, titmice, and warblers. Others attack blossoms and foliage, and here the nimble and sharp-eyed warblers render supreme service, the number of plant lice and lepidopterous larvæ they destroy in a single day almost challenging belief.

Thus our woodland songsters are among the most important of all our birds, and render man unequaled service. Moreover, very few have any injurious habits, and the little harm they do, if any, weighs as nothing in the balance when compared with the good. By reason of their numbers and their activity in hunting insects, our warblers take first place as preservers of the forest.

Our wood warblers are assembled in a rather loosely defined family (the Compsothlypidae), embracing in all about 140 species, of which more than a third are visitors to the United States. They are fairly well distributed over the country at large, although more species make their summer homes in the eastern half of the United States than in the western.

Our New World warblers are quite unlike their Old World relatives, the Sylviidae, or true warblers, whose family includes some 75 genera and between 500 and 600 species. While our warblers are brilliantly colored and many of them sexually dissimilar, those of the Old World are not only small, but plainly plumaged; moreover, the sexes are generally alike in coloration.

The larger number of our warblers, as well as the most characteristic, are included in the one genus Dendroica, which is notable, since it includes more species than any other genus of North American birds.

HAUNTS OF WOOD WARBLERS

Fortunately for the bird lover, our wood warblers are not recluses. They are creatures of light and sunshine. Some of them, it is true, retire to the mountain fastnesses or the depths of coniferous forests during the nesting period; but these are few and their withdrawal is for only a comparatively short time, while the majority at all times of the year favor the edges of the forest, open woods, or brushy clearings.

Despite their name, which would seem to imply musical ability of no mean order, our wood warblers, with few exceptions, occupy no very high place in the musical galaxy. However, all sing, after a fashion, and the musical efforts of some are pleasing, even according to human standards. While most warblers are prodigal enough with their music and sing early and often, especially prior to and during the nesting season, their music is frequently so faint as to be audible only to the trained ear of the bird lover.

As if aware of their musical inferiority, few display much enthusiasm in their vocal efforts, but sing while they work, or while pausing for a brief moment as they move among the foliage hunting for food. With them, singing appears to be an audible expression of general content and well-being, and, no doubt, an effort to please and attract their mates.

Certain members of the thrush and thrasher families, on the contrary, which contain in their ranks the prima donnas of our bird world, as if conscious of their supremacy, are wont to mount a commanding perch when about to sing, and to pour out their melody for all the world to hear. With them, singing is not merely incidental to the day's work. It is a conscious and supreme effort, and is much too important to be slighted or shared with any other function. Apparently they appreciate to a great extent and enjoy their own outpourings, and, if we may interpret their feelings by human standards, are conscious that their musical offerings entitle them to an audience.

Not only do their bright colors suggest a tropical origin, but their whole make-up is in keeping with tropical surroundings. Warblers are thinly feathered and delicately organized and most of them incapable of withstanding any great degree of cold. They are also almost exclusively insect eaters, only a few of the family being at all vegetarian.

Hence, with them, migration is not a matter of choice, but is imperative. They come to us on a particular errand for a few short months, and when family cares are at an end, back they hie to the Tropics, the lands of warmth and sunshine. The true home of our warblers is not where they nest, but where they spend two-thirds of their lives—in the tropical zones.

That wonderful phenomenon, bird migration, is illustrated by few birds so well as by our wood warblers. Assuredly no other birds—unless it be the geese—migrate in such a spectacular manner. The stroller, in late August or September, finds himself in the woods, the silence being broken only by the drumming of a distant partridge, the chirping of insects, or other familiar sounds which only emphasize the general quiet that prevails.

Presto! The scene changes! The woods, apparently almost tenantless but a moment before, are now filled with life of the most animated and intense kind. Every shrub, every tree, has its feathered occupant. Our observer recognizes perhaps a dozen or twenty species, representing several distinct families; but prominent among them, by reason of numbers, variegated plumage, graceful forms, and active motions, are the wood warblers.

THE SUDDEN MIGRATION OF WOOD WARBLERS IS SPECTACULAR

Every individual is alert and busy, gliding from one twig to another, or flying from one tree to the next, while from all sides come the soft calls and notes of individual members of the flock in friendly converse. In a few moments silence again reigns where all was commotion and activity. The birds have passed on their seemingly aimless course.

To solve the mystery of the birds' evident hurry, the observer has only to follow them for a time, when he will find that, however erratic may seem the course of individual members of the flock, the flock as a whole is steering a tolerably straight course southward. He is in the midst of a flock of birds en route to their winter quarters, feeding as they go. This, however, is not the only way warblers migrate, nor is it the most important, since the greater part of the long journey of many is performed by night.

Anyone with good ears has only to listen on a clear, frosty night in fall to hear hundreds of warblers and other birds as they flit by, a few hundred yards above the earth, the call notes coming incessantly out of the darkness. The route of these flying hosts often carries them above cities. The subject of migration has not inspired our poets so often as might be expected, but Longfellow, in his "Birds of Passage," gives us the following wonderfully suggestive lines:

But the night is fair,
And everywhere
A warm, soft vapor fills the air,
  And distant sounds seem near;
And above in the light
Of the star-lit night,
Swift birds of passage wing their flight,
  Through the dewy atmosphere.

I hear the beat
Of their pinions fleet,
As from the land of snow and sleet
  They seek a southern lea.

I hear the cry
Of their voices
high,
Falling dreamily
through the
sky,
But their forms
I cannot see.

Probably because insects constitute such a n important part of their food, warblers, as a rule, migrate early in fall and late in spring. It is true that in fall many linger till frosts nip the vegetation; but insects are abroad even later than this, and it is only necessary to watch these late migrants for a short time to learn that their search for insects is being well rewarded.

Only a few species come north early in spring, the great bulk of the warblers evidently having been taught by bitter experience that in spring, at least, it is not the early bird that finds most worms or finds them easiest.

Photograph by A. A. Allen

WHO'S AFRAID OF A BIG BLACK SHOE?

A black and white warbler with a spider for its young lands on the author's foot, showing that it feels no fear of a human friend.

FLOCKING OF SMALL BIRDS CAUSES SPECULATION

Just why small birds, when migrating, congregate in large flocks and troop through the woodlands has often been the subject of speculation. Juncos, several species of sparrows, woodpeckers, nuthatches, chickadees, creepers, and, above all, warblers, combine to swell the ranks of these migrating companies. As many as a dozen or more species of warblers may often be seen in one flock, which, in addition, may include 200 or 300 individuals, representing a number of families whose tastes and habits in every-day life differ very widely.

Yet here are these incongruous elements mingling together on terms of the utmost friendliness. Since birds are sociable beings, except during the short time when family cares prompt to jealous vigilance, sociability alone may be the bond of union; added, however, to the kindly feeling of companionship probably is a feeling of increased security which comes from numbers. Certainly no enemy can approach one of these bird assemblages without being spied by at least one pair of vigilant eyes, when the flock is immediately notified by a

Photograph by Willard R. Culver

A BICKNELL'S THRUSH MAKES HIMSELF AT HOME

Though so shy as to be difficult to find, these rare birds quickly make friends with their benefactors. This one lived for months in the house of two nature lovers, Mr. and Mrs. George J. Wallace, evincing no desire to escape. His fondness for the bath resulted in his death, when he took a dip in a pan of boiling water. Mr. Wallace has the distinction of being the first to keep this species in captivity.

few sharp chirps—warning for every individual to seek safety in flight or to scurry to cover.

Every few years in some given locality, perhaps embracing a region of considerable size, a particular species of warbler or other bird suddenly becomes rare where before common. After a season or so, though sometimes not for years, the equilibrium is reëstablished and the numbers are as before. These changes very probably are the visible signs of migration catastrophes, the result of the sweeping away of a migration wave, composed of one or of many species, in the path of some sudden storm.

Again, many of us have witnessed the dire effects of a prolonged rain and sleet storm in spring, when thousands of luckless migrants find only too late that they have prematurely left the warmth and plenty of their tropical winter refuges. Under such circumstances thousands of migrants perish from the combined effects of cold and starvation, and among them are sure to be great numbers of warblers.

From the esthetic point of view, our warblers, as a group, occupy a high and unique position. They also occupy no uncertain place in the list of our useful birds. Preëminently insectivorous, they spend their lives in the active pursuit of insects. They begin with the eggs, preying upon them whenever and wherever found, and continue the good work when the egg becomes the larva and when the larva becomes the perfect insect.

WARBLERS SEEK OUT INSECT FOES IN ALL PARTS OF A TREE

They are especially valuable in this respect because of the protection they lend to forest trees, the trunk, bark, and foliage of which they search with tireless energy. Their efficiency is vastly increased because the many different species pursue the quest for food in very different ways. While some confine their search chiefly to the trunks and large branches and examine each crack and crevice in the bark for eggs or larvæ, others devote their energies to the twigs and foliage, scanning each leaf and stem with eager eyes. Still others descend to the ground and examine the rubbish and grass for hidden prey, while nearly all are adept at catching insects on the wing.

Each species, however, has a method of its own, more or less unlike that of its fellows, and each excels in some specialty.

The quantity of animal food required to drive the avian engine at full speed is so very great that it is no exaggeration to say that practically all the waking hours of our warblers, from daylight to dark, are devoted to food-getting. What this never-ceasing industry means when translated into tons-weight of insects, it is impossible even to guess, but the practical result of the work of our warblers and other insectivorous birds is that we still have our forests, and shall continue to have them so long as we encourage and protect the birds.

In the case of orchards and shade trees, there are other means at our disposal of controlling the insect enemy, notably the use of sprays. But for the preservation of our forests we must rely largely upon our birds, since the use of sprays or of other agencies over our vast woodland tracts would be too expensive, even were it not quite impracticable for many other reasons.

Insects are very numerous, and there is reason to believe that much benefit would result if we could multiply the present number of their enemies—the birds. The erection of bird boxes and shelters is an easy way to increase the number of certain species of birds, like swallows and chickadees. Unfortunately, with few exceptions, our warblers do not build their nests in cavities, and hence can not be induced to occupy bird boxes.

Many of them, however, nest in bushes, vines, and shrubbery, and by planting clumps of these near houses something can be done toward increasing the numbers of certain species, as the yellow warbler and the redstart. Because our warblers are chiefly insectivorous, their food habits bar them from the usual bird lunch-counter in times of hard storms.

During migration, warblers are peculiarly exposed to the danger of prowling cats. Many species feed close to or even on the ground, and then they are so much concerned with their own business that any tabby, however old and lazy, is equal to catching one or more individuals daily. The bird lover can do good service by summarily disposing of vagrant cats, which, during migration, work havoc in the ranks of our small birds.

RESTRAINT OF PREDATORY PETS PROTECTS WARBLERS

They can also restrain the pernicious activities of their own pets, for these, however well fed, are still subject to the predatory instincts of their wild ancestry, which impel them to stalk a live bird with all the zeal and cunning of their untamed forebears.

Little difficulty is experienced, even by the tyro, in distinguishing warblers from other birds, but to recognize the several species is not so easy, particularly in view of the fact that the adult males and females of many species are markedly dissimilar, while the young, both in the first and second plumages, often differ from the adults.

So far as possible the several different plumages are shown in the illustrations prepared by the artists, Louis Agassiz Fuertes and Major Allan Brooks. These illustrations are so admirable as to do away with the need of descriptive text. All the figures in the plates of this series are approximately one-half life size.

Maryland Yellow-throat
(Geothlypis trichas)
Average Length, Five and One-third Inches

Mostly green above, yellow below, the male Maryland yellow-throat is distinguished from other warblers by a broad black band across the forehead, bordered narrowly with white.

This little warbler is common throughout the Eastern and Southern States, frequenting thickets and low bushes on swampy ground. He is not a tree lover, but spends most of his time on or very near the ground, where he hunts assiduously for caterpillars, beetles, and other small insects. Among the pests that he devours are the western cucumber beetle and the black olive scale.

He has a cheery song of which he is not a bit ashamed. The yellow-throat has the bump of curiosity well developed, and if you desire a close acquaintance with a pair you have only to "squeak" a few times, when you will have the pleasure of seeing at least one of the couple venture out from the retreat.

This species breeds from southern Canada to southern California, Texas, and Florida; winters from the southern United States to Costa Rica and Haiti. Six forms are recognized

Yellow-breasted Chat
(Icteria virens)
Average Length, Seven and One-half Inches

Its size, olive-green upper parts, and bright yellow throat, breast, and upper belly distinguish this bird at a glance.

The chat is one of our largest and most notable warblers. It is a frequenter of brushy thickets and swampy new growth, and, while not averse to showing itself, relies more upon its voice to announce its presence than upon its green and yellow plumage.

Not infrequently the chat sings at night. The song, an odd jumble of chucks and whistles, brings to mind the western quip, "Don't shoot the musician; he is doing his best." In charitable spirit we must accept the song at the bird's own valuation, which, we may be sure, is not low.

Its nest is a rather bulky structure of grasses, leaves, and strips of bark, and is often so conspicuously placed in a low bush as to cause one to wonder how it ever escapes the notice of marauders fond of birds' eggs and nestlings.

The chat does no harm to agricultural interests, but, like most others of the warbler family, lives largely on insects, among them many weevils, including the alfalfa weevil and the boll weevil so destructive to cotton. Its two forms breed from British Columbia, Wisconsin, Ontario, and southern New England south to the Gulf States and Mexico; winter from Mexico to Costa Rica.

Oven-bird
(Seiurus aurocapillus)
Average Length, Six and One-quarter Inches

The oven-bird, an olive-green, white and black warbler, is one of our best-known birds and one the woodland stroller is sure to get acquainted with, so common is it and so generally distributed.

In moments of ecstasy it has a flight song which has been highly extolled, but this is only for the initiated; its insistent repetition of *teacher, teacher, teacher,* as Burroughs happily phrases it, is all the bird vouchsafes for the ears of ordinary mortals.

Its curious, domed-over grass nest is placed on the ground and is not hard to find. The food of the oven-bird does not differ greatly from that of other warblers, notwithstanding that the bird is strictly terrestrial in habits. The diet consists almost exclusively of insects, including ants, beetles, moths, span worms, and other caterpillars, with a few spiders, millepedes, and weevils.

The oven-bird breeds from southern Mackenzie, Ontario, southern Labrador, and New-foundland south to Wyoming, Kansas, southern Missouri, Ohio Valley, and Virginia; also in mountains of Georgia and South Carolina; winters in southern Florida, southern Louisiana, Bahamas, West Indies, and southern Mexico to Colombia.

Red-faced Warbler
(Cardellina rubrifrons)
Average Length, Five and One-quarter Inches

So differently colored from our own North American warblers generally is the little red-face that one might at once suspect it to be a stranger from a strange land. So at least it seemed to me when, in the mountains near Apache, Arizona, in July, 1874, I saw the first one within our borders. Later that year I found others on Mount Graham.

It is a Mexican species which has obtained a foothold along our southern borders in Arizona and New Mexico. I saw flocks of 10 or 15 among the pines and spruces, the birds frequenting these trees almost exclusively, only rarely being seen on the bushes that fringed the stream.

In habits red-faced warblers are a rather strange compound, now resembling the common warblers, again recalling the redstart, but more often, perhaps, bringing to mind the less graceful motions of the familiar titmice. Their favorite hunting places appear to be the extremities of the limbs of spruces, over the branches of which they quickly pass, with a constant sidewise jerk of the tail.

They range mainly in the Transition Zone in the mountains of southern Arizona and southwestern New Mexico and south through Mexico to the highlands of Guatemala.

MYRIADS OF SUNNY WARBLERS GLEAN INSECTS FROM OUR FOREST TREES

The black mask over eyes and forehead makes it easy to identify the ground-loving male **Maryland Yellow-throat** (upper left, with his mate). A clear, insistent cry of *teacher, teacher* helps to locate the **Oven-bird** (upper right-hand plate), another familiar eastern warbler that rarely leaves the forest floor. Unusually large for its family is the **Yellow-breasted Chat** (lower left) that builds its conspicuous nest in dense thickets. The **Red-faced Warbler,** picking at the spruce tip, is a Mexican species that crosses our southwestern border in small flocks.

Connecticut Warbler
(Oporornis agilis)
Average Length, Five and One-third Inches

Discovered by Wilson in Connecticut early in the last century, the Connecticut warbler remained almost unknown for many years until, September 7, 1870, I found it numerous near Cambridge, Mass. In fall it is common throughout eastern United States in low, swampy thickets. It feeds on the ground, and is so silent and shy as easily to escape notice.

When startled, the warbler flies noiselessly to the nearest shaded perch, and there sits motionless, watching the intruder, till it decides either to renew its interrupted search for food or to seek some distant place. The Connecticut is one of the few species that choose distinct routes of migration; in spring it passes up the Mississippi Valley instead of through the Atlantic Coast States, which form its southern route in fall.

The bird is known to breed in Michigan, Wisconsin, Minnesota, Manitoba, and elsewhere in the North; and to winter in South America. Seton discovered a nest in Manitoba.

Mourning Warbler
(Oporornis philadelphia)
Average Length, Five and Two-thirds Inches

The mourning warbler is a near cousin of the Maryland yellow-throat and, like that bird, sticks to Mother Earth, being no lover of tree-tops. Unlike the yellow-throat, however, it is one of the rarest of the family.

During the spring migration it frequents brushy hillsides and damp thickets, and in the nesting season it places its bulky nest of leaves and stalks in briar patches.

The song is rich and full and has been compared with that of the Maryland yellow-throat and the water-thrush.

The species breeds from east-central Alberta, southern Saskatchewan, southwestern Keewatin, Nova Scotia, and Magdalen Islands to central Minnesota, Michigan, central Ontario, and mountains of New York, Pennsylvania, Massachusetts, and West Virginia; winters from Nicaragua and Costa Rica to Colombia and Ecuador.

Macgillivray's Warbler
(Oporornis tolmiei)
Average Length, Five and One-quarter Inches

Though closely resembling the mourning warbler in appearance and representing that bird in the West, the Macgillivray's warbler differs widely in habits. Thus it is far more generally distributed, both in the mountains and in the lowlands, and is much more numerous. I have found it in summer chiefly in moist thickets of willows or other brush along streams. Other observers, however, have found the bird on dry, brushy hillsides.

This warbler nests from a few inches to a few feet above the ground. It has a short, pleasing song which it repeats often.

It breeds mainly from central British Columbia, central Alberta, and southern Saskatchewan to southern California, Arizona, and northern New Mexico, and from the Pacific coast to southwestern South Dakota; winters from Baja California to Colombia.

Hooded Warbler
(Wilsonia citrina)
Average Length, Five and Two-thirds Inches

The hooded warbler breeds from southeastern Nebraska, southern Iowa, southwestern Michigan, central New York, and the lower Connecticut Valley south to Louisiana, Alabama, and Georgia; winters from Vera Cruz and Yucatán to Panama.

Wilson's Warbler
(Wilsonia pusilla pusilla)
Average Length, Five Inches

This tiny warbler ventures farther north than many bigger and apparently hardier species, and Nelson found it in Alaska "one of the commonest of the bush-frequenting species, . . . extending its breeding range to the shores of the Arctic Ocean wherever it finds shelter." Cooke found it in Colorado breeding at altitudes of 6,000 to 12,000 feet.

The black-cap is a nervous, energetic little fellow, now essaying the rôle of flycatcher, now hunting for insects among the foliage. It has a short, bubbling, warbling song. Its nest, built on the ground, is composed chiefly of grasses, and its eggs are similar to those of other warblers.

The West Coast form of the black-cap (W. p. chryseola) breeds as far south as Los Angeles, and its nest is placed in the crotch of a limb or among weeds or nettles, not on the ground.

Canada Warbler
(Wilsonia canadensis)
Average Length, Five and Two-thirds Inches

Like the Wilson's black-cap, the Canada warbler is half flycatcher, half warbler, and the click of the bird's mandibles as they close on some hapless insect caught in mid-air is often the first indication of its presence. Unlike many of the family, it sings its loud, characteristic song much during its spring migration.

The bird builds a rather bulky nest of leaves and grasses, which it places in a mossy bank or under a moss-grown log. It is an active insect hunter among leaves and twigs.

It breeds from central Alberta, southern Keewatin, northern Ontario, northern Quebec, and Newfoundland south to central Minnesota, central Michigan, southern Ontario, central New York, and Massachusetts, and along the Alleghenies to North Carolina and Tennessee; winters in Ecuador and Peru.

LOVERS OF WARMTH FLY NORTH LATE, LEAVE EARLY FOR THE SOUTH

The three close relatives at the upper left are distinguished by prominent gray about the head and breast. The **Connecticut Warbler** (top) is a shy and silent ground feeder. Of like habits is the **Mourning Warbler** (middle), a species represented in the West by the more numerous and adaptable **Macgillivray's Warbler** (bottom). Like the true flycatchers, the tiny **Wilson's Warbler** (upper right, male above his mate) and the **Canada Warbler** (lower right) snap up insects in mid-air. The **Hooded Warbler** (lower left, male with the black bib) is an abundant bird of southeastern woodlands.

Palm Warbler

(Dendroica palmarum)

Average Length, Five and One-quarter Inches

The palm warbler, including under this name both the eastern and western, or yellow members of the species, is for the most part an inhabitant of the Mississippi Valley and the region eastward, passing its nesting season chiefly north of our northern frontier. It is best known as a spring and fall migrant.

Perhaps the most salient characteristic of this little warbler is the almost incessant tip-up motion of its tail, in which respect it recalls a bird in no wise related to it—the spotted sandpiper, or "tip-up," of pond and stream. It nests on the ground. Its song is a low, faint trill, characteristically warblerlike.

It breeds from southern Mackenzie (Fort Simpson) and central Keewatin south and southeast to Minnesota and Maine; winters from southern Florida and the Bahamas to the Greater Antilles and Yucatán.

Prairie Warbler

(Dendroica discolor)

Average Length, Four and Three-quarters Inches

The prairie warbler, dainty in its variegated black, yellow, and chestnut dress, is common from Florida to New England and from Nebraska and Kansas to the Atlantic.

In Massachusetts it frequents rocky barberry pastures on open hillsides dotted with cedars. About Washington it frequents sprout lands, and when it first arrives from the south is found almost exclusively in groves of the Virginia scrub pine or in junipers.

It is an active insect hunter, moving rapidly among the foliage, ever and again sending forth its characteristic song. Its unusually compact and pretty nest is often placed in the crotch of a barberry bush, in junipers or in low deciduous bushes.

The species breeds chiefly from southeast Nebraska, eastern Kansas, southern Ohio, southwestern Pennsylvania, southern New Jersey, and (along the coast) from Massachusetts south to southwestern Missouri, northern Mississippi, northwestern Georgia, Florida, and the Bahamas, and north locally to central Michigan, southern Ontario, and New Hampshire; winters from central Florida through the Bahamas and the West Indies.

Northern Water-thrush

(Seiurus noveboracencis)

Average Length, Six Inches

In appearance, motions, and habits the water-thrush is more thrush than warbler, and one who sees him for the first time walking sedately along with teetering tail may well be excused for declining to class him with the warbler family. He is partial to swamps and wet places, and is a ground frequenter.

He not infrequently visits gardens even in populous towns, and seems to be quite at home there in the shade of the shrubbery. A sharp and characteristic alarm note often calls the attention of the chance passerby.

The water-thrush is one of the foremost of the warbler choir and a real musician. The bird is a ground builder, placing its nest under the roots of an upturned tree, in banks, or in cavities.

It breeds chiefly from northern Ontario, northern Ungava, and Newfoundland south to central Ontario, northwestern New York, and northern New England, and in mountains south to Pennsylvania and West Virginia; winters from the Valley of Mexico to Colombia and British Guiana, and from the Bahamas throughout the West Indies.

Louisiana Water-thrush

(Seiurus motacilla)

Average Length, Six and One-quarter Inches

The Louisiana water-thrush, though not unlike its northern relative in general appearance, is very different in disposition and habits, and I know of no bird more shy and difficult to watch. It frequents the neighborhood of clear, woodland streams. One hears the sharp note of challenge or the wild ringing song, but seldom sees the singer.

It breeds mainly from southeastern Nebraska, southeastern Minnesota, and the southern parts of Michigan, Ontario, and New York, south to northeastern Texas, northern Georgia, and central South Carolina; winters from northern Mexico to Colombia, the Greater Antilles, Antigua, and the Bahamas.

Kentucky Warbler

(Oporornis formosus)

Average Length, Five and One-third Inches

The Kentucky warbler, with its rich colors and symmetrical form, is to be classed among the elect of the warbler tribe. It is never so abundant that it does not excite interest. It loves the deep, dark forest and shaded ravine.

The bird is a persistent singer, and in its own chosen haunts its loud, sweet song may be heard all day long. This warbler finds most of its food on the ground.

It builds a rather loose, bulky nest, largely of leaves and grasses, which is placed either on or just above the ground. Although this somewhat careless appearing structure may seem to have been a little artlessly located, it is in reality well protected by the surrounding vegetation with which it blends.

It breeds from southeastern Nebraska, southern Wisconsin, southeastern and southwestern Pennsylvania, and the Hudson Valley to eastern Texas, Louisiana, Alabama, and northern Georgia; winters from Tabasco, Campeche, and Chiapas through Central America to Colombia.

PERT FOREST-DWELLERS THRIVE, UNAWARE OF THEIR MISLEADING NAMES

The sweet-voiced **Northern** and **Louisiana Water-thrushes** (upper right, Louisiana on the rock) are warblers that strikingly resemble the real thrushes. The breeding range of the **Kentucky Warbler** (lower right, female half-hidden) actually includes most of the eastern United States. Hard to explain is the name of the **Prairie Warbler** (female below her mate, lower left), an easterner that shuns open country. A sandpiperlike tilting of its tail gives the nickname, "yellow tip-up," to the **Palm Warbler** (upper left, eastern phase above the **Yellow Palm Warbler**).

Bay-breasted Warbler

(Dendroica castanea)

Average Length, Five and Two-thirds Inches

The bay-breast appears to be increasing in numbers. Forty years or so ago it was rare in Massachusetts in fall. Today not a season passes that at the proper time and place careful search will not reveal a dozen or more mingled with others of the warbler family.

In spring the bird has always been uncommon or altogether wanting in the Eastern States, since it migrates up the Mississippi Valley, spreading out to occupy northern Maine and other of its northern summer haunts. In summer it frequents coniferous forests, and often nests in hemlocks.

The bay-breast, one of the larger warblers, is less of a bustler than many of its cousins. Its loud, liquid song is hard to distinguish from those of many of its relatives.

It breeds from northeastern Alberta, southern Keewatin, southern Ungava, and Newfoundland south to southern Manitoba, northern Maine, and mountains of New Hampshire; winters in Panama and Colombia.

Black-throated Gray Warbler

(Dendroica nigrescens)

Average Length, Five Inches

The handsome black-throated gray warbler is exclusively western in distribution, from our southern border to British Columbia. I can recall no especially salient characteristics possessed by the species. Like others of the family, the black-throat is an active insect hunter, among both the oaks and scrub growths of the valleys and the conifers of higher altitudes. In choice of nesting sites it exhibits a wide range of taste, and nests have been found in scrub oaks, pines, and firs, and varying in height from the ground from 3 or 4 feet up to 50 feet or more.

It breeds in the Transition Zone from southern British Columbia, Nevada, northern Utah, and northwestern Colorado south to northern Baja California, southern Arizona, and northern New Mexico; winters in southern Baja California and in Mexico from Durango to Michoacan, Vera Cruz, and Oaxaca.

Black-throated Green Warbler

(Dendroica virens)

Average Length, Five Inches

The very name of black-throated green warbler carries me back to boyhood days and to a certain pine-crested hill in Massachusetts, from which was wafted on an early spring morning the song of this bird. I can vividly recall the pleasure the song occasioned and the satisfaction of knowing a new bird friend.

The black-throated green is one of the commoner of our eastern warblers and one of the first to engage the attention of the bird student. During migration it may be met with in every kind of woodland, where it is at home, both high and low, ever pursuing with tireless energy its quest for insects.

It has two songs, or rather one song delivered in two different ways, sprightly, sweet, and perfectly characteristic. In summer it is partial to coniferous woods, especially white pines and hemlocks, and it frequently nests in these, though also in birches and alders. Though it is a resident of unfrequented woodlands, the black-throated green may grow tame enough to perch on an observer's hat.

It breeds from Alberta, southern Manitoba, central Ontario, northeastern Quebec, and Newfoundland south to Minnesota, Wisconsin, northern Ohio, northern New Jersey, Connecticut, and Long Island, New York, and in the Alleghenies south to Georgia; winters in Mexico (Nuevo Leon to Chiapas and Yucatán), Guatemala, Costa Rica, and Panama.

Wayne's warbler (*D. v. waynei*), a local form, nests from southern Virginia to South Carolina.

Pine Warbler

(Dendroica pinus)

Average Length, Five and One-half Inches

Few of our birds are so aptly named as the pine warbler, which first, last, and all the time, except in migration, resorts to pine woods. It summers in them in the north and it winters in them in the south. Even its feathers often bear conclusive evidence of its predilection for pines, being often besmeared with their gum. Among its bright-hued relatives the pine warbler cuts but a poor show with its somber green and brown coat, which, at least in Florida, is often dingy and smoke-begrimed from contact with burnt timber.

Though distinctly a warbler and not a creeper, the pine warbler is more deliberate in its motions than most others of its kind and, somewhat in the manner of the creeper, moves among the branches or over the trunks in search of its insect.

For a warbler it is an early migrant and reaches the latitude of Massachusetts soon after the middle of April. Indeed, its nest contains eggs or young while the late migrants are still passing north.

Its song has little variation, but while monotonous is pleasing and sweet, far sweeter than the trill of the chipping sparrow, which it recalls. Naturally the pine warbler nests in pines, usually rather high up, on a horizontal limb or among the twigs at limb end.

It breeds from Manitoba, Michigan, Ontario, Quebec, and New Brunswick south to east-central Texas, the Gulf States, and Florida; winters from southern Illinois and coast of Virginia to Florida, eastern Texas, and Tamaulipas.

The Florida pine warbler (*D. p. florida*) nests in southern Florida.

SEVERAL SPECIES, ONCE RARE, ARE NOW ABUNDANT

One apparent reason for the growth in numbers of the **Bay-breasted Warbler** (upper left, female below her mate) and a number of its cousins is the increased area of their preferred open woodlands along migration routes. The handsome **Black-throated Gray Warbler** (lower left) is a far-westerner of varied nesting and feeding habits. Partial to pines are the common **Black-throated Green Warbler** (male above his mate, upper right), and the **Pine Warbler** (lower right), whose nest may contain young while its tardy relatives are still passing north.

Magnolia Warbler
(Dendroica magnolia)
Average Length, Five Inches

The magnolia, or black and yellow warbler, is one of our most beautiful warblers, and fortunately, being one of the commonest of the tribe, is easily met with by anyone willing to take a little pains. When busy at its self-imposed task of hunting insects, it is by no means shy, and may be watched at close range with or without the aid of a field glass.

In migration the magnolia shows no preference for special localities, but occurs in upland woods and lowland shrubbery where there is promise of a harvest of insects. Like its fellows, it finds rich hunting in gray birches.

The magnolia warbler is a versatile, though scarcely an accomplished, songster, and phrases its song in a number of different ways. Many of its nests have been found in the northern woods, some of them in small firs or spruces only a few feet from the ground.

It breeds in the Canadian and Upper Transition Zones from southwestern Mackenzie, southern Keewatin, northern Quebec, and Newfoundland south to central Alberta, southern Saskatchewan, Minnesota, northern Michigan, and northern Massachusetts, and in the mountains of West Virginia, Maryland, Pennsylvania, and New York; winters from southern Mexico (Puebla and Chiapas) to Panama.

Chestnut-sided Warbler
(Dendroica pensylvanica)
Average Length, Five Inches

Since the days of Wilson, Audubon, and Nuttall there is little doubt that the chestnut-sided warbler has increased in numbers, and within its range it is now one of the commoner of the family. It is trim of form and its colors, though not gaudy, have a quiet elegance.

During the fall migration it shows little preference in its hunting grounds, but is found with others of its kin in all sorts of woodland haunts and in deciduous as well as coniferous trees. It frequents open woodland tracts in summer and loves to nest in low thickets of hazel and barberry. Like the redstart, it flits nervously among the undergrowth hunting for grubs and insects. It often perches to sing in bushes along pasture borders. The nests are made of shreds of bark and grasses and are put together so loosely and carelessly that, in connection with their situation, they unmistakably betray their ownership.

It breeds mainly in the Transition Zone from central Saskatchewan, northwestern Manitoba, central Ontario, and Newfoundland south to eastern Nebraska, Illinois, Indiana, northern Ohio, northern New Jersey, and Rhode Island, and south in the Alleghenies to Tennessee and South Carolina; winters from Guatemala to Panama.

Black-poll Warbler
(Dendroica striata)
Average Length, Five and One-half Inches

The black-poll is one of our commonest warblers, in both spring and fall, and probably heads the warbler list in point of numbers. A laggard in spring, it is also a loiterer in fall, and occasionally a flock of black-polls will linger in some sheltered valley where food is abundant till long after others of the family have passed southward. The clear, separate notes of its song help to identify it.

The bird nests chiefly in the far north, though it summers as far south as the Adirondacks. As it winters in South America, there are thus at least 5,000 miles between its extreme northern and southern habitats. Chapman notes that it is one of the very few warblers that migrate directly across the West Indies from South America to Florida. It makes its appearance in the Gulf States about the last of April.

It breeds from tree limit in northwestern Alaska, northern Mackenzie, central Keewatin, northern Ungava, and Newfoundland south to central British Columbia, Manitoba, Michigan, northern Maine, and mountains of Vermont and New Hampshire; winters from Guiana and Venezuela to Brazil.

Blackburnian Warbler
(Dendroica fusca)
Average Length, Five and One-quarter Inches

The Blackburnian, one of the gems of the warbler tribe, has a rather wide range in eastern North America, extending west as far as the Plains and north to Manitoba. Apparently it is nowhere, at least in migration, an abundant warbler, and there are few field observers so seasoned to the sight of its beautiful colors as not to be thrilled by sight of the bird.

The Blackburnian favors very big trees, particularly hemlocks, and passes most of its life high above the ground. As Thayer says, the Blackburnian is the "preëminent forest warbler of the group, the lover of deep mixed growth and the upper branches of the biggest conifers." The bird has a thin, shrill voice and utters at least two songs or variations which some think resemble the black-throated green's. Whatever the tree selected, be it a hemlock or a deciduous tree, the nest is placed well up among the branches and well out toward the end, where it is safe from all enemies that do not possess wings.

It breeds from Manitoba, southern Keewatin, central Ontario, Quebec, and Cape Breton Island to central Minnesota, Wisconsin, northern Michigan, Massachusetts, and Connecticut, and in the Alleghenies from Pennsylvania to Georgia and South Carolina; winters from Colombia to central Peru and less commonly north to Yucatán.

THEIR MIGRATING LEGIONS SHUTTLE BETWEEN TROPICS AND SUB-ARCTICS

Warblers pile up tremendous mileage during their annual flights to and from distant northern breeding grounds. Five thousand miles separate the extreme winter and summer ranges of the abundant **Black-poll Warbler** (upper right, female below). The trim elegance of the **Chestnut-sided Warbler** (male, immature, and female, top to bottom, lower left) and its preference for roadside thickets contrast with the deep woods occurrence and flaming suit of the **Blackburnian Warbler** (male above his mate, lower right). A sprightly wood nymph is the **Magnolia Warbler** (upper left, adult male above an immature bird).

Nashville Warbler

(Vermivora ruficapilla ruficapilla)
Average Length, Four and Three-quarters Inches

I have found only one nest of the Nashville warbler and this was on a little pine-wooded knoll in a small depression in the earth, only partly concealed by thin grass. I should never have found it but for the fact that the bird flushed from between my feet. So far as known, the Nashville always nests on the ground, a habit the more remarkable, since the bird rarely or never hunts there, but prefers to seek its insect food among the foliage, often of the tallest trees.

It breeds from southern Saskatchewan, northern Ontario, central Quebec, and Cape Breton Island south to Nebraska, northern Illinois, northern Pennsylvania, northern New Jersey, and Connecticut; winters from Vera Cruz and Chiapas to Guatemala.

The Calaveras warbler *(V. r. ridgwayi)* is a form allied to the Nashville, but confined chiefly to the Pacific coast. It is found on both sides of the Sierras and as far east as eastern Oregon and Washington and northern Idaho.

Tennessee Warbler

(Vermivora peregrina)
Average Length, Five Inches

The Tennessee warbler is by no means so local as its name would imply, but is likely to be found in migration almost anywhere in eastern United States, although it is much more numerous in the Mississippi Valley. It is not likely to be mistaken for any other species save the Nashville.

During spring migration the Tennessee is apt to be overlooked, since it is prone to keep in the tree-tops. In fall, however, it is found lower, conspicuous among gaudier warblers. Its song is a simple trill not unlike that of the chippy.

It breeds from upper Yukon Valley, southern Mackenzie, central Keewatin, southern Ungava, and Anticosti Island to southern British Columbia, southern Alberta, Manitoba, northern Minnesota, Ontario, New York, northern Maine, and New Hampshire; winters from Oaxaca to Colombia and Venezuela.

Parula Warbler

(Compsothlypis americana)
Average Length, Four and Three-quarters Inches

The beautiful parula, smallest of our warblers, is generally distributed during migration and usually found in company with other warblers in leafy trees, which it explores from the lower to the topmost branches.

It is one of the most active of the tribe, and is untiring in its pursuit of the minute insects which form its food. Its habit of hanging head downward as it explores a cluster of blossoms suggests a chickadee. It is found nesting in summer along streams or in swampy localities where long streamers of usnea moss festoon the trees. The parula has a short, buzzing song of which it is prodigal enough, but it can be heard at no great distance.

The two forms of this bird range from Nebraska, Minnesota, central Ontario, and Anticosti and Cape Breton Islands to central-southern Texas, southern Louisiana, Alabama, Virginia, and Maryland; they winter from the Bahamas and West Indies to Barbados, and from Vera Cruz and Oaxaca to Nicaragua.

Cape May Warbler

(Dendroica tigrina)
Average Length, Five Inches

The Cape May is one of our rarest and most beautiful warblers. This species, however, is far more numerous than it used to be, and in time may even be listed in many of the eastern States as among the more common migrants.

Although the bulk of the species undoubtedly migrates north through the Mississippi Valley, rarely a spring passes that a few individuals are not reported about Washington, D. C., and I have seen several in a day. In spring the Cape May often forsakes the woodlands and appears in orchards or in city parks.

The bird, a rather sluggish, but persistent, insect hunter, is coming into ill repute in parts of Pennsylvania and Virginia because of its fondness for grapes. It is a persistent songster, but its song is weak and squeaky.

It breeds from southern Mackenzie, northern Ontario, New Brunswick, and Nova Scotia to Manitoba, northern Maine, and New Hampshire, and in Jamaica; winters in the Bahamas and the West Indies to Tobago.

Black-throated Blue Warbler

(Dendroica caerulescens)
Average Length, Five and One-quarter Inches

The male black-throated blue warbler is one of the most conspicuous of the warblers, his black throat and blue back always serving to distinguish him. The female, despite her inconspicuous coloration, may be identified by the white spot on the primaries.

Whether in its northern or southern home, the black-throated blue warbler builds its nest of bark, roots, and other pliant material, loose and rather bulky, in a variety of saplings, bushes, and weeds, but always a few inches or a few feet from the ground.

It breeds from Minnesota, Ontario, and Quebec to Michigan, Pennsylvania (mountains), and Connecticut; winters from Key West to the Bahamas, Greater Antilles, and Cozumel Island. Cairns's Warbler *(D. c. cairnsi)*, a darker form, nests in the Alleghenies from Maryland to Georgia.

DESPITE THEIR NERVOUS MOVEMENTS, MOST WARBLERS ARE NOT SHY

Beautiful and quite rare is the **Cape May Warbler** (male above his mate, upper right) whose unpopularity in some regions is traceable to his taste for grapes. The **Nashville** and **Tennessee Warblers** (upper left, above and below), both feeders among the treetops, range widely throughout northeastern North America. The lovely little **Parula** (lower left, male above his mate), smallest of our warblers, thinks nothing of hanging upside down from a twig or blossom. One of the most conspicuous members of the family is the common **Black-throated Blue Warbler** (male below his mate, lower right).

NATURE FURNISHES IDYLLIC SURROUNDINGS FOR THE MOSSY HOME OF A NORTHERN
WATER-THRUSH

Photographs by A. A. Allen

ALL COMERS SERVE THEMSELVES AT A WOODLAND CAFETERIA

Flies, mosquitoes, and black-throated blue warblers find food to their liking and feed side by side.

A YELLOW WARBLER DISCOVERS HIS REFLECTION IN A MIRROR AND CHALLENGES IT
TO A DUEL

Photographs by A. A. Allen

A YELLOW WARBLER GOES WOOL GATHERING

No need to worry where it came from, this material is just the thing for making a nest cozy.

BRIGHT AND DELICATE PLUMAGE BESPEAKS A TROPICAL ORIGIN

During two-thirds of the year warblers "winter" in Mexico, the West Indies, Central and South America. Easy to identify in its eastern haunts is the striped **Black and White Warbler** (upper left). The **Audubon's Warbler** (upper right) of the Far West summers amid the mountain evergreens. Among the commonest of their tribe are the **Yellow Warbler** (below, at the left) and the **American Redstart** (lower right, male below his mate) whose striking finery contrasts with the verdure of the thickets and open forests they frequent.

Black and White Warbler

(*Mniotilta varia*)
Average Length, Five Inches

A warbler in form and general make-up, a creeper by profession and practice, this readily identified species, in its striped suit of black and white, may be observed in any bit of eastern woodland. Here it flits from tree to tree or climbs over the trunks and branches, scanning every crack and cranny for the insects that constitute its chief food.

Though not a lover of open country, it frequently visits the orchard, where it performs its part in the task of keeping insect life within due bounds. It nests on the ground and hides its domicile so skillfully that it is not often found.

None of the warblers are noted as songsters, and this black and white creeper emits a series of thin wiry notes. In scrambling over the trunks of trees it finds and devours many long-horned beetles, the parents of the destructive root-borers; it also finds weevils, ants, and spiders.

It breeds from central Mackenzie, southern Keewatin, northern Ontario, Newfoundland, Nova Scotia, and New Brunswick to eastern Texas, Louisiana, central Alabama, and northern Georgia, west to South Dakota; winters in Florida and from Colima and Nuevo Leon to Ecuador, Venezuela, and the West Indies.

Yellow Warbler

(*Dendroica æstiva*)
Average Length, Five Inches

The "yellow bird," or wild canary, as it is sometimes called, is one of the commonest of the warbler tribe and ranges over a vast extent of territory, being found here and there from ocean to ocean. Unlike some of its relatives, it prefers open thickets, especially of willows, to thick woodland, and often builds its pretty nest by the roadside or in garden shrubbery. Its chestnut-streaked yellow breast contrasts richly with the dark foliage as it searches for insects under leaves and along twigs.

Though not an expert musician, the yellow warbler sings early and often, and in zeal makes up what it lacks in quality of voice.

Because its nest is easily found by the initiated, this warbler is often victimized by the infamous cowbird, and is forced to bring up one, or even two, young cowbirds in place of its own rightful progeny. Sometimes the clever warbler builds a platform over the alien egg, and then continues its domestic affairs as originally planned. Indeed, two cowbirds' eggs have been found in a nest, each covered up by a separate layer of nest material.

Four forms of this species breed from the northern limit of trees south to California, New Mexico, Missouri, and South Carolina; winter in Central and South America.

Audubon's Warbler

(*Dendroica auduboni*)
Average Length, Five and Two-thirds Inches

No other member of the wood warbler family is more characteristic of the group than this beautiful bird. In voice, coloration, and habits it is almost the counterpart of the yellow-rump of the Eastern States, for which indeed it might easily be mistaken were it not for its yellow throat, the corresponding area in the yellow-rump being white.

It summers in the mountains and shows off to advantage against the dark foliage of the pines. It seems to have little fear of man and in winter frequents orchards, gardens, and dooryards. Wherever it may be, it keeps up an incessant hunt for its insect food, in the pursuit of which it sometimes essays the rôle of flycatcher, being very expert and nimble on the wing. It also devours many ants, flies, scale and plant lice, and noxious bugs.

Two forms breed from central British Columbia, Alberta, and southwestern Saskatchewan to our southern border, east to South Dakota and Nebraska; the species winters from California and Texas south to Guatemala.

Redstart

(*Setophaga ruticilla*)
Average Length, Five and One-half Inches

Its beauty of form and plumage and its graceful motions place this dainty bird at the head of our list of wood warblers. The bird appears to be the incarnation of animated motion and fairly dances its way through the forest. It is one of the most vivid frequenters of shadowy forest glades, where its brilliant black and orange plumage is easily seen as it spreads its tail and wings while hopping and fluttering about.

Spanish imagination has coined a suggestive and fitting name for the redstart, *candelita*, the "little torch-bearer."

The redstart is not unknown in some parts of the West; but it is essentially a bird of the Eastern States, where it is a common inhabitant of open woodland districts. While it builds a rather neat and compact structure of strips of bark, plant fibers, and the like, placing it in a sapling not far from the ground, the nest is not the thing of beauty one might expect from such a fairy-like creature.

Ornamental as the redstart is, it possesses other claims on our gratitude, for it is a most active and untiring hunter of insects, such as spittle insects, tree-hoppers, and leaf-hoppers, and both orchard and forest trees are benefited by the unceasing warfare it wages.

It breeds over a wide range from central British Columbia and eastern Canada to the States of Washington, Utah, Colorado, Oklahoma, and North Carolina; winters in the West Indies and from Mexico to Ecuador.

THEIR DROWSY, SIBILANT SONGS PERVADE OPEN EASTERN WOODLANDS

An unobtrusive dweller on shadowy hillsides is the **Worm-eating Warbler** (upper left) that breeds in the middle States from the Mississippi to the Atlantic. The **Orange-crowned Warbler** (upper right), also plainly colored, nests so far north that it is familiar only in migration. The buzzing song of the tastefully clad **Golden-winged Warbler** (lower left, male above the female) is common among elms and birches of the northeastern United States. Very similar in range and habits is the **Blue-winged Warbler** (lower right).

Worm-eating Warbler

(Helmitheros vermivorus)
Average Length, Five and One-half Inches

The worm-eating warbler is a bird of shaded hillside and dark thickets along watercourses. Though nimble in its movements and an active insect hunter, it is garbed in modest colors, and is likely to escape notice.

There seems to be an unusual degree of jealousy among the males, which often chase one another in rapid, zigzag flight through trees and bushes.

The worm-eater has caught the trick of walking, perhaps borrowing it from his thrush neighbors, and he rarely or never hops. His song is so feeble that one must listen carefully to hear it at all.

This warbler nests on the ground, often on a hillside or in a shallow depression, and the pairs seem so much attached to their old home that they may be looked for in the same place year after year.

The species breeds mainly from southern Iowa, northern Illinois, Pennsylvania, and the Hudson and Connecticut River valleys to southern Missouri, Tennessee, Virginia, and mountains of South Carolina; it winters from Chiapas to Panama, in Cuba and the Bahamas.

Golden-winged Warbler

(Vermivora chrysoptera)
Average Length, Five Inches

Though less gaudily colored than certain others of our warblers, the golden-wing ranks high in the family for beauty.

It is almost wholly limited to eastern States, rarely indeed being found west of the Mississippi, and its summer haunts are in the northern parts of its range.

The bird is to be looked for in deciduous timber, and is especially fond of elms and birches as hunting grounds. I have often seen it busy in elms so high up that only with difficulty could it be distinguished from the Tennessee, Nashville, and other strikingly different warblers in company with it. Like the blue-wing, it has the habit of clinging back downward to the tip of a branch or cluster of flowers, which it scrutinizes meticulously.

Once heard, its song is not to be forgotten nor mistaken for that of any other warbler, unless possibly the blue-wing. It possesses a buzzing, insectlike quality well represented by the syllables *ze-ze-ze-ze* in rising pitch.

Numerous nests of the golden-wing have been found, all of them practically on or a few inches from the earth, though usually supported by weed stalks or grass stems.

The species breeds from central Minnesota, southern Ontario, and Massachusetts to southern Iowa, northern Illinois, northern Indiana, northern New Jersey, and northern Georgia; winters from Guatemala to Colombia.

Orange-crowned Warbler

(Vermivora celata celata)
Average Length, Five Inches

The orange-crowned warbler is much better known as a migrant, especially a fall migrant, than as a summer resident.

Seton found it a common summer resident in Manitoba; Kennicott discovered it nesting about the Great Slave Lake among clumps of low bushes; and Nelson found it common in summer in the forests of northern Alaska.

Of late years the orange-crown seems to be a much commoner migrant in Massachusetts, and perhaps generally in New England, than formerly, and the sight of three or four in a day occasions no great surprise. It winters in Florida and in other of the South Atlantic States, and its rarity in the Eastern States in spring is due to the fact that it migrates up the Mississippi Valley.

The orange-crown is one of the most plainly colored of the warbler tribe, and there is little about it to attract the notice of the casual observer. The song consists of a few sweet trills, similar to that of the "chippy."

This warbler breeds from Alaska to Keewatin, and in the Rocky Mountains to New Mexico; winters in the Gulf and South Atlantic States and through Mexico. Two additional forms are found on the Pacific coast.

Blue-winged Warbler

(Vermivora pinus)
Average Length, Four and Three-quarters Inches

Like the golden-wing, the blue-winged warbler is confined to the Eastern States, but it ranges considerably farther west than that species and occurs to the Plains.

It prefers deciduous trees and second growths and shuns the deeper parts of the forests. It has the habit of hanging from the under side of any particular cluster it wishes to investigate, and no doubt it makes sure of insects that defy the less careful search of most other species.

The ordinary song of the blue-wing is comparable to the golden-wing's, being in fact little else than an apology for a song, with the same insectlike quality. This warbler, though of distinctly arboreal habits, prefers to nest on the ground, or a few inches above it, in grass or goldenrods, or at a sapling's base.

The nest is rather bulky, composed of leaves and grasses, put together after the artless manner of its kind; but it is usually well concealed by the surrounding screen of grass or weeds from any but chance discovery.

The bird breeds from southeastern Minnesota, southern Michigan, western New York, Massachusetts (rarely), and southern Connecticut to northeastern Kansas, central Missouri, Kentucky, Maryland, and Delaware; winters from southern Mexico to Guatemala.

TOWERS AND LIGHTHOUSES KILL COUNTLESS WARBLERS ON MIGRATION

Offshore winds and unseasonable cold claim other thousands. Unusual in this family are the bright blue upper parts of the **Cerulean Warbler** (upper left, male above his mate on the slender branches). With them is a southern resident, the **Yellow-throated Warbler.** Rarest of our warblers is the tail-wagging **Kirtland's** (lower left) which breeds exclusively in three counties of Michigan. The **Myrtle Warbler** (lower right, male below the female) often winters in the East wherever myrtle berries are abundant. Above, at the right, perches the southwestern **Grace's Warbler.**

Cerulean Warbler

(Dendroica cerulea)

Average Length, Four and One-half Inches

The winter home of the cerulean warbler is in the forests of Panama, Colombia, Venezuela, and Ecuador, which it leaves in late March so as to arrive in southern Louisiana the beginning of the second week of April. It passes about three weeks in migrating leisurely up the Mississippi Valley, and arrives on its nesting grounds in the first week of May.

While the Ohio River Valley is the center of its abundance, it occurs more or less regularly as far west as Nebraska and Minnesota, and as far east as central New York or even the Hudson Valley. Its song is very similar to that of the parula warbler—starting with a few wiry notes and ending with a buzzy trill.

The rather nondescript grayish female builds her nest of fibers and strips of bark from 20 to 60 feet up in a tall elm or sycamore, saddling it far out on a branch after the fashion of a wood pewee. Like the pewee, also, the cerulean warbler fastens its nest to the branch with cobwebs and decorates the outside with lichens or bits of fungus. The three or four creamy white eggs are rather heavily marked with reddish brown.

Yellow-throated Warbler

(Dendroica dominica)

Average Length, Five and One-quarter Inches

This is a bird of our southeastern States, seldom seen north of Maryland and most abundant from Florida to North Carolina, where it frequents the larger trees.

The yellow-throated warbler places its nest about midway from the trunk on a horizontal branch from 20 to 50 feet from the ground, building a rather compact structure of fine twigs, weed stems, strips of bark, Spanish moss and cottony materials, sometimes with feathers or horsehair in the lining. Its four or five dull, greenish, gray-white eggs are heavily marked with shades of brown, purplish-gray, and blackish.

West of the Alleghenies in the Mississippi Valley as far north as southern Michigan, the yellow-throated warblers have slightly smaller bills, larger white patches on the tail feathers and very little yellow over their eyes. They are considered a distinct subspecies and are called sycamore warblers *(D. d. albilora)* from their habit of frequenting these trees.

The yellow-throated warblers winter from Florida (rarely South Carolina) through the Bahamas and the Greater Antilles; the sycamore warblers from Mexico to Costa Rica.

Kirtland's Warbler

(Dendroica kirtlandi)

Average Length, Five and Three-quarters Inches

This species is considered the rarest of all the warbler family. It was first discovered as a migrant near Cleveland, Ohio, in 1852, but its summer home in Michigan was not found until 1903, long after its winter quarters in the Bahamas had been located and its migration route partly charted.

There is a possibility of the species nesting in the upper peninsula of Michigan and in northern Wisconsin and Minnesota, but at best its range is extremely limited as compared with that of other birds, though there is no evidence of its becoming rarer.

Kirtland's warbler walks like a water-thrush. It selects a conspicuous perch on a dead tree from which to sing its earnest, forceful little song, *chip-chip-che—chee—chee-r-r-r!* It nests on the ground, building its home about the middle of June, usually at the base of a small tree in a dense growth of small jack pines and scrub oak. The three to five white eggs are finely and evenly speckled with brown.

This warbler reaches Florida from the Bahamas about April 20, and northern Michigan about May 15, and between these dates can be searched for in the intervening country in low growth. It nests only in Oscoda, Crawford and Roscommon Counties, Michigan.

Grace's Warbler

(Dendroica graciae)

Average Length, Four and One-half Inches

This western representative of the yellow-throated warbler was first discovered by Dr. Elliott Coues on the summit of Whipple's Pass, New Mexico, in 1864, and named for his sister Grace. It has since been found in summer in the mountains of southern Colorado, Arizona, and northern Mexico, as well as New Mexico, and in winter in Mexico as far south as Nayarit and Jalisco.

Myrtle Warbler

(Dendroica coronata)

Average Length, Five and Two-thirds Inches

This bird is found in summer from the mountains of New England to the limit of trees in northwestern Alaska. It passes the winter from Kansas and southern New England to Mexico, Panama, and the Greater Antilles.

The myrtles are found on migration in all sorts of environments, even venturing out into open fields if insects are abundant. Sometimes they feed like sparrows on the ground; again like flycatchers on the wing; but most of the time they glean from the foliage.

Their song is a rather nondescript junco-like trill and their call-note a sparrow-like *cherk!* While their food is made up chiefly of defoliating insects, they eat also some seeds and during the winter in the Atlantic States they feed on bay or myrtle berries.

The rather bulky nest of the myrtle warbler is usually placed in a spruce tree from five to ten feet from the ground and the grayish-white eggs are heavily marked with brown.

THREE TUNEFUL SOUTHERNERS AND A MODEST PAIR FROM THE WEST

The glowing **Prothonotary Warbler** (upper left) clings to dense undergrowth beside swamps or streams. Unsurpassed in radiant beauty, it has also a ringing song which, however, does not compare with the rich, tender melody of **Swainson's Warbler** (upper right), an inhabitant of marshy thickets in the South. **Bachman's Warbler** (lower left, male above) nests close to the ground, although in migration it flits among the treetops. **Lucy's Warbler** (lower right, above) lives among the willows and mesquite of southwestern lowlands, while **Virginia's Warbler** (below) prefers thickets in the southern Rocky Mountains.

Prothonotary Warbler

(Protonotaria citrea)

Average Length, Five and One-half Inches

In winter the prothonotary warbler is found from Nicaragua to Venezuela, from which it migrates to the United States, apparently across the Gulf of Mexico, since it is never found in Mexico north of Campeche.

It arrives in southern Florida the first week of April, and those that push as far north as Wisconsin or New York reach their nesting grounds usually after the first week of May.

The resounding *sweet, sweet, sweet, sweet!* of the prothonotary warbler coming from any woodland is as indicative of the presence of stream or pond as is the call of frogs.

Its nest is always in a cavity in a dead stub, often standing in water, and the birds have been known to utilize nest boxes arranged for them in suitable places. I have found their nests of grasses and moss in Louisiana in hollow cypress knees, from which they were later flooded out by high water, but more often they select a cavity such as made by a woodpecker or chickadee from four to ten feet above the water. The four or five eggs are creamy white heavily marked with brown.

In the fall these warblers move to northwestern Florida and apparently make a 700-mile flight over the Gulf of Mexico to southern Yucatán instead of crossing to Cuba and thence southward.

Swainson's Warbler

(Limnothlypis swainsoni)

Average Length, Five Inches

In summer the Swainson's warbler is found along streams bordered with a growth of cane or other dense vegetation from Florida and Louisiana north to Oklahoma and southeastern Virginia, and in winter it retires to Jamaica and southern Yucatán. It sings sporadically a rich, ringing song suggestive of that of the northern water-thrush with four or five notes given slowly in the same key followed by a descending series of five or six.

Its bulky nest resembles that of a veery with an outer layer of dead leaves and a lining of pine needles and dry moss placed in a bush or tangle of cane often over or near water. Its three or (rarely) four creamy or bluish-white eggs are unmarked and unglossed.

Bachman's Warbler

(Vermivora bachmani)

Average Length, Four and One-quarter Inches

Like the Swainson's warbler, Bachman's was first discovered by Bachman in 1833. Its nest was not found until May 14, 1897, and its entire summer range has not yet been definitely charted.

Its weak, chippy-like song, its rather shy nature, and the inaccessibility of its haunts in heavily timbered swampy land overgrown with briars, with more or less stagnant water, have combined to keep the species from becoming well known. Apparently, however, it is found in summer in suitable localities from southeastern Missouri and northeastern Arkansas through western Kentucky, northern Alabama to Charleston, South Carolina, and probably also in southern Indiana and eastern North Carolina.

In winter the species is known only from Cuba. It crosses to Florida early in March and returns to Cuba as early as July, belonging to our fauna for only about four months.

In the swampy thickets of its summer habitat Bachman's warbler builds its nest of dead leaves, weed stalks, and fibers in blackberry tangles or similar places, and lays three or four unspotted, glossy white eggs.

Lucy's Warbler

(Vermivora luciae)

Average Length, Three and Three-quarters Inches

This is a bird of the mesquites along the Colorado River and its tributaries in southern Utah, New Mexico, Arizona, and southeastern California, where, because of its small size and activity, it might well be compared with a gnatcatcher or a verdin. Indeed at least one pair has been known to occupy the deserted nest of a verdin, though ordinarily they utilize natural cavities in the mesquite trees or spaces behind loose bark.

The nests themselves are rather frail affairs of grasses and fibers with a lining of feathers and hair; and the eggs are scarcely more than half an inch in length. They are white, handsomely wreathed with reddish brown.

The song of Lucy's warbler is a lively little double trill ending with a *twee!*

Virginia's Warbler

(Vermivora virginiae)

Average Length, Four Inches

Although Virginia's warbler is recognized as a species distinct from the Nashville warbler of eastern North America, it certainly fills the place of this species in the southern Rocky Mountain region from Nevada, Utah, and northern Colorado, south to southern Arizona and northeastern New Mexico.

It was first discovered by Dr. W. W. Anderson in New Mexico, and he sent his specimens to Professor Spencer Fullerton Baird who, in describing the new species, gave it the name of the wife of the discoverer. It has since been found an abundant species of the southern Rockies at an altitude of approximately 5,000 feet where it dwells in the scrub oak and willows bordering cañons and talus slopes.

It nests on the ground at the base of a bush, like the Nashville warbler, and the song of the male is almost indistinguishable from that of the eastern bird. Whether singing or feeding it seldom ventures high in the trees.

BLITHE FEATHERED JEWELS THAT FLASH AMONG THE PINES

High in the mountains of Arizona and New Mexico the **Olive Warbler** (upper left) feeds deliberately among the pine tips. The restless **Townsend's Warbler** (below at the left, upper pair, male with the black throat) is another habitué of western conifers, while the **Golden-cheeked Warbler,** below it, frequents juniper brakes in central and southern Texas. Shy and retiring, the **Hermit Warbler** (upper right, male above) gleams against dark Sierra Nevada forests. The nervous habits of the Southwest's **Painted Redstart** (lower right) resemble those of its namesake, the American redstart.

Olive Warbler

(Peucedramus olivaceus)
Average Length, Five Inches

The olive warbler is really a Mexican species which extends its range into the United States in the mountains of Arizona and southern New Mexico, where occasional birds are found in the open forests of pine and fir. It is fairly common, however, farther south on the Mexican plateau, where it is said by Dr. Frank Chapman to resemble in its habits the more northern pine warbler—creeping leisurely around the branches of the evergreens in its search for insects or even descending to the ground without the fluttering habit of so many of the warblers.

Its song, a rapidly whistled *peto, peto!* is suggestive of that of the tufted titmouse, and its beautiful nest, very seldom found, is placed 30 to 50 feet from the ground on a horizontal branch of pine. The nest, built of rootlets, moss, fir blossoms, and spider webs, is covered on the outside with lichens.

The eggs of the olive warbler are different from those of any other North American warbler in that the ground color is sage green instead of white, marked with shades of brown and gray.

In winter most of the olive warblers retire to the highlands of Mexico and Guatemala, though occasionally a bird remains in southern Arizona. They return to the United States about the first week of April.

Townsend's Warbler

(Dendroica townsendi)
Average Length, Four and Three-quarters Inches

Townsend's warbler is a summer resident of the mountains of our Northwest from Montana to Alaska and winters from central California to Nicaragua. On migration it occurs more or less regularly as far east as eastern Colorado and western Texas, but elsewhere is accidental.

Although Townsend's warbler is common in the forests of fir and spruce, it has apparently escaped detailed study by bird observers and little is known of its habits. In general it keeps to the higher branches and behaves much like a black-throated green warbler and, indeed, its wheezy song somewhat resembles the notes of this species also.

Its nest of grasses, plant fibers, rootlets, hair and plant down has been described as placed in willows four feet from the ground or as high as 60 feet in the firs, and the creamy-white eggs are very heavily marked with chestnut and lavender.

It arrives on its nesting ground in late April or early May and usually leaves before October. From October to April it is found in central California and south along the coast, enjoying the mild sunny climate.

Golden-cheeked Warbler

(Dendroica chrysoparia)
Average Length, Four and Three-quarters Inches

The golden-cheeked warbler has a very restricted summer range in the "Edwards Plateau" region of south-central Texas, where it finds a congenial home among the low junipers and Spanish oaks that cover the eroded sides of the canyons. It builds its nest in an upright fork of a scraggly cedar from six to twenty feet from the ground.

The outside of the nest is made of cedar bark, so that it is quite inconspicuous; the inside is often lined with hair or the feathers of the Gambel's quail and cardinal.

The golden-cheeks arrive on their nesting ground by the middle of March and many of the early nests are destroyed by "northers" in April. By the end of July both old and young have disappeared from their customary haunts and they pass the winter months in the highlands of southern Mexico, Guatemala, and northern Nicaragua.

The hurried song of the golden-cheeked warbler, not very musical, is described as *twee-ah, twee-ah, tweeasy!*

Hermit Warbler

(Dendroica occidentalis)
Average Length, Four and Three-quarters Inches

The hermit warbler is a bird of the Pacific coast where in summer it is found in the high mountains from California to Washington. It winters from Mexico to Nicaragua and is sometimes seen in Nevada and Arizona.

The nest of the hermit warbler is more bulky than the usual warbler type of nest, being made of weed stems, pine needles, and twigs, lined with strips of bark and hair and often decorated with lichens. It is usually placed from 25 to 40 feet from the ground on a pine branch where, despite its size, it is difficult to find. The eggs are white, wreathed with spots of chestnut, brown, and lilac.

The hermit warbler arrives in California the last of April and departs the last of September or first of October.

Painted Redstart

(Setophaga picta)
Average Length, Five Inches

The painted redstart is found in the United States only in the mountains of central Arizona and southern New Mexico, where it frequents the evergreens, oaks, pines, and alders usually near springs or waterfalls. It ranges south over the Mexican plateau to central Mexico, and in winter to Honduras.

The male and female wear the same plumage, and instead of nesting in the second growth they place their nests on the ground in a hollow beneath a projecting rock or bunch of grass, usually near water.

A THRIVING IMMIGRANT KEEPS COMPANY WITH NATIVE WESTERNERS

Our innumerable **Starlings** (center trio; adult male, left and middle, in spring and winter plumage; young at the right) are descended from 100 birds brought from Europe and released in Central Park, New York City, in 1890 and 1891. This interloper ousts bluebirds, flickers, flycatchers, martins, and swallows from nesting holes and bird boxes. Southern Texans are familiar with the glossy black coat and neck ruff of the **Red-eyed Cowbird** (upper left) and with the showy **Audubon's Oriole** (upper right). Below, on the rock, the pure-voiced **Western Meadowlark** pours out its song.

Starling

(Sturnus vulgaris vulgaris)

Average Length, Eight and One-half Inches

One hundred starlings brought over from Europe in 1890 and 1891 and liberated in Central Park, New York City, adapted themselves so well to life in this country that their offspring now number millions. They outnumber that other little immigrant, the English sparrow, that was introduced forty years earlier, not only in New York City but from Maine to Georgia and as far west as Iowa.

What was thought at first to be a most desirable addition to our fauna because of its fondness for insects and its familiarity about our homes and gardens has become a veritable pest. The young are on the wing early in June when they assemble in enormous flocks, and it is not uncommon for 500 or 1,000 to alight in a cherry tree and strip it of its fruit.

Early in the summer these flocks of starlings often roost in the marshes, but later on they sometimes assemble in shade trees along city streets or roost on the buildings or in cupolas where their noise and dirt and peculiar odor often become objectionable. In some places a flock numbering 500,000 comes to a single roost, and the food required to support such a flock is stupendous.

In the Northern States a few starlings remain as permanent residents where a city dump or an arboretum with berries promises sufficient food, but the majority move to Ohio, Maryland, and other more southerly places.

Nesting starts the last of April, and they build in holes in trees or about buildings. Other hole-nesting species such as bluebirds, tree swallows, and flickers usually give way before the starlings' aggressiveness.

The starling's nest is a bulky affair of weed stems, bark, green leaves, and miscellaneous debris, deeply hollowed and lined with feathers. The four or five eggs are light blue and unspotted, like robins' eggs, but paler.

The starlings have in the spring a rather pleasing song of disjointed whistles and clucks intermingled with imitations of many other bird songs which they utter more or less continuously, with wing jerks and tail twitches.

Audubon's Oriole

(Icterus melanocephalus auduboni)

Average Length, Nine and One-half Inches

Audubon's oriole was first discovered by J. P. Giraud in 1841 in southern Texas and named for his friend, the great naturalist, John James Audubon.

It is, however, really a Mexican species that finds the northern limit of its range in the Rio Grande Valley of southern Texas, though it has been known to wander as far north as San Antonio, even in winter. It is a rather shy bird during the summer, placing its half-pensile nest of fine, wiry grasses in open groves of mesquite trees away from habitations, but during the winter it seems bolder and visits orange groves and gardens.

Its large size, brilliant plumage, and magnificent whistled song made it a favorite cage bird in the days when such traffic was legal. This is one of the birds that is often imposed upon by the red-eyed cowbird.

Red-eyed Cowbird

(Tangavius aeneus)

Average Length, Eight and One-half Inches

This is another species which does not range north of southern Texas, seldom being found north of San Antonio, but being very common in parts of eastern Mexico and even as far south as Panama. Its larger size, uniform bronzy plumage, and blood-red eye make it quite distinct from the common cowbird in general appearance, but it has the same strange habit of laying its eggs in the nests of other birds and letting the foster parents hatch them and rear the young. The birds most often imposed upon are the chats, orioles, cardinals, and larger flycatchers.

These cowbirds are often seen in small flocks in pastures or perched on roadside fences. Their courtship displays are usually indulged in on the ground, the enamored male ruffling up the feathers of his cape and back, bowing his head and then bouncing up and down, sometimes even lifting himself several feet above the object of his attentions.

The birds of western Mexico which range northward into southern Arizona are somewhat bluer on the lower back, and have been separated into a distinct form known as the bronzed cowbird *(T. a. involucratus)*.

Western Meadowlark

(Sturnella neglecta)

Average Length, Ten and Three-quarters Inches

Tourists from the East have little difficulty in recognizing the western meadowlark when they see it in Kansas or Iowa because it is so similar to the eastern bird. But one who has trained his ears to the songs of the eastern birds will never mistake the loud warbling whistle for that of the eastern species.

Except for their songs the eastern and western birds seem almost identical in habits as well as in plumage, for they both build dome-shaped nests on the ground with more or less of a tunnel entrance; they both lay from three to five creamy-white eggs spotted with brown, and both pass most of their time in chasing grasshoppers and crickets or in digging out grubs and wireworms.

In Wisconsin, Kansas, Iowa, and Texas the ranges of the two species overlap, and both birds can be heard singing side by side. In the rest of the Western States, however, and from British Columbia to Baja California, the western meadowlark sings alone (page 216).

THE BALTIMORE ORIOLE STARTS A HOME ON A STRING

Photographs by A. A. Allen

WARY BUT UNAFRAID IS THIS RED-EYED VIREO

BLACKBIRDS AND ORIOLES

By Some Strange Law of Distribution These Handsome Flutists Are Confined to the New World

By Arthur A. Allen

IT WAS my first trip to the Tropics. As we stood on the newly finished dam Colonel Gaillard was explaining the probable extent of Gatun Lake when water should finally be admitted to the Panama Canal. But my mind was on other things.

I was an ornithologist craving bird adventure, and while I listened to the Colonel with one ear, the other received most alluring sounds from the undergrowth; and while my eyes took in the enormity of the dam I really perceived only strange shapes and bits of color flitting through the trees in the background.

The next day, as I made my way alone to the beckoning forest, from the train window I glimpsed birds I had never seen before, and yet many of them had a strangely familiar appearance.

There were hawks and swallows and woodpeckers in about the same numbers as one would see from a train window in eastern United States, but other groups flashed by in much greater variety. Instead of one species of hummingbird, for example, there were apparently four or five kinds, and the same was true of the brilliant tanagers. There were many more flycatchers, and there were birds of the oriole family (Icteridae) nearly as large as crows.

A LESSON IN GEOGRAPHICAL DISTRIBUTION

Still other groups of birds that one could never expect to see in the United States were much in evidence. Noisy little parakeets, for example, took the place of house sparrows, and gave the bird landscape an exotic appearance. In the forest I found warblers and vireos somewhat similar to those at home, but also many strange birds belonging to bird families I had never seen except in a museum or a zoölogical park. There were toucans with huge bills, and motmots with long racquet tails, and tree creepers, ant thrushes, cotingas, and honey creepers that one never sees while wandering in the northern forest.

Some groups of birds that are familiar companions in our New York and New England woodlands, like the nuthatches and the chickadees, and the shrikes discussed in this chapter, had no counterpart in this tropical jungle; and others, like the crows and jays and even the sparrows, were rare.

Without realizing it, I was enjoying a lesson in geographical distribution that was to make clear to me, as never before, the origin of our North American bird life and the meaning of bird migration. Had I ventured into a British woodland instead of a Panama forest, the birds might have appeared equally strange to me; but even more striking than the number of new birds seen would have been the absence of representatives of so many families that are found in North and South America.

In Britain there would have been no hummingbirds, no tanagers, no flycatchers, as we know them; no wood warblers, and no blackbirds and orioles.

On the other hand, there would have been more sparrows and buntings, more titmice, more crows and jays, more shrikes, and more of the birds belonging to the kinglet family.

How, then, can we explain the absence of hummingbirds from the English landscape and of titmice from Panama, and the presence of both in New England? Why are blackbirds and orioles, vireos and phainopeplas confined to the New World, while waxwings and shrikes are found on both sides of the Atlantic and Pacific Oceans?*

Evolution has taught us that not all species of birds and animals were developed at the same time, and that there has been a gradual extension of range as well as an evolution of structure. It is thus not difficult to conceive that each group of birds originated in some one part of the globe in distant past ages, and in succeeding ages endeavored to populate the world.

* The bird called "blackbird" in Britain is really a thrush, closely related to our robin.

THE MOTHER REDWING CLEANS THE NEST

After feeding her brood, she removes the bird lime from the nest and makes her home neat and comfortable

The reason that some should have been more successful than others is that some birds are much more prolific, aggressive, and adaptable than others.

NORTH AMERICAN BIRD LIFE HAS COME FROM TWO SOURCES

Compare the starling and the skylark, for example. Repeated attempts to introduce the skylark into North America have thus far been unsuccessful and the birds liberated have gradually disappeared. The starling, on the other hand, from an initial start in New York City in 1890, has in four decades spread to Florida, Texas, and Wisconsin, and over a great deal of this range is now one of the commonest birds.

And so it is with all of our birds; some groups have never spread very far from the place of their origin, while others —the hawks and the owls, the woodpeckers, the sparrows, the thrushes, and many more—are now found over the greater part of the earth.

North America has apparently become populated with birds from two sources. The Old World, by way of Alaska, has contributed such groups as the shrikes, the chickadees, and the nuthatches, which have not yet extended their range to Central and South America. It has given as well families such as the sparrows, thrushes, woodpeckers, and waterfowl, which are now cosmopolitan. South America has obviously contributed the hummingbirds, the warblers, the vireos, and the blackbirds and orioles.

These families have not yet extended their ranges to any part of the Old World, in spite of the wealth of species to be found in the land of their origin. Of the birds discussed in this article, therefore, we have the blackbirds and orioles, the vireos and the phainopeplas, that are manifestly of New World origin with no representatives in the Old World, and the shrikes and waxwings that have come into North America from the Old World.

One reason, perhaps, why the blackbirds and vireos have not spread more rapidly is that they are migratory, and each winter retire toward the land of their ancestors. The bobolinks, for example, spend scarcely more than three months on their breeding grounds in northern United States, and the other nine on the pampas of Brazil and Argentina, and in traveling back and forth.

Leaving the daisy fields of New York and New England before the middle of August, they assemble in flocks about our marshes, making their way by easy stages to the lowlands of the Southern States. About the last of October, while food is still very abundant and before the huge

Photograph by A. A. Allen

AN "EARTHQUAKE" UPSETS A REDWING'S HOUSE

Because of the growth of the sedges to which one side of the nest was fastened, the whole structure was gradually tilted until it capsized.

flocks of blackbirds that might compete with them for food have arrived from the North, they leave the United States entirely.

Flying a little east of south, they cross Cuba and Jamaica and the Caribbean Sea to Venezuela. Not content with this long flight, however, they continue in the same southeasterly direction over the llanos of Venezuela and the forests of the Amazon until they come to the wide prairies of southern Brazil and northern Argentina. What draws them to this vast area of sedge and marsh no one knows, unless it be that here the original bobolinks sprang from the ancestral blackbird stock.

But whether or not this area represents the original home of the bobolink, there they return with unfailing regularity each winter and there they spend about as much time as they do on their nesting grounds in the North, although, of course, like other birds, they do not nest at this season because they are physiologically unable to do so. So they merely travel about in small flocks until February, when they begin to feel the urge to start northward again.

Most members of the blackbird family are fine songsters, although their notes consist of relatively simple piping whistles. The simple *spring-is-here* piping of the eastern meadowlark, the clear, flutelike calls of the Baltimore oriole, *here, here; look right here, dear,* and the liquid *gurgle-lee* of the redwing are familiar to all Nature lovers in northeastern United States.

The more finished production of the western meadowlark and the finchlike warblings of the more southern orchard orioles are less familiar, though perhaps more to be admired. On the other hand, the rasping notes of the grackles and the shrill, squeaky whistle of the cowbird, and the squeals of the yellow-heads can scarcely be classified as music by any stretch of the imagination.

Even those species which cannot sing, however, have some method of appearing bigger and better than they really are, and thus intimidating their rivals. When the male redwing is at rest the scarlet epaulets often do not show at all. He then presents a modest appearance, with a narrow bar of buff across the wing. But when the bird takes flight the flash of red is a dazzling surprise which he apparently takes pleasure in displaying.

During the breeding season the redwing is often seen balancing on a cattail or flying up into the air with the scarlet feathers standing up on end and all the feathers of its body fluffed out. At such times he gives his *gurgle-lee* song with the greatest fervor.

The various grackles also have the habit of fluffing out their feathers and spreading their wings and tails when they utter their squeaky notes. This is carried to the extreme in the cowbird, which, while spreading its wings and tail and raising its feathers as it gives forth its shrill, squeaky note, pitches forward over the branch with a disquieting resemblance to seasickness.

FOOLED BY A STUFFED FEMALE

Apparently display of plumage is purely instinctive and a natural reaction, during the nesting season, of the male to the presence of a female or, indeed, of another male in his territory.

A few years ago, in connection with the study of the cowbird made at Cornell by Dr. Friedmann, we kept a captive male in a large flying cage, and, in an effort to obtain photographs of his display, we gave him a mounted specimen of a female cowbird for company. Although the female was far from being a well-mounted specimen, so captivating was she to the male bird that he displayed for her again and

again with all the ardor that he would bestow upon a live bird.

I have since repeated this experiment with other species and usually with the same result: that the male bird, during the mating period, cannot differentiate between the living and stuffed specimens.

BLACKBIRDS' BUILDING DIVERSIFIED

In nest building the members of the blackbird family show as much diversity as they do in color and habitat. The bobolink builds an open nest like a sparrow's in the meadow; in a similar situation the meadowlark makes a nest of long grasses and roofs it over like an old-fashioned Dutch oven; the redwing and the yellow-head hang their nests in the reeds of marshes; the grackles build plastered nests like robins', usually in trees; the orioles build long, beautifully woven, pocketlike nests, suspended at the tip of a branch; and the cowbirds build no nest at all.

In general, the duty of building the nest, whether it be simple or elaborate, falls on the female bird. The male's duty is to sing, announcing to others of his kind that he is prepared to drive them out of his territory should they dare to intrude, and to spread the alarm at the appearance of a hawk or other enemy.

Birds feel a greater attachment to their nesting sites than to their mates, and if one mate is lost another is promptly secured.

Ordinarily the bird allows six or seven days for nest construction, three for the outside and three or four for the lining. This is approximately the time required for the yellow yolk to be deposited about the ovum in the ovary, which starts concomitantly with the building of the nest.

Just how much control the bird can consciously exercise over her egg-laying is not known, but ordinarily one egg is laid each day until the normal number of four or five is complete. Some birds lay only every other day, and some can be stimulated to lay many more than the normal number by removing the second egg as often as laid. If the nests or eggs of birds of the blackbird family are interfered with before incubation begins, they usually desert and choose other sites.

The incubation periods of parasitic birds of this family are shorter than those of other birds which lay eggs of similar size. The period of the cowbird, for example, is ten days, while those of most birds which

Photograph by A. A. Allen

"YOU SHALL NOT HARM CROPS," SAYS THE BOBOLINK

Two enemies of the farmer, a grasshopper and an army worm, will soon become a meal for this little bird's young.

it parasitizes, such as sparrows, warblers, and vireos, average eleven or twelve. This gives the young cowbird a day's start on the rightful young, which is a great advantage, for birds do not feed their young in rotation and make sure that each has had an equal share of the food. Instead, they feed the hungriest one first, which is the one with the longest neck and the widest mouth.

Since the young cowbird is always thus equipped, he regularly gets the lion's share.

Members of the blackbird family do not feed their young by regurgitation, as do the waxwings and many birds, but ordinarily carry the food, consisting of insects and the like, in the bill and insert it into the gaping mouths of the youngsters. The contraction of the throat muscles in the action of swallowing is entirely automatic and dependent upon the mechanical stimulus of touching the base of the tongue.

The parent bird inserts its bill with food far enough into the throat of the young bird to produce the proper reaction. If she should not do this, the food, whether worm or grasshopper, would certainly crawl out, as many with good intentions have

learned when attempting to succor an orphaned bird.

After placing the food in the throat the mother watches to see whether it has been swallowed, and, if the throat muscles do not give the proper response immediately, she reaches down and pulls out the last bug and gives it to the next youngster.

After feeding, the nest is scrupulously cleaned, and in this group of birds the feces are enclosed in a mucous sac, so that they can be carried away. The young birds are ordinarily brooded by the female; at any rate, no male bird of this family has been observed sheltering the young from heat or cold, although he may be very diligent in feeding them. After they once leave the nest, they are never brooded again by either parent, no matter how hot or cold it may be, and they never return to the nest, although they may be fed by their parents for two or even three weeks longer.

Frequently meadowlarks, redwings, and yellow-heads have second nestings, and cowbirds are known to lay eggs as late as July. The bobolinks, orioles, and grackles, however, seem to be content with one brood, excepting when nests are broken up early.

Cowbird

(Molothrus ater)

Average Length, Seven and Three-quarters Inches

The cowbird is a social parasite that lays her eggs in the nests of other birds and foists her maternal duties on the foster parents.

If she lays her egg before her hostesses have laid theirs, the latter often desert their first nests and start again; but if they have already laid eggs they hatch hers out and rear her youngster with their own. In this task smaller birds—the redstart, or the yellow warbler, or the red-eyed vireo—are least successful.

These smaller birds are not able to raise any of their own young when they have hatched a cowbird in their tiny nest. Sometimes, however, they floor over the cowbird's egg and raise their family in safety above it.

A few species have learned to throw out the cowbird's egg, but the majority accept it as one of their own and are quite as solicitous for the care of the intruder as for their own young, although he may have pushed out or smothered all of them.

Experiments with those species, such as wrens and robins, that seldom or rarely accept cowbirds' eggs, indicate that this ability to note differences in size or color of eggs does not extend to recognition of the young; for, if young cowbirds hatched by some other bird are placed in robins' or wrens' nests, they accept them as their own.

I once removed a young cowbird from a yellow-throated vireo's nest and placed it in a house wren's nest in my garden. The young were approximately the same age, though far from the same size. The wrens succeeded in rearing four of their own young in addition to the cowbird. When, at the age of 10 days, the cowbird was ready to leave the nest, I put him in a cage beneath the nest box and the wrens continued to feed him for 12 days longer, at which time he finally escaped.

When the young cowbird leaves the nest he develops a most insistent food call and often waylays birds other than his foster parents and successfully begs food from them. Finally he joins a flock of young house sparrows and roosts in the ivy on the house; then he joins others of his kind and makes evening flights to the marsh to roost with redwings and starlings.

All over the United States and southern Canada, except in the southeastern corner and in the high mountains, small birds have these cowbirds to contend with. In western United States the species is divided into several varieties, but their habits are uniformly the same and they look almost identical.

The cowbird derives its name from its habit of following cattle for the insects attracted by them or stirred up by them as they plod along, and they are often seen feeding on the animals' backs. In early accounts of prairie life they were referred to as "buffalo birds."

Eastern Meadowlark

(Sturnella magna magna)

Average Length, Ten and Three-quarters Inches

The loud, clear whistle of the meadowlark, *Spring is here,* brings to my mind scenes of my boyhood in moist meadows, with pockets full of frogs and shoes caked with mud. The meadowlark has always said this to me and I suppose always will, long after my children have stopped catching frogs and tracking mud into the kitchen.

All winter the meadowlarks in small flocks gather in the old fields and barren pastures from Washington, D. C., southward to the Gulf. But as often as March comes round they start for their more northern nesting grounds. Why they should care to brave snow and ice by arriving early in March when they never start nesting until May is a mystery.

The males usually appear first in the spring and select certain song perches, from which they sally forth to drive others of their kind from the territory which they claim for themselves. The meadowlark is a rather shy bird, but I have often amused myself and members of my classes after an unsuccessful attempt to stalk a singing male by sitting quietly and imitating his song.

The whistle of the meadowlark is rather easy to approximate, and not much more is necessary at this season when he is "territory-mad." On quivering wings he approaches a supposed rival and circles about us, looking for the bird that dares to sing in his territory. The bird that had been so shy a few moments before now flies round us within 20 feet, and we have a wonderful opportunity to see his brilliant yellow breast with its black crescent and the conspicuous white patches in his tail.

By the middle of May one or more females have usually accepted each male's territory, the males being sometimes polygamous, and the nests are started under the dried grasses of the previous year. Sometimes they tunnel for a foot or more under the flattened grasses before they start the nest, which usually is arched over. In this safe retreat the four or five speckled eggs are laid and are incubated by the female, but the male is quite assiduous in feeding the young.

The eastern meadowlark ranges northward into southern Canada and westward into Kansas, Iowa, and Texas, where it meets the western meadowlark *(Sturnella neglecta)*, a paler species with the yellow extending to the cheeks (see page 208). The songs of the two species are more dissimilar than their plumages, that of the eastern species being short whistles, that of the western long and bubbling.

The smaller southern meadowlark *(S. m. argutula)* nests from southern Illinois and South Carolina southward, while the paler Rio Grande meadowlark *(S. m. hoopesi)* is found from Arizona to Texas.

A SOCIAL PARASITE AND A BIGAMIST

Too lazy to build nests or rear their own young, the **Eastern Cowbirds** (upper pair) play a tragic rôle in the lives of smaller birds. The female (right) has sneaked one of her large speckled eggs into a chipping sparrow's nest. Unless the foster mother builds a floor over the unwelcome present or ejects it, she will rear a ravenous Cowbird almost twice her size, while her own young may be crowded out, or starved. The **Eastern Meadowlark** (lower, and flying), sweet songster of our daisy fields, has induced more than one female to become his wife, but normally he is monogamous.

Bobolink

(Dolichonyx oryzivorus)

Average Length, Seven and One-quarter Inches

In this family of orioles and blackbirds the bobolink is so different that he has been placed in a genus by himself, and some would no doubt place him in a different family.

His bill is more sparrowlike than the others except the cowbird; his female is decidedly sparrowlike in her coloration and nesting habits; and his species is different from all other blackbirds in having pointed tail feathers, the reason for which has never been explained.

Besides this, the fact that most birds are colored lighter below than above, while the bobolink is just the reverse, and the fact that his song, given on the wing, has neither oriole nor blackbird quality, give us a peculiar sort of bird.

The bobolink passes the winter south of the Tropic of Capricorn, in southern Brazil and northern Argentina, nearly 5,000 miles south of his breeding grounds, in the northern United States and southern Canada.

The bobolink travels farther than any other member of his family. His migration exceeds by several thousand miles the distance traveled by the meadowlarks, cowbirds, and the different kinds of blackbirds, which merely retire to the Southern States or northern Mexico; and exceeds by more than a thousand miles even that of the orioles, which go to central and northern South America.

Despite the distance traveled, the bobolinks return with great regularity to their nesting grounds. In comparatively recent years the bobolink has extended its range to eastern Washington and British Columbia, and these birds are said to migrate eastward in the fall, so as to leave the United States by way of Florida or the Gulf coast.

The bobolinks' nests are difficult to find in the hayfield, because the birds prefer to place their inconspicuous cups of grasses in a little depression in the ground among dense grass or clover and they never fly directly to these homes. The gray eggs, heavily blotched with reddish brown, are likewise quite inconspicuous, and the yellowish-brown young, resembling the female, match well the dead grasses covering the ground.

During the summer they feed almost entirely upon insects destructive to the meadows and gardens, such as grasshoppers and army worms, and are among our most beneficial birds.

Before the bobolinks leave the fields and marshes of northern United States, they change all their feathers, and the new feathers of the males resemble very closely those of the females. With most birds, including the other members of the blackbird family, this complete post-nuptial moult is sufficient for the year, but the bobolinks change all their feathers and become bright again in the spring.

Brewer's Blackbird

(Euphagus cyanocephalus)

Average Length, Ten Inches

Out where the real West begins, the Brewer's blackbird takes the place of the bronzed grackle both in appearance and in habits. It has the same iridescent black plumage and pale yellow eye, and the same habit of walking about lawns with wings slightly drooped, and the same sort of rusty, squeaky notes.

It is a decidedly smaller bird, however, and the female is much grayer, more the color of a female cowbird, though its bill is longer and more slender. About the ranches and even in towns it is a familiar back-yard bird and is more given to lording it over the English sparrows and poultry than the eastern grackle.

It nests in small colonies, usually in a thick tree, but sometimes in bushes about marshes and on the outskirts of the colonies of yellowheads or redwings. With these birds it associates often in large flocks, after the nesting season is over, and then may do considerable damage in grain fields.

Brewer's blackbird breeds in the western United States, north to southern Canada, and east to Texas, Kansas, and Minnesota. It winters over most of this range and south to Guatemala.

Rusty Blackbird

(Euphagus carolinus)

Average Length, Nine and One-half Inches

During the summer the rusty blackbirds are confined to the boreal zones, and though found in western Canada as well as eastern, they begin where the Brewer's leave off and extend well up into Alaska. When migrating, they swing eastward and pass the winter mainly south of the Ohio and Delaware Valleys to the Gulf coast. Only occasionally are they found within the range of the Brewer's blackbird.

In fall and winter the edges of the feathers are margined with brown, those of the young females so widely as to make their whole bodies look brown like that of a sparrow. But these edges all wear off during the winter, leaving the males blue-black and the females almost as gray as catbirds.

Swampy thickets and the edges of wet woodlands afford feeding grounds for flocks of this blackbird, which we see mostly in the fall or winter when it comes south to more temperate latitudes. In willows, alders, or evergreens, usually close to water, it builds a bulky nest of twigs, grass and mud in which are laid four to six greenish-gray eggs thickly blotched with chestnut and purple.

When frightened from some woodland pool where they have been feeding, the whole flock will rise as a body into the trees and almost immediately start a concert of interesting if not musical gurgles and squeaks.

"BOB O' LINCOLN" TRAVELS IN DISGUISE AND UNDER ASSUMED NAMES

To the rollicking banjo songs of the "bridegroom" in his black, white, and buff "wedding dress," the **Bobolinks** (upper) nest in northern meadows. Then the male dons a dull suit for the flight of nearly 5,000 miles to the winter home south of the Amazon. In southern States farmers call them "rice-birds" and formerly many were shot as pillagers. Others are eaten as "butter-birds" in Jamaica. A handsome westerner is **Brewer's Blackbird** (right center pair). The **Rusty Blackbirds** (lower trio) vary from the greenish black of the pair at the left in summer to the rusty brown of the young deb in her fall frock (lower right).

Northern Shrike
(Lanius borealis)
Average Length, Ten and One-third Inches

There are more than 90 species and sub-species of true shrikes in the Old World, but only two have become established in the New World, although these two have split up into eight subspecies.

Once glance at the feet of shrikes and hawks will convince anyone that the two species are not related, for all the hawks have very strong feet, with sharp, curved talons that are used in catching their prey, while the shrikes depend upon their bills.

In spite of their predacious habits, the shrikes are songbirds of no mean ability, and in March, while still on their winter quarters, they may sometimes be heard singing much like a catbird. During the summer they move to northern Canada.

They are often called butcher birds because of the strange habit of impaling their prey of large insects, small birds, or mice on thorns.

I recall an unhappy day when a cardinal, which is a rare bird in New York State, came flying through my garden toward the house, pursued at some distance by a shrike. The cardinal could easily have eluded the shrike, but apparently was so frightened that it dashed against a window and fell dead at my feet.

The northern shrike nests from Ungava to southern Ontario and Quebec, in winter going south to Kentucky and North Carolina. The paler northwestern shrike (L. b. invictus) nests from Alaska and Mackenzie to Saskatchewan and winters from California to Texas.

Loggerhead Shrike
(Lanius ludovicianus)
Average Length, Nine Inches

This familiar bird divided into six related forms is a smaller and bluer edition of the northern shrike, with the black lores connected by a black line above the bill. It is represented in all parts of the United States, no kind differing greatly from the parent stock.

Being smaller, this bird feeds more upon insects than his Northern cousin, but he can be quite objectionable around feeding stations where small birds are numerous. He builds a bulky nest during April in a thick bush, leafy tree, or vine and is quite a devoted parent.

Because of their predacious habits, logger heads perch where they can view the landscape.

Bohemian Waxwing
(Bombycilla garrula pallidiceps)
Average Length, Eight Inches

This is the larger cousin of the cedar waxwing, but is very similar to it in habits. It nests in the Canadian Northwest from southern Alberta to Alaska, and in winter wanders irregularly southward and eastward, often joining bands of cedar waxwings.

Cedar Waxwing
(Bombycilla cedrorum)
Average Length, Seven and One-quarter Inches

The waxwing family, though distinctive in appearance and widely distributed, contains only three species. One species, the Japanese waxwing, is confined to eastern Asia; another species, the cedar waxwing, is confined to the United States and southern Canada; the third species, the Bohemian waxwing, is found almost throughout the Northern Hemisphere, though it is rare in eastern United States and also west of the Rockies.

The cedar waxwing has done a good job of colonizing North America, for it now breeds throughout southern Canada and most of the United States except California.

In migration, however, the species seems not to know what to do and is very erratic. Some years large numbers winter throughout the Northern States and the next winter none may appear over this area; instead they will swing south into Mexico and even to Panama.

Usually they congregate in the Southern States wherever dried berries are abundant and migrate northward in apple-blossom time. At this season they fill their throats with petals as few other birds do, or eat cankerworms or elm-leaf beetles from infested trees.

Their liking for fruit has given them the name of cherry bird in farming communities, and it is no uncommon sight to see a row of waxwings on a branch where only the outermost can reach the fruit, passing the cherry or mulberry from one to the next until one swallows it or passes it back.

Waxwings are late nesters, seldom starting before the middle of June and continuing into September, making rather untidy nests of grasses and woolly materials in tall bushes or in low branches of thickly leaved trees.

They feed their young, by regurgitation, a mixture of insects and berries, usually bringing back enough for the whole family in their distended throats. They often permit close approach while they are feeding their young.

Phainopepla
(Phainopepla nitens lepida)
Average Length, Seven and One-half Inches

The phainopeplas, or silky flycatchers, as they are called, belong to another strictly New World family, the Ptilogonatidae.

In habits they are like the flycatchers, perching on exposed branches and darting out at passing insects. They undoubtedly had their origin in the New World Tropics, and only one species, the phainopepla, has extended its range to include the United States, where it is now resident from western Texas to California.

In the phainopepla sex duties seem to be reversed. The males are often seen building nests and incubating eggs, but both parents help feed the young.

SONGBIRDS ALL—BUT SOME ARE HOOK-BEAKED KILLERS!

From the Old World immigrated the shrikes, or "butcher birds" (lower trio), which impale their prey on thorns and combine such predatory habits with a surprising ability to sing. Holding a field mouse is a young **Northern Shrike** with adult above. At the left is the smaller **Loggerhead Shrike.** Although related to them, the waxwings (upper right trio) have straight beaks and are gentle eaters of insects and fruit. The largest is the **Bohemian Waxwing,** and above him are **Cedar Waxwings** (young left, adult male right). The Southwest's **Phainopepla,** or silky flycatcher, eating peppertree berries, builds the nest for his somber, gadabout wife and helps to hatch the eggs.

Vireos

Average Length, Four and One-half to Six and
One-quarter Inches

The vireos constitute another New World family of birds of which the majority of the 75 species are confined to tropical America, only twelve reaching the United States. Were it not for their songs they might easily be overlooked, for they have neither the active flitting habits nor the bright colors of the warblers and flycatchers.

These greenish little birds, which are smaller than sparrows, spend their lives gleaning among the leaves of forest and shade trees or in the undergrowth, where their coloration is very protective. They are principally insectivorous, though they also feed to some extent on fruits and berries. Different kinds of larvæ and hairless caterpillars are among their most numerous victims, but any insect species is devoured greedily.

So loud and so oft-repeated are their songs, however, that anyone with an ear for bird music has no difficulty in finding them.

The nests of the vireos are pendent little baskets fastened at the rim in a small fork and made of fine vegetable fibers, mosses and lichens. The white eggs are usually spotted. The white-eyed and least vireos build in the undergrowth; the red-eyed and blue-headed in the lower branches of small trees; the yellow-throated in the center of a tree, on lateral shoots from the trunk; and the warbling vireo in the tree tops.

Most vireos are rather fearless of man, especially when nesting, and I have many times enjoyed the sensation of stroking a blue-headed or red-eyed vireo on its nest or of watching a yellow-throated at arm's length.

The song of the warbling vireo is a continuous warble, like that of a purple finch, but with a rising inflection at the end fitting the words, "If I could see it, I would seize it, and would squeeze it till it squirts."

The red-eyed vireo seems to say, "Look up—way up—tree top—etc.," while the yellow-throated sings more slowly and huskily, "Cherries—sweet cherries—have some." Both species keep up their refrains during the nesting season from daylight until dark.

The red-eyed vireo (Vireo olivaceus) everyone hears but few recognize. Widespread in summer throughout North America wherever there are trees, from central Florida to central British Columbia, it sings continuously from the time it arrives, in April or May, until it leaves for South America, in September or October. It frequents shade trees, woodlands and orchards. Its harsh, complaining call, red eye, and distinct white line above the eye are helpful identification marks. The red-eye has been called "preacher bird" because of its unceasing vocal efforts, continued even during the hottest parts of the hottest summer days when

most feathered creatures are silenced. This vireo is one of the birds that the female cowbird frequently selects to hatch her young.

In spite of its wide range, the red-eyed vireo shows remarkably little variation and has not been divided into any subspecies as have so many of the other vireos.

The warbling vireo (Vireo gilvus) is found from the Atlantic to the Pacific north of North Carolina and south of central Ontario. Its persistent warbling is often heard issuing from the singer's favored haunts among the tops of elms and other shade trees. This song is steadier and richer than that of the more abundant red-eye. Perhaps because of its inconspicuousness, it is one of the few North American birds whose winter home is not definitely known, though of course it is somewhere south of the United States. The red-eyed vireo winters from Colombia to Brazil, but the warbling probably does not go so far, for it returns to nest nearly a week earlier.

The least vireo (Vireo belli) lives in the thick brush of our arid Southwest and is more often heard than seen. It is a drab little bird that clings close to willows and thickets.

The blue-headed vireo (Vireo solitarius) is a striking bird, with its blue-gray head, pronounced white eye-ring, wing bars, and white throat. Its confiding ways and early migration northward before the leaves have unfurled make it better known, even though it is much less numerous than the red-eyed or warbling vireos. It ordinarily winters in the Gulf States and passes the summer in southern Canada. While resembling the notes of several of the sweetest-singing vireos, the song of the blue-headed is considered by some listeners to be the most flexible and beautiful of them all. This bird is remarkably tame, sometimes even permitting itself to be stroked while on the nest. The cool depths of evergreen forests are its favorite haunts during the nesting season. A great eater of caterpillars, it is one of our most useful forest guardians.

The white-eyed vireo (Vireo griseus griseus), because of its brushy haunts, is difficult to get acquainted with. In summer it is found throughout eastern United States as far north as southern New York and New England. A saucy, scolding voice and jerky, abrupt manners characterize this solitude-loving bird which has a reputation for mimicry.

The yellow-throated vireo (Vireo flavifrons) nests from northern Florida to central Texas and northward to Maine and east-central Saskatchewan. Its throaty song somewhat resembles that of the red-eyed vireo, but is louder, slower, and more buzzy. A conspicuous yellow breast makes it possible to pick it out up among the tree tops which it prefers.

The Hutton's vireo (Vireo huttoni huttoni) can be found west of the Sierras from Vancouver Island to Baja California.

WELL CAMOUFLAGED ARE THE VIREOS, WHOSE NAME MEANS "I AM GREEN"

They all build pendent nests, as do the orioles. Tireless singers, some repeat the same musical phrase over and over, as many as 4,000 times a day. At the left (top to bottom) are the **White-eyed Vireo,** which volubly scolds intruders; the West's **Least Vireo;** the **Warbling Vireo,** whose song ripples up to a marked crescendo; and the **Red-eyed Vireo,** or "preacher-bird," whose reiterated phrases suggest the robin's carol. At the right (top to bottom) are **Hutton's Vireo** of California; the **Yellow-throated Vireo;** and the **Blue-headed,** or solitary vireo, a wild, sweet, woodland singer of the northeastern United States and Canada.

A MEADOWLARK CAPTURES WHITE GRUBS AND BLACK CRICKETS

Aside from its cheerful call this avian policeman wins popularity by destroying crop pests.

Photographs by A. A. Allen

FOUR DAYS OLD, AND MOSTLY APPETITE

These young redwings sound a call for dinner. Their stomachs have amazing capacity.

OUR STATE BIRDS

OF LATE years the custom has developed of adopting a "State Bird." Already choice has been made by the organizations of 46 States and the District of Columbia.

In Alabama the question of which bird should be chosen created hot discussion. In the end the "yellow-hammer" was decided upon. The fight for its name was led by a women's patriotic organization, members of which directed attention to the historic fact that a company of Alabama youths had placed the bird's feathers in their caps and, designating themselves "yellow-hammers," had marched away, singing, to the Civil War.

OFFICIAL BIRDS HAVE BEEN CHOSEN BY MANY STATES

All the Commonwealths excepting Connecticut and Massachusetts have chosen representative birds. The list follows:

Alabama, the yellow-hammer.
Arizona, the cactus wren.
Arkansas, the mockingbird.
California, the California quail.
Colorado, the lark bunting.
Delaware, the cardinal.
District of Columbia, the wood thrush.
Florida, the mockingbird.
Georgia, the brown thrasher.
Idaho, the mountain bluebird.
Illinois, the cardinal.
Indiana, the cardinal.
Iowa, the eastern goldfinch.
Kansas, the western meadowlark.
Kentucky, the cardinal.
Louisiana, the brown pelican.
Maine, the chickadee.
Maryland, the Baltimore oriole.
Michigan, the robin.
Minnesota, the goldfinch.
Mississippi, the mockingbird.
Missouri, the bluebird.
Montana, the western meadowlark.
Nebraska, the western meadowlark.
Nevada, the mountain bluebird.
New Hampshire, the purple finch.
New Jersey, the goldfinch.
New Mexico, the road-runner.
New York, the bluebird.
North Carolina, the Carolina chickadee.
North Dakota, the western meadowlark.
Ohio, the house wren.

Oklahoma, the bobwhite.
Oregon, the western meadowlark.
Pennsylvania, the ruffed grouse.
Rhode Island, the bobwhite.
South Carolina, the Carolina wren.
South Dakota, the western meadowlark.
Tennessee, the mockingbird.
Texas, the western mockingbird.
Utah, the sea gull.
Vermont, the hermit thrush.
Virginia, the robin.
Washington, the willow goldfinch.
West Virginia, the tufted titmouse.
Wisconsin, the robin.
Wyoming, the western meadowlark.

Many people in Massachusetts regard the veery as their State bird, but this has not been officially recognized, the State Legislature having voted it down on the ground that it goes to Florida for the winter. In some cases the choice of a bird has been made by legislative or executive authority, but more often by State federations of women's clubs or Audubon societies.

It would be strange indeed if our land, with its vast extent of territory, its diversified landscape, its extensive forests, its numerous lakes and streams, with its mountains, prairies, and plains, had not been provided by Nature with an abundant and diversified bird life. As a matter of fact, America has been favored with many kinds of birds famed both for beauty and for song. Little wonder, then, that the States have given recognition to feathered friends.

STATES RECOGNIZE BIRD FRIENDS AS A POLICE FORCE

In considering the many kinds of birds in the United States from the practical side, they may not inaptly be compared to a police force, the chief duty of which is to restrain within bounds the hordes of insects that, if unchecked, would devour every green thing.

To accomplish this task successfully, the members of the force must be variously equipped, as we find they are. The nearly 800 species of birds that inhabit the United States and Canada can be grouped in families which resemble each other in a general way, yet among the members of the several families are marked variations of form and plumage and still greater variation of habits, fitting them for diversified duties.

A SUMMER FLAME FROM THE TROPICS IS DAPPER "LORD BALTIMORE"

Sporting the colors of Maryland's founder, the male **Baltimore Oriole** (upper right) surveys his domain and whistles cheerily—while his lady weaves a beautiful hanging home of strings and plant fibers. Dressed richly and in perfect taste, an adult male **Orchard Oriole** (center) sings a bubbling song to his spouse (below) and to a second-year male, who matches the mother except for his black "bib." Not until the third summer can the youngster wear the gay colors of his father. The birds feed largely on insects, with a dessert of mulberries or cherries in season.

Baltimore Oriole

(Icterus galbula)

Average Length, Seven and One-half Inches

There is a silver maple shading my drive where for the last 15 or 20 years a Baltimore oriole has hung its nest. It has not been the same pair of birds all these years, for one year both birds were taken by a screech owl and other fatalities also have occurred. Once a pair of orioles decide a tree is to their liking, and raise their young in it successfully, it is likely to be used by them or other orioles indefinitely.

Securely woven from strings and milkweed fibers, the nest hangs to the tips of the branches through the storms of winter to give mute testimony that an oriole family chose this tree for their home the preceding year, and perhaps that in itself is sufficient to encourage others to accept it.

And so each May 4 or 5 we welcome the cheery whistle of Lord Baltimore when he comes back to look over his domain. If he arrives on time we assume that all has gone well with him during the winter in Central America; but if he is late we fear that something has happened to him.

A few days after the male has taken up his stand, a female arrives, and his song is redoubled. A whistled imitation of it brings him like a flash to drive out the intruder. We put out short lengths of light-colored yarn or string, and in a few days Lady Baltimore is busy weaving her nest, usually starting at the top and working down and putting on all the finishing touches from the inside.

Then the eggs are laid—one each day for four or five days; and though from my window I can no longer see the female deep down in the nest, I can occasionally see the flexible pocket shake as she adjusts the eggs beneath her, and I know that in twelve days the male, too, will be absorbed in family duties from which thus far he has escaped all responsibility.

For about two weeks we can see them flying to the dark spot, now concealed by leaves, wherein the youngsters are doubling and trebling in size and budding and growing feathers, but all is relatively quiet. On a certain day, however, a change comes over the household. We are now aware of different voices in the tree. Lord Baltimore himself has become quiet—the cares of filling four hungry mouths and the lack of necessity for defending his territory have calmed him. But we hear insistent cries from hungry youngsters. It is a sign they are nearly ready to leave the nest and have developed the food call which will enable their parents to find them after they have scattered from the nest. And what crybabies they are from early dawn until dark!

Through June and July they all visit the mulberry tree and occasionally we hear fragmentary whistles from the male. But this does not last long, for in late summer they all moult and grow new feathers for the winter which, strangely enough, are similar to those worn during the summer. Usually, brightly colored birds such as tanagers and goldfinches wear dull feathers like the females during the winter. But the Baltimore oriole wears the same colored suit winter and summer.

While the Baltimore oriole's nest must originally have been made entirely of natural materials, these are now relinquished in favor of yarn, string, cotton, paper, cloth and hairs that man has brought with him. Apparently the birds have a keen eye for protective coloration, for some have been seen avoiding bright colored stuff where more sober materials were available. However, individuals that have confidence in the protection assured by the location and shape of their nests have been known to use gaudy and dull materials impartially. Nest-building is the female's task, and while she is busy with strings, plant fibers and vegetable downs, Mr. Baltimore sits affably, whistling his love and preening his feathers.

Cotton boll-weevils form part of its food, but caterpillars are the largest dietary item. Many other kinds of insects are eaten, among them plant lice, grasshoppers, ants and spiders.

This oriole prefers rather open country among shade and orchard trees, road- and creek-side groves and the edges of woodlots. Towns and cities, if they provide suitable nesting trees, are readily accepted places of residence. The bird's call and song notes are quite varied and very difficult to reproduce in words or combinations of letters, though many entertaining attempts have been made to do this. Thoreau translated an oriole's whistle as, "Eat it, Potter, eat it!"

During the summer the Baltimore oriole is found from southern Canada nearly to the Gulf and west to the Rockies, and shows so little variation that it is not divided into subspecies. It winters from Mexico to Colombia.

Orchard Oriole

(Icterus spurius)

Average Length, Seven and One-third Inches

Of less widespread distribution is the orchard oriole, which scarcely ever reaches the Canadian border. It is most numerous in the South Central States, where it frequents orchard and shade trees and weaves a nest of freshly dried grasses, which hangs less freely than that of the Baltimore, usually resting against the branch. For some reason it seems partial to trees where kingbirds have already established themselves, and lives in friendly relations with this ordinarily quarrelsome bird.

During the winter the orchard orioles frequent the same range as the Baltimores.

Both orioles are insectivorous and very beneficial, being among the comparatively few birds that like to dine on hairy caterpillars.

SOME BRIGHT AND BREEZY ORIOLE COUSINS FROM THE OPEN SPACES

    Bullock's Oriole (upper trio) is a favorite with western bird lovers, as the Baltimore is in the East. His song may be a bit less musical, but his flashing colors are more conspicuous among the cottonwoods. Like the orchard oriole, the young male (upper right) masquerades in lady's dress with black V-neck. **Scott's Oriole** (lower left pair) haunts the misshapen Joshua trees of the arid Southwest and hangs its cup-shaped, fiber nest to the undersides of the yucca's stiff leaves.   Perched in a mesquite is a pair of **Hooded Orioles** (lower right).

Bullock's Oriole
(Icterus bullocki)
Average Length, Seven and One-half Inches

What the Baltimore oriole is to eastern United States the Bullock's oriole is to the west, the ranges of the two species overlapping only from the foothills of the Rockies to central South Dakota, Nebraska, Kansas, and Texas. In winter the Bullock's oriole retires to Mexico and Central America. In summer it ranges from the tableland of Mexico to southern British Columbia and Alberta. It occurs less frequently on the Pacific coast than in the Great Basin regions, where it is abundant, particularly in brushy lowland growths beside desert water courses. It comes north from its winter haunts in Mexico toward the end of March and takes a month or six weeks to attain the northern sections of its range.

It is fond of tall sycamores and cottonwoods, though where these are not found it may nest in low willows, especially along irrigation ditches or streams.

Its nest, like that of the Baltimore oriole which it closely resembles, is a hanging masterpiece of woven vegetable fibers, bark and horsehair skilfully lined with wool and other soft materials. Because the builder frequents less populous regions, on the whole, than the Baltimore oriole, less string and other man-made stuff is found in its nests. Some nests are so carefully wrought that they survive the winds and storms of several winters.

The ability to turn out a finished nest is not inherited by the young birds, which at first build coarse and imperfectly supported homes. This lag indicates a gradual maturing which is borne out by the fact that it takes a young male three or four years to attain his finest appearance. This oriole's three to six eggs are a trifle paler than those of the Baltimore. Incubation seems to be done exclusively by the female and takes about two weeks.

In the summer, Bullock's oriole adds wild fruits and some cultivated cherries and apricots to its diet of bugs and caterpillars. On the whole, it is a friend of the farmer and gardener. Its call notes are like those of the Baltimore, but the song lacks the sweetness and melody of that of the eastern relative.

After the breeding season the bird, like all other birds, changes all its feathers. The new plumage is similar to that shown in the plate, except that most of the feathers are edged with grayish or whitish, causing the birds to appear much duller. As spring advances, these gray tips wear off and the bird appears to become much brighter. This masking of the bright colors during the winter and brightening the plumage by feather-wear occurs in all the species of orioles and blackbirds and, indeed, is commoner among all birds than actual renewal of feathers in the spring.

Scott's Oriole
(Icterus parisorum)
Average Length, Eight Inches

In the semiarid regions of our Southwest this handsome lemon-yellow and black oriole is particularly welcome. Of active disposition and often making long flights from one clump of yuccas to the next, his flash of color gives many a thrill to the traveler. His high, clear whistled song is somewhat suggestive of the western meadowlark, and while it has not the wide range and throaty quality of the meadowlark, it has perhaps greater vivacity. The female Scott's oriole, too, in her plain grayish brown and yellow, sings nearly as well as the male, though not so loudly or long.

This oriole often places its nest only a few feet above the ground under the drooping leaves of a yucca. Two to four blotched eggs are laid in a neatly woven basket of grass, plant fibers, horsehair and cotton which usually is not as free hanging as the abodes of other orioles.

Among the most familiar sounds of nature in the deeply scored canyon country of the Southwest are the clear whistled notes of the Scott's oriole which is found on steep rocky slopes among agaves, yuccas and other sparse desert vegetation. This bird's food is largely made up of caterpillars, insects and their larvæ, wild fruits and berries, and is like that of other orioles.

During the winter months the Scott's oriole retires into Mexico, but comes back again the following April to remain until August or September.

Hooded Oriole
(Icterus cucullatus)
Average Length, Seven Inches

The hooded oriole ranges through the chaparral and cottonwoods of southwestern New Mexico, southern Arizona, and southwestern California.

Dense groves in the bottom lands along water courses are enlivened by this bird's harsh calls as it flits from bush to bush. It is always on the alert for insects and their larvæ, caterpillars and grasshoppers.

The nest is a firmly suspended basket and is usually woven, in large part, of the fibrous portions of the particular kind of tree in which it is built and lined with soft vegetable downs. The three to five bluish-white eggs are spotted and penciled in brown, principally on the large end.

During the winter these brilliant birds retire into Mexico, but by the first of April they are back in their old haunts and ready once more to hang their beautiful cuplike nest to the edge of a palm leaf or a yucca, or in the upper branches of a cottonwood.

THEIR COATS OF MANY COLORS MAY SWIFTLY CHANGE TO DEEPEST MOURNING

Iridescent greens and purples vary with the sunlight in the plumage of the grackles, and at times disappear altogether, leaving the birds a gloomy black. As if in pain, the "crow blackbird," or **Purple Grackle** (upper, with mate), grates out raucous squeaks like the creaking of a rusty wheelbarrow. Sometimes it gobbles the eggs and nestlings of smaller birds. Larger and partial to marshland is the South's **Boat-tailed Grackle** (lower). The males have a way of deserting their brownish wives until the work of raising the young is over. Where they abound, their appetite for young sprouts is the farmer's despair.

Purple Grackle

(Quiscalus quiscula quiscula)

Average Length, Thirteen Inches

Crow blackbirds we called them as young-sters, and I can never forget the wonder of it when once at close range in full sunlight I saw one and discovered that he was not black like a piece of coal, but wonderfully and iridescently purple and green and bronze; and then as he turned and the sun struck him at a different angle he was just a plain blackbird once more. Another discovery was his yellow eye, which looked so pale in the sunlight as to be almost white; and then, when the pair of birds flew and the male held his long tail half spread toward the tip and folded so as to appear like the keel of a boat, I had still another surprise.

Every fall long files of crow blackbirds flew southward over the city—sometimes only 50 or 75 birds wide, but the flocks were possibly a mile long. People complained then as now of the noisy roosts where the birds congre-gated by the tens of thousands before moving to the southern States for the winter.

Every March, however, we were glad to have the "blackbirds" come back and we watched them carry dry crusts to the water and soak them before trying to eat them. Late in April we watched them carrying grasses and rags and bills full of wet mud into the tops of the Norway spruces, where they built nests like those of large robins, with an outer layer of coarse materials, a middle layer of mud, and a lining of grasses.

How we boys prized those large greenish-white eggs with their varied scrawls of dark brown and black! No two of them were ex-actly alike and we had great times bartering with each other, because this bird was not pro-tected by law and we felt then that we had a perfect right to all the eggs we could find. Thus does lack of legal protection stigmatize any species.

These were the bronzed grackles, found west of the Alleghenies. All those crow blackbirds that breed between the Rockies and the Alle-ghenies north to Great Slave Lake, and south to Georgia, are recognized as belonging to this subspecies, the bronzed grackle *(Q. q. aeneus)*, while those east of the Alleghenies from New England to Georgia are the purple grackle. The Florida grackle *(Q. q. aglaeus)* ranges from South Carolina and Florida.

The purple grackle is a bird that does much good in the springtime by gleaning grub worms from newly plowed fields and by seizing multi-tudes of insects to feed to its young. It can-not be condemned for eating a few fish, mice and snails, but its taste for grain, which makes up 45 per cent of its total food, is certainly reprehensible. It is also to be blamed for its nest-robbing propensities.

The grackle's attempts at song are pathetic and discordant. A raucous squeak is the best it can produce, but it never loses hope and keeps right on practicing.

But in spite of all this that can be listed against it, the purple grackle is a handsome bird, with its iridescent plumage on head, neck and shoulders. It takes itself very seri-ously as it walks stiffly and sedately over fields and lawns. This appearance of pompous self-importance is accentuated by the fishy stare of its prominent yellow eyes.

Boat-tailed Grackle

(Cassidix mexicanus major)

Average Length, Sixteen Inches

One familiar with the purple grackle will immediately recognize the boat-tail as a larger edition of the same bird unless perchance he sees the female first. In her brown plumage she might be very puzzling; but the males of the two species are quite alike except that the boat-tail is some four inches longer. In the South, this bird goes by the name of "jackdaw" or "thrush blackbird." It is quite unlike the European jackdaw, however. Like the others of its kind, this grackle passes a good part of its life on the ground searching for food with the absurd strutting walk characteristic of its smaller purple cousin.

The boat-tails are partial to water and may often be seen wading clear up to their breasts in the shallows, snatching aquatic insects, scuds, or little fish. They feed in small flocks, even during the nesting season, and, for some reason, the males seem always to outnumber the females. Sometimes they nest in the saw grass like redwings, sometimes in the willows among the herons, and again they may conceal their nests in the curtains of Spanish moss hanging from cypress trees.

The nest is a compact, bulky assemblage of sticks, grass, roots and seaweed, usually stiff-ened with a core of mud. Three to five drab bluish-white eggs spotted and marked with purplish-brown and black are usually laid be-tween March 20 and the beginning of May, depending on the geographical situation.

The males desert their mates either as soon as the eggs are laid or after the young can take care of themselves. Gathering together in flocks, they range up and down the country-side, pilfering and squalling. After household cares end, the females also band together.

Much of the boat-tailed grackle's food comes from the sea—small mollusks and crustaceans, occasional dead fish and offal. It also eats in-sects. But as a consistent consumer of corn, this grackle is an enemy of the agriculturist. It is found in the South Atlantic and Gulf States, north to Chesapeake Bay and west to Texas. The related great-tailed grackle *(C. m. mexi-canus)* ranges from Texas to Colombia.

GENERALS OF THE MARSHES PARADE IN GOLD BRAID OR BRILLIANT EPAULETS

Across the western plains and prairies fly the legions of the **Yellow-headed Blackbird** (upper pair and flying). His wings are marked with white chevrons and his "song" is a series of uncouth cries, like a choking spell. Below him at the left clings California's **Tricolored Redwing,** with his drab spouse. Best known of the group is the **Eastern Redwing** (bottom trio). The veteran at the left proudly displays blazing "shoulder straps," edged with buff instead of white, while he sends forth his liquid *ok-a-lee*. His mate (center) and two-year-old son (right) wear just a hint of his insignia.

Yellow-headed Blackbird

(Xanthocephalus xanthocephalus)

Average Length, Ten and One-half Inches

This denizen of the marshes helps make the waste areas attractive, though I must admit he can lay no claims to being a musician. What he lacks in musical ability, however, he makes up in effort, puffing out his throat and spreading his wings and tail as he balances on a reed and gives vent to a song that sounds more like "the drawl of a discontented hen" than that of many of his clear-voiced relatives.

The heavy, rolling song of the young birds is much less harsh and ridiculous than that of the parents, though even that is not melodious enough to inspire such poetry as has been written about other blackbirds' notes.

In his other habits, however, he is much like the redwing, hanging his nest in the reeds of the marshes, gathering in large flocks after the nesting season, moving to the uplands to feed on grain and weed seed, and returning at evening to the roosting place in the marshes.

This is one of the most striking of the blackbirds in its sleek black coat, contrasting yellow cap, scarf and apron, and two prominent white epaulets. Yellow-headed blackbirds are very sociable, usually nesting in compact colonies. But during the breeding season they apparently do not get along very well with other kinds of blackbirds. At least they take care to nest at a distance from other species.

Their swaggering walk contrasts absurdly with ineffectual vocal attempts. One of the borderline birds from the point of view of its effect on agriculture, the yellow-head does harm by eating cultivated grains and much good by destroying injurious insects and their eggs and larvæ.

During the summer the yellow-heads are found from Mexico north to central Manitoba and Mackenzie, east to Wisconsin, Illinois and Indiana. In winter they retire for the most part into Mexico.

Tricolored Redwing

(Agelaius tricolor)

Average Length, Nine Inches

Just what happened to separate the redwings of the San Joaquin and Sacramento Valleys of California and Oregon from the parent stock and make them uniformly different we shall probably never know. At present, however, the males show a clear white edging to their scarlet shoulders, their bills are more slender, and their females are uniformly darker. Their voices, too, perhaps because of the Pacific coast climate, perhaps for some other reason, have changed and lost some of the liquid quality of the Eastern redwing.

In other respects, however, the habits and appearance of the tricolored redwing are essentially the same as those of the other redwings.

Eastern Redwing

(Agelaius phoeniceus phoeniceus)

Average Length, Nine and One-half Inches

Each spring for the last twenty years it has been my privilege to introduce a group of students to the bird life of the eastern United States. Most of them have never before ventured near the marshes.

Early in March the redwings come back from the Southern States, where they have been passing the winter, the males sometimes two weeks ahead of the streaked females and the old birds ahead of the immature males, which can be recognized by their orange shoulders. At first they travel in flocks, being most often seen in daytime on the uplands and at night in the marshes, but when the summer resident males arrive in late March they select their territories, and will be found in the marsh all day long.

Nesting, however, does not begin until about the middle of April, and is not in full swing until the middle or last of May. Even at this time immature females are still arriving from the South, and sometimes they settle down in the territories of mated pairs, for redwings are sometimes polygamous.

A large percentage of the early nests are capsized by the rapidly growing vegetation to which one side of the nest may be fastened. Many a time I have found nests tipped on one side, and only a single half-grown young remaining to give mute evidence of what must have become of his unfortunate nest-mates. Later nests and second-brood nests are usually safely suspended in the growing vegetation.

By the last of June the young birds are gathering in flocks and moving around, sometimes accompanied by a few old males, though the majority of old birds are still busy with their second broods.

The immature birds, even the males, resemble the females in their streaked gray and black plumage; but before fall they shed all these feathers, and then the young males resemble more the old males in winter plumage, except that their shoulders are orange instead of red and the black feathers are much more broadly edged with brown.

There is no spring moult, but the brown edges wear off completely by March, leaving the familiar coal-black.

The redwing deserves full protection throughout most of its range. By eating weed seeds, and weevils and other harmful insects, it more than makes up for the comparatively slight damage done to grain crops.

The redwing is found from the Atlantic to the Pacific and from the Gulf of Mexico to Alaska, but from place to place it differs somewhat in size and proportions, especially of its bill and wing, so that the species has been divided into fourteen subspecies.

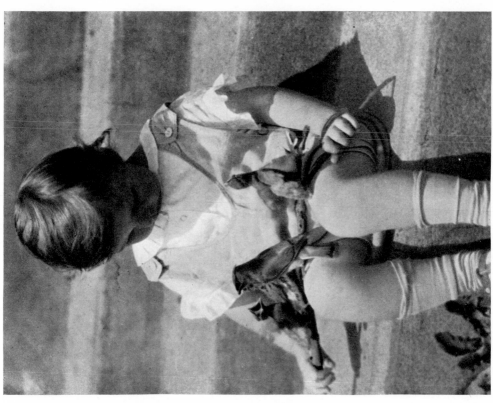

Photographs by A. A. Allen

WHAT A TEA PARTY, WITH MOTHER WAXWING BRINGING FOOD

It is a fortunate little girl who can win the confidence of such playmates. The female bird feeds her young without fear.

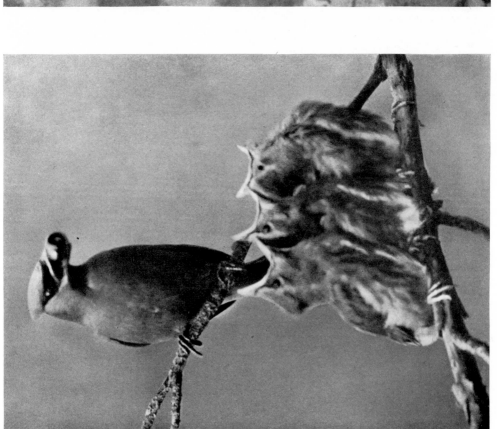

"ME FIRST," THEY SEEM TO SAY

No matter which of the three little cedar waxwings gets the berry the mother holds in her bill, she has in her throat other tidbits for the rest.

THE TANAGERS AND FINCHES

Their Flashes of Color and Lilting Songs Gladden the Hearts of American Bird Lovers East and West

By Arthur A. Allen

ROSO, our Indian hunter, was obviously excited. He was familiar with most of the birds in the rain forest which caps the central Andes of Colombia, where we were camped, and he knew of our interest in any new or rare species. Whenever he discovered any bird strange to him, his natural reticence gave way to captivating enthusiasm.

Silently we stole down the dank trail through the moss-covered oaks until we came to a clearing where stood a large tree in full bloom with inconspicuous, greenish-white flowers. If the flowers were inconspicuous, the birds which flitted through the branches certainly were not.

COLORS FLASH LIKE JEWELS

There were bright-green cotingas with red faces, others with heavenly blue backs and flashing yellow breasts; there were iridescent Callistes, other tanagers of several varieties, and honey creepers and hummingbirds that flashed like jewels.

But all these we had seen before and had learned to expect in the flocks that frequented the treetops of this temperate area near the Equator. Where, then, were the wonderful new birds that Roso had discovered?

"Look!" Roso pointed his finger toward a smaller tree as a flash of yellow and black and red marked their presence. To my eye they were no more brilliant than the tree full of chatterers and honey creepers, but to Roso they were "new birds," wonderful in their yellow bodies blending into red on their heads and set off by black wings and tails. They were tropical tanagers of a kind so similar to our own western tanagers that at first I thought some of these must have strayed southward from their winter quarters in Costa Rica instead of going north into the United States. I told Roso that they were birds from the North.

"Ah," he exclaimed, "we have many lovely birds here in the Tropics, but when your birds come down from the North they are so much more beautiful!"

Previously I had explained to him how the little redstarts and the yellow and the Blackburnian warblers, which he knew as winter visitors, passed the summer with me in New York. He could hardly be blamed for thinking of the United States as having the most beautiful birds, even though we in the North are equally certain that all the most brilliant birds are to be found in the Tropics.

THERE IS NO BLUE PIGMENT IN COLORS OF BIRDS

It will not be surprising if many readers ask why there is not a more tropical setting to the accompanying beautiful paintings by Major Brooks, or if all these lovely colors exist on our own birds.

"Look! An indigo bunting!" We direct a friend's glance to the telegraph wire where we have heard a familiar song and see a well-known figure with its head thrown back and its bill open.

"What! That little black sparrow sitting on the wire? Why do you call it indigo? There is nothing blue about it." Such is the response of our prosaic friend. The next instant the bird flies down to a dandelion by the roadside and what was a little black bird on the wire becomes an intense indigo-blue creature, merely by a change in the angle at which the light comes from it to our eyes.

There is no blue pigment in the feathers of birds; neither, with rare exceptions, is there any green. The only pigment colors in ordinary birds' feathers are reds and yellows and blacks, and all the other colors are due either to a combination of these or to the superficial structure of the feathers overlying some other pigment.

Blue feathers, for example, contain only brown or blackish pigment overlaid by a layer of prismatic cells which reflect only blue light rays. Sometimes the structure

Photograph by A. A. Allen

THIS WAS HARDLY THE MOTHER'S IDEA OF A HELPING HAND

But female scarlet tanagers are often fearless, and she went right ahead feeding her youngsters despite the strange "nest" in which she found them.

is that of minute pits on the surface of the feathers. When they become filled with water during a rain, they lose their refractive power, and the birds, apparently, change from blue to white, as in the tropical swallow tanagers.

Again, the blue color is due to minute air spaces in the superficial layer of cells, just as the blueness of the sky is due to minute dust particles, and the blueness of the milk on the boarding house table to the minute cream droplets. So long as our blue birds remain between us and the source of light, they are not blue birds at all and therefore may go unnoticed.

YELLOW BIRDS ARE CONSPICUOUS

Yellow birds are usually conspicuous because our eyes are very sensitive to yellow. But many birds have a blue-producing structure overlaid by a yellow pigment, so that the combination sends green light to our eyes. Then we say these birds are green. Wet the back of a parrot and it be-

comes brown, or scratch the surface of one of the green feathers with a knife and a dark mark is left. This is not because any green pigment is scratched off, but because the yellow and the prismatic cells have been removed and the dark layer beneath exposed.

But there seem to be many red birds among these tanagers and finches. Why do we not see them more often? Certainly we have no trouble seeing a red traffic light—indeed, most of them seem to be that color when we are in a hurry. There are some reds, such as the iridescent throats of the hummingbirds, for which the structure of the feathers is responsible. But most reds, such as those of the tanagers and finches here shown, are due to pigment, and they register as red under all light conditions. To be really effective, however, the red must be exposed to direct sunlight.

Should a scarlet tanager alight in the middle of a sunlit lawn or a cardinal fly across the open space in a garden, either bird would attract attention, but most of the time they are sitting among the shadows of green leaves, where they are poorly lighted. The sunlight is reflected from the leaves more readily than from the birds, especially since our eyes are peculiarly sensitive to greens. Anyone who has trained his ear to recognize the songs and calls of the birds can easily find ten tanagers, while another, who has not learned to use his ears, will have difficulty in finding one.

During the winter many birds have their conspicuous marks veiled by gray edges to the feathers. These edges break off during the spring, exposing the color underneath. The male house sparrow, for example, in winter seems to have only a narrow line of black on his throat, because the rest of his black cravat is concealed by the gray tips of the feathers, which break off during April.

THE FEMALES ARE NOT BRIGHT HUED

Red finches display no such gray edges to the feathers. But upon examining a feather with a lens, one will find that the red pigment occurs only in the main branches of the leaflike structure, the parts called the shaft and the barbs, while the more minute branches, or barbules, are gray. As these barbules wear off, the barbs with their color become more exposed and the feathers apparently get brighter. Thus the red finches (the purple finch, house finch, and redpolls) apparently brighten as spring advances.

Were we to classify birds by color alone, we should have to place the males and females of these tanagers and finches in separate species; indeed, almost in distinct families. The greatest confusion would occur when we had to put the same individual in two distinct species during winter and summer, for many of the brightest males, like the scarlet tanagers, rose-breasted grosbeaks, and indigo buntings, become dull like their mates during the winter.

It would be convenient if we could say that whenever males and females are different, the males assume the plumage of the females during the winter. But this is true only with certain species, while others persist in breaking the rule.

Thus the summer tanager male remains red throughout the year, and so do the cardinal, the purple finch, the pine grosbeak, and the crossbills. The yellow evening grosbeak never becomes gray like his mate, once he has acquired maturity, though the male goldfinch does.

No one has yet advanced a satisfactory explanation for these differences in seasonal styles among the males, but the inference is that the females are dully colored so as not to attract attention to the nest. Usually the brilliantly colored males in this family never assist in incubating the eggs, but even here there are exceptions, as in the rose-breasted and black-headed grosbeaks. Males of these birds not only sit on the eggs, but even break all rules of bird conduct by singing as they do so.

Whether because of the singing, or because of the bright colors of the incubating male, or because of the general fragility of the nest, there is a relatively high nest mortality among the rose-breasted grosbeaks, and some years very few young are reared. Then the species becomes scarce, because grosbeaks are not so persistent about re-nesting as are some other birds.

There is no one place in North America where all of the birds here illustrated can be found. The pyrrhuloxia, hepatic tanager, beautiful bunting, and Sharpe's seed-eater, for example, are not found very far north of the Mexican border. The pine and evening grosbeaks, redpolls, and crossbills are northern birds that, even in migration, seldom reach the southern States.

EAST AND WEST DIVIDE SPECIES

The lazuli bunting, black-headed grosbeak, western tanager, rosy finch, house finch, green-backed and Lawrence's goldfinches are birds of the Pacific coast and the Rocky Mountain region, while the rose-breasted grosbeak, scarlet tanager, and indigo bunting are primarily birds of the eastern United States.

It is difficult to explain why each species has a restricted summer home when it is free to come and go as it pleases and often migrates extensively. It is still more difficult to explain how this whole group of birds got into North America originally. Certain of them, such as the tanagers, the cardinals, the blue, rose-breasted, and black-headed grosbeaks, and the "buntings," have close relatives in Central and South America and none in the Old World. Hence, we feel that our species came originally from the south. Furthermore, most of them are quite migratory and tend to return to the land of their ancestors each winter.

Photograph by A. A. Allen

HIS WINTER SUIT IMPROVES WITH WEAR

Gray tips to new feathers, grown in the fall, conceal the black, white, and chestnut of the male house sparrow, but the ends wear off before spring. Then the fresh, black throat-patch and chestnut head-stripe make this chirping English immigrant look his best.

On the other hand, the evening grosbeak and several other kinds of birds described here have almost exact counterparts in Asia and Europe. This leads us to suppose that either our species came from Asia, when Alaska and Siberia were continuous and when a subtropical climate existed clear to the Arctic Circle, or else that the Old World species emigrated from North America at that time.

In attempting to arrange all birds in an orderly series to show their relationships, ornithologists derive the family of finches (Fringillidae) from the families lower in the scale of evolution through the tanagers or tanagerlike birds, and they place the Fringillidae at the top of the avian series. Certainly today, the family of finches is more numerous than any other, more than 800 species and subspecies being known from the Western Hemisphere alone.

FINCHES FOUND EVERYWHERE EXCEPT AUSTRALIA

All grosbeaks, finches, sparrows (except the English, or house, sparrow), buntings, linnets, juncos, towhees, and crossbills,

belong to the Fringillidae. The tanagers form a separate but closely related family.

The members of the finch family are found all over the world, except in Australia. The family includes such familiar cage birds as the canary and linnet, but is now thought to exclude the familiar little house sparrow, which everyone calls a sparrow. Recent studies indicate that this street gamin really belongs to the family of weaver birds (Ploceidae), best represented in Africa, where the bright colors of some species and the interestingly woven nests of others have long made them famous as cage birds. The Australian "finches" also are assigned to this family of weaver birds.

Occasionally the house sparrow builds a nest among the branches of a tree instead of in a cranny of a building. Then he shows his weaver-bird affinity, for the nest is a large, untidy, globular affair with the hole near the bottom of one side.

The tanagers and finches are relatively poor nest builders, though an exception is the goldfinch, which makes a beautiful abode of cotton or thistledown (see illustration, page 239). The nest of the indigo

Photograph by A. A. Allen

THE LAST WORD IN HOMEMAKING—A COTTON NEST

For nest lining, goldfinches readily adopt this material in place of thistledown. Put it out in a conspicuous place, and the birds may make their home in a garden that otherwise would fail to attract them.

and the other "buntings" also is more elaborate and thick-walled, with a mixture of dead leaves among the grasses, fibers, and rootlets that compose it, so that it will stand considerable abuse before falling apart.

With the majority of the others, the nests are flimsy cups of rootlets and weed stems, often dislodged by windstorms, and so poorly and openly constructed that the eggs are sometimes visible from below.

SOME CHEERFUL SONGSTERS

Reports of female grosbeaks and purple finches singing are usually traceable to one-year-old males still in female plumage, though I believe females occasionally sing a weak song somewhat like that of the males.

The finches include some of our favorite songsters, such as the canary already mentioned. The rose-breasted and black-headed grosbeaks have delightful, full-voiced, rob-inlike songs; the purple and house finches utter loud warbles; and the cardinal, while his piping whistles are comparatively simple, is perhaps the cheeriest of them all.

None of them has the pensive type of song of our thrushes, the European nightingale, or our southern mockingbird, but their voices have a freshness and cheer that awaken thoughts of woods and fields, blue skies, and bright flowers.

YOUNG ARE FED ON "CEREALS"

As the shape and strength of their bills indicate, the finches are primarily seed-eaters, but they consume many insects during the summer and wild fruits during the fall. The goldfinch brings up his young-sters almost wholly on "cereals." These are served warm, for the parent birds swallow the seeds after cracking their hard coats and feed the youngsters by regurgitation.

Purple finches occasionally eat the hearts out of fruit blossoms and summer tanagers sometimes catch honeybees. But, for the most part, these birds do little harm to man's interests and often they are of direct value because of the insects they destroy. The rose-breasted grosbeak, for example, is one of the few birds that feed on the Colorado potato beetle.

Scarlet Tanager
(Piranga erythromelas)
Average Length, Seven and One-quarter Inches

Louis Agassiz Fuertes used to tell of over-hearing two bird observers on the Cornell campus. One was complaining that he had not seen a scarlet tanager all spring, and the other was agreeing that they must be very scarce. Yet, in the tree directly over their heads, a tanager was singing at the top of its voice during their entire conversation.

Hurry, worry, flurry, blurry, the tanager seems to say, like a robin in a hurry with a cold, and *chip-burr* he calls when alarmed. Anyone in the northeastern United States and southern Canada who recognizes these calls can find scarlet tanagers.

Arriving about the first of May, the tanagers may be conspicuous at first, if the vegetation has been retarded, but they soon lose themselves in the treetops (see page 249).

Female tanagers are often remarkably tame, or, rather, have their maternal instinct powerfully developed, so that they will sometimes let one stroke them on the nest or will feed their youngsters even when they are held in one's hand. Their nests are usually out of reach of the ground, on a horizontal branch of an oak or a hemlock and are rather carelessly built of rootlets and weed stems.

The greenish-blue eggs are heavily marked with reddish-brown specks. The nests are often parasitized by cowbirds, and many a time I have glanced up into our mulberry tree at the call of a tanager, only to see a fluttering young cowbird receiving a berry from a deluded mother tanager.

Young tanagers in the nest resemble the female, but are slightly streaked beneath. These streaks, however, soon disappear. After nesting season the male changes his red for a greenish-yellow coat, but his wings and tail are black, edged with green.

After they leave the nesting grounds in October for Colombia or Bolivia, where they winter, scarlet tanagers are not seen again until the following spring, when the males have once more molted their body feathers for red and have worn off the green edges on their wing feathers.

They nest from Saskatchewan and Nova Scotia south to eastern Kansas and Virginia, and in the mountains to Georgia.

Summer Tanager
(Piranga rubra rubra)
Average Length, Seven and One-half Inches

This is the common tanager of our southeastern States, west as far as eastern Texas and Nebraska. Its arrival early in April from northern South America, where it has passed the winter, is often first made known by its curious call, which Dr. Chapman describes as a "clearly enunciated *chicky-tucky-tuck.*" Its song is much clearer than that of the scarlet tanager. Common in the open pinewoods of the South, it seems to prefer those with an undergrowth of oaks and hickories.

Summer tanagers build careless nests about 20 feet from the ground near the ends of horizontal branches, and, with their families, leave the United States in October. The eggs are similar to those of the scarlet tanager.

From New Mexico to California a variety known as Cooper's tanager (*Piranga r. cooperi*) lives among the cottonwoods of the river bottoms. It is slightly larger, with a somewhat longer bill and rosier under parts.

House Sparrow
(Passer domesticus domesticus)
Average Length, Six and One-third Inches

House sparrows were introduced from Europe at Brooklyn, N. Y., in 1850 and 1852 by Nicolas Pike to destroy cankerworms, which had become a pest in the shade trees. Being naturally prolific and adaptable, they were quick to spread in the eastern United States. For some 20 years they were confined largely to cities of the Atlantic coast, but by 1900 there was scarcely a hamlet from Maine to California that did not awaken to the chirp of this little immigrant.

The house sparrow is not really a sparrow. From the true sparrows it differs, among other ways, in building a covered nest.

House sparrows have three to six young in a brood and breed throughout most of the year. A warm day in January or February starts them carrying nesting material, and the male is as assiduous as the female in this. The nests are usually placed in vines or crannies about buildings and are often objectionable on account of the litter.

As the automobile has replaced the horse, and the sparrows' food supply in the cities has become less certain, their number has lessened.

A change in the appearance of the male sparrow in the spring is accomplished in true economy, without the change of a feather. The new feathers grown in the fall after the nesting season are all edged with gray, which largely conceals the color patterns of chestnut, white, and black. By April, however, these gray tips break off and the black throat and chestnut head-stripe stand out freshly. Young sparrows in their first plumage resemble their mothers, except for slightly streaked breasts.

Sparrows' eggs are grayish white, with speckles or streaks ranging from green to black or brown and numbering from none at all to enough to obscure the ground color.

The house sparrow is found all over Europe and Asia, except in the Mediterranean countries and India, where it is replaced by close relatives of similar habits. Africa and Asia have paler and smaller varieties.

VIVID TANAGERS AND DINGY SPARROWS PRESENT A STUDY IN CONTRASTS

In spite of their brilliant colors, the North's **Scarlet Tanager,** with its jet-black wings, and the duller-red **Summer Tanager** of the South are more often heard than seen, so modestly do they move about among the green leaves. The yellowish olive-green females are so different that some observers mistake them for another species. The immigrant **English,** or **House, Sparrow** (below), whose lively chirrup is so familiar in city streets and farmyards, now is thought to belong to the interesting family of weaver finches, some of whose members in Asia, Africa, and the East Indies weave elaborate nests.

Pyrrhuloxia
(Pyrrhuloxia sinuata)
Average Length, Eight and One-half Inches

On the King Ranch near Corpus Christi I first made the acquaintance of this delightful bird. Mr. Richard Kleberg had shown us the last of the whooping cranes making their final stand against extinction on the muddy shores of Laguna Larga. We had seen innumerable white-fronted geese and little brown cranes.

Suddenly a slender, soft-gray bird darted across our path from one scrubby mesquite to another. Or was it gray? My eye seemed to catch a glow of red as it passed.

Out came my binoculars. But its back was toward me and at first I was almost sure it was only a female cardinal—a little grayer than our eastern bird.

A moment later, however, the gray bird turned, displayed a beautiful rose-red vest, and raised a saucy and most expressive scarlet crest. Its short, heavy, almost parrot-like bill gave it a patrician expression that left no doubt that it was a real Texas aristocrat.

Later we saw others—cardinal-like in most of their actions, sometimes on the ground, sometimes in the bushes, but never far from some thorny tangle. Their calls were thinner than those of the cardinals and their whistles clearer, with less inflection.

In their nesting and other habits the pyrrhuloxias are much like cardinals, building rather bulky nests of twigs, weed stems, and inner bark, bound with fine grasses, in thickets of mesquite or other thorny growth, and laying three to five finely speckled eggs.

The Texas pyrrhuloxia *(P. s. texana)* is resident from southern Texas into Mexico. The somewhat paler Arizona pyrrhuloxia *(P. s. sinuata)* is found from southern Arizona and western Texas to Sinaloa, and the smaller San Lucas pyrrhuloxia *(P. s. peninsulae)* in southern Baja California.

Hepatic Tanager
(Piranga flava hepatica)
Average Length, Eight Inches

To the ordinary observer the hepatic tanager and the summer tanager are almost identical. In reality, however, the hepatic tanager is a larger bird, with a more scarlet breast, a browner back, and much grayer cheeks.

The summer tanager ranges widely throughout our southern States, but one is not likely to see a living hepatic tanager unless one ventures into the mountains of western Texas, New Mexico, or Arizona, or into Mexico itself.

There, among the oaks and pines of the mountains that rise from the desert, the hepatic tanager is sometimes found in comparative abundance. Its song is remarkably like that of the scarlet tanager, and its feeding and nesting habits are likewise similar.

Western Tanager
(Piranga ludoviciana)
Average Length, Seven Inches

Bird lovers in California look forward to the return of the western tanagers much as we in the East watch for the coming of their scarlet cousins. About the first week in May the birds can be expected to pass through the lowlands and foothills and a week later they appear in the black oaks and incense cedars of Yosemite. For the rest of the summer they are among the most conspicuous birds throughout the forests of the Rockies up to 10,000 feet, as far east as Colorado and Nebraska.

Western tanagers are never so abundant as robins or chipping sparrows, but, because of their conspicuous colors, courage, fondness for the open woods, and breezy songs, they are not easily overlooked. Their drawling two-syllable call note of *chee-tik,* and their song, consisting of a rapid repetition of the syllable *chēē wēr,* as Dr. Grinnell puts it, suggest the utterances of the scarlet tanager. The song is heard at all times of day from the middle of May until mid-July.

Early in the season they feed largely on insects, but they are never so active in their pursuit as are warblers. Seeming to realize that they are conspicuous when moving, they pass much time sitting around or peering under leaves for caterpillars. A little later, however, when berries begin to ripen, they venture into the open to feed on buckthorn berries.

Nesting begins the last of May, when females may be seen gathering nesting material, often on the ground, and flying directly to their nests. The work of nest building devolves entirely upon the female.

The nest is rather loosely constructed on a horizontal branch, usually about 20 feet from the ground, and the eggs, like those of other tanagers, are greenish blue, speckled with brown. Once incubation starts, the two birds are rarely seen together, but the males remain conspicuous as foragers. Although the male does not assist with home-building or hatching, he helps feed the young, both while they are in the nest and afterward.

During July and early August, when the families feed largely in the trees, they are less conspicuous than in late August and September, when they come down to eat berries. At this time, those which have been nesting higher in the mountains move down toward the lower land, so that during the few weeks just before starting South the western tanagers seem more numerous than at other times. The males then wear winter plumage and their heads are only slightly reddish.

By the first of October these tanagers have deserted California for their winter home, the Mexican plateau and the mountains of Central America as far south as Costa Rica.

THEIR STRIKING COLORS BLAZE AMID THE SCENERY OF OUR WEST

The red-crested and red-waistcoated **Arizona Pyrrhuloxia** (at the top with his consort) is better known in the southwestern United States as "gray cardinal" or "parrot-bill." They win man's affection by their cheery whistle and their habit of eating boll weevils. **Hepatic Tanagers** (perched at the bottom) live in the mountains of Texas, New Mexico, and Arizona. In the Far West, often near camps in our national parks, the **Western Tanager** (left), crimson of face, pours out to his yellow-green mate a song like the lay of the East's scarlet tanager.

Rose-breasted Grosbeak

(Hedymeles ludovicianus)

Average Length, Eight Inches

I have always felt sorry for the male rose-breasted grosbeak since the first time I caught him in the act of sitting on the eggs and singing to himself.

Nature endowed him with beautiful colors and a rich, rollicking voice. A few minutes before, I had seen him glorying in both on the dead branch of a butternut over the elderberry bushes in which the nest was located.

Yet there he was in all his black and white and rose red, inviting attention to the nest, while his mate, designed and colored by Nature especially for the work he was doing, was off gadding by herself and doing no good for anyone. With most pairs the males spend fully as much time on the eggs as do the females.

During winter the male rose-breasted grosbeak looks much more like the female as he roams through the forests from Mexico to northern South America, for the feathers of his upper parts and breast are edged with brown, and he has a light line over his eye. By the time he reaches his nesting grounds in the northern United States and Canada, the last of April or the first of May, he is once more in his full breeding regalia. Then his voice rings out like that of a glorified robin, each phrase slurring into the next.

The plain, sparrowlike females would easily escape detection were their mates not so attentive, but as they gather dead twigs for their crude nests the males fly back and forth with them, apparently taking keen interest in the undertaking. An intruder is always greeted with a few metallic chipping notes, but soon is ignored.

The favorite location for a nest seems to be an elderberry bush five to ten feet from the ground, although horizontal branches of small oaks or elms are also used. The nests are poorly woven of twigs or weed stems, and often the eggs, spotted with chestnut and brown, can be seen from below.

The exact function of the heavy bills is not evident during the summer, when the birds are feeding their young and themselves largely on soft-bodied insects or fruit. Even the potato beetles, of which they are fond, do not require any such crushers to reduce them to a suitable swallowing condition. What they feed on in winter that needs such a bill I do not know.

Immature grosbeaks resemble the females, except that the linings of the wings of the males are rose red instead of yellow, and there is a suffusion of rose on their streaked breasts. The youngsters wear some of their brownish wing and tail feathers during their first nesting season after they have changed the rest of their plumage to a dress like that of their fathers. First-year birds are, therefore, easily distinguished from the adults.

Cardinal

(Richmondena cardinalis)

Average Length, Seven Inches

From Ohio and Pennsylvania southward the cardinal often nests in the vines on the porch and performs in many lovable little ways before the eyes of his hosts (see page 248).

Cardinals are not really migratory, but the young birds do much wandering in all directions after they are grown. This doubtless accounts for individuals appearing north of their normal range in winter as often as in summer. Their nonmigratory habit is likewise the underlying reason why the Florida, the Texas, and the Arizona birds are now recognized as forms distinct from birds of the eastern United States as well as from the four or five other varieties of Mexico proper and Baja California.

In late April or early May the female cardinal selects her nesting site in a thick bush or vine, constructs her nest of rootlets, strips of bark, and grasses, and lays three or four bluish-white, brown-speckled eggs. During the entire time the male is attentive, often feeding her on the nest as well as feeding the young. With comical seriousness he usually takes charge of the young when they leave home, and the female starts building another nest.

Young cardinals are at first a dull, dark brown, with blackish bills, but before long they get lighter below, and the crests of the males are slightly reddish. Before winter they change all their feathers and become indistinguishable from their parents.

Blue Grosbeak

(Guiraca caerulea)

Average Length, Eight and One-quarter Inches

You may be disappointed in your first blue grosbeak. He may look like a cowbird. It all depends on the angle at which the light comes from his feathers to your eye.

Blue grosbeaks, like indigo buntings, prefer tangles of weeds and berry bushes or willows, but they do not venture so far north as getting north of Maryland in the East or central California in the West. From east to west the species has been split up into three varieties, but the ordinary observer would not recognize differences among the eastern, western, and California forms.

In the fall the plumage of the adult male becomes edged with brown, while the immature males are fully as brown as the females.

The blue grosbeak's nest, a rather flimsy, shallow affair of rootlets and weed stems, is placed like the buntings' nests, in weeds, usually not far from the ground. The three or four eggs are bluish white and unspotted.

The blue grosbeak's song, oft repeated from one perch, is like that of the other grosbeaks, though weaker and sometimes finchlike.

GROSBEAKS AND CARDINALS COMBINE FINE MANNERS AND FINE CLOTHES

A model husband—though somewhat henpecked—the East's handsome **Rose-breasted Grosbeak** (above) sings sweetly to his somber-clad spouse in a tree-top. These birds endear themselves to farmers by a fondness for potato bugs. The **Cardinal,** or "redbird" (male left, female right), beloved in the southeastern States, ranges as far north as Pennsylvania. Often grain tossed on doorsills or window ledges will attract groups of a dozen or more of these flashing birds in winter. The **Blue Grosbeak** (right pair) is a shy denizen of South Atlantic and Gulf States.

Indigo Bunting

(Passerina cyanea)

Average Length, Five and One-half Inches

It is the middle of May before this charming bit of color appears in my garden, but he makes up for his late appearance by singing to us long after the other birds have ceased in late August.

His song is not the full-voiced type we get from the grosbeaks or the purple finches, but inclines to be thin and wiry. Many bird students have difficulty distinguishing it from that of the goldfinch, but if one listens attentively, one will notice that the bunting's notes are usually paired: *sweet, sweet—where, where, here, here—seeit, seeit.*

When he sings, he is usually high in a tree or on a telegraph wire and, seen against the sky, appears only blackish, except as he turns his head occasionally and sends a flash of blue light to the observer's eye. Soon, however, he darts down to the undergrowth, for he always has one eye on the shrubbery beneath him for the appearance of his mate.

The indigo bunting is a bird of the eastern United States, spreading as far west as central Texas and as far north as southern Quebec; it winters in Yucatán, Central America, and Cuba. It arrives in the southern United States in April and does not leave until October, but it is more conspicuous in late summer when other birds have quieted down.

The nest is placed in a weed, fern, or berry bush within a few feet of the ground, and is well constructed of grasses and weed stems, usually with a few dead leaves woven into the bottom.

The male never incubates the eggs or broods the nestlings, but he often brings food to the female on the nest and is always assiduous in feeding the young. In this respect he is much more normal than the grosbeak. In summer the indigo bunting eats chiefly insects.

The indigo bunting's four or five eggs are pale bluish white, with no spots. Normally, two broods are reared each season, a new nest being built for the second family.

Beautiful Bunting

(Passerina versicolor pulchra)

Average Length, Five and One-half Inches

Just as the lazuli bunting replaces the indigo bunting in the West, so the beautiful bunting replaces the lazuli along our southern border and southward into Mexico. Mesquite thickets of southeastern California and Baja California furnish the shelter into which this variegated little finch can disappear at the approach of an enemy or from the top branches of which he can pour forth his wiry song with much enthusiasm. In brushy areas along the lower Rio Grande is an allied form, the varied bunting *(P. v. versicolor).*

Lazuli Bunting

(Passerina amoena)

Average Length, Five and One-half Inches

One familiar with the indigo bunting in the eastern United States finds its exact counterpart in the lazuli bunting of the West.

The song of the lazuli bunting, however, though divided into short phrases, is less clear than that of the indigo, and the phrases are not so regularly of only two notes in length.

This species ranges from British Columbia and North Dakota to Baja California and Texas. It winters from Mexico to Cuba and Panama.

Black-headed Grosbeak

(Hedymeles melanocephalus)

Average Length, Eight Inches

Visitors to some of the western camp sites, such as those in Yosemite National Park, are sure to get acquainted with this large-billed, golden-brown and black bird foraging for crumbs around the tents or buildings. Here, constant association with man and his works has destroyed their natural timidity and they often hop about within a few feet of visitors.

At such times their ridiculous little call note, *eek,* is in strong contrast to the loud, beautifully modulated song that bursts from their throats when they mount to the treetops.

At the height of the courtship period they can sometimes be heard singing in chorus at sunset, like our robins in the East. In his ardor the male grosbeak sometimes mounts into the air and sings on the wing.

The black-headed grosbeak passes the winter in central and southern Mexico, arriving in the United States in April and reaching its northern limits in May, where it stays until September. It is found throughout the Rocky Mountain region as far north as southern Canada, and from California as far east as western Texas and North Dakota.

The Pacific coast birds are considered a different variety from those found in the rest of the Rocky Mountain region. Thus, in the western United States, where the rose-breasted grosbeak is unknown, this bird replaces it. Indeed, it is very similar to the rose-breast in all its habits, even including that of the males helping to incubate eggs and brood young.

Its food habits, too, are similar. Although it occasionally is objectionable about cherry orchards and may develop a fondness for green peas, the damage it does is relatively insignificant compared with its destruction of injurious insects, such as the black olive scale, potato beetle, alfalfa weevil, cankerworm, and codling moth.

The young resemble the female, but have paler coloring on the under parts of their bodies. In winter plumage the black of the males is replaced or concealed by brown.

BRILLIANT BUNTINGS SEEM DIPPED IN THE SKY'S OWN HUES

The **Indigo Bunting** (upper left) has the blues in his feathers only. Gaily this easterner sings and bustles about, while his mousy mate stays in the background. Sunset colors blend in the gorgeous "Joseph's coat" of the Southwest's **Beautiful Bunting** (upper right). Radiant silvery blue adorns the male of the West's **Lazuli Bunting** (right center pair), whose coloring recalls that of the familiar bluebird. The **Black-headed Grosbeak** (lower pair) is a westerner closely resembling, in all but plumage, the East's rose-breasted grosbeak.

RANDOM NOTES ON TANAGERS AND FINCHES

By Arthur A. Allen

ALL WINTER a beautiful male cardinal had been visiting our feeding log, regaling himself on the sunflower seed which we purchased for his benefit. Occasionally he nibbled at the suet which we put out for the woodpeckers or picked at the chick feed we scattered for the juncos and tree sparrows, but he obviously preferred the sunflower seed.

He was welcome to all he could eat, for he was the only cardinal, so far as we knew, that had dared venture as far north as central New York. We rejoiced more at his discovering our food log than we had when the flock of evening grosbeaks found it earlier in the winter.

BIRDS OF NORTH AND SOUTH TOGETHER

These grosbeaks are northern birds that only occasionally wander in winter as far south and east as Ithaca, N. Y. They were still visiting our log on the day when the cardinal announced his presence with a loud, cheery whistle. I conceived the idea of getting a photograph of the two together and thus showing on one photographic plate birds from the opposite ends of the country. This became a longer job than I had expected, because, though they both became regular boarders, their meal hours were different. For ten days I kept a camera focused on the log, with a thread to one of our windows, before the opportunity arrived.

One noon, when I came home to lunch, the cardinal was munching away on the seeds, and one of the male grosbeaks was calling in the tree overhead. Having set the camera in the morning, I knew it was ready. Several thrilling moments of suspense ensued, and then the grosbeak dropped to the log. Just as I pulled the thread to take the picture, the cardinal lifted his crest in a beautifully expressive fashion, raised his wings, opened his bill, darted at the grosbeak, and knocked him off the end of the log. It all happened so quickly that the camera recorded not much more than a blur.

My second experience with a cardinal at Ithaca was less amusing. All winter this one had been coming to our window feeding station, braving the zero temperature and apparently not minding the icy blasts from the northwest, despite his southern origin. Spring was in the March air one noon when I stepped from my car near the feeding station window. I had scarcely looked around before I heard a scream from a bird in distress. The cry seemed familiar, yet I was sure I had never heard it before.

Looking up the hill toward the rock garden, I saw a flash of red as the cardinal headed straight for the spot where I was standing. Behind him came a northern shrike in hot pursuit.

Had I realized what was to happen, I might almost have caught the cardinal in my hands like a baseball as he flashed by. The next instant he had pitched headlong into the closed window and lay quivering at my feet. Blind instinct had directed him in distress toward the spot which had protected him all winter, but it had not taught him the meaning of glass.

GOLDFINCHES DO NOT GLITTER IN THE WINTER

From my study window I look out upon a hemlock tree full of little hanging cones. Busily working on these cones is a flock of a dozen small birds and the snow beneath is covered with the scales they have removed to get at the seeds.

I have just looked the flock over with my binoculars in the hope of finding some siskins or redpolls, but I find they are all goldfinches. How different they are from the brilliant yellow and black birds that frequented my garden during the summer and went bounding over the maples during July and August!

Of course, they look much like the summer females, only they are browner, and one can hardly distinguish the sexes, except that the males have somewhat blacker wings, with more prominent white markings. None of the birds is streaked, however, a fact which eliminates entirely the possibility of identifying them as siskins or redpolls, which feed in similar flocks.

Goldfinches never seem so pugnacious toward others of their kind as are many other birds when nesting. Perhaps their type of food is so abundant that there is little competition for territories. They travel around in pairs for some time before nesting starts, but about the first of July the male alone joyously cuts great circles over some tree where soon the nest will be built. At times, he hovers overhead on rather slowly beating wings, giving vent to his feelings in a canarylike song, but generally he keeps time with his undulating flight by a happy *per-chic-o-ree* call.

Standing at my front door early in June, at the height of the nesting season, I can hear from different directions the songs of three or four male tanagers. Yet we seldom see one. Indeed, one year we found a nest in a pear tree within 25 feet of the porch, but we rarely saw the birds unless we watched expressly for them and then it was only when they took flight at our close approach.

We could always find the male by following his song, or, if we watched the nest continuously, we would occasionally see him slip in with a fat green caterpillar for his mate. After the eggs hatched, and especially when the young were leaving the nest, he was always around with a worm in his bill, and his *chip-burring* attracted our attention as he brought food to the youngsters.

THE TANAGER IS ONE OF NATURE'S MOST THRILLING SIGHTS

Of the extraordinary pleasure derived from one of Nature's most startling sights, the first glimpse of a scarlet tanager, Dr. Elliott Coues wrote: "I hold this bird in particular, almost superstitious, recollection, as the very first of all the feathered tribe to stir within me those emotions that have never ceased to stimulate and gratify my love for birds. More years have passed than I care to remember since a little child was strolling through an orchard one bright morning in June, filled with mute wonder at beauties felt, but neither questioned nor understood.

"A shout from an older companion—'There goes a scarlet tanager!'—and the child was straining eager, wistful eyes after something that had flashed upon his senses for a moment as if from another world, it seemed so bright, so beautiful, so strange.

"'What is a scarlet tanager?' mused the child, whose consciousness had flown with the wonderful apparition on wings of ecstasy; but the bees hummed on, the scent of the flowers floated by, the sunbeam passed across the greensward, and there was no reply—nothing but the echo of a mute appeal to Nature, stirring the very

depths with an inward thrill. That night the vision came again in dreamland, where the strangest things are truest and known the best; the child was startled by a ball of fire, and fanned to rest again by a sable wing.

"The wax was soft then, and the impress grew indelible. Nor would I blur it if I could—not though the flight of years has borne sad answers to reiterated questionings—not though the wings of hope are tipped with lead and brush the very earth, instead of soaring in scented sunlight."

A CHARMING BIRD MAY BE FORGIVEN HIS DEPREDATIONS

The scarlet tanager's close cousin, the summer tanager, seldom reaches the Northern States, but two years ago a beautiful male visited Buttermilk Falls State Park, south of Ithaca, New York, and, true to his reputation as a bee-eater, took up his station for several days near a hive belonging to the caretaker. When the bee owner discovered how many visitors the bird brought to the park, he cheerfully resigned himself to the loss of a few bees.

The pine siskin is a bird we share with the Old World, for, although ornithologists put the European siskin, or tarin, in a separate species, the two birds look almost exactly alike. Indeed, many believe that the siskins represent the ancestral stock from which the redpolls, goldfinches, crossbills, and even the buntings have been derived. Certainly their heavy streaking suggests the plumage of most young sparrows, irrespective of their adult plumage.

Passing through the northern United States, often in large numbers, during April, they are sometimes overtaken by the mating urge before they reach their normal breeding grounds; so they settle down and rear families considerably south of where they are usually expected. Such an invasion of siskins occurred on the Cornell University campus in 1925, where they never nested before or since.

In behavior siskins are much like winter goldfinches, and the little patches of yeilow in the wings and base of the tail might be confusing were it not for the almost black streaks that enliven their plumage both above and below. They are usually much more friendly than the goldfinches and will permit the cautious bird lover to approach within a few feet of them without showing signs of fear or ceasing their usual activities.

A GAUDY FELLOW, A MIDGET, A WANDERER, AND A MASQUERADER

The **Painted Bunting** (upper left), with his perfectly camouflaged greenish mate, hides his beauty in southern swamps and thickets; but many know him as "nonpareil" or "Mexican canary." A tiny finch of eastern Mexico and Texas is **Sharpe's Seedeater** (upper right pair). Flocks of eastern **Evening Grosbeaks** (center) ramble in winter over all northern States. The cheery, grasshopper-loving **Dickcissel** (lower), resembling a miniature meadowlark, forsook the eastern seaboard for interior States some 65 years ago and only rarely do individuals return.

Painted Bunting

(Passerina ciris)
Average Length, Five and One-quarter Inches

Like the cardinal, the male painted bunting or "nonpareil," as it is sometimes called, retains its bright colors even in its winter plumage. While the majority move southward into Mexico, or Central America, or Cuba for the winter, a goodly number always remain in southern Florida, feeding on seeds of grasses and weeds and ready to eat the chick feed or bread crumbs that friends provide.

About the middle of April the migration northward starts; for though the painted bunting is distinctly a bird nesting south of an indefinite line connecting southern North Carolina and southern Kansas, it does not nest south of central Florida. At least two, possibly three broods may be reared each season.

The song suggests that of the indigo bunting, but lacks something of its energy and rhythm. It has been compared more with the singing of the Canada or the magnolia warbler.

Like the indigo bunting, the painted bunting prefers thickets and weedy places along the edges of woods or the borders of towns. The nest is usually in a bush or a low tree, and the bluish-white eggs have numerous speckles of chestnut or rufous brown.

Sharpe's Seedeater

(Sporophila morelleti sharpei)
Average Length, Four and One-half Inches

Wherever one travels in the arid Tropics of the New World from Mexico to Paraguay, one finds some species of seedeater, an abundant roadside bird living on the seeds of weeds and grasses. In general, seedeaters are decidedly smaller than the average sparrow.

Sharpe's seedeater is one of eight species found north of Panama. It is the only one, however, which enters the United States and then only for a relatively few miles along the lower Rio Grande in southeastern Texas, especially in the region of Brownsville.

Evening Grosbeak

(Hesperiphona vespertina)
Average Length, Eight Inches

The most striking things about this unusual bird are its fearlessness and the irregularity of its appearance about civilization. It passes the breeding season largely in the pine forests from northern Michigan to western Alberta and (the western and Mexican varieties) in the mountains from central British Columbia to New Mexico, Arizona, and Mexico.

Ordinarily, it nests during June on the horizontal branches of spruces, more or less in scattered colonies. In Manitoba, however, two nests were found in shade trees in the town of Selkirk and others in river-bottom willows. The nests were loosely constructed of twigs and rootlets and the eggs were pale greenish blue, rather heavily marked with gray, olive green, and brown.

At irregular intervals, sometimes years apart, the birds move eastward and southward from their breeding grounds and appear sometimes in large flocks in New England and the Middle Atlantic States, even as far south as Washington, D. C.

Their natural food is the seeds of ashes, box elders and maples, the pits of chokecherries and dogwoods, weed seed, and the seeds of conifers. They will often peck through frozen apples for the seeds, apparently not caring for the pulp. At feeding stations they seem to prefer sunflower seeds and, in summer at least, have a fondness for salt.

A flock that found my feeding station in February came regularly every day until the first of May. One could almost set a watch by the birds' first appearance at 6:30 each morning. Their chirping call notes made them sound like glorified house sparrows.

The birds are rather swift in flight, but on the ground or in trees they appear sluggish and pass a great deal of time sitting quietly.

Young evening grosbeaks, when they leave their nests, all resemble their mother, but before winter the males have acquired their yellow body feathers, though they retain their juvenile wings and tails until the following fall. Old birds molt but once a year after the nesting season.

The pleasing name is based upon the mistaken notion of the original collector that the bird dwelt in dark woods and came out only at evening to sing.

Dickcissel

(Spiza americana)
Average Length, Six Inches

This Mississippi Valley bird is found in summer from southern Texas and Mississippi to Minnesota and North Dakota.

Before 1880 the dickcissel was more or less common in the Middle Atlantic States, but now is of very rare occurrence east of the Alleghenies. No good reason for its disappearance in the East has yet been discovered. The bird gets its name from its curious little song: *dick-dick—cissel-cissel-cissel*.

In clover fields this bird usually nests on or near the ground; in brushlands, sometimes as much as six feet from the ground. The nest is rather bulky, of coarse grasses and leaves, lined with finer grasses or hairs, and the four or five eggs are pale blue with no spots.

Dickcissels gather in large flocks in August and winter in Central America and northern South America. They return in equally large groups the following April; but these break up into pairs and scatter.

SOME FINCHES ARE SPLASHED WITH WINE COLOR AND FILLED WITH SONG

Few birds have richer melodies than that of the eastern **Purple Finch,** here engaged with his mate in gulping mountain-ash berries. Sometimes the impassioned minstrel mounts skyward, singing ecstatically. **Cassin's Purple Finch** (top) dwells on western mountain slopes. The **House Finch** (the male wearing a red crown and cravat, right) is numerous in California and has a habit of raiding orchards. Into the northern United States in winter roams that boreal nomad, the Canadian **Pine Grosbeak** (bottom), whistling melodiously. The male is tinged with red.

Purple Finch

(Carpodacus purpureus)

Average Length, Six and One-quarter Inches

Originally a wild forest bird, the purple finch has adapted itself to man's ways and frequently nests in dooryard spruces and pines. Especially has it become a familiar patron of bird lunch counters, where its appetite for sunflower seeds and its habit of congregating in large flocks sometimes taxes hospitality.

Like many other members of their group, the purple finches are erratic in their migrations and may disappear for years from a locality where they have been unusually abundant.

In summer this finch ordinarily restricts itself to the northern United States and Canada, as far west as northwest British Columbia. The form known as the California purple finch extends its range to the Pacific coast and in the mountains to Baja California. In winter the purple finches are scattered more or less throughout the United States even as far south as Florida and Texas.

About the first of May they repair to their nesting grounds, but even before that the songs of the males have redoubled and are often given with so much energy and enthusiasm that the bird is carried right up into the air with his continuous bubbling warble.

The courtship performance, "the dance of the straw," begins with the male's picking up a straw and ends, after an elaborate display, with his falling over as if dead until a peck from the female rouses him.

At the end of a display, I once saw a male strike a pose with his head thrown back, his chest up, and his tail braced against the ground. Thereupon, the female hopped upon his chest, bent over, and clasped bills with him; then dashed away to lead him a merry chase through the trees.

The nest, made largely of rootlets and weed stems, often has a lining of hair or woolly material. The three to five eggs are bluish with brown spots wreathing the larger ends.

Young purple finches resemble their mother for more than a year and, in their streaked brown plumage, might be confused with some of the sparrows. Young males, in female plumage, sing well their first spring.

Cassin's Purple Finch

(Carpodacus cassini)

Average Length, Six and One-third Inches

Similar to the purple finch but larger, with paler breast and rump, is this dweller in the Cascades and high Sierras, and other mountains from British Columbia to Baja California, and east to Colorado.

In all its habits it seems to be like the other species, nesting rather high in the spruces, traveling in small flocks, and singing a loud, warbling song, usually somewhat louder and more varied than those of its relatives. In winter it visits the lowlands.

House Finch

(Carpodacus mexicanus frontalis)

Average Length, Six Inches

From central Texas and western Kansas to Oregon and California this is one of the most abundant birds, being nearly as numerous and friendly as the robin, or even the house sparrow, in the East.

Except during the nesting season, these "California linnets" are found in flocks, sometimes of large size, feeding about weed patches. When alarmed, they fly up and away instead of dodging for cover like most sparrows. They often circle high in the air and apparently make off for distant parts.

At this season the flocks are naturally made up largely of dull-colored birds, because, in addition to the females, there are included all the young of the year and the immature males of the preceding year. The latter do not get their red markings the first year.

The nesting season begins in April, when the flocks break up into pairs, and the singing, which is heard off and on all winter, is redoubled.

The courtship and display are similar to those described for the purple finch. Once nesting starts, the males are very attentive to the females, remaining close in flight as well as when foraging. After incubation begins, they select perches close to the nests.

Pine Grosbeak

(Pinicola enucleator)

Average Length, Eight Inches

The pine grosbeak is one of the birds we share with the Old World, for it is found in coniferous forests throughout the northern parts of the Northern Hemisphere.

In western mountains, where these grosbeaks live just below timber line, they apparently seldom venture to the lowlands.

In eastern North America, however, and especially in New England, one occasionally has opportunity to see pine grosbeaks without climbing mountains or traveling nearly to Hudson Bay. Occasionally their food supply in the far North seems to fail, and the birds move southward where they find a better living during the winter.

On their nesting grounds their favorite food seems to be the seeds of spruce and hemlock, but when they move south in winter they also feed on sumac and berries of mountain-ash, wild grapes, and Virginia creeper.

The flocks are not usually large, and in one comprising a dozen birds there are likely to be not more than two or three of the rosy-red adult males.

Seven forms are recognized in the extensive range of this species in North America.

STOUT-HEARTED, THEY WREST FOOD FROM THISTLES OR CONIFERS IN SNOWY WASTES

The gay little **Eastern Goldfinch,** a bit of bright summer sunshine, swings along in lilting flight and utters ecstatic canarylike love songs. They have earned the nickname of "thistle birds" by gleaning thistle seeds or down for nest-lining. Through northern fir forests and meadows wander flocks of the **Pine Siskin** (upper right) ; the more gaily garbed **Common Redpoll** (right center pair) ; and the rarer, more northerly **Hoary Redpoll** (clinging just below). The **Gray-crowned Rosy Finch** (lower left pair) lives on wind-blown seeds and insects in western mountains.

Goldfinch
(Spinus tristis)
Average Length, Five Inches

Goldfinches are found in summer throughout most of the United States, except the Gulf States, and southern Canada. In the Rocky Mountain region there is a variety called the pale goldfinch *(S. t. pallidus)*, and, on the Pacific coast, another, the willow goldfinch *(S. t. salicamans)*, all essentially alike and more or less resident throughout their ranges, though they roam much. In winter some move southward to the Gulf or into Mexico.

During winter goldfinches travel in flocks. They are equally at home in the hemlocks and birches of the woodlands and the weeds of the wind-blown fields. At this season they seem restless and timid. During summer, they are confiding little creatures, feeding on thistles and dandelions by the roadside, or on sunflowers, cosmos, and bachelor-buttons in gardens. They are also fond of beet leaves.

There are relatively few goldfinches in the northern States in winter, but during April they move northward in large flocks, the males now wearing spotted yellow and gray plumage. In early May the seeds of the elms attract them and our shade trees resound with their twittering. Nesting, however, awaits July and August, when fresh thistle and other seeds are assured for the young.

The nest, built largely of thistledown and vegetable fibers, is placed high in a bush or the outer branches of trees, especially maples, from 10 to 30 feet from the ground. Occasionally, however, nests are found on thistles or cornstalks. The four to six eggs are bluish white and normally are unspotted.

The female alone incubates and is fed on the nest by the male. He regurgitates the seeds which he has cracked and swallowed, while she flutters her wings like a young bird.

Pine Siskin
(Spinus pinus)
Average Length, Five Inches

Our siskins are found in summer throughout the southern half of the coniferous forests, in the mountains to North Carolina in the East and to southern California in the West. In winter they roam erratically over most of the United States and northern Mexico (page 249).

At feeding stations they often respond to kindness by perching all over their host. A remarkable case of this response is described in *Bird-Lore* by E. R. Davis. A large flock of siskins which fed at his window learned to come in and awaken him by pulling his hair or tweaking his ear.

The nest is usually placed near the end of a branch of a hemlock or other coniferous tree 10 to 50 feet from the ground. It is made of rootlets and lined with hair, feathers, or plant down. The eggs are pale greenish blue speckled with brown. The female builds the nest and incubates the eggs, and the male feeds her on the nest by regurgitation.

The siskin's song is a rather weak warble interrupted by hissing notes suggestive somewhat of a leaky valve on a radiator.

The Redpolls
(Acanthis linaria and Acanthis hornemanni)
Average Lengths, Five and Five and One-third Inches

Usually the hoary redpoll *(Acanthis hornemanni exilipes)* appears much whiter and less heavily streaked than the common redpoll *(Acanthis linaria linaria)* and its white lower back is without streaks, but females of the hoary species often seem as dark as the males of the common redpoll.

In the summer of 1934 we found both species nesting almost side by side and in about equal abundance at timber line on Hudson Bay. The nests were in spruces and willows from two to ten feet from the ground.

The nests were made of spruce twigs and plant fibers and always lined with ptarmigan feathers. About their homes the birds were rather tame, just as they often are in winter when feeding on birch or alder catkins or on pigweed along roadsides. The eggs were bluish or greenish white specked with brown.

As with goldfinches and siskins, the females, closely attended by the males, build the nests and incubate the eggs. Similarly, the males feed the incubating females, as they later feed the young, by regurgitation.

The common redpoll nests from Alaska and Quebec to Alberta and the Gulf of St. Lawrence, and wanders in winter to the Northern States. The hoary redpoll has a similar range but reaches Siberia and is rarer in the south.

Gray-crowned Rosy Finch
(Leucosticte tephrocotis tephrocotis)
Average Length, Six Inches

Rosy finches are birds of the mountain tops and glaciers, making their summer home above timber line and coming down to lower levels in winter only when forced to do so by lack of food. Six varieties, belonging to four species, have been described from North America, and at least one from northeastern Asia, but their plumage and affinities seem somewhat variable.

The best known is the gray-crowned rosy finch, which appears in summer on mountain tops from Alaska to northwestern Montana and in winter descends to the lower levels as far south as Utah and Colorado.

They are friendly little birds and entirely terrestrial, picking up benumbed insects at the edge of snow in summer and weed seed in winter. The nest is a cup of grasses or moss in a niche in a cliff or under a bowlder. The four or five eggs are pure white.

NATURE TWISTED THE CROSSBILL'S BEAK FOR A SPECIAL PURPOSE

The bill, with its curiously crossed tips, looks malformed, but actually it makes a perfect tool for opening the cones of evergreen trees and exposing the seeds on which these northern and eastern wood wanderers (lower trio) largely feed. The **White-winged Crossbill** at the bottom is less prevalent than the pair of **Red Crossbills** with him. The **Green-backed Goldfinch** (upper left pair) is common in weed-grown fields of California and east to Colorado. The **Lawrence's Goldfinch** (upper right pair) inhabits the Southwest from New Mexico to California.

Crossbills

(Loxia curvirostra and *loxia leucoptera)*
Average Length, Six and One-quarter Inches

Here is a case of extreme specialization which has apparently been successful. One unfamiliar with the habits of crossbills and noting the curiously crossed mandibles for the first time is likely to think them a malformation and feel sorry for the bird that must make its living with such a handicap.

Nor does one's sympathy grow less upon seeing one of these birds trying to eat ordinary food. A white-winged crossbill, for example, came to the hemlock tree near my bird feeding station and, after watching the chickadees, nuthatches, and woodpeckers eating suet, thought he would like some of it.

He had no trouble hanging on to the suet that was fastened to the side of an upright log, but when he tried to use his beak to detach a piece, he found that the peculiar crossed tips of his bill obstructed his purpose. He apparently was faced with a new problem.

I sat in a blind about three feet from the bird, and could see exactly what he was doing. Finally, he clamped his wide-open bill into the suet and I could see his hard, pointed, scooplike tongue scraping little crumbs of suet into his mouth.

It was a rather clumsy performance at best and I felt sorry for him. I cut off a twig of hemlock with several cones and fastened it over the suet. This was quite a different story. I was interested to see how he could get at the seeds, because the scales of the cones were tightly shut.

With one snip of his bill he cut off one of the cones, turned it upside down between his feet and, opening his bill until the tips just met, he slipped this instrument under the edge of one of the scales.

As he opened his bill still further, I could see there was sufficient lateral motion to pry up the scale, whereupon his little tongue scooped out the two seeds underneath as neatly as could be desired. On the heavier cones of pine and spruce the crossbills hang upside down and perform the same feat without snipping them off.

Here, then, was the secret of the crossbills' great success in populating the coniferous world with their kind. They had been able to take advantage of an almost continuous food supply closed to most other birds. We find today that crossbills, in spite of what seems a deformity, have been able so to increase that they are found practically all over the Northern Hemisphere wherever there are coniferous trees.

In the red crossbill *(Loxia curvirostra)* several minor variations in size of bill, length of wing, or intensity of red have naturally developed, so that in North America alone we recognize five varieties. The common crossbill of Europe is a somewhat larger form of the same species.

Ordinarily, plenty of cones are available in the northern forests every year and throughout the year. During such times the crossbills do not migrate at all and may even start nesting in January. But once in a while, for some unknown reason, the spruces stop fruiting, and the crossbills are robbed of their main support. Then they move southward into the northern United States in large numbers and feed upon whatever bits of food they can find.

They seem to have little fear of man and sometimes permit one to walk among them.

In these flocks the olive plumage of the female usually predominates, for the young wear this garb for two years and then the males change rather gradually. On their erratic wanderings the crossbills may associate with other finches and grosbeaks. The nests of the crossbills are in coniferous trees, 15 to 30 feet from the ground.

The white-winged crossbill *(Loxia leucoptera)* with more slender bill is confined to the evergreen forests of Alaska and Canada. A few birds are also sometimes found in summer in the higher Adirondacks of New York, the White Mountains of New Hampshire, and the spruce forests of Maine. With its pinkish-red color and conspicuous wing bars, it is quite easily distinguished from its brick-red cousin, but its habits are apparently the same.

Green-backed Goldfinch

(Spinus psaltria)
Average Length, Four Inches

Californians have three goldfinches, or "wild canaries." to our one in the East. The western representative of our common goldfinch is called the willow goldfinch. It is similar to the eastern, but has shorter wings and tail. The other two are the green-backed and the Lawrence's.

The habits of the latter two are not very different from those of our eastern bird, though their call notes are quite distinct. The green-backed is the commoner, frequenting weedy borders of fields. Pairs keep together much, even during winter.

Lawrence's Goldfinch

(Spinus lawrencei)
Average Length, Four and One-quarter Inches

Lawrence's goldfinch *(Spinus lawrencei)* is found in the hotter, drier parts of southern California, and in winter as far east as Arizona.

The song of this goldfinch is lower in pitch and somewhat rougher than the songs of the other species, and it has among its call notes a harsh *kee-yerr* that is quite different from any of the notes of the others.

THE YELLOW-THROATED VIREO IS JUSTLY PROUD OF HER SKILFULLY BUILT NEST

Photographs by A. A. Allen

THE ROSE-BREASTED GROSBEAK HAS A RAMSHACKLE HOME

TOWHEES, SPARROWS, AND LONGSPURS

These Happy Little Singers Make Merry in Field, Forest, and Hedgerow Throughout North America

By T. Gilbert Pearson

ONE sultry September afternoon, when I was having difficulty holding the attention of my zoölogy students, I suddenly asked how they would like to put aside their note-books and go with me to look for birds. Surprised, but willing, they arose and followed.

It was a quiet day; there was no soughing of the pines, or even a ripple along the tops of the broom-sedge that extended across the field beyond the old rail fence. A blue haze hung along the horizon, as it often does in North Carolina during the autumn days. We advanced stealthily along a sandy road running through a cutover woodland. Presently we heard from a near-by thicket a great commotion among the fallen leaves.

"A flock of quail," one whispered. "Or a big wild turkey," said another.

A BIRD CALL DIFFICULT TO LOCATE

Then there came a sharp call, *chewink, joree,* repeated many times. At once a discussion arose as to the direction from which the sounds were coming. Some thought they were from a bush in front of us; and others were just as sure that they were from our left, or our right.

Suddenly the feathered ventriloquist appeared, and with pounding, jerking flight dashed away and vanished. It was a redeyed towhee. When I told the students that all the scratching they had heard had been made by that eight and one-third-inch bird, I saw on every face a look of incredulity. Murmurs of surprise were the only audible replies.

A towhee's personality dominates the thicket which he enters. His colors are striking and he is full of energy and industry. The call notes are clear and far-reaching. If you intrude too closely upon his privacy, he may briefly mount to some limb for a better view of you. If it is springtime, you may even find him singing from some elevated perch.

Ordinarily this is not a bird of the dooryard, although, now and then, hunger may force him to your feeding station. He lives, in part, upon ants, cockroaches, flies, boll weevils and grasshoppers. In fact, he devours almost every kind of insect found on or near the ground. Seeds and grain also are staple articles of his diet, and sometimes gooseberries are eaten.

The towhee tribe is numerous, 24 kinds being recognized in North America. All but one belong to the genus called *Pipilo,* which contains five distinct species, three of which, in turn, are divided into 21 subspecies. The one species found east of the Mississippi River is the well-known redeyed towhee. North America's five remaining species occupy western ranges from Alaska to Texas and northern Mexico.

One of these birds, the coloration of which remains the same throughout its entire range, and which therefore is not divided into subspecies, is the green towhee. I first made its acquaintance in northern California, and since then have seen it in many places; but I still find it difficult to think of it as a towhee, so much does it differ from representatives of the genus *Pipilo* I knew in former days.

It is an inhabitant of the western and southwestern United States, and often is found on the mesas and brush-scattered rock slides.

Of all the kinds of towhees with which the far western States are so bountifully supplied, none is so well known as the somber-colored brown towhee. Not only is it an abundant species, but its habit of making itself at home in gardens and bushy lawns brings it constantly to human attention. It is a bird of town and wilderness, of the flat deserts and the wild arroyos where few birds are more in evidence.

Furthermore, it may be seen throughout the year. When the dry season approaches and many other birds depart for the verdure of higher altitudes, the brown towhee stays in the parched chaparral. Most people know it but not everyone calls it "towhee." Many speak of it as "brown bird" and others call it "bush bird." However, under one name or another, there are parts of California where it is as well known as any other species of feathered life.

There are eight varieties of the species we call brown towhee, three of them inhabiting each its own particular region in California; three others are found in Baja California and one each in Oregon and Arizona, the latter ranging to Colorado.

In the classification of birds the most numerous family is the Fringillidae, containing some 1200 species and subspecies distributed throughout the world. In North America the representatives of this group are enrolled in three subfamilies, one of which, the Emberizinae, includes the towhees, sparrows, juncos, longspurs, and snow buntings—169 birds in all.

STOUT BEAKS CRUSH WEED SEEDS

In the color plates presented with this article are reproduced paintings of 61 of the more typical forms of this subfamily. All possess short, stout beaks well adapted for crushing seeds, of which they are voracious consumers. As destroyers of weed seeds, their value to farmers is incalculable.

To the field ornithologist, the mention of any section of the country is likely to bring to his mind some bird that he has seen and enjoyed in that particular region. When I hear "Great Plains," my instant mental response is "lark bunting."

In western Nebraska, in Colorado, and in southern Saskatchewan, this striking white-winged, black bird has filled me with delight. A male will rise from a rock or a slight elevation of ground, fly upward for 15 or 20 feet and, after hovering for a moment, burst into a melody which ceases only when it sinks again to the earth.

When we come to consider the true sparrows, we find a large and widely scattered assemblage of small birds with streaked plumage predominantly brown and gray. They are denizens of fields, old pastures, fence rows, and open groves. They gather their food almost entirely from the ground, and their colors render them inconspicuous, a fortunate protection when winged enemies are abroad.

There is a general superficial resemblance among most of the sparrows, and inexperi-

enced bird observers often find difficulty in identifying them. However, not many species are met in any one neighborhood; therefore, with patience, one may learn to know at least the sparrows of the immediate locality. Although they are the plainest of all the feathered tribes, they are extremely interesting, and one soon discovers that each species possesses its individual traits.

Near my home in New York there is a college campus with an adjoining small park. Here every spring I find three kinds of sparrows. Early in April I begin to watch for the chipping sparrow, which is due to arrive any day after its winter sojourn in the southern States.

Generally my first knowledge of its presence is the sound of its voice. It cannot sing much of a song, only a monotonous *chippy-chippy-chippy,* repeated many times with virtually no variation. With my field glass I soon locate the little bird, his brownish-red cap and the white stripe over his eye easily identifying him.

He and his mate will build a nest close by in the vine on a veranda or in some small evergreen, or perhaps out on a horizontal limb of a shade tree. I have never seen a nest except close to dwellings of man. Not once have I found one in heavy woodlands or forests.

HAIR LINES CHIPPING SPARROW NEST

The nest is constructed mainly of little twigs, grasses and rootlets, and lined with hair. Where, in this age of automobiles, the millions of chipping sparrows of the land find enough long hairs for their nest linings is indeed a mystery to me. These hairs sometimes become tangled about a sparrow, and, catching on a limb, cause tragedy to occur in the orchard.

The chipping sparrows stay near my home for seven months, and in November depart from the New York City region.

The second visitor that comes to my hunting grounds on the New York University Campus is the song sparrow. Usually I find him by an old stone wall that borders a thicket on the slope. He is larger than the chipping sparrow; in fact, a typical specimen is fully six and a third inches in length, exceeding the measurement of the chippy by a full inch.

His name correctly describes one of his characteristics. I know few other birds so habitually given to song. He may be heard anywhere, day or night, singing even when on the wing. The song sparrow is not so tame as some other birds, and while it sometimes comes into your yard it is ever alert and ready to dash to cover. Look for it along hedgerows and in bushes bordering streams in the fields.

THE SONG SPARROW TRAVELS FAR

When you startle a sparrow from the grass and it flies away with a sharp chirp, watch its tail; for if the tail jerks and pounds as the bird flies you are most certainly looking at a song sparrow.

You might remember too that you are watching one of the great biological successes in the bird world. His range is enormous. Go to the Alaska Peninsula and you will find him; follow down the Pacific coast until you are among the semi-barren hills of Baja California and in many places you will meet the song sparrow. Turn eastward through the great mountain chains, traverse central Canada all the way to Nova Scotia, go through the United States anywhere as far south as northern South Carolina and in nearly every suitable region of this vast domain the song sparrow lives, rears its young, and sings to the delight of man.

It does not breed in the far southern States, but even there you may find it in winter, flitting and singing in the brushy red gullies of Georgia, in the palmetto thickets of Florida, and along the hyacinth-choked bayous of Louisiana.

Throughout its range 26 subspecies have developed under Nature's magic laws, but, in any garden, the song sparrow that you find is just the same alert vivacious singer as any other song sparrow, although found half a continent away.

A third visitor that I welcome near my home every spring is the field sparrow. Sometimes I see him on mild days late in March before the chippy has arrived. He comes early, and in autumn seems reluctant to leave; some individuals, I am told, even pass the winter on Long Island. He is larger than the chipping sparrow, and longer by a quarter of an inch.

When you find this bird in your orchard do not confuse it with the chipping sparrow. Notice that its cheeks are gray, while the other bird has a clear white stripe over its eye. The field sparrow has a real song, *che-wee, che-wee, che-wee,* followed by a trill, while the chipping sparrow sings only *chippy* with many rapid reiterations all strung closely together.

On the western shore of Lake Champlain there is a large sheep pasture, where spreading junipers grow, and a cedar swamp with ferns and bane berries. Here, in June, I sometimes go to listen to the white-throated sparrows sing, and to renew my search for one of their nests.

The song I hear is clear and pleasing, carrying far across the rocky pasture. It begins with two or three measured high-pitched notes, followed by a quavering trill which diminishes until I do not always catch the ending. New Englanders say that the bird sings *old Sam Peabody, Peabody, Peabody;* but men from the other side of the St. Lawrence stoutly aver that what it says is *sweet, sweet, Canada, Canada, Canada.*

WHITE-THROAT HIDES ITS NEST

I have been very anxious to find its nest, which, I have read, is "sunk to the rim in moss or earth, and so cunningly concealed by surrounding and overhanging vegetation that it is difficult to find."

In this pasture, whenever I see a pair of white-throats exhibiting uneasiness at my presence, I begin a systematic hunt for their nest. I crawl over many square rods of earth, peering under every little bush, and pushing aside the tops of every cluster of thick grass.

All this effort is vain, however, for never, as yet, have I been able to discover the hidden treasures of the white-throat and his mate. Before the goldenrod has reached its glory, I have heard the young ones calling in the thicket where the bane berries are turning red, and I have known that they are being fed not far away from the nest which I have so vainly sought.

From Massachusetts westward to Montana, and throughout much of Canada as far northward as trees are found, the white-throats make their summer home. They pass the winter in the United States eastward of Missouri, and southward to Mexico and Florida. In the region including Georgia, Tennessee and the Carolinas, they tarry for as long as seven months.

Hedgerows, bushes, and the brushy margins of woodlands are their favorite haunts, and often they are associated with other sparrows. They are a delight to have about the home, for they will visit the feeding station and often they will sing.

Photograph by A. A. Allen

"SCRAM, SPATZY," SAYS THE NUTHATCH TO THE HOUSE SPARROW

A food log often becomes a scene of warfare when birds of different species seek the same viands.

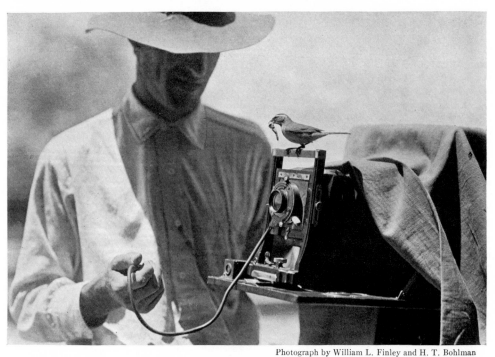

Photograph by William L. Finley and H. T. Bohlman

IS THE WORM FOR PHOTOGRAPHER OR CAMERA?

This desert sparrow knows no fear of human friends, for it is of a species little persecuted.

Photograph by Raymond S. Deck

EIGHT SPARROWS OF SIX SPECIES EAT GRAIN SCATTERED ON SNOW

Two "English sparrows"; a white-throat; a fox sparrow; a tree sparrow; two juncos; song sparrow.

Photograph by Jacob Gayer

THE WHITE-CROWNED SPARROW HIDES ITS NEST

Fortunate is he who can find the eggs of this species. The picture was taken in Labrador in July.

Red-eyed Towhee

(Pipilo erythrophthalmus erythrophthalmus)

Average Length, Eight and One-third Inches

This bird has been known to naturalists since Catesby published an account of it in 1758. It breeds in the Transition and Upper Austral Zones in most of the region from southeastern Saskatchewan and southeastern Nebraska eastward to southern Maine and northern Georgia. It winters from eastern Nebraska, and the Ohio and Potomac Valleys to Texas and central Florida.

It is a thicket-loving species, being especially fond of cut-over land where sprouts and young saplings abound, or of scrubby lands with patches of brush and briars. Often it frequents hedges and old walls or rail fences bordered with brush and vines.

In the mountains of North Carolina, years ago, there arose complaints, probably ill-founded, that the towhee made a business of pulling up newly planted corn. Therefore the State Legislature decided to place its name on the list of birds having no legal protection. By error, however, it was listed among the game birds; and for 25 years thereafter the towhee was officially a game bird in that State. Not until 1928 was the statute corrected and the handsome bird given the legal status it so justly deserves.

Towhees are not gregarious by nature and rarely are many of them seen together, although at times several may collect where food conditions are particularly favorable. Of course, in some regions they are more plentiful than in others. Standing on the scrubby slopes of Blue Hill, Massachusetts, I counted one day eight male towhees singing within my hearing, but to me this was a most unusual experience.

The nest of the towhee is built on the ground or in low bushes or brush piles. It is constructed of twigs, weed stems, leaves, and strips of bark, all skillfully woven together and finished with a lining of grass or of hair.

Three to five spotted eggs are laid. When a female is sitting on her nest, her colors blend so well with the surroundings that one may come within a few feet without noticing her presence. At times the male shares with his mate the duties of incubation, and both exhibit the greatest solicitude for the young when danger threatens.

The towhee is one of nearly 200 varieties of birds that the parasitic cowbird depends upon to hatch her eggs and rear her young. As many as six cowbird eggs have been found in one towhee's nest.

In 1871 Coues reported the discovery that the towhee breeding in central Florida has white eyes, and that only two instead of three of the outer tail feathers are tipped with white. Thus it was proclaimed that the towhee of eastern North America consists of two climatic varieties, one of which henceforward was to be known as the white-eyed towhee *(P. e. alleni)*.

Howell in 1913 reported still another subspecies, the Alabama towhee *(P. e. canaster)* from Alabama and Georgia. In general all these birds bear such a close resemblance that at a little distance only the most experienced students can distinguish between them.

Spurred Towhee

(Pipilo maculatus montanus)

Average Length, Seven and Three-quarters Inches

In the three southwestern Provinces of Canada and in the United States, westward of a line running through eastern Colorado and down into Mexico, there is found a bird that closely resembles the common towhee of the eastern States. The chief difference is that there is more white on the tail and that there are white spots on the back.

The specimens first described in 1831 are now called arctic towhees. Eighteen years later it was learned that the spotted-backed towhee found in southwestern British Columbia and western Oregon was slightly different, and the Oregon towhee was described.

In 1858 a third climatic variety came to light. Thirty-three years later another subdivision was recognized. Today we have 10 subspecies of this one bird.

Their names and the dates of their recognition by scientists are as follows:

Arctic towhee—1831, Oregon towhee—1849, San Diego towhee—1858, large-billed towhee—1891, San Clemente towhee—1897, San Francisco towhee—1900, spurred towhee—1905, Nevada towhee—1911, Sacramento towhee—1913, Cape Colnett towhee—1926.

These birds are so nearly alike that the average observer in the field could scarcely be expected to distinguish among them. There seems to be little known difference in their habits and almost any basic fact that is stated regarding the habits of the spurred towhee may be taken to apply with equal truthfulness to all of the others.

Texas Sparrow

(Arremonops rufivirgatus rufivirgatus)

Average Length, Six Inches

For a long time after this bird was described to science in 1851, it was known as the "green finch." The olive-green colors of the upper parts, including wings and tail, do not readily suggest a sparrow, for generally the sparrows run strongly to shades of gray and brown.

It is an inhabitant of the chaparral regions of lower Texas, and southward into Tamaulipas, Nuevo Leon, and San Luis Potosí, Mexico. The nest of twigs, weed stems, bark, grasses, and sometimes hair, is built in low bushes. The eggs, usually four in number, are white.

TOWHEES ARE HANDSOME SONGSTERS OF THE BRUSH LANDS

They are often heard but seldom seen. The brisk, bustling **Red-eyed Towhee** (male and his mate, right and left, above) is fully at rest only when pouring out its passionate love song. This bird's other common name, "chewink," is derived from its call note. Of even more striking appearance is the **Spurred Towhee** (male and a young bird, center pair), a far westerner with ten close subspecific relatives. Chaparral thickets of the Southwest are "home" to the inconspicuous **Texas Sparrow** (lower right), once known as the "green finch."

Green-tailed Towhee
(Oberholseria chlorura)
Average Length, Six and Three-quarters Inches

Deposited one morning at a small railway station in California with three hours to wait before the next train, I obtained a horse and rode off among the hills in search of birds new to my experience. In the clearing mist the sun was lighting up the dripping foliage on every side, an ideal condition to expect activity to begin among the birds, and it was not long before my hopes were realized.

I heard a *mew, mew,* and looking around at once discovered, in the top of a small tree, the author of the notes. Its size and its grayish-yellow color suggested a greatly overgrown warbler, but its throat was white like that of some of the sparrows, and it wore a very distinct cap of reddish-brown.

Eagerly I studied the tail, but my binoculars revealed only dark yellowish feathers. In the angle of light which played upon it, I could detect no green, but there was no mistaking the bird; it was indeed a green-tailed towhee.

Neither on this occasion, nor later when I came to know it better, did its colors or its movements ever completely satisfy me that it should be called a towhee, with which I had so long been familiar. I have always felt like calling it the red-capped sparrow-warbler, or some other such descriptive name.

The familiar voice of this towhee is often heard even when its owner is well-hidden behind a screen of desert shrubbery. With much flashing of its green tail, this trim, glossy-coated beauty scratches busily among the brush. Seemingly, it is very proud of the red feathers of its cap, for it has a way of raising these when faced by an intruder.

The green-tail places its nest on or near the ground in chaparral, mesquite, sagebrush or cactus. The nest is made of grass, small twigs, and shreds of bark and is lined with fine grass or, occasionally, with horsehair. The four whitish eggs are freckled with brown.

For a time this bird was classified with the genus *Pipilo;* then it was called an *Oreospiza;* but of late it has been given a distinctive generic name of its own, *Oberholseria.*

It inhabits the country from the western edge of the Great Plains to the Coast Ranges. In summer it is found from Oregon to southern California and eastward into western Texas. The winters are passed along the southern fringe of its summer range and southward in Mexico to Cape San Lucas and Guanajuato.

Cañon Towhee
(Pipilo fuscus mesoleucus)
Average Length, Eight and One-half Inches

This bird is closely allied to the California towhee, but the rich brown cap and sparsely spotted breast make its identification easy. It is found in the Upper Austral Zone from southeastern Colorado and western Arizona to western Texas and northern Sonora. Like other towhees, it is a brush-loving species and builds its nest indifferently in mesquite trees, in cholla cactus, or among the daggers of the yucca, but rarely at a distance of more than ten feet from the ground.

In their selection of food, the brown towhees are omnivorous. Any insect that comes near is quickly snapped up and swallowed. Seeds of many kinds are eaten, and gardeners often find it desirable to cover their lettuce and peas with mosquito netting or brush to avoid replanting after the towhees have visited them.

California Towhee
(Pipilo fuscus crissalis)
Average Length, Nine Inches

We now come to a bird popularly known as the "brown towhee" throughout its range in California. It and the cañon towhee are two of the eight races of this western species. It is abundant in western California from Monterey to the Mexican border and eastward to the San Joaquin Valley region, and also in California's southeastern desert country.

It not only haunts bushy places in the wilderness but also comes to city lawns and parks. As an excuse for a song it gives vent to a series of squeaky notes which do not rank high as music. Most of the time it is content to voice its emotions with sharp metallic chirps uttered with whatever emphasis the occasion may require. A fluffy, friendly bird, it darts about in awkward bobbing fashion.

Abert's Towhee
(Pipilo aberti)
Average Length, Eight and One-half Inches

This very plain brownish towhee is found chiefly from southwestern Utah to Arizona, New Mexico and northeast Baja California.

This is a common bird throughout the region of the Colorado River Valley and the delta country bordering the Gulf of California. About Phoenix, Arizona, the bird student may readily find Abert's towhees inhabiting the mesquite thickets and the groves of cottonwoods. As a rule it resents close inspection, and will slip into cover at the first alarm. It may be recognized by its cinnamon-colored plumage and by the additional fact that it is the largest of the towhees to be met with in that part of the country.

Its nest is a rather large, bulky affair, more or less loosely put together. Weed stalks, strips of bark, grasses, and sticks are used in its construction. From two to four sparsely marked eggs are laid in the nest which may be lined with inner bark or with horse hairs.

Insects of many kinds, as well as berries and seeds, constitute its usual diet. It is not known to be harmful in any way to man's agricultural or horticultural interests.

Allan Brooks -

MODEST PLUMAGE OF WESTERN TOWHEES BLENDS WITH THEIR ARID RANGE

The intense industry of the **Green-tailed Towhee** (upper left), as it busily scratches among the brush, seems to say, "Bird at work. Do not disturb." The green-tail's resemblance to a sparrow, or a flycatcher, has led ornithologists to give it a private generic name of its own. The very plain brownish **Abert's Towhee** (lower right) is common throughout the lower Colorado River Valley. Close cousins are the **California** and **Cañon Towhees** (upper right and left center). They are both subspecies of the bird popularly known as the "brown towhee."

Lark Bunting

(Calamospiza melanocorys)
Average Length, Six and One-half Inches

The male of the lark bunting is one of the most conspicuous of the small birds that in summer inhabit the Great Plains region of central and western North America. Its black plumage with large white wing patch renders it a bird not easily overlooked.

The lark bunting likes the untilled prairies and rocky hillsides, and often it has been driven from favorite regions by the advent of the plow. On the grassy plains it occupies much the same place in the bird world as does the bobolink of more eastern regions. Also, like the bobolink, it undergoes unusual molting processes. In winter plumage the black feathers of the male have largely disappeared and he much resembles the female.

In autumn these buntings desert their prairie home and in flocks roam the country from Arizona and Texas southward well on to the cactus-strewn plateau of Mexico. Here they remain until the approach of spring, when they begin to move northward, the white and black plumage of the males once again in evidence. A flood of song announces that another mating season is close at hand.

Its four or five pale blue eggs are laid in a nest of grass and fine roots.

Eastern Savannah Sparrow

(Passerculus sandwichensis savanna)
Average Length, Five and One-half Inches

The Savannah sparrow is another of those small species that breed over a surprisingly large part of North America.

Its summer range extends from arctic Alaska to Labrador and southward to New Jersey, Indiana, and northern New Mexico. In winter it spreads over the country from New Jersey, Indiana, and California to Guatemala.

At present it is classified into six closely related subspecies. The eastern Savannah sparrow breeds from northern Montana and northern Quebec southward to Iowa and southern New Jersey, and winters from the southern part of its summer range to Cuba, the Gulf coast and northeastern Mexico. It is abundant in many regions, frequenting meadows, especially damp ones where long grass abounds.

About one-half of its food consists of seeds, the remainder of insects. When startled, it flies low over the grass for a distance, then darts suddenly out of sight. It is supposed to consume more beetles than does any other bird of the sparrow tribe. Its song, usually delivered from a weed stalk or low bush, consists of a brief trill, musical but weak.

The nest of the eastern Savannah sparrow is built of grass, moss, and hair. The four or five bluish-white eggs are speckled and splotched with reddish brown.

Belding's Sparrow

(Passerculus beldingi)
Average Length, Five Inches

Belding's sparrow inhabits the salt marshes of California from the neighborhood of Santa Barbara southward along the coast to San Quintín Bay in Baja California. It prefers wet or damp marshes, but I have seen it on the dry sand not far from the road leading northward from Los Angeles.

It usually lays three spotted eggs in a nest built in marsh grass just above the ground.

Ipswich Sparrow

(Passerculus princeps)
Average Length, Six and One-quarter Inches

On December 4, 1868, C. J. Maynard while walking among the sand dunes of Ipswich, Massachusetts, shot a bird hitherto unknown. It was named Ipswich sparrow.

No one knew where it came from until May, 1894, when Dr. Jonathan Dwight found the species breeding near the beach on Sable Island, Nova Scotia. Its nest has not been found elsewhere. The bird winters along the beaches of the Atlantic coast as far south (rarely) as North Carolina.

Besides characteristic sparrow-like chirps, it has a song described by Dr. Dwight as a "sad little chant" repeated several times a minute.

The same authority wrote: "Those who care to visit in winter the bleak, winter-swept sand hillocks of our Atlantic coast will find this bird much less rare than it was once supposed to be. It never strays far from the waving tufts of coarse beach-grass that scantily cover the sand-drifts, and single individuals may be found skulking among such surroundings. They seldom allow a near approach, but fly wildly away to considerable distances, and on alighting run off so rapidly that they are difficult to find a second time. The flight is rapid and irregular, and the birds may easily be mistaken for Savannah sparrows, with which, during the migrations, they are sometimes associated. On rare occasions a sharp chirp is heard, but as a rule they are silent."

Large-billed Sparrow

(Passerculus rostratus rostratus)
Average Length, Five and One-half Inches

This bright brownish bird inhabits salt marshes about the head of the Gulf of California, in northeastern Baja California and in northwestern Sonora. In winter it migrates as far southward as southern Sonora and Cape San Lucas and northward into southern California.

At times it comes into coastwise towns and runs about the docks and warehouses, but as a rule it dwells in the open, more unsettled country. The other two subspecies of this sparrow are found only in Baja California.

THE BLACK-AND-WHITE LARK BUNTING IS A CONSPICUOUS BIRD OF THE PRAIRIE

In sharp contrast to his pale, streaked mate and four neat but soberly clad sparrows is the striking **Lark Bunting** (above, male beside his mate and flying). In the spring this bird's rich song floods the untilled grassy plains and rocky hillsides of the West. Among the long grass of wet meadows dwells the **Eastern Savannah Sparrow** (right center). The nest of the **Ipswich Sparrow** (left center) has been found only on Sable Island, Nova Scotia. The **Belding's Sparrow** and **Large-billed Sparrow** (at the bottom, left and right) inhabit salt marshes in southern California and Baja California.

Eastern Grasshopper Sparrow
(Ammodramus savannarum australis)
Average Length, Five and One-third Inches

Four subspecies of this bird are recognized by ornithologists. The eastern grasshopper sparrow is widely distributed in eastern United States, inhabiting much of the territory east of the Great Plains from southern Wisconsin, southern Ontario, and southern New Hampshire southward to northern South Carolina, northern Georgia, and central Alabama. It winters from Illinois and North Carolina southward to Cuba, Yucatán, and Guatemala.

This sparrow has very marked peculiarities. Its shape is odd in that its head seems unusually large for a sparrow, and its tail is ridiculously short. Its song is a splendid imitation of the buzzing sound produced by a grasshopper. It lives in grass and weed patches, mounting a weed stalk now and then for seeds or flying to the top of a fence to sing.

When taking flight, it flutters wren-fashion for a short distance and then, as if completely exhausted, drops quickly into cover again.

The nest, made on the ground, is skillfully hidden in a slight depression. This the bird approaches and leaves by slipping quietly through the grass.

In appearance it is much like the Savannah, but its breast is unstreaked and there is yellow at the bend of the wing. The grasshopper sparrow is distinctly a ground bird, for it not only nests and feeds on the ground, but usually sings on the ground, and it is supposed always to sleep on the ground.

There is a western grasshopper sparrow *(A. s. bimaculatus)* found from Minnesota to California and a Florida grasshopper sparrow *(A. s. floridanus)* of the Kissimmee Prairie.

Baird's Sparrow
(Ammodramus bairdi)
Average Length, Five and One-half Inches

When in 1843 Audubon was on his trip to the Yellowstone country, he discovered and named the Baird's sparrow. He explained that he named it for his friend, Spencer F. Baird, who in later years became Secretary of the Smithsonian Institution. Although the bird occurs commonly on many of the western prairies, it is a curious fact that after its discovery by Audubon 30 years elapsed before its presence was again noted by ornithologists.

It closely resembles the Savannah sparrow, though its song contains more of a warble than that of the Savannah. It flies in a characteristic zigzag course. It haunts dry uplands, preferably those with clusters of dead grass.

Baird's sparrow is found in summer from Minnesota westward to Saskatchewan and central Montana. It winters from central Texas southward into Mexico.

Eastern Henslow's Sparrow
(Passerherbulus henslowi susurrans)
Average Length, Five Inches

This modest bird is a retiring little inhabitant of unwooded country from New York and New Hampshire southward. In summer its favorite habitat is wet meadows where, early in June, one may find its nest with the four or five dainty, spotted eggs.

It passes the winter in the southeastern States, going as far south as Florida and frequenting abandoned fields grown up in broomsedge. Like the grasshopper sparrow, it is very skillful in keeping out of sight.

Mr. William Brewster named this bird in 1918, the type specimen coming from Falls Church, Virginia, near Washington, D. C.

Eastern Henslow's sparrows begin to reach the Washington region in spring about April 10. Here they are locally common summer residents. After the young are hatched and reared, the augmented families linger on through much of October before joining the last of those hosts of birds which for weeks have been hurrying southward every night.

While these sparrows stay six or six and a half months in the middle latitudes, those that go on to New England usually do not reach their destinations until May. The more northerly migrants leave early in October for the South and so their sojourn in the North is usually shorter by a month than that of the birds that stay in the Middle Atlantic States.

Belonging to a species that is distinctly ground-loving, eastern Henslow's sparrows are seldom seen perched aloft, except in the spring when an ardent male may come to the top of a fence post or to a low weed to pour out his vigorous little song. Like other birds of terrestrial habits, Henslow's sparrow hides its nest on the ground among grass or weeds.

The western Henslow's sparrow *(P. h. henslowi)* breeds from Ontario and South Dakota to Ohio and northern Texas. It winters from southern Texas to western Florida.

Leconte's Sparrow
(Passerherbulus caudacutus)
Average Length, Five Inches

One of the unobtrusive feathered inhabitants of swamps and bogs is Leconte's sparrow. It closely resembles the Savannah sparrow and its song is very similar to that of the grasshopper sparrow, an insect-like buzz of about one second's duration, delivered as the bird stands with gaping bill pointed skyward.

It is found in summer from Great Slave Lake to North Dakota and southern Minnesota. Its nest is usually hidden in clusters of dead grass in wet meadowlands. The species winters from southern Kansas and Tennessee to Texas and Florida.

SPARROWS BELONG TO THE MOST NUMEROUS OF ALL BIRD FAMILIES

The sparrows form a branch of the great finch family, which is represented by about 200 species in the United States and 1,200 throughout the world. A grasshopperlike buzzing song has named the **Eastern Grasshopper Sparrow** (upper left) which, also like the insect, lives in grass and weed patches. The **Eastern Henslow's Sparrow** and **Leconte's Sparrow** (at the right, above and below) nest and sing among the tall grasses of wet meadows. **Baird's Sparrow** (lower left) haunts dry uplands in the West.

Sharp-tailed Sparrow

(Ammospiza caudacuta caudacuta)

Average Length, Five and Three-quarters Inches

The sharp-tailed sparrow is one of several species of sparrows inhabiting the salt marshes of the Atlantic coast of the United States. It breeds from New Hampshire to Virginia and winters from New Jersey to northern Florida. In many localities it is very abundant.

When found, the birds seek to escape observation by running along the ground, as a rule being very reluctant to take wing. In the spring they frequent the same marshes inhabited by the seaside sparrow. In the autumn mixed flocks of the two species may be found running about the marshes or clinging to reeds that grow in or near the salt water.

The sharp-tailed sparrow is about the length of the chipping sparrow. It is, however, stouter and more robust and its head is noticeably larger than that of the chippy, while its tail is shorter. The young bird of the year is very fluffy and the plumage of its back and underparts bears dark stripes like those that adorn a young bobolink.

As the bird is continually creeping and running through the coarse grass of the beaches its feathers are subjected to great wear. Partially to offset this, it acquires two new sets of feathers each year. The molt that occurs just before the beginning of the nesting season results in an almost complete change of plumage, while that which takes place at the end of the breeding period produces an entirely new suit of feathers.

The breeding grounds of this dweller by the sea are limited to salt or brackish marsh lands on or near the beach, along the margins of estuaries, and up the river valleys as far as there is any tidal influence. The nest is built in tussocks of grass or clusters of dried seaweed or other waste matter left by the tide above the usual high water mark. Seaweed and dry grasses are used in the construction. The four or five eggs are about three-quarters of an inch in length and are covered with dots clustered thickly about the larger end.

These birds show a marked sociability, especially in the breeding season when they are inclined to colonize. One may search the marshes for some time without finding any sharp-tails and then come upon several pairs of them nesting close together.

From stomach examinations it has been learned that four-fifths of the food of this marsh bird in summer consists of animal matter, which includes sandfleas, spiders, crickets, moths, and various bugs. About twenty per cent of the nourishment taken is vegetable food, mostly seeds of grasses and weeds.

Close relatives of the sharp-tailed sparrow are the subspecies called the Acadian sparrow and the Nelson's sparrow. The Acadian sparrow *(A. c. subvirgata)*, found in Nova Scotia and Maine, winters from South Carolina to western Florida. The Nelson's sparrow *(A. c. nelsoni)* of Alberta, Manitoba, Minnesota and South Dakota also winters on the South Atlantic and Gulf coasts. In a general way the three birds resemble each other very closely both in appearance and in habits of life.

Cape Sable Seaside Sparrow

(Ammospiza mirabilis)

Average Length, Six Inches

Known only to the coastal marshes of Cape Sable, Florida, where it was discovered by Howell in 1918, this bird has an exceptionally small range. So far as known, it nests only in a brackish-water marsh six miles long and one-half mile in width. Storm tides sometimes inundate this marsh.

These birds breed in small isolated colonies, the nests being attached to the tall marsh grass. Their food consists of spiders, several kinds of insects, small Mollusca, and some vegetable matter.

Dusky Seaside Sparrow

(Ammospiza nigrescens)

Average Length, Six Inches

The dusky seaside sparrow inhabits salt marshes chiefly on or near Merritt Island, near Titusville, on the Atlantic coast of Florida. It has been studied very little, but its unusually short flights when frightened from cover and its extremely limited range are among the facts that have been noted.

Northern Seaside Sparrow

(Ammospiza maritima maritima)

Average Length, Six Inches

These birds have been well named. Never yet have I seen one except within sight or sound of the ocean. One may never expect to find them except in a salt marsh, or perhaps in vegetation growing on the sands in the immediate vicinity of the marsh.

The northern seaside sparrow inhabits, in summer, the vicinity of the ocean beaches from Massachusetts to Virginia. Its nest is built on the ground, and its three or four eggs are heavily spotted with cinnamon-brown.

The song consists of a few unmusical notes, which are sometimes uttered when the performer takes a short upward flight.

In winter it is found from Virginia to Florida, often in regions also frequented by sharp-tailed, swamp, and Savannah sparrows. There are seven subspecies of the seaside sparrow distributed along the Atlantic and Gulf of Mexico coasts from Canada to Texas. In song as well as in nesting, feeding, and migratory habits, little essential difference has been detected among them.

DWELLERS AMONG THE SALT SEA MARSHES

At the top is the locally abundant **Sharp-tailed Sparrow** of the Atlantic coast. Very reluctant to take wing when surprised, it prefers to run for cover among the coarse reeds of the seashore. The **Cape Sable Seaside Sparrow** (left center) breeds sociably in small colonies in a single Florida marsh. Also of very local distribution is the **Dusky Seaside Sparrow** (right center), found chiefly on or near Merritt Island, Florida. The **Northern Seaside Sparrow** (below, with a young bird) nests along the shore from Massachusetts to Virginia.

Eastern Vesper Sparrow

(Pooecetes gramineus gramineus)

Average Length, Six and One-quarter Inches

The eastern vesper sparrow is a bird of the fields and dry meadows. It breeds from Minnesota, Ontario, and Nova Scotia south to Nebraska and North Carolina, and winters from the southern part of its summer range to the Gulf of Mexico. The western vesper sparrow *(P. g. confinis)* ranges from British Columbia to California and Texas.

This rather pale, streaked sparrow is often found along country roadways. To many its song is even sweeter than that produced by the song sparrow; especially late in the evening, when to some ears its melody is the most inspiring music to be heard in the fields.

Mr. John Burroughs was especially attached to this bird. He enlarged on the exquisite beauty of its evening song and in the 1880's was in part responsible for the adoption of the name "vesper" sparrow. Before this it bore the name "grass finch" and sometimes "bay-winged bunting." Personally, I have never considered the evening song of this bird superior to the music it renders at other times. The natural hush of evening and the absence of distracting artificial sounds at the close of the day make all bird songs stand out more clearly. But to me there is no essential difference between the daytime and evening notes of this modest, sprightly vocalist.

Although chiefly a bird of the ground, the vesper sparrow frequently perches on fences, telephone wires, and the limbs of trees. It sings from such elevations, and, in the mating season, often flies aloft and pours out its music.

During nesting time it rarely is seen in marshy ground because it builds the cradle for its eggs and young in dry upland fields. The nest is sunk in some slight depression in the earth, often in a grass clump or the shelter of a weed or beside a clod. It is made entirely of dried grasses, rootlets, inner bark and hair. The eggs are four or five in number and are marked with brown dots and splashes. The principal breeding season is from mid-April until the middle of June.

Western Lark Sparrow

(Chondestes grammacus strigatus)

Average Length, Six and One-half Inches

There is many a dusty road in the West where one may come upon a lark sparrow that prefers to run ahead of one, rather than take flight. The white and chestnut stripes on its head make it by far the most conspicuously marked ground bird of the region.

Even as one watches, it may leap into the air to seize a passing insect, or it may mount some boulder or a convenient fence post and entertain the listener with a song of unusual sweetness and charm. Its song consists of numerous clear, rich notes, intermingled with trills. In autumn perhaps a score or more of these birds may burst into song from a fence.

The nest of grasses, rootlets, and perhaps long hairs, is secreted on the ground or a low bush. The eggs are three to five in number, and the white or pinkish shell is spotted and scrawled with black and purple markings.

There are two forms of this bird, one being the eastern lark sparrow *(C. g. grammacus)* which inhabits the country from western Minnesota and southern Ontario southward to Alabama and Louisiana. Eastward, it is found as far as western Pennsylvania and Maryland. It winters as far south as eastern Mexico.

The western lark sparrow breeds from British Columbia and Saskatchewan southward into northern Mexico. It passes the winter from northern California and southern Texas southward to Guatemala.

In spring the male often entertains his mate while singing by dancing about with many fluttering gestures, during which his white-rimmed tail is widely spread.

Rufous-winged Sparrow

(Aimophila carpalis)

Average Length, Five and One-third Inches

Arizona and northwestern Mexico are regarded as the range of the rufous-winged sparrow. Good field marks to watch for are the rufous wing patches and the rufous stripes on the head. The bird often associates with other sparrows, especially the western chipping sparrow, the general habits of which are similar. It is found up mountain slopes to an elevation of 4,000 feet.

Scott's Sparrow

(Aimophila ruficeps scotti)

Average Length, Five and One-half Inches

This bird might well be called the "ground-creeping sparrow." Its unhurried movement as it passes from sight behind a bush does not suggest a creature stricken with terror because of an observer's presence, but rather it reveals a dainty little feathered object exhibiting a nonchalance that is most charming. It prefers thus casually to pass from sight rather than to depart in panic on swiftly beating wings.

This species is classified as one of the eight subspecies of a far western bird known as the rufous-crowned sparrow.

From southern Colorado it ranges through much of Arizona, New Mexico, and southwestern Texas to Durango, Mexico, and is common in many of the little mountain ranges that one finds in that portion of America. In summer it is sometimes found up to an altitude of 10,000 feet. It haunts hillsides and gullies and where small bushes or cacti abound.

In its nest, on or near the ground, three to five pale bluish unspotted eggs are laid.

THE VESPER SPARROW'S PLAINTIVE MELODY PIERCES THE EVENING CALM

The hush that mantles Nature at sunset time throws into relief the sweet carolling of the **Eastern Vesper Sparrow** (on the post, above). The white and chestnut stripes on the head of the **Western Lark Sparrow** (left center) make it easily identified as it runs along dusty roads in the West. Desert mountain slopes in Arizona and northwestern Mexico are frequented by the **Rufous-winged Sparrow** (right center). **Scott's Sparrow** (lower left) is a ground-creeping bird of the Southwest.

Desert Sparrow

(Amphispiza bilineata deserticola)
Average Length, Five Inches

The strikingly marked desert sparrow is one of the numerous western representatives of this subfamily of birds. I especially recall enjoying these handsome songsters in southern Arizona, where I found them quite common.

The breeding season had passed and probably those I noted were settled for the winter. As I rode among the cacti and other prickly plants that throng the desert floors, these birds often would appear on the bushes, only to depart a moment later.

In many regions this is a numerous species, and its songs may be heard on all sides. One who works his way through the thorny brush, or climbs the hills where the grease-wood and squaw-grass flourish, will probably not long be out of sight or sound of this denizen of the desert wastes. It lives in the region where the scaled quail, the verdin, and the road-runner dwell. No other desert bird is more solicitous of its nest and young than is the desert sparrow. When danger approaches, the excitement of the parents becomes intense. They call continually and fly excitedly from bush to bush, the male sometimes bursting into song.

Desert sparrows breed generally farther north, as in Nevada, Utah, and Colorado. However, some are found in summer also in California and western Texas. They winter largely in Mexico.

Bachman's Sparrow

(Aimophila aestivalis bachmani)
Average Length, Five and Three-quarters Inches

The Bachman's sparrow was discovered by Audubon about one hundred years ago near Charleston, South Carolina, and named for his friend, Rev. John Bachman. It ranges from southern Indiana and central Virginia southward to northern Florida and central Texas.

It is one of my favorite birds of the southern yellow-pine lands where, among the ever-present clusters of wire grass, it runs before me like a mouse. If flushed, it flies for a short distance near the ground and then drops from sight. Its nest is well concealed on the ground, and its eggs are white.

In Guilford County, North Carolina, is situated an old Friends' cemetery known as New Garden Burying Ground. Here about fifty British and American soldiers, who died after a near-by battle between the forces of Greene and Cornwallis, lie buried together near a great oak. It was amid the grass and the weeds that cover the common grave of these men that, one May day, I stumbled upon my first Bachman's sparrow's nest.

It was made of grass and was domed over like the nest of the oven-bird or that of the meadowlark. It contained four eggs of the purest white. Later I found that the eggs had hatched, and the whole family avoided me so successfully that I was unable to follow further the fortunes of either the old birds or their young, although at times I heard the male singing. The plaintive appeal of its song reminds one somewhat of the field sparrow's chant, but the Bachman's melody is louder.

Neglected fields as well as open pine and oak woodlands are the haunts of this dweller in southern uplands. There is no distinction between the plumage of the male and female, both being sandy-ferruginous above with pale-reddish wing coverts.

Closely related to Bachman's sparrow is the pine-woods sparrow *(A. a. aestivalis)* of southern Georgia and Florida. In that southeastern corner of the United States there are large regions thinly covered with pine forests and an undergrowth of scrub palmetto. There are scattered "bay-heads" and at times cypress-heads, but mostly the country is open and one can see a great distance through the woods. Such regions are beloved by the pine-woods sparrow.

It spends its time almost entirely upon the ground, hunting in long wire-grass for its food. At times it seeks an elevated perch, usually for a brief survey of the surroundings but sometimes to sing. At the approach of an intruder, it drops to the ground where it is very difficult to flush. When stirred to flight, it goes but a short distance before again dropping to cover.

Its song, which is loud, clear, and plaintive, is delivered mostly in the early morning and late afternoon. Like the Bachman's sparrow, this species builds its nest on the ground, and its eggs are white.

Cassin's Sparrow

(Aimophila cassini)
Average Length, Five and One-half Inches

From Kansas and Nevada southward to Texas and Mexico is the homeland of Cassin's sparrow. It is particularly an inhabitant of the semi-arid regions, where numbers of the birds may often be found together in the mesquite singing in chorus.

In the spring the males engage in their melodious entertainments throughout all the daylight hours. The eggs are white or bluish-white, and unspotted.

Botteri's Sparrow

(Aimophila botterii botterii)
Average Length, Five and Three-quarters Inches

Botteri's sparrow ranges from southern Arizona and the lower Rio Grande Valley into Mexico. This little-known species has the general feeding and nesting habits of the desert sparrows, and is one of the varieties of sparrows that lay pure white, unspotted eggs.

THE DAPPER DESERT SPARROW OUTSHINES THREE PLAINER COUSINS

While few of our native sparrows boast bright plumage, all are clean-cut and neat. Among mesquite and cactus dwells the black-bibbed **Desert Sparrow** (upper left) that shares its southwestern range with the scaled quail and the road-runner. Two other sparrows of the Southwest are **Cassin's Sparrow** (lower left) and **Botteri's Sparrow** (lower right). **Bachman's Sparrow** (right center) frequents open southeastern oak and pine groves and builds a domed nest of grass.

Bell's Sparrow
(Amphispiza belli belli)
Average Length, Five and Three-quarters Inches

There are two sparrows of the desert country of southwestern North America that are similar in habits and general appearance and are often confused, the present species and the sage sparrow. Bell's sparrow, and its relation the gray sage sparrow (A. b. cinerea) of Baja California, are distinguished by lack of streaks on the back.

Bell's sparrow lives in California, west of the Sierra Nevada range, from Shasta County southward into Baja California, and on some of the adjacent islands. Its habits do not differ materially from those of the sage sparrow.

In a nest made of grasses and weed stems, the female Bell's sparrow lays three or four pale speckled eggs.

Northern Sage Sparrow
(Amphispiza nevadensis nevadensis)
Average Length, Six Inches

Over a vast domain from the State of Washington southward through California and Texas, and for hundreds of miles over the plateau of Mexico, the country is largely open with great expanses of sagebrush, creosote, and general chaparral. This semiarid region is the dwelling place of the northern sage sparrow and its fellow subspecies, the California sage sparrow (A. n. canescens).

It is distinctly a bird of sagebrush, feeding in its shadow, building its nest in part of sagebrush twigs and placing it among the stems of the sagebrush. The grayish tones and faint streakings of its plumage blend well with the surrounding vegetation.

As if the barrenness of the desert exercised a depressing effect upon the spirits of the sage sparrow, it is, during most of the year, a very silent bird, refraining from any vocal outbursts that would indicate special joy in life. Only in spring and early summer does its song show the gayer and more joyous side of its nature. When it sings, however, it gives a serious performance and, to the accompaniment of the voices of other male sparrows in the neighborhood, it shouts aloud its simple and exquisitely sweet lay. Far and wide the sagebrush rings with the music of innumerable sage sparrows. All the suppression of the previous silent months is at an end, and the writer of old, who observed that "the time of the singing of birds is at hand," might well have received from the sage sparrows the inspiration for this remark, if his sandaled feet had trod the thorny growths of the New Mexican wilds.

This light-colored sparrow dwells chiefly in sagebrush, creosote, and mesquite regions from Washington to Texas and California; winters in Chihuahua and States bordering on Mexico.

White-winged Junco
(Junco aikeni)
Average Length, Six and One-half Inches

Of all the 16 kinds of juncos in North America, the one called the white-winged is marked by large size, plain light gray coloration and, usually but not always, by white wing bars.

Its summer range is confined largely to Wyoming, the Black Hills country of South Dakota, and northwestern Nebraska. It winters from South Dakota southward through Colorado, western Kansas, and westward casually to New Mexico. Like the other members of this family, it subsists chiefly on insects and various weed seeds.

The nest of the white-winged junco is placed on the ground, often along the sides or at the bottom of canyons. It is a soft, cozy little structure composed almost entirely of dried grasses and hair. The eggs, four or five in number, have a greenish-white background and are sparingly marked with spots of varying shades of brown and lavender.

Like that of other juncos, its song is weak and is rarely heard except in the mating and nesting seasons.

Slate-colored Junco
(Junco hyemalis hyemalis)
Average Length, Six and One-quarter Inches

The common, dark-gray snowbird so well known throughout the colder months in eastern North America is the slate-colored junco. The line of demarcation on the breast where the slate-colored feathers stop and the white plumage begins constitutes a splendid field mark to look for. Also, the bird in flight usually displays the white outer tail feathers.

People who place food in their yards look for the junco as one of their regular winter guests. In summer it ranges from Alaska through central Alberta to Michigan, Nova Scotia, New York, and Pennsylvania, placing its nest generally on the ground in well-hidden situations. It winters from eastern Canada to the Gulf of Mexico.

I have often wondered where the juncos spend the night. One would naturally suppose that their resting place would be within the shelter of some convenient bush. Many of us have come upon them in such situations after the birds evidently had settled for their night's repose. But once I found one roosting in a broken gourd lying on a shelf in a buggy-shed. For more than a week one spent each night on a veranda rafter, a hiding place I discovered by the cautious use of a flashlight. It is safest to say that these juncos usually roost in trees and bushes.

Their feet must become very numb on cold, snowy nights, and many have been found with toes partly gone, presumably from frostbite.

WINTER BRINGS CHEERY "SNOWBIRDS" TO THE DOORYARD

Deep woods of Canada and mountainous regions of the eastern United States provide nesting sites for the plump **Slate-colored Junco** (lower left, facing a streaked young bird), known to many only as the "snowbird." The **White-winged Junco** (right center), a species of the northern Great Plains, is large and gray and has white bars on the wings. Sagebrush and chaparral deserts of the West are the haunts of the **Northern Sage Sparrow** (upper left), a close relative of the Californian **Bell's Sparrow** (upper right).

ADVENTURES WITH SPARROWS AND JUNCOS

By T. Gilbert Pearson

AFTER a serious illness in the early winter of 1926, I was very weak, but my kindly doctor allowed me to go out from the sanitarium every morning and trudge slowly about the Maryland fields. I rested on stumps, munching withered turnips and persimmons touched by the frost, but chiefly I watched for birds.

My favorite seat was in a patch of stalwart weeds bordering an extensive thicket. There were always birds about, and some of them often came very near.

Thinking of this place recalls my most vivid memories of close acquaintance with tree sparrows. They were winter visitors, maybe from Labrador or perhaps from regions beyond the icy waters of Great Slave Lake. Once seen, these birds are easily remembered. They remind one of chipping sparrows, but the brown on the back is of a redder hue, and in the very center of the grayish-white breast there is a clearly marked spot of black.

TREE SPARROWS ARE HAPPY SINGERS

Where I sat among the weeds those mild winter days, I caught many glimpses of the tree sparrows as they fed all around me. Now and then one would mount to the top of some weed stalk to gather the seeds not yet fallen to the earth, and at times some would fly up to rest on the limbs along the edge of the thicket. When not alarmed, they chirped among themselves, their little twitters and cheerful notes producing a subdued melody that spoke of contentment and happiness.

The next summer I found the western tree sparrow in the land where it mates and sings and builds its nest. It sings much as a canary sings, but with less volume and a noticeable absence of assertive boldness in its notes. The birds were not in flocks, but in scattered pairs.

To me the tree sparrow makes a strong appeal, whether seen in an old field where the broom-sedge grows and the sumac and the persimmon ripen their fruit, or up near the Arctic Circle where scattered bushes and evergreens adorn those great hills that bolster the bulk of Mount McKinley.

There are many kinds of sparrows in the world. In North America alone there are no less than 11 genera represented by 37 species, many of which present climatic variations of plumage. We may say that 119 kinds of sparrows are found on this continent north of Mexico.

The list does not include the house sparrow (*Passer domesticus*) of western Europe, which has so amply proved its amazing adaptability to new environment by readily becoming acclimated in this as well as in many other countries where it has been introduced.

This so-called "English sparrow" is classified as one of the weaver finches, which places it in a different family from the Fringillidae to which the North American sparrows belong.

Sparrows are all small; for example, the tree sparrow weighs about seven-tenths of an ounce; and it takes a lusty towhee to tip the scales at an ounce and a half.

As a rule all birds of this group fly very well, but they do not take such long migratory journeys as do the warblers, many of which annually go for the winter to northern or central South America.

In their tails there are 12 rectrices instead of 10 as in the powerful-flying swifts, but all are well developed, the outer two not being rudimentary as is the case with woodpeckers.

JUNCOS FREQUENTLY CONSORT WITH WHITE-THROAT SPARROWS

A bird often associated with the roadside sparrows is the slate-colored junco, generally, in the South, called "snowbird." Juncos seem especially fond of the companionship of the white-throats. They feed together in the same weed patches, dash together to the same cover when alarmed, and when in early spring the white-throat begins to sing lustily, the juncos join in as best they can with their small, modest voices.

The head and back of the junco are deep slaty-gray, in the male almost black. One should remember that a junco is darker than the common sparrows and that the white feathers at each side of its tail flash when the bird darts away. I have found Carolina juncos, incubating eggs or caring for young, at Blowing Rock and on Grand-

Photograph by Acme

"UNTO THE LEAST OF THESE"

A New York policeman gives a drink to a sparrow overcome by heat. This picture was published in the New York *Herald-Tribune* on Wednesday, December 11, 1935. Titled "None so Small," by Victor Twyman of *The Daily News*, it won second prize in a national snapshot contest.

father Mountain in North Carolina, and in winter have seen the ordinary junco almost as far south as the Gulf of Mexico.

On another occasion, in central Alaska, 3,500 miles from the Carolina mountains, I came upon juncos feeding their young. On foot, I left Dawson where in all its plainness and haunting memories of golden romance it lies by the mouth of Klondike river, and followed a trail for miles over the hills toward an Indian village on the right bank of the Yukon.

THE DISTANCES JUNCOS TRAVEL ARE AMAZING

The place seemed so far removed from my usual haunts that I was far from expecting to see a familiar friend. Of course I knew that many of my bird acquaintances travel far, but here was wilderness where I was looking for new and little-known species.

Suddenly close at hand I heard the sharp metallic, kissing click of a slate-colored junco. There were two of these birds, one of them carrying food for its young. What a tremendous part of North America some of these birds cover in their migrations twice each year—and I was still nearly 700 miles from the junco's extreme northwestern summer range where Point Barrow looks to the waters of the Arctic Ocean!

To the wanderer far from home there is something comforting in seeing a familiar form. Many a homesick traveler has been cheered by the presence of a person he has seen only casually in his own land, and a "bird from home" offers a heart-warming thrill almost equal to that of meeting an old friend in a strange country.

MARKINGS OF RUSTY PINK ADORN FAR WESTERN JUNCOS

The **Pink-sided Junco** (upper left) of the northern Rocky Mountain region largely depends on insects during spring and summer and on weed seeds, berry pits, and grains in the winter. Slight plumage differences distinguish the several subspecies of the **Oregon Junco** (right center, black-headed male beside an immature female) which breeds on the northwest coast as far as Alaska. Two species of the red-backed junco are the **Arizona Junco** (lower left), a ground-loving southwesterner, and the **Gray-headed Junco** (lower right), an abundant resident of the southern Rocky Mountains.

Pink-sided Junco
(Junco mearnsi)
Average Length, Six and One-quarter Inches

To find the pink-sided junco in summer one must look for it in the territory from southwestern Saskatchewan southward through the Rocky Mountain region to northern Wyoming and southern Idaho. In winter it may be found from Montana southward to the Mexican border of Arizona and New Mexico.

Extensive russet-pink areas on the sides and breast distinguish this bird from other juncos. The plumage of the male and female is alike. This is one of the distinct species of North American juncos. Its plumage is virtually the same wherever the species is found.

Insects form a large part of the food of the pink-sided junco during the spring and summer. Particularly is this true of the nestlings' diet which for a time must be composed exclusively of the soft bodies of immature as well as adult insects. Later on, and especially throughout the winter, weed seeds, small grain, and pits of small berries are eaten.

This bird is slightly smaller than the common English sparrow and about the size of the house finch so common in the Far West. It has the usual junco character of white feathers on either side of the tail.

Oregon Junco
(Junco oreganus)
Average Length, Six Inches

The head feathers of the male Oregon junco are noticeably black, a color which in the female is replaced with gray. The *Junco oreganus* is a western species that is found over a vast region of widely varying environmental conditions. Certain differences in plumage have therefore developed and today this bird is classified into three subspecies.

One of these is called Shufeldt's junco *(J. o. shufeldti)*. It breeds from the interior of central British Columbia eastward to central Alberta and south into northern Oregon and winters from the Rocky Mountain tablelands southward into Mexico as far as Chihuahua and Sonora. Another one of this group is the Montana junco *(J. o. montanus)*. It is found in summer in the Canadian Zone elevations from southern Alberta to northwestern Montana, northern Idaho, and eastern Oregon. It winters in the various States to the southward as far as northern Mexico.

The Oregon junco itself *(J. o. oreganus)* is more of a coast-wise bird than either of the other two subspecies. It breeds from Yakutat Bay, Alaska, southward to Vancouver Island, British Columbia, and winters in the coast regions throughout much of the length of California. A few have been known to wander off their regular migration routes as far as eastern Oregon and Nevada.

Arizona Junco
(Junco phaeonotus palliatus)
Average Length, Six and One-quarter Inches

In the older bird books we used to read descriptions of the red-backed junco. Later it was determined that there were two distinct geographic forms of this bird and so it has been divided into two subspecies. One of these bears the name red-backed junco *(J. p. dorsalis)*. It ranges in summer in the high mountains of western Arizona and New Mexico, breeding in the Transition and the Canadian Zones.

When winter approaches it leaves its abode on the heights and descends to lower altitudes. Many migrate to western Texas and the Mexican States of Sonora and Chihuahua.

The other representative of this species is the Arizona junco *(J. p. palliatus)*. A distinguishing characteristic is its brown iris, whereas the red-backed junco has a yellow eye. This is a ground-loving species with habits like those of other southwestern juncos.

Gray-headed Junco
(Junco caniceps)
Average Length, Six Inches

One of the most abundant bird species in parts of the Rocky Mountains is the gray-headed junco, another red-backed species. I have found it exceedingly tame in the summer and so unsuspicious that one morning I saw a cat catch two within a few minutes.

It breeds from Wyoming and Utah southward to New Mexico. It leaves the higher mountains in winter and inhabits regions of lower altitude southward to northern Mexico.

The gray-headed junco rears its young in lofty regions which it seems reluctant to leave even after the young are fully grown and strong upon the wing. It leaves the high altitudes only when the heavy snows of winter drive it to lower levels in quest of food, when it often appears about cabins or wilderness camps in astonishing numbers.

The nest of the gray-headed junco is usually built on the ground. The birds seem to prefer open situations for nesting rather than thick woods or tangles of brush. The nests are well hidden, however, among clumps of weeds or tufts of grass. So closely do the brooding juncos sit that it is only by watching a bird carrying building materials or, later on, food for the young that a nest may be found, unless, of course, one actually steps close enough to a nest to startle the setting parent into flight.

Like many other small birds inhabiting the far north or higher mountain levels, this junco does not start nesting until June or July. The necessity of waiting for weather warm enough to hatch out the insects on which the bird partly depends seems to cause this delay.

THE "CHIPPY" HAS PROFITED FROM MAN'S CULTIVATION OF THE LAND

The well-loved **Eastern Chipping Sparrow** (left center, with young bird) has largely forsaken wilder regions to live in gardens, fields, and orchards where its favorite foods are more abundant. One of our sweetest-singing birds is the **Eastern Field Sparrow** (upper figure). The very abundant **Eastern Tree Sparrow** (lower right) nests in Canada and in October appears in hordes in the Eastern and Southern States. At the lower left is the little-known **Worthen's Sparrow** of New and Old Mexico.

Eastern Chipping Sparrow
(Spizella passerina passerina)
Average Length, Five and One-third Inches

One of the birds that undoubtedly has profited by the advent of the white man to North America is the eastern chipping sparrow. It has largely forsaken the wilder regions to dwell near the abode of man. Here the open fields and orchards are more to its liking and there is less molestation from its natural enemies. Over much of Canada and eastern United States, as far southward as Georgia and central Texas, it is a well-known inhabitant of gardens and lawns.

It winters abundantly in the southern States from Oklahoma and southern New Jersey to the Gulf of Mexico. Here it often congregates in flocks, especially as spring approaches. In a field near Summerville, South Carolina, one day at sunrise, a friend and I watched a company of 60 or more that alighted in a leafless tree.

Soon they began to drop down, a few at a time, among the dry, dead cottonstalks. Many settled near our bird trap to feed on the seed scattered as a lure for them. When I pulled the string of the trap 14 were captured.

My companion placed bird bands around their legs and released them one by one to join their friends in the tree-top. Half an hour later when the trap was again sprung we found that several of the prisoners wore aluminum bands they had recently acquired. We may in time learn that some of them have been handled by bird banders in New Jersey, Ontario, or elsewhere, who, reporting the numbers on the bands, will add to our knowledge.

From British Columbia and Alberta southward to the mountains of Chihuahua, the western form of this species *(S. p. arizonae)* may be found; but it is not so distinctly an inhabitant of the cultivated lands, being quite at home in regions uninhabited by man.

Eastern Field Sparrow
(Spizella pusilla pusilla)
Average Length, Five and Three-quarters Inches

Among the flocks of sparrows of different species that we find in the brown fields of autumn, there often occurs the eastern field sparrow. From New Jersey, Pennsylvania, and Missouri southward to the coast of the Gulf of Mexico, it is a common winter resident, being distributed more or less locally according to the natural food conditions.

It does not have the habit of collecting in large flocks like the chipping sparrow, and often is found quite singly and alone. It is one of our sweetest-singing birds, and its clear, plaintive notes are among the most common sounds of our northern fields and meadows in spring and summer.

The song is delivered from a low perch, often a dead limb on some bush or tree, and begins with four or five clear whistled notes, all of which descend in pitch and lead quickly to a terminating, almost insectlike, trill. Thus the performance, which begins in leisurely fashion, ends with a breathless rush.

In spring the field sparrow is partial to abandoned fields overgrown here and there with bushes or briars. In such an environment it builds its finely lined nest of grasses, weeds and rootlets. Often the cradle for the eggs and young is nestled in the fork of a low huckleberry or in a cluster of small blackberry vines. Now and again it is built on the ground, but even when one is placed in a bush it is never at an altitude of more than a few feet. The spotted eggs number either four or five. Two broods are raised each year.

The western subspecies of the field sparrow *(S. p. arenacea)* is found in summer from Montana and North Dakota to Nebraska. It passes the winter from the southern limits of its breeding range to Texas, Louisiana, and Nuevo Leon.

Eastern Tree Sparrow
(Spizella arborea arborea)
Average Length, Six and One-third Inches

Early in October small flocks of eastern tree sparrows begin to enter the United States from their summer home in Canada. By the last of the month their numbers have grown to large proportions, for by then some hundreds of millions are well distributed throughout the eastern and southern States.

Before departing for the North the next March or early April, they have consumed thousands of tons of weed seeds. To the farmer they are one of the most valuable of Nature's helpers.

As warmth begins to creep into the air of early spring, tree sparrows begin to sing, and the volume and frequency of the bursts of song increase until they depart for their summer home in the lands lying between Newfoundland on the east, and far-away Mackenzie near the Canadian Rockies. A western race *(S. a. ochracea)* is slightly paler.

Worthen's Sparrow
(Spizella wortheni)
Average Length, Five Inches

Almost identical in general appearance with the western chipping sparrow is the Worthen's sparrow of New Mexico and northern Mexico to Tamaulipas. The brown of the crown is not so reddish, nor are the stripes on the side of the head so distinct.

Little is known of the habits of this rather obscure bird, described in 1884 from a specimen taken at Silver City, New Mexico.

IN THE SPARROW TRIBE, BOTH SEXES SHARE SIMILAR COLORING

The quiet, streaked plumage of most sparrows is an impressive example of protective adaptation. A characteristic sparrow of the Great Plains, the **Clay-colored Sparrow** (upper left), may easily be overlooked. The pale **Brewer's Sparrow** (upper right) inhabits sagebrush flats and barren mountain slopes from British Columbia to Arizona. Brushy, semiarid hills of southern California are frequented by the **California Black-chinned Sparrow** (left center). The Far West's **Golden-crowned Sparrow** (lower right, adult with the yellow head stripe, and an immature bird) prefers alder and evergreen thickets.

Clay-colored Sparrow
(Spizella pallida)
Average Length, Five and One-quarter Inches

A very characteristic bird of the interior of North America is the clay-colored sparrow which breeds abundantly from Great Slave Lake to Colorado and Illinois. It winters chiefly in the northern half of Mexico.

Its little song of three notes and a trill is generally uttered from the top of some bush or stake. It is a thin musical buzzing sound not unlike the syllable *ze,* many times repeated. The usual note is a simple *chip,* not thrilling but serving at least to inform the observer of some sparrow's presence.

Although found in open country, the clay-colored sparrow is fond of brush-covered hillsides and open woodlands. The nest is made of grasses, fine twigs, and sometimes hair, and is placed in a bush from one to six feet from the ground. The spotted eggs range from three to five in number.

This bird derived its name from the flaxen, or clay-colored, feathers that cover its crown and back.

The clay-colored is by nature secretive and is such an inconspicuous bird that it is often overlooked in a neighborhood where it may not be at all a rare species. For example, it is a common summer resident in northern Wisconsin and also breeds in northwestern Illinois. It seems altogether likely that many individuals of those regions, in the course of their autumn and spring migrations to and from Texas or the eastern States to Mexico, would pass through central and eastern Illinois, including the Chicago region. Yet a Chicago ornithologist reported that although he had worked in that section for twenty years it was not until the spring of 1931 that he was so fortunate as to identify a clay-colored sparrow. He did not claim that during all that time it had been absent from the area, but the fact that an alert local bird observer had failed to recognize a single specimen for twenty years illustrated how easily the species may be overlooked.

Like many other birds, this sparrow sometimes wanders far from its usual migration routes and may be discovered in most surprising places. Some years ago there was a record of a clay-colored sparrow in British Columbia, and wanderers have been found as far east as Massachusetts and South Carolina.

Brewer's Sparrow
(Spizella breweri breweri)
Average Length, Five Inches

Among the scattered clumps of sagebrush that find precarious footing in the lava beds of Siskiyou County, California, I came upon the Brewer's sparrow at home, and was much delighted with its sweet canary-like trillings.

One may look for it in summer in the semi-arid regions from British Columbia to southern Arizona and western Texas; or in winter through much of northern Mexico.

Although commonly inhabiting the sagebrush flats of the desert, it also ascends the near-by mountain slopes and has even been found singing at snow line on the Sierras at an elevation of many thousands of feet.

The nest is built of small bushes or sagebrush, being made of leaves and grasses with a lining of long horse hairs. Three or four spotted eggs are laid. Its food consists of insects and seeds of many kinds.

California Black-chinned Sparrow
(Spizella atrogularis cana)
Average Length, Five and One-quarter Inches

The black-chinned sparrow nests in small colonies. Half a dozen pairs may be found in a few hundred square rods, with no other breeding birds within a dozen miles.

This bird loves the brushy hillsides of southern California and southward to Cape San Lucas. A related race *(S. a. atrogularis)* occurs in Arizona and New Mexico. Observers differ in their estimation of the strength of its singing notes, some stating that these are scarcely audible at a little distance. Others assert that they may be heard clearly for a quarter of a mile.

Golden-crowned Sparrow
(Zonotrichia coronata)
Average Length, Six and Three-quarters Inches

This unusually handsome bird ranges from the Aleutian Islands to central British Columbia in summer, and passes the winter from central Oregon to Baja California. In the parks of San Francisco it is often seen. Perhaps some of those that recently have been captured and illegally brought to New York for sale as caged birds were taken within a radius of 50 miles from the Golden Gate.

This traveler from the north also occurs in the Santa Barbara Islands and has been seen on Guadalupe Island off the coast of Baja California. Stragglers have appeared in Nevada and Colorado, and lost or wind-blown individuals have wandered to Wisconsin and even eastward as far as Massachusetts. It is a large sparrow, specimens usually measuring seven inches in length. The plumage is alike in both sexes.

The golden-crowned sparrow is not a bird of the open fields. It distinctly prefers woods and thickets where it often frequents evergreens. In its usual summer haunts the alders grow along many streams and sloughs. In the bushes and trees of such waterside thickets the golden-crown habitually constructs its nest in a suitable fork. Four or five pale greenish blue eggs are laid in the bulky structure of coarse grass, weeds and rootlets.

PERSISTENT EATERS OF WEED SEEDS, SPARROWS ARE FARMERS' FRIENDS

Their stout beaks are perfect seed crushers. An aristocrat of its family is the **White-crowned Sparrow** (upper right, adult above an immature bird), which nests in the higher western mountains and most of northern Canada to the limit of trees. In winter its flocks spread over the southern United States and northern Mexico. A subspecies of the white-crown is the well-known western **Gambel's Sparrow** (lowest figure of trio). **Harris's Sparrow** (adult left and immature right, below) is another fine-looking westerner.

White-crowned Sparrow
(Zonotrichia leucophrys leucophrys)
Average Length, Six and Three-quarters Inches

The white-crowned is an aristocrat of the great sparrow family. Its pleasing garb of gray and brown, its black and white crown stripes, and its neat form quickly arrest the attention of the bird observer. In many ways it resembles the white-throat, although it is a distinct species. Like most of our North American small birds it is migratory in habit. In winter it is spread over most of a great territory extending from lower Baja California and eastward through Arizona, Kansas, the Ohio and Potomac River Valleys, and below this line as far as Florida, Louisiana, and much of the plateau of western Mexico. Its summer range includes suitable localities in the higher mountains of California, New Mexico, Wyoming, Oregon, and northward and eastward to the tree limit in northern Manitoba and Quebec. It occurs accidentally in southern Greenland.

Early in April, northward-moving white-crowns begin to appear in the middle States. Some years they are fairly common migrants, other years but few are seen. By the middle of May or a little later, the wave of these migrants has passed on toward the north and bird observers in the southern region see no more of them until the early days of autumn. During the fall migration their appearance in this region is confined almost entirely to the month of October, though some late arrivals, or early comers that are reluctant to leave, may linger on for a week or two after most of their associates have left for more southern regions.

In the spring the transient white-crowns often frequent open pastures and fields, or may appear along roadsides. In autumn I have found them mingling with other sparrows in cornfields, or in weed thickets where the ripened seeds lie scattered and furnish a food supply that is easy to garner.

In the eastern United States we are seldom privileged to hear the song of this bird given with the full power with which it is rendered in its summer home. Usually we catch only snatches of song which, however, are pleasing, even if sad, in their cadence. The white-crown's melodies may be heard on warm days in early spring and often come from the shelter of woodlands rather than from the open fields. The full song consists of two long-drawn-out notes, the second one followed by three rapidly repeated lower whistles. The effect is rich, plaintive and very pleasing.

One day shortly after we had made camp in the valley of the Snake River in Wyoming, I discovered that a pair of white-crowned sparrows were carrying food to a spot a few rods from my tepee. On each trip an old bird would alight in a cluster of growing plants forming a bed about forty feet across.

These plants were from twelve to fourteen inches in height.

After watching for some time and noticing that the birds always alighted at about the same place, I went to look for the nest. The most painstaking search failed to reveal their hiding place. Whenever I retired to a little distance, feeding operations would be resumed. I searched virtually every square foot of that weed patch in vain. At length I climbed a tree, field glasses in hand, and spotted the nest.

Adjoining one side of the weed patch there was an area well covered with smaller weeds that were only three or four inches high. Here, eighteen feet from the border of the area of larger plants, the nest was discovered on the ground. The parents would alight among the tall plants, then run out to the border and, mouselike, slip through the thin growth of short weeds to the nest and its four hungry young.

The white-crowned sparrow feeds upon many kinds of insects, including ants, caterpillars, various beetles, and grasshoppers, also spiders. It also consumes many seeds and waste grain in their season. At times it samples small fruits, including grapes, and now and then eats buds and the blossoms of shrubs and trees. But on the whole it is an economic asset to the agricultural and horticultural interests of the country.

It was described in 1772 and is thus one of the earliest members of our great sparrow group to be given scientific recognition.

Gambel's Sparrow
(Zonotrichia leucophrys gambeli)
Average Length, Six and Three-quarters Inches

One of the four subspecies of the white-crowned sparrow is the well-known Gambel's sparrow of western North America. It breeds as far north as the tree limit in Alaska and northern Mackenzie, and winters from northern California and Utah south to central Mexico. Occasionally these sparrows wander far beyond the confines of their usual range. Thus specimens of this western species have been taken in various central and eastern States, as, for example, in Iowa, Michigan, and South Carolina.

In habits of nesting and feeding as well as in song, the Gambel's sparrow does not differ essentially from its close relative, the white-crowned sparrow.

Harris's Sparrow
(Zonotrichia querula)
Average Length, Seven and One-quarter Inches

This is another western sparrow. It breeds in northern Canada, even to the edge of the Barren Grounds. Extremely little is known of its exact range or its breeding habits. In winter it reaches Kansas and southern Texas.

FIFTEEN VARIETIES OF FOX SPARROWS ARE SCATTERED THROUGH THE WEST

Sixteenth variety of the species is the reddish **Eastern Fox Sparrow** (right center) whose rich, full-toned song is unsurpassed among the sparrows. The **Stephens's Fox Sparrow** (left center) is a large, dark-colored subspecies found only in restricted areas of California. All too brief is the clear song of the **Sooty Fox Sparrow** (lower right) of the northwest coast. Above at the left perches a male **White-throated Sparrow** above a plainer immature female. The sad, sweet whistle of this so-called "Peabody bird" is a welcome voice of the northern wilderness.

White-throated Sparrow
(Zonotrichia albicollis)
Average Length, Six and Three-quarters Inches

The so-called "Peabody bird" or white-throated sparrow breeds from Great Bear Lake to northern New York, Massachusetts, northern Michigan, northeast Wyoming, eastern Montana; winters from Baltimore, Louisville, and St. Louis to Florida and Texas.

Few birds are more sociable, and a group of them may be found almost anywhere, often in company with other sparrows. At times they feed with their friends,the slate-colored juncos. In late winter, spring, and summer they give vent to a beautiful song. Their ordinary call notes are metallic *chips,* which, however, are softer as roosting time approaches.

In the white-throat's northern breeding haunts, in the evergreens or in bushy undergrowth among the burnt timber, its clear, sweetly melancholy whistle accentuates the emptiness of the wilderness and yet cheers the listener. Its bulky nest, made chiefly of grasses and moss, is placed on the ground or in low bushes, preferably in burnt-over clearings.

Eastern Fox Sparrow
(Passerella iliaca iliaca)
Average Length, Seven and One-quarter Inches

The colors of this bird, suggesting those of the red fox, render it a very conspicuous inhabitant of the countryside. It is not inclined to come near man's abode except on rare occasions, although in winter the hope of food may draw it to your feeding station. In small flocks it inhabits thickets, patches of large weeds, and the brushy borders of woodlands. As such regions are the dwelling places of red-eyed towhees and various other sparrows, it is not uncommon to find them all in the same thicket searching for their dinner.

Fox sparrows are continually turning over dead leaves that strew the ground, scratching with both feet at the same time. Vigorously they dig with the beak, sharp eyes ever alert for any tiny seed or insect. They consume the seeds of various kinds of small wild fruit and such dormant or active insects as they find. At feeding stations they have shown a liking for millet or hemp seeds.

An early spring snowfall which may cause the song sparrow to go supperless to roost does not daunt the fox sparrow. Unhesitatingly it digs away the snow and goes right on with its search among the fallen leaves.

The summer home of this bird extends over a vast territory from Newfoundland to Manitoba, and northward as far as trees are growing, from northern Quebec to northwestern Alaska. The nest is built on the ground, at times in low bushes.

The advance guard of the southward-bound fox sparrow migration enters the United States in September, and within the next six weeks millions of individuals are scattered generally over the eastern and southern States. Few of them winter as far north as New England or even Washington, D. C., the great bulk of them passing on south of the Potomac and Ohio rivers. Some journey to Florida and others to Texas.

The fox sparrow's song is unsurpassed among the sparrows. The bird does not wait for warm weather to begin its music. There are records of its singing in Massachusetts as late as October and as early as January, February, and March. The migration song, however, is far inferior to that produced in the lands where it raises its family.

Sixteen varieties of this beautiful sparrow are recognized by bird students. With the exception of the eastern fox sparrow, they are all found in western North America. The western representatives vary slightly in plumage, and generally are darker than the eastern form. Reference will be made to two typical examples of the other climatic varieties.

Stephens's Fox Sparrow
(Passerella iliaca stephensi)
Average Length, Seven and One-half Inches

In 1895, A. W. Anthony published the description of a new fox sparrow which had been taken in the San Jacinto Mountains of California. It received the name Stephens's fox sparrow. It is a large, dark-colored variety, with a larger bill than its near relatives. It is known to breed only in certain restricted regions of California. Thus it has been discovered in the nesting season in the Sierra Nevada, also on Mount Pinos, and in the San Gabriel, San Bernardino, and San Jacinto mountains. In winter it descends to Los Angeles and Santa Barbara counties.

Naturalists working in the San Bernardino Mountains have found Stephens's fox sparrow partial to regions where thick low clumps of mountain misery abound, and also where the wiry chinquapin thrives. The nests they discovered were built in bushes from a foot and a half to two feet from the ground. Other nests have been found on the ground in the San Gabriel Mountains. Buckthorn bushes seem to be especially favored as nesting sites.

Three eggs is the usual number laid, and so closely does a brooding parent sit that at times it will allow the intruder to approach within a foot or two before taking flight.

Sooty Fox Sparrow
(Passerella iliaca fuliginosa)
Average Length, Seven Inches

This sparrow breeds on the mainland of southeastern Alaska southward to Washington, and winters from Vancouver Island to central California. Like others of the species, it has a clear, full-toned and all too brief song.

TWO THOUSAND DIFFERENT MELODIES OF THE SONG SPARROW HAVE BEEN RECORDED

The cheerful song sparrow is the most familiar and widely distributed species of its family. Best known is the exuberant **Eastern Song Sparrow** (center pair, adult and young bird) which breeds over most of eastern North America. Very similar are the songs and nesting habits of the numerous western subspecies. Here are depicted the Southwest's **Desert Song Sparrow** (upper figure), the **Aleutian Song Sparrow** (lower left), named for the Alaskan islands it inhabits, and the **Sooty Song Sparrow** (lower right) of the coasts of southern Alaska and British Columbia.

Song Sparrows

(Melospiza melodia)

Average Length, Six to Seven Inches

Very rarely is there published a local or State list of birds in the United States or Canada that does not contain the name of the song sparrow. No other native sparrow is so widely distributed in North America and none is better or more favorably known.

This streaked bird with the identifying dark brown spot in the center of the breast may be found in almost any bushy field, along fence rows, or the borders of marshes and swamps, in gardens, about lawns, or in fact almost anywhere except in thick woods and in regions barren of vegetation. Its song—so loud, so cheerful, and so melodious—is hailed with delight by thousands of nature lovers who may hear it at almost any time of day, and, in some localities, any day of the year.

It has a very sprightly, exuberant spirit and is one of those birds that seem especially clean and healthy. Observers have commented on its comparative freedom from parasites.

That these birds have strong individuality and are well adapted to their environment is well known. Few observers, however, realize how rewarding a close study of their daily activities can be.

Mrs. Margaret Morse Nice, whose home is in the outskirts of Columbus, Ohio, is one outstanding student of the song sparrow. For years she has worked unremittingly, often for weeks and months at a time, spying upon the intimate home life of several pairs of these birds that live near her home. She has learned many new facts and has been able to correct certain long accepted but inaccurate statements about this sparrow's habits.

Mrs. Nice has found that many of the song sparrows that breed in the neighborhood are not migrant birds that have spent the winter farther south and returned in spring to the Columbus region, but are permanent residents that have passed the winter close at hand. By the time the migratory waves of song sparrows from the south begin to sweep by in March, the local pairs of birds have already preëmpted favorable nesting sites and are ready to defend them against the new arrivals. The intruding migrants are promptly attacked and encouraged to leave at once for other parts.

The resident song sparrows begin to sing by the latter part of February and soon are producing their full volume of melody. Frequently, one will render his song as many as two or three hundred times in an hour. While song sparrows are usually secretive and retiring, their fear of discovery seems to vanish in the spring. At this season they come boldly into the open to sing or to fight others that trespass on their territories. They often invade the domain of neighboring song sparrows and get into fierce battles with them.

When the nest building instinct becomes strong, both birds of a pair look for a site. The male shows his intense interest by carrying dried grasses, fragments of weeds or bits of chips to a number of places that he seems to think would be suitable locations for a nest. The female has ideas of her own and there is much bustling about before a site is finally chosen. This is usually under sheltering weeds, or it may have the protection of a clump of grass. Building operations then proceed rapidly.

The female makes the nest and incubates the eggs. She also continues to brood the young for some time, undoubtedly to protect them from the weather and from prying enemies. The male brings food to the nest. As a rule, the eggs hatch in twelve days and the young remain in the nest from twelve to fourteen days longer.

One year Mrs. Nice found that sixty-four pairs of song sparrows were inhabiting approximately fifty acres in the region where she studies. She made notes on the nests that came to grief. The eggs, young, or nests are destroyed chiefly through natural causes, such as rats, snakes, cats, wandering dogs and rain storms. When a nest is ruined or its contents taken, another is built at once. Thus as many as four are often built in a single season. Even if the first nest is unmolested, at least one more brood of young will be reared by the same pair of sparrows.

It was found that two-thirds of the first nests came to grief. The percentage of successful nests increased as the season advanced. On the fourth attempt the birds were successful in bringing up their young in sixty per cent of the cases.

One amusing discovery was the way a male song sparrow can tell the sex of a strange song sparrow. He cannot tell by the color of the feathers because the plumage of both sexes is alike. His method is to attack the intruder. If it is a male it flees. If it simply sits still and says *eee eee eee* it is a female!

The plumage of the song sparrow and, in some cases, its size vary in different parts of its range, which extends from Alaska to Mexico and from the Atlantic seaboard to the Pacific coast. The eastern song sparrow *(M. m. melodia)* breeds from Mackenzie and Cape Breton Island to northern Georgia, and winters from Massachusetts to the Gulf of Mexico. Three others of the twenty-six subspecies of the song sparrow are the Aleutian *(M. m. sanaka)*, inhabiting the Aleutian Islands and the Alaska Peninsula; desert *(M. m. saltonis)*, distributed locally from Utah to Mexico; and sooty *(M. m. rufina)*, found on islands off southern Alaska and British Columbia.

The Aleutian, desert, and sooty sparrows are all far western forms, and their nesting habits and songs are very similar.

FLOCKS OF ELEGANT LONGSPURS DECORATE THE OPEN PLAINS

The **Chestnut-collared Longspur** (center pair, male on the stone) places its nest on an open patch of ground, scorning the protection of weeds or grass. This beautifully marked bird shares a breeding range in the prairie Provinces of Canada and the north central States with the **McCown's Longspur** (male and female, right and left, below). Primarily a westerner, the shy **Lincoln's Sparrow** (upper left) has a bubbling song suggesting that of the house wren. The **Swamp Sparrow** (male above a young bird, upper right) rarely leaves the marshy bottomlands except in winter.

Lincoln's Sparrow

(Melospiza lincolni lincolni)

Average Length, Five and Three-quarters Inches

An exceedingly shy bird is the Lincoln's sparrow. It enjoys a wide range, chiefly in central and western North America, comparatively few occurring in the Atlantic Coast States. It has many of the habits and actions of the song sparrow, although more secretive. The chest markings easily distinguish the two.

Along vine-covered walls and other places where the vegetation is thick it hides so successfully that its presence in many communities is never discovered except by the most alert, patient, and painstaking bird student. It has an unusual song for a sparrow, a song that suggests more the bursting, gurgling notes of a house wren. Upon discovering that it is being watched, it abruptly stops singing.

In its northern breeding grounds it may be found in small flocks or scattered pairs among bushes or low evergreens in damp thickets. It feeds primarily on weed seeds.

Its four or five pale greenish white eggs, heavily blotched with reddish brown, are laid in a nest placed on the ground and made principally of coarse and fine grasses.

It breeds from Alaska and Ungava to California, Minnesota, and Nova Scotia, nesting on the ground. The winter home is from California, Oklahoma, and Mississippi through Texas and Mexico to Guatemala.

Swamp Sparrow

(Melospiza georgiana)

Average Length, Five and Three-quarters Inches

Among the rank grasses, rushes and cattails growing in bogs and wet meadow low grounds, the swamp sparrow makes its summer abode. It creeps in and out among the vegetation and climbs nimbly the reeds and bushes.

Its simple, musical song issues on every hand, although the performer is not easily seen, unless perchance the observer is close at hand, or the bird appears in one of its infrequent flight songs. Its notes somewhat resemble those of the chipping sparrow but are more varied. It may be distinguished from the song sparrow by its darker back and wings, its unmarked breast and underparts, and its gray nape and cheeks.

The nest, built almost wholly of grasses, is placed on or near the ground. From four to six heavily spotted eggs are laid.

In winter, swamp sparrows often desert their swampy surroundings for the dry fields grown up in tall grass.

Their summer range extends through the southern Provinces of central and eastern Canada and south to northern Illinois, Missouri, and the mountains of West Virginia. The species passes the winter from Nebraska and New York to the Gulf of Mexico.

McCown's Longspur

(Rhynchophanes mccowni)

Average Length, Six Inches

The longspurs are beautifully marked sparrow-like birds. There are four distinct species.

A characteristic of this group is the very long nail on the rear toe; hence the name. McCown's longspur breeds mainly in Alberta, Saskatchewan, Colorado, North Dakota, and Minnesota, winters south to northern Mexico.

This bird was named for Captain John P. McCown, of the United States Army, who was its discoverer. He found it in western Texas about 1851, and thus his name has been preserved by the ornithologists of America.

When startled from the ground, these birds fly about in a circling, erratic, undulating manner, which would seem to indicate a disinclination to leave the neighborhood.

Chestnut-collared Longspur

(Calcarius ornatus)

Average Length, Six and One-quarter Inches

Meadows and lands with scattered weed patches are this longspur's favorite haunts in summer. At a little distance, its actions and dark appearance suggest to the passerby the bobolink that frequents the same fields. The male perches and swings on the bending weed stalks or soars aloft in erratic butterflylike swoops and darts. Its weak, sweet song is often poured forth as it pauses for a moment between flights. With fluttering wings and extended tail it begins its daylight serenade, and with wings held high sinks again to the earth, singing continuously. As a rule it prefers dry lands to the marshes or wet meadows.

An unusual habit of this species is that of nesting in exposed situations. Instead of following the custom of most ground-nesting birds and hiding its treasures under some weed or in a sheltering cluster of grass, it prefers to use areas of ground where vegetation is scanty. In such a place are deposited the three to five spotted eggs.

Apparently the female assumes the entire responsibility of incubation. However, when the young have hatched, the male does his share in guarding and feeding them. Caterpillars and insects of various kinds, including grasshoppers, are the favorite articles of diet for the young chestnut-collared longspurs in their flimsy nest out there under the broiling sunlight. Both old and young migrate to the winter range in Mexico. With the return of the warm days of April and early May, those that have survived the perils of travel return to their summer homes in the prairie States.

In summer the chestnut-collared longspur lives in the open country of the three prairie Provinces of Canada and the neighboring States from Wyoming to Minnesota. In winter it drifts southward well into central Mexico.

DRIFTING "SNOWFLAKES" ENLIVEN WINTRY FIELDS

Visitors to the arctic tundras tell of the sweet, tinkling mating song of the **Lapland Longspur** (male in summer and winter dress, upper left) in its breeding range at the top of the world. In winter this great traveler joins **Smith's Longspur** (upper right) in the south central States where their flocks devour weed seeds by the ton. A picturesque winter visitor, popularly called "snowflake," is the **Eastern Snow Bunting** (lower right, male in summer plumage on the rock and in winter garb below it) which breeds in the polar regions. **McKay's Snow Bunting** (lower left, in summer plumage) never leaves the Arctic.

Lapland Longspur

(Calcarius lapponicus lapponicus)

Average Length, Six and One-half Inches

The best known of this little group of birds with long rear toenails is the Lapland longspur. It breeds in Siberia, in Lapland, and over much of Arctic America. With the approach of cold weather it moves irregularly through the central States to Texas, and occasionally on the east coast to South Carolina.

Observers of its habits on the tundras tell of its beautiful tinkling song, which it delivers usually on the wing after an upward flight of 30 or 40 feet.

In migration or on its winter feeding grounds it often associates with horned larks or snow buntings. Sometimes hundreds of thousands of these birds may be seen in flocks in the western Central States, and it is an experience long to be remembered when one of these great assemblages is seen flying overhead, all singing at once and flooding the prairies with their music.

It is well known that there are sometimes tremendous losses of bird life during periods of stormy or unseasonable weather. Such a misfortune overtook a vast migratory movement of Lapland longspurs in Minnesota on the night of March 13-14, 1904. The night was cold, very dark, and a heavy wet snow was falling. In the morning it was discovered that an incredible number of northward-moving longspurs had perished. Dr. T. S. Roberts conducted a careful investigation of the catastrophe. On the ice of two small lakes covering about two square miles lay the bodies of not less than 750,000 longspurs! In the surrounding country, dead birds lay on house roofs, in the streets, in fact, everywhere. Literally millions perished that fatal night within an area of approximately 1,500 square miles. Examination of a large number of these birds revealed that in all cases their stomachs were empty. Weakness resulting from hunger may have contributed to their destruction.

Smith's Longspur

(Calcarius pictus)

Average Length, Six Inches

Smith's longspur passes the summer on the Barren Grounds between Mackenzie and Hudson Bay, and winters from Kansas to central Texas. In the winter the birds feed upon weed seeds which they are wont to gather along old roads, in fields, and on prairies.

Nelson records that when a flock of these birds is flushed they rise into the air, circle a few times and then fly off straight, rising higher and higher. The bill of Smith's longspur is slenderer and more pointed than that of the Lapland longspur.

This species builds its nest of grass and moss, placing it on the ground.

Eastern Snow Bunting

(Plectrophenax nivalis nivalis)

Average Length, Seven Inches

The eastern snow bunting is in summer distinctly a polar species, breeding as far north as there is land on which to place its nest. Along the vast arctic wastes of North America, extending from northern Greenland to northwestern Alaska, it is one of the few small birds that the traveler is likely to encounter. It is also found in the arctic regions of the Old World. In winter, snow buntings may be seen in flocks almost anywhere in central Europe, and at times even in northern Africa.

In America, on rare occasions, they wander as far south as Florida. In southern Canada and in the northern States they are quite common winter residents; but where, in all the world of frozen whiteness, the "snowflakes" are able to find enough seeds to keep them in excellent physical condition is a difficult question for man to answer. However, they certainly find abundant food. A scientific collector found in the stomach of one of them 1,000 pig weed seeds.

One of the most stimulating sights in a winter landscape is a flock of these white birds moving erratically here and there over the snow-clad fields. In perfect unison they wheel, mount, veer to the left or right, and make sudden swoops toward the earth. You are sure they have alighted, and the next instant discover you were mistaken, for there they go close to the snow, then up and away. Again you may see them on the surface of the snow, pausing here and there, running, walking, or even jumping from place to place. Sometimes they come about haystacks or swarm over the barnyard, always active and full of an abundant vitality. Their happy calls are sweet.

The snow bunting's nest is placed in a slight depression on the ground. It is constructed of moss, grasses, and rootlets, with a lining of fine grasses usually mixed with feathers. Four to seven spotted eggs are laid.

In early spring snow buntings often collect in vast assemblies and slowly, irregularly, begin their erratic flight toward the frozen ground of the North, chirping musically.

This bird is larger than most of the other representatives of the subfamily to which it belongs, being nearly seven inches in length and having a wing spread of more than a foot.

McKay's Snow Bunting

(Plectrophenax hyperboreus)

Average Length, Seven Inches

More completely white than the common snowflake, the McKay's snow bunting is seen only by the few inhabitants or travelers to the region of the Bering Sea. It breeds on Hall and St. Matthew Islands, and in winter comes to the mainland of western Alaska.

AN UNUSUAL BIRD RECORD

A REMARKABLE record for density of bird population is held by a farm within ten miles of the White House. It is owned by Dr. Gilbert Grosvenor, the President of the National Geographic Society and Editor of THE NATIONAL GEOGRAPHIC MAGAZINE.

In 1913 Dr. Grosvenor bought a farm of 100 acres, half in forest and half in field, in Maryland, about four miles north of the District of Columbia, moving there early in the spring.

Being interested in the work of the Audubon societies, he determined to see what he and his family could do to get birds around the home. He had such success that Dr. Henry W. Henshaw, then Chief of the U. S. Biological Survey of the Department of Agriculture, became interested and delegated Dr. Wells W. Cooke of the Survey to visit the Grosvenor farm.

FIFTY-NINE PAIRS OF BIRDS NESTING ON ONE ACRE

Dr. Cooke found so many birds there that he suggested a census be taken of those living on an acre or two adjacent to the house, as he thought the count would establish a world's record. Up to that time the record was held by a family at Chevy Chase, Maryland, which had attracted thirteen pairs of birds to half an acre.

The prospect of establishing a world's record was so inviting to the Grosvenor family that its members encouraged Dr. Cooke to count the nesting birds on an acre adjoining their house and barns, with the result that they found 59 pairs of birds with young or eggs in the nest on that acre, the highest number of land birds inhabiting one acre that has yet been reported to the Department of Agriculture or to any Audubon society.

A similar census was made of a second acre, and it was found that this acre had 33 pairs of nesting birds.

In an article contributed to *Bird-Lore*, the bimonthly organ of the Audubon societies of the United States, Dr. Grosvenor tells a fascinating story of the birds which have come to dwell at "Wild Acres," as his farm is named.

"Wild Acres" is a typical Maryland farm, with an old-fashioned farmhouse surrounded by an apple and pear orchard, with a vegetable garden, hedges, and open fields. Surrounding the fields is a tract of 50 acres in woods, with a beautiful stream and several springs scattered around in both the fields and the woods.

The bird census taken in the week of June 15 to June 21 showed that on the first acre they had one pair of flickers, one pair of bluebirds, one of yellow warblers, two of orchard orioles, two of catbirds, one of song sparrows, two of chipping sparrows, one of phoebes, 14 of house wrens, seven of robins, one of kingbirds, and 26 of martins.

On the second acre there were one pair each of song sparrows, Carolina wrens, flickers, Maryland yellow-throats, brown thrashers, catbirds, chipping sparrows, screech owls, and towhees. There were also 18 pairs of martins, four of house wrens, and two of robins.

"I attribute our success primarily," writes Dr. Grosvenor, "to shooting the English sparrows and driving the cats away, to putting up many boxes, and to keeping fresh water handy at all times. We do everything we can for the comfort of our birds. For instance, we put on twigs little pieces of the oiled paper that our butter was wrapped in, and we left mud in convenient places for the martins. The catbirds used the oiled paper for their nests; in fact, they used all kinds of scraps.

"Imagine the delight of the family when, on examining one of the catbirds' nests in the autumn, we found one of the children's hair ribbons and also a piece of an old dress of the baby!

"We had read a great deal about how tame birds become when they are protected, but we were constantly amazed at the quickness with which they perceived the care taken of them.

PHOEBE RAISES HER FAMILY WITHIN REACH OF HAND

"Perhaps the most remarkable nest was that of a phoebe, which was built under the cornice of the piazza within reach of my hand. We had a little school in the morning at the house, and ten children were continually running up and down the piazza, shouting at the top of their voices; but the phoebe went on building her nest, then hatched her eggs, and fed her young without fear, though she could see everyone and everyone could see her.

"I was also surprised to find how friendly birds, even of the same species, can become. For instance, we had 14 pairs of wrens on a single acre, some of the nests being not more than 15 feet apart. We also had robins' nests only 12 yards apart. The bluebirds, on the other hand, do not like each other, and would not tolerate another pair of bluebirds nearer than 100 yards.

"The first year we had no flickers, but there was a pair nesting in an old apple tree on our neighbors' property. During the winter the tree was blown down and our oldest son obtained permission to get it. He cut out the portion of the tree which contained the nest, cleaned out the hole and then hung the nest in a dying cherry tree. The nest was not more than ten yards from the house, but was taken possession of in 1914 and again in 1915.

"In 1915, we had 75 pairs of martins in an area approximating 10 acres. We had one pair of red-shouldered hawks nesting in our apple orchard, and kept them for two years; but they developed such a fondness for poultry, having frequently been caught thieving, that finally we had to shoot them.

"We have in the woods a splendid pair of barred owls. They come around the barns at night, and I suspect them also of attempts at chicken thieving, but they are too handsome and rare a bird in these parts to shoot. We suspect screech owls of having been the cause of the mysterious disappearance of many young birds from their nests.

A STUFFED OWL PROVIDES FUN

"If anyone wants excitement, I suggest that he buy or borrow a stuffed owl and put it out in the garden in the daytime during the nesting season. All of the birds in the neighborhood will soon congregate to scold and fight the unpopular 'interloper,' and the children will learn to recognize their feathered neighbors more quickly than in any other way."

A census of the species in the 100 acres of fields and woods in Dr. Grosvenor's "Wild Acres" showed that the next summer 60 species were nesting on the farm.

Commenting upon the story of the birds at "Wild Acres," Dr. Frank Chapman, the editor of *Bird-Lore*, says:

"The birds which Dr. Grosvenor has brought about him are unquestionably more his birds than if he had shot them and placed their skins in a cabinet. With their death his responsibility for their welfare would cease. But a living bird, to which we feel we owe protection, is exposed to so many dangers that our fears for its safety are correspondingly aroused.

"These birds of our garden are our guests. Through the erection of birdhouses and by other means we have invited them to live with us, and when they accept as they have with Dr. Grosvenor they make us realize not only our responsibility, but they awaken the strongest sense of hospitality."

Interesting changes have occurred since this record was achieved, Dr. Grosvenor reported in 1937.

"When our growing family required more accommodation and it became necessary to replace the old farmhouse with a more comfortable structure, we worried lest our bird friends shun our new quarters. But the workmen had hardly packed their tools before the birds were crowding about again. The first summer, robins, phoebes, and barn swallows nested on the new house, swifts in the chimney (we had arranged to leave the inside of one flue rough), and cardinals close enough to touch from the window.

"Starlings occasionally take possession of the martin houses in spite of all our efforts. But we take pleasure in ever-increasing barn swallows, mockingbirds, thrashers, bluebirds, wood thrushes, catbirds, bobwhites, cardinals, red-bellied and other woodpeckers, and many varieties of flycatchers and sparrows. I have watched the great crested flycatcher fight the starling furiously and whip the pest. We have known four families of starlings, 9 to 11 in each brood, to be reared in one nest in one season. Their nests are foul.

"A green heron for years has nested on 'Wild Acres,' and one August two American egrets were daily visitors. In May an Audubon class once identified on 'Wild Acres' more than 100 varieties before lunch.

"One March evening a Japanese girl visiting us tumbled down the stairs, crying hysterically, 'Big chickee in my room! Big chickee frighten me.' We found a solemn, monkey-faced owl (barn owl) blinking on her dressing table. To the Japanese, she wept, the visit of an owl portended evil. When we explained that in America an owl entering through the open window is a welcome guest, she was consoled, but not until her mother in Tokyo wrote her that all at home were well was she reassured."

"Of many interesting experiences searching for birds in the United States and Canada (Vol. I, pages 18, 68, and 235), the most unusual was in company of Dr. T. Gilbert Pearson.

"Together one July we landed on an uninhabited island opposite Cape Dauphin, Cape Breton Island. The island is a bird sanctuary carefully protected by the Canadian Government. European cormorants, puffins, guillemots, gulls, and terns in thousands were nesting on the cliffs.

"Climbing to the summit, we noticed many burrows in the turf. 'Petrels dug the holes and nest in tiny rooms at the end of the tunnels,' Dr. Pearson remarked.

"Dr. Pearson thrust his arm deep into one of the burrows and then gently withdrew his hand, clutching a small dark-colored bird with a white rump. He turned to me and said:

"'This is a Leach's petrel, one of Mother Carey's chickens. Watch when I let the bird free; watch carefully. You will note something extraordinary. These thousands of great gulls and swiftly flying terns that shriek at us so savagely overhead will hush their cries when I release this tiny creature. Are you ready? Away, little chicken!'

"Instantly the deafening din of the screaming birds hushed. Not a shriek, not a sound broke the silence that settled across the island. The petrel darted speedily to sea, and after a moment the gulls and terns resumed their loud protests at our presence.

"Will someone please explain why the birds overhead became silent at sight of the apparently harmless little creature, much smaller than themselves? Were they expressing respect for this hardy child of the ocean? For its home is the distant seas and it comes to land only when nesting.

"That birds have means of communication with one another most naturalists believe. The *caw! caw! caw!* of the raven and crow, the shouts of the blue jays back and forth surely are messages exchanged. At my summer home on the Bras d'Or Lakes, Cape Breton, I watch for hours the parent raven schooling its young in aerial maneuvers. It requires little fancy to interpret the varying inflections of these calls —scolding, laughing, teasing, warning, encouraging, praising."

PROTECTION AGAINST ENEMIES

"My garden will be a bird sanctuary" is today the usual hope of the fortunate possessor of a piece of land suitable for growing flowers, however small the piece may be. But many have not yet learned that however attractive the arrangement and setting, birds cannot rear their nestlings nor can they survive, so long as a cat is permitted on the premises. The cautious naturalists of the U. S. Biological Survey after fifty years' experience and observation publish the following warning:

"The house cat is one of the greatest obstacles in efforts toward increasing bird life in urban or suburban communities. The mere presence of a cat, regardless of whether it is or is not a habitual bird killer, has a demoralizing effect on nesting birds and may entirely defeat the most energetic efforts to attract and increase their numbers. Young birds just out of the nest are the easiest prey for the house cat and are liable to arouse the predatory instincts of the most docile and well-mannered. During the nesting season even the well-trained house cat must be kept away from the vicinity of birdhouses, and the vagrant animal must be carefully guarded against or dealt with summarily." *

* From "Homes for Birds," by E. R. Kalmbach, Senior Biologist, Bureau of Biological Survey, page 16, Farmers' Bulletin No. 1456, U. S. Department of Agriculture.

OUR GREATEST TRAVELERS

The Seasonal Movements of Birds Revealed By Birdbanding

By Frederick C. Lincoln

Senior Biologist in Charge, Distribution and Migration of Birds, U. S. Biological Survey

WHERE each fall go the birds that have nested in our dooryards and frequented the neighboring woods, hills, and marshes? Will the same ones return again to their former haunts next spring? What adventures do they face on their round-trip flights and where are their winter homes?

The migrations of birds were probably among the first natural phenomena to attract the attention of man. Recorded observations date back nearly 3,000 years—from the times of Hesiod, Homer, Herodotus, Aristotle. In the Bible are several references to the periodic movements of birds, as in the book of Job (39:26): "Doth the hawk fly by thy wisdom and stretch her wings toward the south?" Jeremiah (8:7) wrote: "The stork in the heaven knoweth her appointed times; and the turtle (dove) and the crane and the swallow observe the time of their coming."

The flight of quail that saved the Israelites from starvation in their wanderings in the wilderness of Sinai now is recognized as a vast movement of migratory quail (*Coturnix coturnix*) between their breeding grounds and their winter home in Africa.

A TOURIST REGISTER OF BIRDS

For half a century the United States Biological Survey has been collecting facts on the migration of North American birds.* Field men of the Bureau have gathered information about the distribution and seasonal movements of the different species in many extended areas, from the Arctic coast south to the pampa region of Argentina.

Supplementing these investigations are the hundreds of volunteer ornithologists and bird students throughout the United States and Canada, who each year, spring and fall, forward reports on the migrations observed in their localities.

Added to this mass of data is a rapidly growing file of records of birds that have been banded.

These cards, together with other records gleaned by the Survey are in files that now contain well over 2,500,000 entries, the largest existing accumulation of information about the distribution and movements of North American birds. Facts thus assembled make it possible to chart the ranges and migrations of the different species, and form the basis of regulatory action for their protection.

Aristotle, often right, sponsored some superstitions on bird migration that persisted for centuries. He accounted for the autumnal disappearance of swallows, storks, doves, etc., by their passing the cold season in a torpid state hidden in hollow trees, in caves, and in the mud of marshes. This hibernation theory became so firmly rooted that in 1878 Elliott Coues listed the titles of 182 papers on the hibernation of swallows. Some early naturalists wrote fantastic accounts of the flocks of swallows congregating in the marshes until their accumulated weight bent the reeds on which they clung and submerged the birds. It was even recorded that fishermen in northern waters sometimes drew up their nets with a mixed "catch" of fish and hibernating swallows.

The hibernation theory still is repeated to account for failure to locate definitely the winter home of the chimney swifts (*Chaetura pelagica*). Each autumn they gather in immense flocks in southern Georgia and northern Florida and then suddenly disappear. It is probable that they winter in the great rain-forest area of the Amazon Valley in Brazil, passing most of the daytime high in the air with other swifts that are local residents.

Persons who accepted the larger birds as

* In the preparation of this paper the author has made free use of the writings of all leading students of bird migration, to whom grateful acknowledgment is made. Much of the material originally appeared in U. S. Dept. Agriculture Circular 363.

IN SUCH TRAPS, 28,000 CHIMNEY SWIFTS WERE CAUGHT FOR
STUDY IN EIGHT WEEKS

The screen, its sides lined with black oilcloth, is put over the chimney after the
large migrating flocks have gone to roost. When they attempt to escape next
morning, they fail to cling to the smooth walls and as a result flutter unharmed
into a large gathering cage. A speedy day migrant, this species sometimes flies
more than 100 miles an hour. Its winter home is not definitely known, but investigators hope the recent wholesale banding will result in addition of reliable
data (page 313).

of small birds
that congregate
on the shores of
the Mediterra-
nean Sea, await-
ing opportunity
for this kind of
passage to their
winter homes in
Africa.

Even as re-
cently as the au-
tumn of 1936
press dispatches
from a town in
British Columbia
alleged that a
hunter brought
down two birds
in one shot, "a
Canadian goose
and a passenger
—a hummingbird
traveling south
nestled in the soft,
warm feathers of
the larger bird."

BIRDS RETURN
WITH SURPRIS-
ING REGULARITY

The weather at
any point has lit-
tle, if anything,
to do with the
time of arrival of
migratory birds.
This is contrary
to the belief of
those who have
thought they
could foretell the
appearance of
the several spe-
cies by a study
of weather condi-
tions.

migratory travelers were unable to understand how the smaller species, some of
them notoriously poor flyers, could make
similar journeys. They contended that the
larger species, such as the storks and cranes,
carried their small companions as living
freight.

In some of the Mediterranean countries
it is still believed that these broad-pinioned
birds serve as aerial transports for the hosts

Though the insistent crescendo note of
the oven-bird is ordinarily associated with
the full verdure of May woods, this bird has
been known to reach its breeding grounds in
a snowstorm, and the records of its arrival
in southern Minnesota show a temperature
variation from near freezing to full summer warmth. Temperatures recorded at
the time of arrival of several other common birds show variations of 14° to 37°

Photograph by Arthur A. Allen

THIS VIEW OF THE DOMED NEST SHOWS WHY THE OVEN-BIRD IS SO NAMED

The parent stands in front of the entrance like a housewife attending to her baking. For peculiarities
of the migration of this species, see opposite page.

Fahrenheit, the average variation being about 24°.

Migration is so ingrained that each species moves north in spring when the average weather encountered is endurable. The hardy birds travel early, fearless of the blasts of retreating winter. The more delicate species come later, when there is less danger of inclement weather.

Some of the stout-hearted birds pause and allow the spring season to advance, and then by rapid travel again overtake it, or actually outstrip it. At times this results in hardship and occasionally in the destruction of many individuals. That has happened when early migrating bluebirds have been overwhelmed by a late winter storm.

The advance of average temperature lines, or isotherms, is found to correspond closely with the northward movements of certain species. For example, the northward travels of the Canada goose are found to coincide with the advance of the isotherm of 35° Fahrenheit (page 305).

THEY FOLLOW THE FOOD SUPPLY

The tendency in many species to move southward at the approach of winter is not always due to the seasonal low temperatures, since experiments have demonstrated that many summer insect feeders, when confined in outdoor aviaries, comfortably withstand temperatures far below zero.

The main consideration is the depletion of the food supply, caused either by disappearance or hibernation of insects, or by the mantle of snow or ice blanketing the seeds and other ground food. Possibly, also, shortened hours of daylight restrict the time of obtaining sufficient food when the cold requires an increased supply to maintain body heat.

THEORIES OF MIGRATION

Chickadees and some others of our smaller birds have no fear of Arctic weather, since their food sources are mainly arboreal. Also, when there is a good supply of cones in the Canadian woods, red-breasted nuthatches and crossbills will remain through the winter. When these birds appear abundantly in winter in southern latitudes, there probably is a shortage of their food in the north.

Migration long since has become a definite hereditary habit that recurs in annual

ing conditions and a yearlong food supply. This is the condition today in the Tropics, and it is noteworthy that most tropical birds are nonmigratory.

Gradually, however, the glacial ice fields advanced southward, forcing the birds before them, until finally all bird life was concentrated in southern latitudes. As the ages passed and the icecap gradually retreated, the birds endeavored each spring to return to their ancestral homes in the north, only to be driven south again at the approach of winter. As the size of the ice-covered area diminished, the journeys made became ever longer, until eventually the habits of migration were fixed to accord with the climatic conditions of the present age.

Photograph by Ada B. Copeland

THIS CROSSBILL CAME DOWN FROM THE MOUNTAINS FOR FOOD

It was banded at Grand Junction, Colorado, in January, 1925. In the East, members of the species do not migrate from the Canadian forests unless the harvest of evergreen cones fails there (see page 303).

cycles, probably because of physiological stimuli in the bodies of the birds, associated with the reproductive period. To seek its origin, one must study the history of the birds' occupation of their present ranges, and consider all reasonable theories. The two now most commonly accepted are diametrically opposed to each other.

According to one theory, nonmigratory birds swarmed over the entire Northern Hemisphere in earlier ages, when food and habitat permitted them to remain in their haunts throughout the year. The entire northern area then afforded the two important avian requirements—suitable breed-

The actions of the birds lend some support to this theory; every bird student has noted the feverish impatience with which certain species push northward in spring. It is probable, however, that the reproductive impulse urges the birds on to their northern breeding grounds.

The opposing theory supposes that the ancestral home of all birds was in the Tropics, and that since all bird life tends to overpopulation there was a constant effort to seek breeding grounds where competition would be less keen. Species that strove for more northern latitudes would be kept

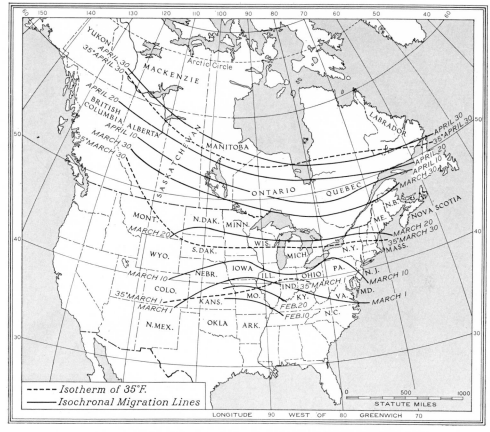

IN STEP WITH THE SPRING, THE CANADA GOOSE GOES NORTH

As the isotherm of 35° Fahrenheit advances toward the Arctic Circle, the movement of these birds keeps pace with it. Isochronal migration lines make this statement clear. The speed is increased in the upper part of the range where warm weather begins more quickly (page 303).

in check by the ice and forced to return southward with the recurrence of winter conditions.

As the ice retreated, vast areas of virgin country became successively suitable for summer occupancy, but the winter habitat remained the home to which the birds returned after the nesting season.

Some species do linger briefly on their breeding grounds. The orchard oriole, for example, passes only 2½ months in its summer home, arriving in southern Pennsylvania about the first week in May and leaving by the middle of July.

THE NIGHT AND DAY THEORY

Both theories have been criticized on biological and geological grounds; neither can be accepted without qualification. It is apparent, however, that the search for conditions favorable for breeding in summer and for feeding in winter has been a princi-

pal factor underlying the origin of migration.

A modern view holds that quantity of light and length of day are the stimulating causes of migration. Its proponents urge that migration is a phenomenon far too regular to be created anew each season, and that it began before the necessity for a change in latitude became pressing.

Such birds as swallows, nighthawks, shore birds, and others may start their southward movement while the summer food supply in the north is at peak abundance; robins, bluebirds, and others may leave abundant food in the south in spring and press northward when the food supplies there are almost entirely lacking, and when severe cold and storms are likely to play havoc with them.

The regularity of arrival and departure is one of the most impressive features of migration, and since birds travel in almost

A RAPID MIGRANT IS THE GRAY-CHEEKED THRUSH

From Louisiana to Alaska, about 4,000 miles, this songster advances at an average speed of 130 miles a day. The last part of the journey is covered, isochronal migration lines show, at a rate several times as fast as that attained in the Mississippi Valley (page 314).

strict accordance with the calendar, the advocates of the theory ask: What phenomenon to which we may attribute the stimulating impulse occurs with such precise regularity as the constantly increasing light in spring?

Experimental work has demonstrated the effects of increased light upon the growth, flowering, and fruiting of plants. Similarly, experiments with the common junco, or snowbird, reported by Professor William Rowan, of the University of Alberta, re-

sulted in increased development of the sexual organs by the end of December, although the birds were confined in outdoor aviaries in Canada and had been exposed to temperatures as low as 44 degrees below zero.

After a consideration of all evidence, including the fact that no ultraviolet rays were used, it was concluded that the explanation lay in the increased exercise taken during the periods of increased light. If development of the sexual organs be ac-

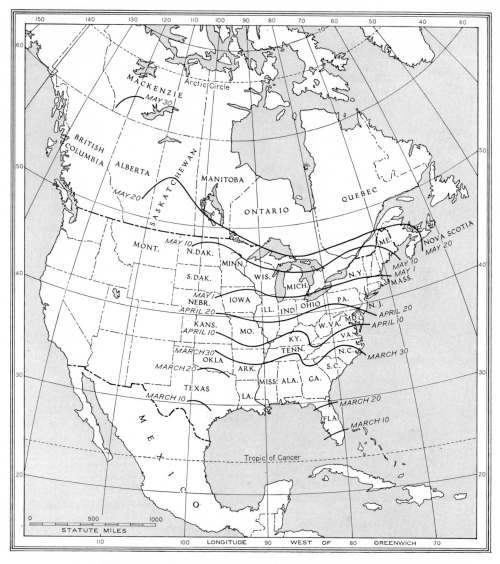

THE BLACK AND WHITE WARBLER IS A SLOW MIGRANT

About 50 days are required for these birds to travel from their winter quarters in Florida, the West Indies, central Mexico, Central America, and northwestern South America to breeding grounds extending west and northwest from South Carolina and New Brunswick as far as Great Bear Lake in northwestern Canada. The isochronal migration lines on the map show a slow and uniform advance, apparently only about 20 miles a day across the United States (page 310).

cepted as a controlling cause of migration, then these experiments are of great importance.

However, this theory also is open to serious objections. It might be asked, for example: If the lengthening day is the stimulating factor, why should our summer birds wintering in the Tropics ever start northward, since in their winter quarters the variation in the length of day from winter to summer is imperceptible?

At any given point many species depart in fall and return in spring. In some species one of the parent birds (rarely both) frequently returns and nests in the same tree, bush, or box that held its nest the previous season. Thus, one ordinarily thinks of the world of birds as quiescent during two seasons each year, at nesting time and in winter. For individual species this is obviously the case, but when the entire avifauna of the continent is

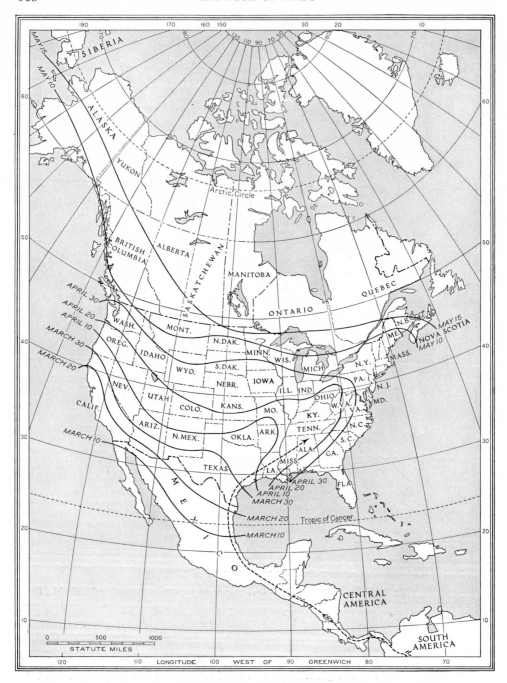

THE CLIFF SWALLOWS MIGRATE BY DAY

Instead of flying across the Caribbean Sea as does the black-poll warbler (opposite page),
they follow the coast of Central America, where their food, flying insects, is readily obtained. The
isochronal lines show the places at which the birds arrive at the same time (pages 312 and 317).
Instead of appearing first in Florida and Texas, then in the Rocky Mountains, and last on the Pacific
coast, these birds are common in north-central California before they are seen in the southeastern
part of the United States.

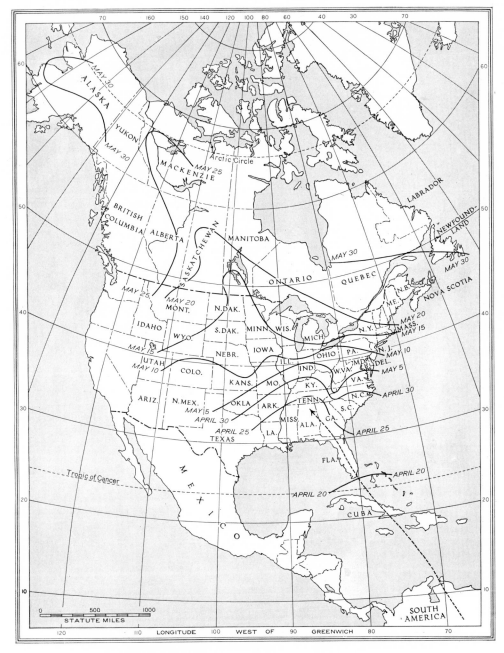

THE BLACK-POLL WARBLER MIGRATES AT NIGHT

The solid isochronal lines show the places at which these birds arrive at the same time, moving north from South America across the West Indies to Florida. As the birds move northward, these lines become farther apart, showing that the warblers move faster with the advance of spring. From April 30 to May 10 the average speed is about 30 miles a day, while from May 25 to May 30 it is increased to more than 200 miles. The migration of the warbler is made up of a series of long, nocturnal flights, alternated with days of rest and feeding in favorable localities. Besides warblers, many birds migrate at night, including shore birds, vireos, thrushes, and the large family of sparrows—in fact, the majority of small birds.

considered there are some latitudinal movements at almost all periods.

Some species begin their fall migrations in midsummer, and in some parts of the country distinct southward movements can be detected from then until the beginning or middle of winter. For example, many shore birds start south in the early part of July, while the goshawks, snowy owls, redpolls, Bohemian waxwings, and many others do not leave the north until forced to do so by severe winter weather or by lack of customary food.

Thus, an observer in the northern part of the United States may record an almost unbroken southward procession of birds from midsummer to midwinter, and he may note some of the returning migrants as early as the middle of February.

Purple martins have been known to arrive in Florida late in January on their way north, and the northern movement may continue among late arrivals into the first week of June. In some species the migration is so prolonged that the first arrivals in the southern part of the breeding range will have performed their parental duties while others of that species are still on their way to more northern nesting grounds.

These facts indicate that sometimes there exists a definite relationship between what we may term northern and southern groups of individuals of the same species. A supposition, on which further banding work is expected later to give definite facts, is that in some species, which have an extensive latitudinal breeding range and a normal migration, the individuals that nest farthest south migrate first in fall and proceed to the southern part of the winter range; those that occupy the central parts of the breeding range migrate next, and travel to regions in the winter range north of those occupied by the first group; and, finally, the individuals breeding farthest north are the last to begin their fall migration, and these remain farthest north during the winter.

This theory supposes that the southward movement of the species is normally such that the different groups maintain their relative latitudinal positions, both spring and fall.

The black and white warbler furnishes an example. The breeding range of this bird extends west and northwest from South Carolina and Nova Scotia as far as Great Bear Lake in northwestern Canada. The bird spends the winter in southern Florida, the West Indies, central Mexico, Central America, and northwestern South America (map, page 307).

In the southern part of its breeding range it is nesting in April, but the summer residents of Nova Scotia do not reach their breeding grounds before the middle of May. Therefore, about 50 days are required for these northbound birds to cross the breeding range, and if 60 days be allowed for nest building, egg laying, incubation, care of the young, and molt, they would not be ready to start southward before the middle of July.

Then another 50-day trip south, and the earliest migrants from the northern areas would reach the Gulf coast in September.

But both adults and young have been observed at Key West, Florida, by the middle of July, and on the northern coast of South America by August 21. Since the birds at Key West were fully 500 miles south of the breeding range, it is evident that they must have come from the southern part of the nesting area.

THE REASONS FOR NIGHT FLYING

Since most birds appear more or less helpless in the dark, it seems remarkable that many should select the night hours for extended travel. Among those that do are the hosts of shore birds, rails, flycatchers, orioles, most of the large family of sparrows, the warblers, vireos, and thrushes, and, in fact, the majority of small birds.

The passage of flocks of ducks and geese frequently is observed by sportsmen sitting in their blinds, but vast numbers of these birds also pass through at night. The clarion call of the Canada goose and the conversational gabbling of a flock of ducks are familiar night sounds in spring and fall in many parts of the country.

The sibilant, nocturnal calls of the upland plover and other shore birds during their spring and fall flights form vivid memories.

Observations made with telescopes focused on the full moon have shown processions of birds. One observer estimated that birds passed his point of observation at the rate of 9,000 an hour.

The bulk of the flocks pass during the earlier hours of the evening and toward daylight in the morning, the periods from 8 o'clock to midnight and from 4 to 6 a. m.

Photograph by Arthur A. Allen

COZILY ENSCONCED, THE FEMALE BLACK-POLL WARBLER IS HARD TO SEE

She has made her rather loosely constructed nest in a spruce tree near Hudson Bay (see page 309).

seeming to be favorite times for nocturnal flight.

It has been asserted, with some reason, that small birds migrate by night the better to avoid their enemies, and that most of the nocturnal travelers are those that are timid, sedentary, or feeble-winged.

Included in this group are not only small song and insectivorous birds, but also such weak flyers as the rails, the wrens, the small woodland flycatchers, and other species. These, living habitually more or less in concealment, probably are safer under the protective cloak of darkness.

Nevertheless, this explanation cannot account for such night migrants as the snipe, sandpipers, and plovers, birds generally found in the open and rated powerful flyers, some of them winging more than 2,000 miles across the ocean. Such long flights, of course, require both day and night flying.

Night travel is probably best for most birds from the standpoint of feeding. Digestion is rapid, yet the stomach of a bird killed in the day usually contains food.

To supply the energy for long flight, food must be obtained at comparatively short intervals.

If the smaller migrants were to make protracted flights by day they might arrive at their destination at nightfall almost exhausted, but unable to obtain food until the following morning, since they are entirely daylight feeders. This would delay resumption of flight.

Traveling at night, however, they pause at daybreak and devote the daylight to alternate feeding and resting. This permits complete recuperation that makes them ready to continue the journey at nightfall.

Many species of wading and swimming birds, able to feed at all hours and seeking no safety in concealment, migrate by day or by night. Some diving birds, including ducks that submerge when in danger, sometimes travel over water by day and over land at night.

The day migrants include, in addition to some of the ducks and geese, the loons, cranes, gulls, pelicans, hawks, swallows,

Photograph by Alfred M. Bailey

WINGS OVER A LOUISIANA MARSH

A flock of blue geese darken the sun as they spring into flight from a swamp in Vermilion Parish. The blue goose is a late but rapid spring migrant that winters on the coast of Louisiana and breeds on Baffin and Southampton Islands and flies between summer and winter homes practically without stops (see page 340).

nighthawks, and swifts—all strong-winged birds. The swifts, swallows, and night-hawks (sometimes called bull-bats) feed entirely on flying insects, and use their short, weak feet and legs only for grasping a perch during periods of rest or sleep. Thus they feed as they travel, the circling flocks being frequently seen late in summer working gradually southward.

DAY AND NIGHT MIGRANTS TAKE DIFFERENT ROUTES

Both the black-poll warbler and the cliff swallow pass the winter as neighbors in South America.

But when they start northward toward their respective breeding grounds, the warblers strike straight across the Caribbean Sea to Florida, while the swallows begin their journey by a westward flight of several hundred miles to Panama. Thence they move leisurely along the western shore of the Caribbean Sea to Mexico and, continuing to avoid a long trip over water, they go completely around the western end of the Gulf of Mexico.

This circuitous route adds more than 2,000 miles to the journey of the swallows that nest in Nova Scotia. The explanation is that the swallow is a day migrant, and the warbler travels at night.

The migration of the warbler is made up of a series of long, nocturnal flights, alternated with days of rest and feeding in favorable localities.

The swallow, on the other hand, starts its migration several weeks earlier and catches each day's ration of flying insects during a few hours of aerial evolutions, which carry it slowly in the proper direction. Flying along the insect-teeming shores of the Gulf of Mexico, these birds cover in the 2,000 extra miles but a fraction of the distance that they travel in pursuit of their food.

Although most of our smaller birds make their longest flights at night, travel is continued to some extent by day. This is particularly the case during the latter half of a migratory season, when the birds desire to hasten to their breeding grounds. At this time flocks of birds while feeding maintain a movement in the general direction of the

Photograph by R. D. Sloane

A BANDED CANADA GOOSE NESTS ON JACK MINER'S BIRD SANCTUARY

There are nine eggs in the nest, an unusual number, for this species regularly lays only six. At this haven near Kingsville, Ontario, much information has been obtained by recovery of individuals marked and released in Kansas (map, page 342).

seasonal journey. Sometimes they travel hurriedly, and, while their flights may be short, they cover considerable distance in a day.

SPEED OF FLIGHT AND MIGRATION

It is not unusual to hear accounts of birds flying "a mile a minute." Some birds attain a speed even greater, but such cases are exceptional. Even when pressed, few can develop an air speed of 60 miles an hour.

They do, however, have two speeds, one the normal rate for everyday purposes and for migration, and an accelerated speed for escape or pursuit. In some cases the latter may be nearly double the normal rate. Nevertheless, the effort required for the high speeds could not be long sustained, certainly not for long-distance migratory journeys.

During the last few years reliable data on the speed of birds have accumulated slowly. It has been found that the common flying speed of ducks and geese is between 40 and 50 miles an hour, but that of smaller birds is much less.

Herons, hawks, horned larks, ravens, and shrikes, as timed with the speedometer of an automobile, fly 22 to 28 miles an hour, while some of the flycatchers are such slow flyers that they attain only 10 to 17 miles an hour. Even such fast-flying birds as the mourning dove rarely exceed 35 miles an hour.

All these birds can fly faster, but at training camps during the World War airplanes having a maximum speed of about 80 miles an hour easily overtook flocks of ducks making every effort to escape. Aviators have asserted that at 65 miles an hour they can overtake the fastest ducks, though cases are on record of ducks passing airplanes that were throttled down to 55 miles an hour.

FASTEST-FLYING BIRDS

The highest bird speeds reliably recorded are of the swifts and the duck hawk, or peregrine falcon (*Falco peregrinus*). An observer in an airplane in Mesopotamia (Iraq) reported that swifts easily circled his ship when it was traveling 68 miles an hour. To do this, the birds certainly were flying at a speed as high as 100 miles an hour.

Once a hunting duck hawk, "stooping" at its quarry, and timed with a stop watch, was calculated to have attained a speed between 165 and 180 miles an hour.

The speed of migration, however, is quite different from that attained in forced flights for short distances.

It is probable that the barn swallows I saw in May on Beata Island, off the southern coast of the Dominican Republic, may have reached that point after a non-stop flight of 350 miles across the Caribbean Sea from the coast of Venezuela. Nevertheless, it is doubtful that birds continue such long journeys day after day from winter quarters to breeding grounds.

It seems more likely that migrations are performed in a leisurely manner, and that after a flight of a few hours the birds pause to feed and rest for one or several days, particularly if they find themselves in congenial surroundings. Some indication of this is found in the records of banded birds.

Considering only the shortest intervals that have elapsed between banding in the north and recovery in southern regions, it is found that usually a month or more is taken to cover an air-line distance of a thousand miles.

FASTEST FLIGHT YET RECORDED

Among the thousands of banding records obtained in recent years, evidences of rapid flight are decidedly scarce, for with few exceptions all 1,000-mile flights have required two to four weeks, or more.

The highest speed thus far recorded for a banded bird is that of a mallard banded on November 23, 1930, in Green Bay, Wisconsin, and shot five days later, 900 miles away, near Georgetown, South Carolina. This bird doubtless flew at least 1,000 miles in the five days, since its route probably was not in a direct air line; but, even so, the average daily distance was only 200 miles, which could easily have been covered in five hours.

The Canada goose affords a typical example of regular, but slow, migration. Its advance northward is at the same rate as the advance of the season. In fact, the isotherm of 35° Fahrenheit appears to be a governing factor in the speed at which these geese move north, and over their entire trip the vanguard follows closely the advance of this isotherm.

Only a few species, however, perform such regular migrations, the majority waiting in their winter homes until spring is well advanced and then moving rapidly to their breeding grounds. Sometimes this advance is so rapid that the later migrants actually catch up with species that for a month or more may have been pressing slowly northward.

One of the best examples of rapid migration is found in the gray-cheeked thrush. This bird winters in Colombia, Ecuador, Peru, Venezuela, and British Guiana, and does not start its northward journey until many other species are well on their way. It does not appear in the United States until the last of April—April 25, near the mouth of the Mississippi, and April 30 in northern Florida.

A month later, or by the last week in May, the bird has reached northwestern Alaska, having made the 4,000-mile trip from Louisiana at an average speed of about 130 miles a day (see map, page 306).

CATCHING UP WITH SPRING

Coming from the Tropics, the yellow, or summer, warblers reach New Orleans about April 5, when the average temperature is 65° Fahrenheit. Traveling north much faster than the season, they reach their breeding grounds in Manitoba the latter part of May, when the average temperature is only 47°. Encountering progressively colder weather over their entire route, they cross in the 15 days from May 11 to 25 a zone that spring takes 35 days to cross.

This "catching up" with spring is habitual in species that winter south of the United States and in most of the northern species that winter in the Gulf States.

To this rule there appear to be only six exceptions: the Canada goose, the mallard, the pintail, the crow, the red-winged blackbird, and the robin.

The blue goose presents a striking example of a late but rapid spring migration. Practically all members of the species winter in the coastal marshes of Louisiana, where 50,000 or more may be seen grazing in the "pastures" or flying overhead in flocks. Their breeding grounds are chiefly on Baffin Island, and on Southampton Island, in the northern part of Hudson Bay, a region where severe cold prevails except for a few weeks each year.

The birds seem to realize that even though the season in their winter quarters

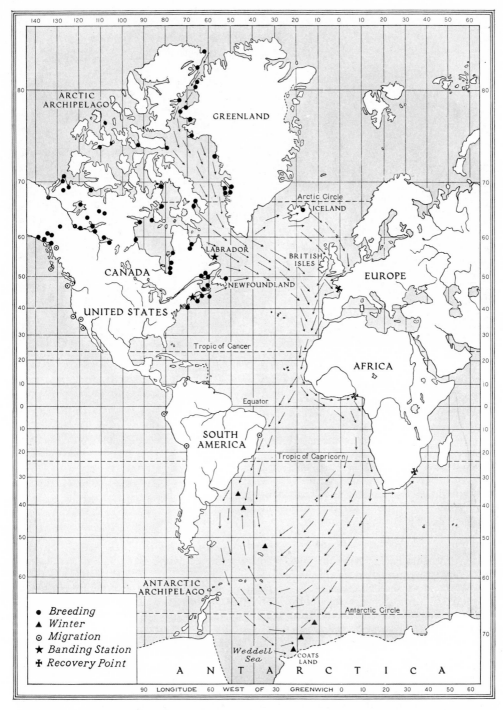

THE WORLD'S GREATEST TRAVELER IS THE ARCTIC TERN

For an individual bird the longest flight known was accomplished by one of these which flew from the coast of Labrador to the coast of southeastern Africa in three months. The map shows the distribution and the migration of the Arctic terns of eastern North America. Since no other species is known to breed abundantly on this continent and to cross the Atlantic Ocean to and from the Old World, their route is unique. They enjoy more hours of daylight than any other animal, for their summer and winter homes are 11,000 miles apart at the extremes, and they fly circuitously, covering probably at least 25,000 miles each year (pages 329, 343).

Photograph by Paul W. Hoffman

A BLACK TERN REMOVES THE EGGSHELL FROM ITS NEST

More than a thousand of these birds have been banded, but only one has been recovered.

is advancing rapidly, their nesting grounds are still covered with a heavy blanket of ice and snow. Accordingly, they remain in the coastal marshes until the last of March or the first of April, when the local birds are already busily engaged with reproduction.

The flight northward is rapid, almost nonstop across the United States. Although the birds are sometimes recorded in considerable numbers in the Mississippi Valley, including eastern South Dakota, and in southeastern Manitoba, there are few records along the route of such large flocks as are known to winter in Louisiana.

When the birds arrive in the James Bay region of Canada they apparently enjoy a prolonged rest, for they are not noted in the vicinity of their breeding grounds until early June. During the first two weeks of that month they pour into the tundra country by the thousands, and each pair immediately sets about rearing a brood.

The robin has been mentioned as a slow migrant, and as a species it takes 78 days to make the 3,000-mile trip from Iowa to Alaska, a stretch of country that is crossed by advancing spring in 68 days. This fact, however, does not mean that individual robins are necessarily slow, for probably the northward movement of the species depends upon the continual advance of birds from the rear, the first individuals to arrive in a suitable locality remaining to nest.

THE GULF-TO-ARCTIC ROUTE

Special interest attaches to the wide variation in the speed of bird travel in different sections of the broad flyway extending from the Gulf of Mexico to the Arctic Ocean by way of the Mississippi and Mackenzie Valleys.

The black-poll warbler winters in north-central South America and migrates in April across the West Indies to Florida. From there some individuals fly northwest to the Mississippi Valley, north to Manitoba, northwest to the Mackenzie River, and thence almost due west to western Alaska.

A fairly uniform average speed of 30 to 35 miles a day is maintained from the Gulf to Minnesota. Then comes a spurt, for a week later the black-polls have reached the central part of the Mackenzie Valley, and by the following week they are observed in northwestern Alaska.

Accordingly, it appears that during the

Photograph by Olin Sewall Pettingill, Jr.

THE WORLD'S GREATEST TRAVELER ALIGHTS BESIDE ITS EGGS

For only ten weeks the Arctic tern is at home in the north country. The rest of the year it travels, for it passes the winter south of the Antarctic Circle. Each year it enjoys eight months of continuous daylight (pages 315 and 329).

latter part of the journey, many individuals must average more than 200 miles a day. Increased speed across western Canada to Alaska is shown also by many other species (see map, page 309).

A study of all species traveling up the Mississippi Valley indicates an average speed of about 23 miles a day.

Change in speed seems to have a direct relation to a corresponding change in the isothermal lines, which turn northwestward west of the Great Lakes.

As indicated, the advance of spring in the northern interior is much more rapid than in the Mississippi Valley and on the Gulf coast. In the north spring comes with a rush, and during the height of the migration season in Saskatchewan the temperature in the southern part of the Mackenzie Valley just about equals that in the Lake Superior area, which is 700 miles farther south. Such conditions, coupled with the diagonal course of the birds across this region of fast-moving spring, are the chief factors in the acceleration of speed.

Variations in speed of migration in different parts of the country are illustrated also by the movements of the cliff swallow, which breeds from Mexico to Alaska and winters in Brazil and Argentina. It would be expected in spring to appear in the United States first in Florida and Texas, then in the southern Rocky Mountain region, and finally on the Pacific coast.

As a matter of fact, however, the earliest spring records come from north-central California, where the bird usually is common before the first arrivals are observed in Texas or Florida (map, page 308).

The route taken, for many years a migration problem, was solved when it was found that these swallows went around the Gulf of Mexico rather than across it. The isochronal lines show the more rapid advance along the Pacific coast. By March 20, when the vanguard has not quite reached the lower Rio Grande in Texas, the species is already north of San Francisco in California.

HOW HIGH DO BIRDS FLY?

Since the development of the airplane, it has become common knowledge that rarefied atmosphere adds to the difficulties of flight.

Photograph courtesy U. S. Biological Survey

MALLARDS AND PINTAILS IN A WIRE-MESH TRAP SET ON THE ICE

Pintails are trimmer than most other ducks, with longer, slimmer necks and a more elegant and dignified carriage. They are extremely shy and quick to take alarm and, not possessing any great degree of curiosity, they are not easily fooled by decoys. This baited trap was about 100 feet long and in one day caught 414 ducks.

This is because of the reduction in oxygen, whether for a gasoline engine or the lungs of a bird, and to the lack of buoyancy of rarefied air.

Such birds as vultures, pelicans, cranes, and some of the hawks feel this the least, since compared with body weight the supporting surface of their wings is very great. But for the smaller and shorter-winged birds lack of buoyancy at high altitudes presents an obstacle in flight. Even when flying close to the earth, small birds have to keep their wings in rapid motion.

Knowledge of the altitude of migratory flight is scanty, though estimates obtained with the telescope, and still more accurate data by altimeter observation from airplanes, are accumulating.

It is, of course, obvious that some birds crossing mountain ranges during migration must attain high altitudes. Observers at 14,000 feet in the Himalayas have recorded storks and cranes flying so high that they could be seen only through field glasses. Being beyond the range of unaided vision, they must have been at least 6,000 feet above the observers, or at an actual altitude of 20,000 feet above sea level.

Such cases are exceptional. Aviators have reported that they rarely meet birds above an altitude of 5,000 feet.

Migration in general is performed below an altitude of 3,000 feet. Observations made from lighthouses and elsewhere indicate that migrants commonly travel at altitudes of a very few feet to a few hundred feet above sea or land. Sandpipers, sanderlings, and northern phalaropes, observed in migration on the Pacific Ocean route, sometimes fly so low that they are visible only as they top a wave. Observers off the English coast have similarly recorded the passage of land birds, which sometimes flew just above the surface of the water, rarely above 200 feet.

Of several hundred records of World War airplane pilots only 36 were of birds flying above 5,000 feet, and only seven above 8,500 feet.

Cranes were once recorded at an altitude of 15,000 feet, and the lapwing was the bird most frequently seen at high levels, 8,500 feet being its greatest recorded altitude.

These observations relate only to daytime travelers, but there is no reason to

Photograph courtesy U. S. Biological Survey

YOUNG CASPIAN TERNS CORRALLED FOR BANDING

This "haul" netted more than 700 birds. Returns from birds banded at this station in northern Lake Michigan have been received from as far south as Colombia and as far east as Nova Scotia.

believe that nocturnal migration is performed at higher altitudes.

BIRDS FLY THROUGH FOG WITH ACCURACY OF COMPASS-DIRECTED SHIP

Birds challenge admiration by the unerring certainty with which they cover thousands of miles of land and water to come to rest in exactly the same spot where they passed the previous summer or winter. The faculty that enables them to point their course accurately over vast expanses of land and water may, for want of a better term, be called a "sense of direction." Man recognizes this sense in himself, though usually it is imperfect and frequently at fault. This sense likewise is possessed by many mammals as well as by some insects and fishes. The well-known migrations of the salmon and the eel are notable examples.

The theory is sometimes advanced that the older and more experienced birds lead the way, showing the route to their younger companions. However, the young cowbird, reared by foster parents, flocks with others of its kind when grown and in many cases can hardly be said to have adult guidance in migration.

An inherited migratory instinct with a definite sense of the objective to be reached and the route to be followed must be attributed to these birds.

Birds possess remarkable vision. If they also have retentive memories, subsequent trips over a route may well be steered in part by recognizable landmarks. True, much migration is by night and long stretches of the open sea are crossed. Nevertheless, nights are rarely so dark that all terrestrial objects are totally obscured; coast lines and rivers usually may be seen in the faintest light, particularly by the acute vision of a bird and from the air.

But some birds fly unerringly through the densest fog. Members of the Biological Survey, going by steamer from the island of Unalaska to Bogoslof Island in Bering Sea through a heavy fog which made invisible every object beyond a hundred yards, recorded that flocks of murres, returning to Bogoslof, after quests for food, broke through the wall of fog astern, flew by the vessel, and disappeared into the mists ahead.

The ship was heading direct for the island by compass and chart, but its course was no more sure than that of the birds.

Some investigators have asserted that the

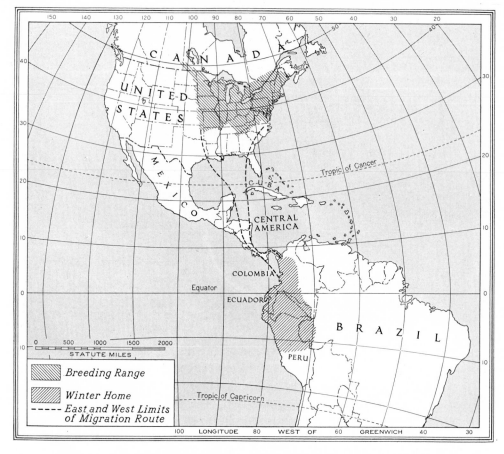

MIGRATION LINES OF THE SCARLET TANAGER PASS THROUGH A BOTTLENECK

During the season of laying eggs and rearing young, individuals of this species may be 1,900 miles apart in an east and west line across the breeding range. In their flights to and from their winter habitat, however, they draw nearer until in Central America not more than 100 miles separate them.

sense of direction has its seat in the ears or nasal passages, and that through these organs the birds can identify air currents and other phenomena. Experiments have demonstrated that disturbance of the semicircular canals of the inner ear will destroy the homing instinct of the racing pigeon, but tests by delicate operations, or closing the ears with wax, are such a serious shock to the sensitive nervous system of the bird that they cannot be considered conclusive evidence.

MANY BIRDS HAVE THE HOMING INSTINCT OF PIGEONS

Several years ago careful studies were made of the homing instinct of the sooty and noddy terns, tropical species that in the Atlantic region reach their most northern breeding point on the Dry Tortugas Is-

lands, off the southwest coast of Florida. They are not known to wander regularly any appreciable distance farther north. Some returned to their nests on the Tortugas after they had been taken on board ship, confined in cages below deck, and carried northward for 400 to 800 miles before being released. (See Vol. I, pages 300-1.)

Even the lowly cowbird, which, because of its habit of depositing its eggs in the nests of other birds, we would expect to have little attachment for its nesting territory, has demonstrated remarkable ability to return when carried for long distances from the area it has selected for breeding purposes.

Five of these birds, trapped and banded at Waukegan, Illinois, and shipped in a cage to New Orleans, Louisiana, for release, made the 1,000-mile flight back to

Photograph from S. Prentiss Baldwin

AN AUTOMATIC TRAP THAT WORKS

Dr. S. Prentiss Baldwin is driving the birds into a small "gathering cage," which enables the bander to take the birds in hand without the difficulty and danger to them that are attendant on their seizure in the traps.

Waukegan in periods from 14 to 30 days.

Another cowbird was sent across the mountains to Washington, D. C., but in less than a month it was again taken in the traps at the Waukegan banding station.

Still another, sent 1,200 miles west to Denver, Colorado, into the range of a different race of this species, was recaptured at Waukegan 26 days after release.

For instances of similar experiments with pintails, see pages 352-3; with song sparrows, see page 360.

Landmarks of all kinds were entirely lacking, and the birds were liberated in regions where they had no previous experience.

The "homing instinct" as shown by these terns, by the man-o'-war-birds, which are trained and used as message carriers in the Tuamotu, Gilbert, and Marshall Islands, and by the homing pigeon, may not be identical, but it seems closely akin to the orientation sense that directs the flights of migratory birds.

Although homing may involve flight from a point that the bird has not before visited, the flight is always to a known point—that is, the bird's nest—while, on the other hand, the first migratory flight is always from the region of the bird's birth to a region it has not before visited. The spring migration might, of course, be more nearly considered as true "homing."

The migratory instinct appears to be more or less transitory; that is, it is not persistent over an extended period. Migratory birds may be arrested en route, either by natural conditions, such as unusual food supplies, or forcibly by the act of man, and detained until the end or nearly the end of the migratory season, and then may not attempt to finish the journey.

In the fall and early winter of 1929, abundant food and an open season caused an unusual number of mallard ducks to arrest their migration and remain in western Montana and northern Idaho. Later, however, a heavy snowfall with subzero temperatures suddenly cut off the food supply, with the result that large numbers of the birds starved to death, when a flight of a few hours would have carried them to a region of open water and abundant food.

TRAVEL IN MIXED COMPANY

At the height of the spring migration the woods and thickets may be suddenly filled with several species of wood warblers,

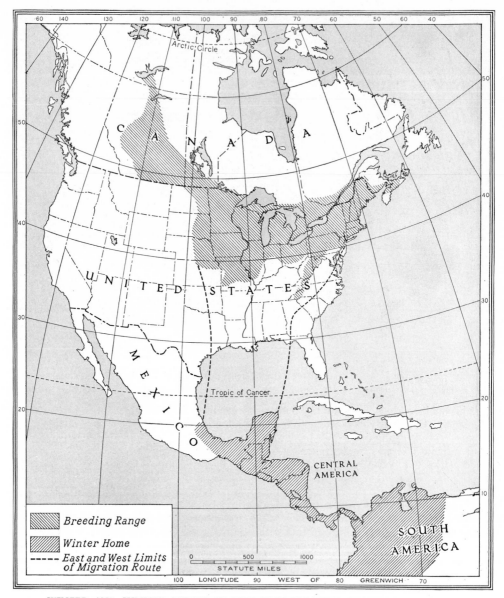

WINTER AND SUMMER HOMES OF THE ROSE-BREASTED GROSBEAK FORM AN
"HOURGLASS"

Though the width of the breeding range is about 2,500 miles, the migratory lines converge until the
boundaries are only about 700 miles apart when the birds leave the United States.

thrushes, sparrows, flycatchers, and others, which it is natural to conclude have traveled together and arrived simultaneously. Probably they did, but such combined migration is by no means the rule for all species.

As a group the wood warblers probably travel more in mixed companies than does any other single family of North American birds. The flocks are likely to be made up of several species, spring and fall, with both adults and young. Sometimes swallows, sparrows, blackbirds, and some of the shore birds also migrate in mixed flocks.

In fall, large flocks of blackbirds frequently sweep south across the Plains States, and occasionally one flock will contain bronzed grackles, red-winged blackbirds, yellow-headed blackbirds, and Brewer's blackbirds.

Many species keep strictly to themselves.

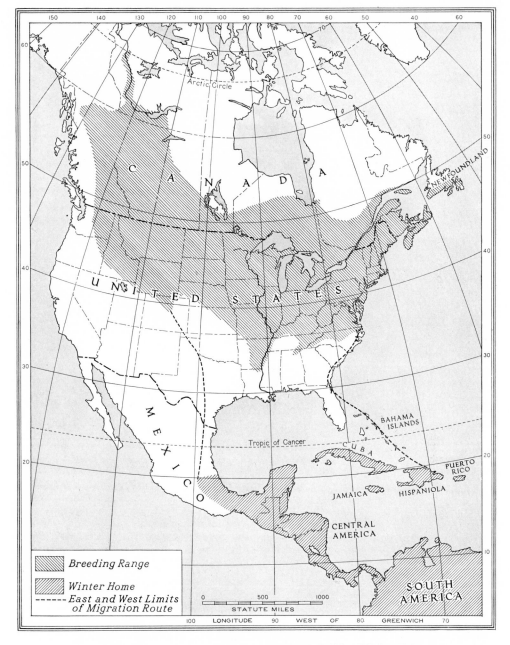

REDSTARTS USE A FLYWAY MORE THAN 2,000 MILES WIDE

Since birds of this species cross all parts of the Gulf of Mexico, or may travel from Florida to Cuba and through the Bahamas, the lines of their travel do not converge, as do those of the rose-breasted grosbeak (opposite page), but form an outstanding example of a wide migration route.

It would be difficult for others to keep in company with such rapid flyers as the chimney swift.

Nighthawks, or bull-bats, also fly in separate companies, as usually do crows, waxwings, crossbills, bobolinks, and kingbirds.

Occasionally a flock of ducks will be observed to contain several species, but usually when they are actually on migration the individuals of each species separate and travel with others of their own kind.

Flocks of blue geese frequently have with

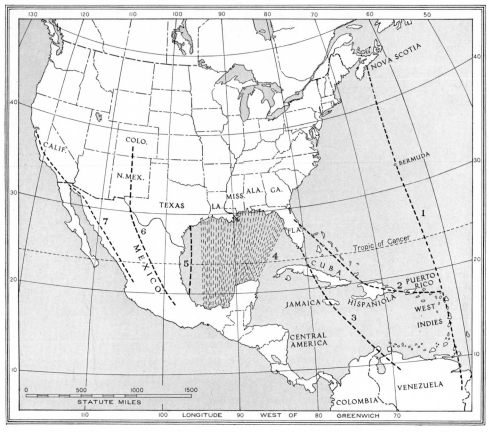

FEATHERED TRAVELERS GOING SOUTH FOR THE WINTER FOLLOW THESE WAYS

In passing from North America to the West Indies, Central America, and South America, birds use principally the seven migration routes shown on the map. Number 4 is the one taken most extensively. Only a few species make the 2,400-mile flight from Nova Scotia to South America.

them a few of the closely related snow geese, particularly in the eastern part of their winter range.

The adults of most perching birds drive the young away when they are grown, probably to be relieved of providing for them. This also affords the parents opportunity to rest and renew their plumage before starting for winter quarters. The young birds are likely to drift together and, having no further responsibility, may start ahead of their parents.

Canada geese and some others remain in family groups, the parent birds undergoing the wing molt that renders them flightless during the growth of their young, so that old and young acquire their full plumage at the same time and thus start south together.

The large flocks are composed of many families that band together, and when they separate into V-shaped units it is probable that an old bird leads the group. Where there is segregation of the sexes, the young birds usually accompany their mothers, as do some of the ducks. After the females start to incubate their eggs, the males of most species of ducks flock by themselves and remain together until fall.

MARSH WRENS BUILD "MODEL HOMES"

The males and females of some species may migrate either simultaneously or separately. In the latter event the males usually arrive first, sometimes huge flocks of male birds, as in the case of the red-winged blackbird, reaching a locality several days before any of the females. This is particularly the rule in spring; the first robins are usually males, as also are the first song sparrows, rose-breasted grosbeaks, and scarlet tanagers.

Photograph by Arthur A. Allen

A LITTLE MIGRATING MYRTLE WARBLER COMES ABOARD SHIP IN A FOG OFF THE
LABRADOR COAST

Soon it found a warm spot by the steam pipes, tucked its head under its wing and went to sleep.

The males' early arrival has been explained on the theory of territorial possession. This holds that the male selects the area where it elects to breed, each individual attempting to protect a claim from trespass by other males of its own kind, at the same time singing or otherwise inviting the later arriving females to examine the "homestead" it has selected for nesting. The long-billed marsh wren males may build several dummy nests before the females arrive.

In a few species, males and females arrive at the breeding grounds together and begin nest building. Among the shore birds, ducks, and geese, courtship and mating may take place, in whole or in part, while the birds are in the south or on their way north. When they arrive at the northern nesting grounds they are paired and ready to raise their families.

Mallard and black ducks pair as early as January, the female leading and the male following when they take flight. Naturally these mated pairs migrate north in company, and it was largely to protect such birds that duck shooting in spring was prohibited by Federal law.

Many shore birds nest well within the Arctic Circle, and it is the opinion of ornithologists that most of these birds share, at least in part, the habits of the phalaropes, a family in which the male assumes the entire care of the eggs and young. If this be true, it explains why in southern latitudes so many of the earliest fall arrivals are females that may have deserted the breeding grounds after the eggs were laid.

Migratory flights are frequently accomplished in close-flock formation, as with the shore birds, blackbirds, waxwings, and especially some of the sparrows—the snow buntings, longspurs, juncos, and tree sparrows.

Other species, however, though they travel in flocks, maintain a very loose formation; examples are the turkey vultures, the hawks, swifts, blue jays, swallows, warblers, and bluebirds.

TRANSCONTINENTAL MIGRANTS

Still others, the grebes, great horned owls, winter wrens, shrikes, and belted kingfishers, ordinarily travel alone. When several are found in proximity they have been drawn together by unusual conditions, such as abundant food.

A COOT STANDS BY ITS NEST IN A MONTANA MARSH

But it might have been photographed equally well in California or New Jersey, for marsh life is
remarkably uniform the country over.

The length and the duration of the migratory journey vary greatly. The bobwhite and the western quails, the cardinal, the Carolina wren, and probably some of the titmice and woodpeckers, may round out their existence without going more than ten miles from the nest where they were hatched.

Also song sparrows, meadowlarks, blue jays, and some other species make such short migrations that the movement is difficult to detect.

Eventually it may be possible to say definitely just how far the song sparrows that nest in northern New England and the Maritime Provinces of Canada travel to their winter quarters, and whether the blue jays of New York and the upper Mississippi Valley remain throughout the winter in their breeding areas, or move farther south and relinquish their places to individuals from southern Canada.

The robin is found in the Middle Atlantic States throughout the year, in Canada only in summer, and along the Gulf coast only as a winter resident.

On the Atlantic coast its movements are readily ascertained. For example, in the country about Washington, D. C., the breeding robin is the southern variety, found there from the first of April to the last of October, when its place is taken, in smaller numbers, by the northern robin, which arrives about the middle of October and remains until the following April.

It is probable that a similar interchange of individual robins occurs in the rest of its range, the hardy birds from the north being the winter tenants in the abandoned summer homes of the southern birds.

The red-winged blackbirds that nest in northern Texas are almost sedentary, but in winter they are joined by representatives of other subspecies that nest as far north as the Mackenzie Valley.

The difference in characters between subspecies has been used to discover other interesting facts concerning variations of migratory flight between closely related birds that breed in different latitudes.

The familiar eastern fox sparrow, for example, breeds from northwestern Alaska to Labrador, and in winter is found concentrated in the southeastern part of the United States. It thus travels a long distance each year.

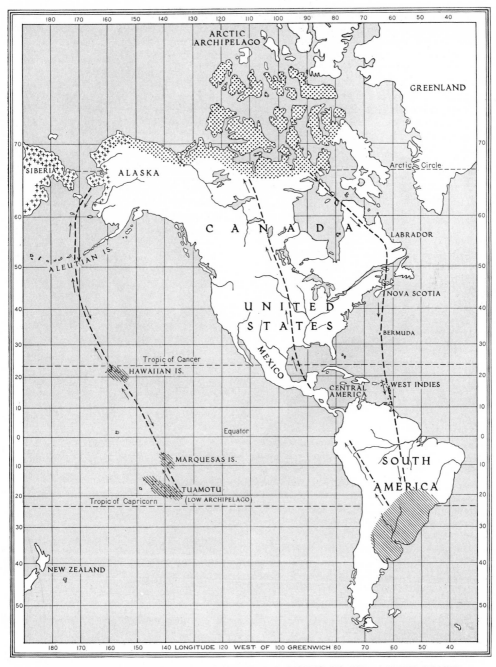

LONG AIRWAYS JOIN SUMMER AND WINTER HOMES OF THE GOLDEN PLOVER

Adults of the eastern form (*Pluvialis dominica dominica*) migrate across northeastern Canada and then by a nonstop flight of 2,400 miles reach South America (page 334). They return by way of the Mississippi Valley. Since all birds of this species travel both day and night, their entire route makes an ellipse with a major axis of 8,000 miles and a minor of 2,000. The Pacific variety (*P. d. fulva*), which breeds in Alaska, apparently wings without pause 2,000 miles across the ocean to the Hawaiian Islands, thence to the Marquesas Islands and the Tuamotus, and returns in spring over the same course (see page 343). A golden plover, found with a broken leg on Laysan Island, of the Hawaiian group, was cared for by the lighthouse keeper, who amputated the leg and later released the bird. Dubbed old "Stump-leg," it returned every fall and departed as regularly every spring for five years.

On the west coast of the continent, however, six subspecies of this bird breed in rather sharply delimited ranges, extending from the region of Puget Sound and Vancouver Island to Unimak Island, at the end of the Alaska Peninsula.

One of these, known as the sooty fox sparrow, breeds in the Puget Sound area and makes practically no migration at all, while the other races, nesting on the coast of British Columbia and Alaska, are found in winter chiefly in California.

BIRDS THAT BREED FARTHEST NORTH WINTER FARTHEST SOUTH

The forms that breed farthest north are in winter found farthest south, illustrating a tendency for those birds that are forced to migrate to pass over those so favorably located that they have no need to leave their breeding areas, while the northern birds settle for the winter in the unoccupied areas farther south.

Maryland yellow-throats of the Atlantic coast occupying the most southern part of the general range are almost nonmigratory, residing throughout the year in Florida. Those breeding as far north as Newfoundland go to the West Indies for the winter, thus passing directly over the home of their southern relatives.

The palm warbler, which breeds from Nova Scotia and Maine west and northwest to southern Mackenzie, has been separated into two subspecies. Those breeding in the interior of Canada make a 3,000-mile journey from Great Slave Lake to Cuba, passing through the Gulf States early in October.

After most of this form have passed, the palm warblers from the Northeastern States and Provinces drift slowly into the Gulf coast region, where they remain for the winter. Their migratory journey is about half as long as that of the northwestern subspecies.

Some other species that have extensive summer ranges, for instance, the pine warbler, rock wren, field sparrow, loggerhead shrike, and black-headed grosbeak, are found to concentrate during the winter season in the southern part of the breeding range, or to occupy additional territory only a short distance farther south.

The entire species may thus be confined within a restricted area for the winter, and then, with the return of warmer weather, spread out to reoccupy the full range.

There are many species, including the tree sparrow, slate-colored junco, and Lapland longspur, that nest in Canada and winter in the United States; while others, including the vesper sparrow, chipping sparrow, grackles, red-winged blackbird, bluebird, the woodcock, and several species of ducks, nest in the northern United States and move south for the winter to areas along the Gulf of Mexico.

This list includes the more hardy species, some individuals of which may linger in protected places well within the reach of severe cold, as, for example, Wilson's snipe, or jacksnipe, which I have frequently found during subzero weather in parts of the Rocky Mountain region where warm springs assured a food supply.

More than 100 of our summer birds leave the United States entirely and pass the winter in the West Indies, in Central America, or in South America. For example, the Cape May warbler, which breeds from northern New England, northern Michigan, and northern Minnesota north to New Brunswick, Nova Scotia, and nearly to Great Slave Lake, is concentrated in winter chiefly in the West Indies, its metropolis at this season being the island of Hispaniola.

SOME MARATHON MIGRATIONS

Some of the common summer residents are not content with a trip to northern South America, but push on across the Equator and finally come to rest for the winter in the pampa region of Argentina, or even in Patagonia. Thus some species that are more or less associated with each other in summer, as nighthawks, barn swallows, cliff swallows, and some of the thrushes, may also occupy the same general winter quarters in Brazil.

Some individual nighthawks and barn swallows travel still farther, and of all North American land birds these species probably have the longest migration route, since they occur north to Yukon and Alaska, and south to Argentina, 7,000 miles away.

THE CHAMPION "GLOBE-TROTTERS"

Such seasonal flights are exceeded in length, however, by the journeys of several species of water birds, chiefly members of the suborder of shore birds. In this group there are 19 species that breed north of the Arctic Circle and winter in South America,

BOBOLINKS MIGRATE OVER AN UNBROKEN STRETCH OF OCEAN

In crossing to South America most of this species fly directly from Jamaica to their winter home, adhering to ancestral flyways. Even the colonies of the birds that have established themselves in the western United States show no tendency to take the short cut across Arizona, New Mexico, and Texas (pages 337 and 345).

six of them going as far south as Patagonia, traveling each year over a migration route of more than 8,000 miles.

The Arctic tern is the champion "globe-trotter" and long-distance flyer. Its name "Arctic" is well earned, as its breeding range is circumpolar and it nests as far north as it can find a suitable place.

The first nest to be found in this region was only 7½° from the North Pole, and it contained a downy chick surrounded by a wall of newly fallen snow that had been scooped out by the parent. In North America the bird breeds south in the interior to

Great Slave Lake, and on the Atlantic coast to Massachusetts (map, page 315).

After the young are grown, the Arctic terns disappear from their North American breeding grounds, and a few months later arrive in the Antarctic region, 11,000 miles away. Until recently their route was a mystery. Although a few scattered individuals have been noted south as far as Long Island, the species otherwise is practically unknown along the Atlantic coasts of North and South America. It is, however, known as a migrant on the west coast of Europe and Africa.

By numbered bands the picture now is developing of what apparently is the longest and one of the most remarkable of all migratory journeys. The evidence consists of only three definite cases. All three birds were banded as downy chicks, one on July 3, 1913, at Eastern Egg Rock, Maine,* and the other two at the Red Islands, Turnevik Bay, Labrador, on July 22, 1927, and July 23, 1928.

The first was found dead in the Niger River Delta, West Africa, in August, 1917, while the Labrador birds were recovered near La Rochelle, France, on October 1, 1927, and at Margate, near Port Shepstone, Natal, South Africa, on November 14, 1928.

The flight shown by the last record is the longest known. The trip, between 8,000 and 9,000 miles, was accomplished in less than three months and for a bird not more than three months old is a truly remarkable record.

Thus it seems likely that the Arctic terns of eastern North America originally found their way here from the Old World, probably by way of Iceland and Greenland. Consequently, when the time comes for them to migrate to winter quarters they do not go directly south, as do the common and Forster's terns, but fly back eastward along their ancestral route across the Atlantic to the shores of Europe, and then go south along the African coast to their winter home.

It seems likely that those nesting in the northwestern part of the continent, as in Alaska, migrate chiefly down the western coast, for the species is not infrequently reported on the coast of California and also on the western coast of South America.

SUN SELDOM SETS ON THE ARCTIC TERNS

Probably no other animal in the world enjoys so many hours of daylight as does the Arctic tern. For these birds the sun never sets during their nesting season in the northern part of the range, and during their sojourn in the south daylight is continuous. During several months of the year they have 24 hours of daylight and during the other months considerably more daylight than darkness.

The term "migration route" is concerned with the lines of general advance or retreat of a species, rather than the exact course

* Recorded at the time of banding as a common tern, a natural error, as the downy young of common and Arctic terns look almost exactly alike.

followed by individual birds. Even the records of banded birds usually show no more than the places of banding and recovery. One must have recourse to intermediate records and to reasoning from probabilities to fill in details of the course.

The choice of migration highways is so wide that it seems as if the routes of no two species coincide. Differences in distance traveled, in time of starting, in speed of flight, in geographical position, in latitudes of breeding and of wintering grounds, and in other factors, all contribute to this wide variation of migration routes.

Nevertheless, certain factors serve to guide the avian travelers along more or less definite lines, and it is possible to define general lines of migration for the majority of species.

Bird migration is generally thought of as a north-and-south movement, with the lanes of heavier concentration following the coasts, mountain ranges, and principal river valleys. To a considerable extent this is true, particularly in North America, where those natural features in general run north and south. Students of American birds thus have exceptionally good opportunities to study migratory movements.

Where the migration is long, however, many species seem to disregard utterly such apparently good natural lanes of travel as river valleys.

For example, the Arkansas River has a general east and west course for most of its length, and while it does constitute a highway for many perching birds en route from the Mississippi Valley to the Rocky Mountain region, some of the hawks and many ducks and shore birds pay the valley scant attention. They may arrest their fall journey to feed among the cottonwoods or along the sand bars, but when ready to resume their flight they leave the river and fly directly south over the more or less arid region that lies between the Arkansas and the Rio Grande.

WIDE AND NARROW MIGRATION LANES

When birds start their southward migration, the movement necessarily involves the full width of the breeding range. Later, there is a convergence of the lines of flight taken by individual birds, because of the conformation of the land mass, and as the species proceeds southward the width of the occupied region becomes less and less.

The common kingbird breeds from New-

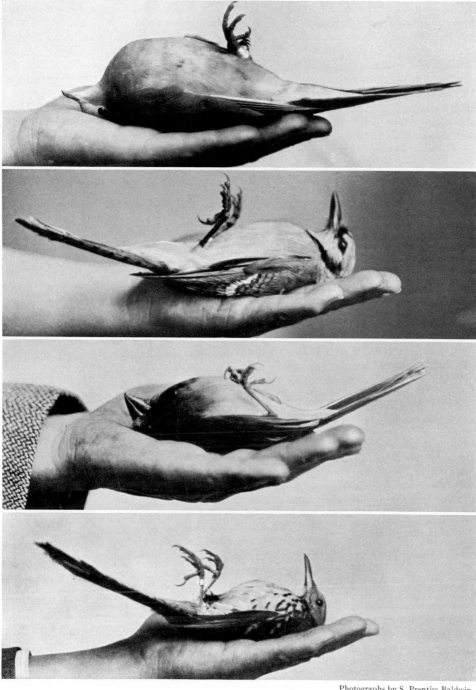

Photographs by S. Prentiss Baldwin

HYPNOTIZED, OR JUST "PLAYIN' POSSUM"?

When held in the hand for a short time and then turned over on their backs, birds appear to be affected hypnotically. Practically all species react similarly, but some are slower than others in becoming quiescent. They remain quite rigid for from a few seconds to several minutes and then dart away. From top to bottom, the birds shown here are a mourning dove, blue jay, cardinal, and brown thrasher.

foundland to British Columbia, a summer range 2,800 miles wide. On migration, however, its paths converge, until in the southern part of the United States the occupied area extends from Florida to the mouth of the Rio Grande, only 900 miles, and still farther south the migration path is further restricted.

In the latitude of Yucatán it is not more than 400 miles wide, and the great bulk of the species probably moves in a belt less than half that width.

Whatever main routes are described, there also remain a multitude of tributary and separate minor routes. In fact, with the entire Continent of North America crossed by migratory birds, the different groups of species frequently follow lines that may repeatedly intersect those taken by others of their own kind or by other species. The arterial routes, therefore, merely indicate paths of migration on which there is tendency to concentrate.

Certain species, such as the knot and the purple sandpiper, normally found only along the coasts, must have extremely narrow routes of travel. They are limited on one side by the broad waters of the ocean and on the other by land and fresh water, both of which are unsuited to furnish the food desired.

The Ipswich sparrow has probably the most restricted migration range of all land species. It is known to breed only on Sable Island, Nova Scotia, and it winters along the Atlantic coast south to Georgia.

Living constantly within sound of the surf, it is rarely more than a quarter of a mile from the outer beach, and is at home among the sand dunes and their sparse covering of coarse grass.

Harris's sparrow is known to breed only in the region from Churchill, on the west shore of Hudson Bay, northwest to the shores of Great Bear Lake. Few actual breeding records of the species are available, but these indicate that the breeding range is in the strip of stunted timber country just south of the tree limit.

When it begins its fall migration, this bird necessarily covers the full width of its breeding area. Then it proceeds almost directly south, or slightly southeasterly, the area becoming gradually constricted. By the time it reaches the United States it is most numerous in a belt about 500 miles wide, extending across North Dakota to central Minnesota.

Harris's sparrows are noted on migration with fair regularity east to the western shore of Lake Michigan, and west to the foothills of the Rocky Mountains, but the bulk of the species moves north and south through a relatively narrow path in the central continent.

This narrow migration range probably is determined by the close association Harris's sparrow maintains with a habitat which includes brushy places, thickets, edges of groves, and weed patches.

The winter range extends from southeastern Nebraska and northwestern Missouri, across eastern Kansas and Oklahoma, and through a narrow section of central Texas, at places hardly more than 150 miles wide.

THROUGH A 100-MILE "DOOR"

The scarlet tanager follows another narrow migration route, its breeding range extending in greatest width from New Brunswick to Saskatchewan, about 1,900 miles. As the birds move southward in fall, their path becomes more and more constricted, until at the time they leave the United States all are included in the 600-mile belt from eastern Texas to the Florida Peninsula.

Continuing to converge through Honduras and Costa Rica, the boundaries there are not more than 100 miles apart. The species winters in northwestern South America, where it spreads out over most of Colombia, Ecuador, and Peru (page 320).

The rose-breasted grosbeak also leaves the United States through the 700-mile stretch from eastern Texas to Apalachicola Bay, but thereafter the lines do not further converge, since this grosbeak enters the northern part of its winter quarters in Central America and South America through a door of about the same width (page 322).

The cases cited represent extremes of convergence, but a narrowing of the migratory path is the rule for the majority of North American birds. The shape of the continent tends to affect this, and so the width of the migration route in the latitude of the Gulf of Mexico is usually much less than in the breeding territory.

FOUR FLYWAY SYSTEMS

The redstart represents a wide migration route, although even in the southern United States this is much narrower than the breeding range. These birds, however, cross all parts of the Gulf of Mexico and pass from Florida to Cuba and Haiti by

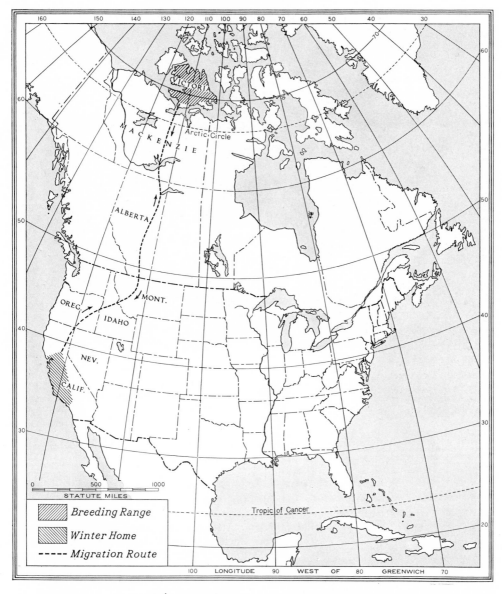

ROSS'S GOOSE FOLLOWS A UNIQUE ROUTE

This is the only species of which all members apparently breed in the Arctic regions, migrate south through the Mackenzie Valley, and upon reaching the United States turn to the southwest rather than the southeast. The southern part of this line of travel, however, is followed by some mallards, pintails, baldpates, and possibly other ducks.

way of the Bahamas, so that here their route has a width of about 2,500 miles.

Four great flyway systems cover practically the entire width of the North American Continent and extend from the Arctic coast to Patagonia.

By reference to map, page 324, it will be noted that route Number 1 is almost entirely oceanic, passing directly over the Atlantic Ocean from Labrador and Nova Scotia to the Lesser Antilles, and then through this group of small islands to the mainland of South America.* It is not used by any

* Discussion of the principal routes of North American birds relates chiefly to the fall migration, for, except as otherwise noted, the spring flight generally retraces the same course. The routes indicated on the maps must not be considered as representing paths with clearly defined borders, but rather as convenient subdivisions of the four great flyway systems.

Photograph by Arthur A. Allen

"THIS CAPS THE CLIMAX," SAID THE KILLDEER

To obtain this unique photograph, Professor Allen placed his head covering over the bird's eggs. The picture was taken at Ithaca, New York; but since the species nests from Hudson Bay to Florida and from Massachusetts to California, a similar snapshot would be possible almost anywhere in the country.

of the smaller land birds, but is followed chiefly by thousands of water birds and by shore birds of several species, the adult golden plover being a notable example.

This overseas route is definitely known only at its terminals and from occasional observations made at Bermuda and other islands in its course. Some of the shore birds that breed on the Arctic tundras of Mackenzie and in Alaska fly southeastward across Canada to the Atlantic coast and follow the oceanic route to the mainland of South America.

THE GOLDEN PLOVER'S ROUTE

The golden plover, flying day and night, may accomplish the entire 2,400 miles without pause; in fair weather the flocks pass Bermuda and sometimes even the islands of the Antilles without stopping. Since the bird swims lightly and easily, it may make a few short halts along the way; it has even been seen resting on the ocean.

Other shore birds have been observed busily feeding in that vast area of ocean known as the Sargasso Sea, where thou-

sands of square miles of floating seaweed teem with marine life.

The annual flight of the adult golden plover is remarkable. It is an exception to the general rule that spring and fall movements are over the same routes.

After reaching the South American coast the birds halt briefly, then continue overland to the pampa region of Argentina, where they remain from September to March.

Leaving their winter quarters, they cross northwestern South America and the Gulf of Mexico, and reach the North American mainland on the coasts of Texas and Louisiana. Thence they proceed slowly up the Mississippi Valley, and by early June are again on their breeding grounds, having performed an elliptical round-trip journey with the minor axis about 2,000 miles, and the major axis 8,000 miles, extending from the Arctic tundras to the pampa region of Argentina (map, page 327).

The older birds probably are accompanied by some of the young, perhaps those from early nestings, but most of the immatures leave their natal grounds late in summer and move southward through the interior of the country. They return in spring over essentially the same course.

THE ATLANTIC COAST ROUTE

About 50 different kinds of land birds that breed in New England follow the Atlantic coast southward to Florida and travel thence by island and mainland to South America.

A seemingly natural and convenient highway extends through the Bahamas, Cuba, Hispaniola, Puerto Rico, and the Lesser Antilles to the South American coast (map, p. 324). Resting places are afforded at convenient intervals, and at no time need the aerial travelers be out of sight of land.

It is not, however, the favored highway. Only about 25 species go beyond Cuba to Puerto Rico along this route to their winter quarters, while only six species are known to reach South America by way of the Lesser Antilles. The obvious drawback is lack of adequate food.

The total area of all the West Indies east of Puerto Rico is slightly more than that of Delaware. If even a small part of the birds of the eastern United States were to travel that way, it is doubtful whether the luxuriant tropical flora and fauna would provide sufficient food.

THE TRAVELS OF CANVASBACKS, REDHEADS, AND MALLARDS

The Atlantic flyway receives accretions of waterfowl from three or four interior migration paths, one of first importance, since it includes large flocks of canvasbacks, redheads, scaup ducks, Canada geese, and many of the black ducks that winter in the waters and marshes of the coastal region south of Delaware Bay.

The canvasbacks, redheads, and scaups come from their breeding grounds on the great northern plains of central Canada, follow the general southeasterly trend of the Great Lakes, cross Pennsylvania over the mountains, and reach the Atlantic coast in the vicinity of Delaware and Chesapeake Bays.

Black ducks, mallards, and blue-winged teal that have gathered in southern Ontario during the fall leave these feeding grounds and proceed southwest, apparently headed for the Mississippi Valley. Many do continue this route down the Ohio Valley, but others, upon reaching the vicinity of Lake St. Clair, between Michigan and

Ontario, swing abruptly southeast and, crossing the mountains in a single flight, reach the Atlantic coast south of New Jersey.

The white-winged scoter, which also breeds in the interior country from northern North Dakota north to the Arctic coast, is another bird having an elliptical migration route. This duck breeds near fresh water and winters entirely on the ocean along both the Atlantic and Pacific coasts of the United States (page 343).

Those wintering on the Atlantic side leave their breeding grounds west of Hudson Bay and fly 1,500 miles almost due east to the easternmost part of Labrador, whence they proceed southward across the Gulf of St. Lawrence to their winter home, which extends from southwestern Maine to Chesapeake Bay. The return flight in spring is made by an interior route that traverses the valleys of the Connecticut, Hudson, and Ottawa Rivers, and thence passes west and north to the breeding grounds.

A study of the Canada geese that winter abundantly in the waters of Back Bay, Virginia, and Currituck Sound, North Carolina, reveals another important tributary to the Atlantic coast route. The principal breeding grounds of these birds are among the islands and on the eastern shores of Hudson Bay. From this region they move south in the fall to the point of lower Ontario between Lakes Erie and Huron. Some of the banded geese are recovered in the Mississippi Valley, but the great majority are retaken either on their breeding grounds or on the Atlantic coast south of Delaware Bay—another instance of a long cross-country flight by waterfowl.

Although migrating Canada geese are abundant on the coast of New England, birds taken there do not include any banded in southern Ontario. New England visitants come from other breeding areas, chiefly Newfoundland and the coast of Labrador, and their migration is entirely coastwise.

THE "BOBOLINK ROUTE"

While not yet well understood, a hitherto unsuspected migration route across the Alleghenies to the Mississippi Valley has been revealed by the banding of blue-winged teal on the coastal saw-grass marshes of South Carolina. Birds marked there have been retaken in Tennessee and Kentucky as well as in States farther north in the Mississippi Valley.

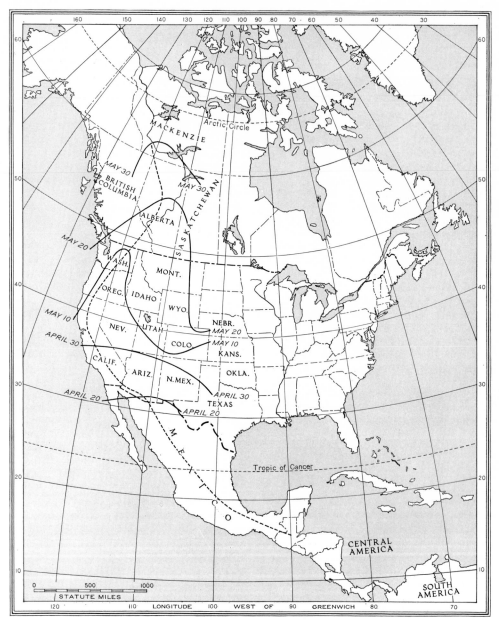

WESTERN TANAGERS CLING TO THE PACIFIC COAST MOST OF THE WAY TO
BREEDING GROUNDS

The birds that arrive in eastern Alberta by May 20 do not travel along the eastern base of the
Rocky Mountains, for in that region the van has then only reached northern Colorado. Instead, the
isochronal lines indicate that they migrate through California, Oregon, and Washington, and do not
cross the mountains until they are in British Columbia (page 343).

Route Number 3 (page 324) presents a much more direct line of flight for the Atlantic coast migrants to South America than the others, although it involves much longer flights. It is used almost entirely by land birds.

After taking off from the coast of Florida, the migrants find only two land masses on the way. Nevertheless, tens of thousands of birds of some 60 species cross the 150 miles from Florida to Cuba, where about half of them elect to remain for the winter.

The others fly the 90 miles between Cuba and Jamaica.

From that point to the South American coast, however, there is a stretch of unbroken ocean fully 500 miles across, and scarcely a third of the North American migrants leave the forested mountains of Jamaica to risk the perils of this ocean trip.

Chief among those that do is the bobolink, which so far outnumbers all other birds using this flyway that it may well be called the "bobolink route." Along this route the bobolinks may meet vireos, kingbirds, and nighthawks from Florida; the chuck-will's-widow of the Southeastern States; black-billed and yellow-billed cuckoos from New England; gray-cheeked thrushes from Quebec, bank swallows from Labrador; and black-poll warblers from Alaska (p. 329).

Sometimes this scattered assemblage will be joined by a tanager or a wood thrush.

FROM ALASKA TO PATAGONIA

Easily the longest flyway in the Western Hemisphere is that from the Mackenzie Valley past the Great Lakes and down the Mississippi River, including its tributaries. Its northern terminus is on the Arctic coast in the regions of Kotzebue Sound, Alaska, and the mouth of the Mackenzie River, while its southern end lies in Patagonia.

During the spring migration some shore birds traverse the full extent of this long path, and it seems likely that the nighthawk, the barn swallow, the black-poll warbler, and individuals of several other species that breed north to Yukon and Alaska must twice each year cover the larger part of it.

For more than 3,000 miles—from the mouth of the Mackenzie to the Delta of the Mississippi—this flyway is uninterrupted by mountains. In fact, there is not even a ridge of hills on the route high enough to interfere with the movements of the feathered travelers, and the greatest elevation above sea level is less than 2,000 feet. Well timbered and watered, the entire region affords ideal conditions for the support of its hosts of migrating birds.

THE WORLD'S BIGGEST BIRD BOULEVARD

Over it fly such vast numbers of ducks, geese, shore birds, blackbirds, sparrows, warblers, and thrushes that observers stationed at favorable points in the Mississippi Valley—such as Keokuk, Iowa; Blue Island, Illinois, and the vicinity of Madison,

Wisconsin—during the height of migration can see more species and individuals than can be noted anywhere else in the world.

Starting in the region of Kotzebue Sound, the route extends eastward across northern Alaska and joins another that has its origin at the mouth of the Mackenzie River. The line of flight then trends a little east of south through the great lake system of central Canada, where it is joined by two or three other routes from the northeast that have their origin on the central Arctic coast.

Continuing southward, the migrating flocks are constantly augmented as they pass over the extensive breeding grounds of central and southern Canada. Upon reaching the headwaters of the Missouri and Mississippi Rivers the route follows these streams to the Gulf coast.

Arriving in this latitude, many species, including ducks and geese, the robin, the myrtle warbler, and some others spread out east and west for their winter sojourn. Others, despite the perils of a flight of several hundred miles across the Gulf of Mexico, strike out boldly for Central America and South America. This part of the route is a broad "boulevard" extending from northwestern Florida to eastern Texas and reaching southward across the Gulf of Mexico to Yucatán and the Isthmus of Tehuantepec.

Many birds that breed east of the Allegheny Mountains parallel the seacoast as they move southwestward in fall, and, apparently maintaining the same direction from northwestern Florida, cross the Gulf to the coastal regions of eastern Mexico. Birds that have come directly through the Mississippi Valley and the region west to the Rocky Mountains reach the coastal plains of Mississippi, Louisiana, and Texas, and continue directly across the Gulf.

During the height of the migration the winged travelers fairly swarm over some islands off the coasts of Louisiana and Texas.

THE NORTH-SOUTH TRUNK LINE

One short cut that may be considered a part of this water artery of migration extends a few hundred miles from the coast of Texas to the northern part of the State of Vera Cruz. Since the neighboring coast is arid and thus entirely unsuited to the needs of moist-woodlands birds, it is not surprising to find this Gulf route used by such species as the golden-winged warbler,

Photograph by H. L. Stoddard

NOT MEMBERS OF A BUTTERFLY BALLET; JUST HUNTERS TRYING TO CATCH BIRDS FOR BANDING

Bamboo rods rise from sockets in the operator's belt and spread the clap net. When robins or blackbirds are flushed from their roosts and fly into the trap, the hunter sweeps the two side rods forward like a pair of wings, closing the net on the captives.

THE CLARK'S CROW, OR NUTCRACKER, GETS HIS CLIMATIC CHANGES BY MOVING UP THE MOUNTAIN

His migration is vertical, a few hundred feet of altitude being equivalent to hundreds of miles of latitude (see text, page 345). Many a trapper inveighs against these mischievous pilferers when they steal his food, but sometimes, as here, they earn their board by neatly and completely cleaning surplus fat and flesh from pelts.

Photograph by George A. Lewis

AN UNWELCOME GIFT

A cowbird has dropped its large egg in a redstart's nest (see opposite page).

the worm-eating warbler, and the Kentucky warbler.

A second route that joins the main artery on its eastern side is used by the blue goose, which flies more nearly due north and south than any other North American bird. The breeding grounds, recently discovered, are in the Foxe Basin region of Baffin Island and on Southampton Island.

In fall these geese work southward, chiefly along the eastern shore of Hudson Bay, and upon reaching the southern extremity of James Bay, they take off for a practically nonstop flight to the great coastal marshes of Louisiana west of the Mississippi Delta.

In some seasons the flocks make intermediate stops among the islands and sand bars of the Mississippi; they are occasionally common in the general vicinity of Memphis, Tennessee. Most of the birds push on, however, and from the first of November to the last of March fully 90 per cent of the species are concentrated between the Sabine and the Mississippi Rivers.

On the return trip northward some blue geese veer off toward the northwest, and they are occasionally abundant in eastern South Dakota and southeastern Manitoba.

While some geese and many ducks start northward at the first sign of spring, the blue goose remains in its winter quarters until the season there is far advanced, seemingly aware that its own breeding grounds in the Arctic are still in the grip of winter.

A GREAT WESTERN ROUTE

A great western highway also has its origin in the Mackenzie River Delta area and in Alaska. This is used chiefly by the pintail and the baldpate, which fly southward through eastern Alberta to western Montana. Some localities—for example the Flathead Valley, Montana—normally furnish enough food to induce these birds to pause in their migratory movement. (See map, Flyways of North America.)

Upon resuming travel, some flocks move almost directly west across Idaho to the valley of the Columbia River, from which they turn abruptly south to the interior valleys of California. Others leave the Montana feeding and resting areas and turn southeastward across Wyoming and Nebraska either to join the flocks that are moving southward through the Great Plains, or to continue across Arkansas to the main Mississippi Valley flyway.

Photograph by Arthur A. Allen

AN UNWELCOME GUEST USURPS ITS HOST'S HOME

The young cowbird fills the nest; the young redstarts have been starved or crowded out. It is strange that the cowbird, which is notorious for foisting the incubation and care of its young on other species, should be passionately devoted to its home territory (page 320).

Many redheads that breed in the Bear River Marshes in Utah take a westerly route across Nevada to California, but some leave these breeding grounds and fly northeastward across North Dakota and Minnesota to join the flocks of these ducks that come out of the prairie regions of Canada, and travel southeastward to the Atlantic coast. This route is well traced by records of ducks banded in summer in the Bear River Marshes and retaken the following fall in eastern Montana, Wyoming, South Dakota, North Dakota, Minnesota, Wisconsin, Michigan, and Maryland.

Another route from these great marshes crosses the mountains in an easterly direction, but almost immediately turns southward through Colorado and New Mexico, and continues to winter quarters in the Valley of Mexico. This route also represents the travels of many of the land birds of the Rocky Mountain region. Such birds perform comparatively short migrations, most of them being content to stop when they reach the middle districts of Mexico. Only a few pass east beyond the southern part of that country.

Because of equable conditions, many species of birds along the Pacific coast from the Northwestern States to southern Alaska either do not migrate at all or else make relatively short journeys. This route has its origin chiefly in Alaska, the general region of the Delta of the Yukon River marking its northern terminus, although a few species join it after a flight westward along the Alaskan Arctic coast.

Some of the scoters and other sea ducks of the North Pacific region, and the diminutive cackling goose, which breeds in the Delta of the Yukon River, use the coastal sea route for all or most of their southward flight.

The journey of the cackling geese has been traced southward across the Alaska Peninsula and apparently across the Gulf of Alaska to the Queen Charlotte Islands, the birds following the coast line south to near the mouth of the Columbia River. There the route swings toward the interior for a short distance before continuing south by way of the Willamette River Valley. The winter quarters of the cackling geese are chiefly in the vicinity of Tule Lake, near

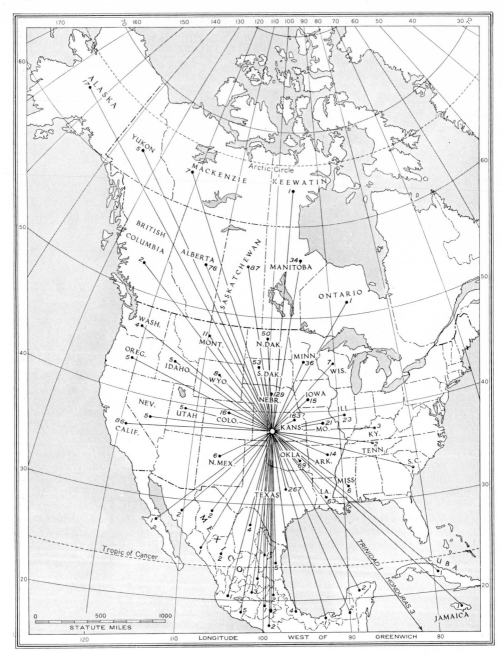

LIKE WHEEL SPOKES GO OUT ROUTES OF DUCKS BANDED IN KANSAS

Ducks banded at Cheyenne Bottoms, Kansas, close to the 100th meridian, disperse to all quarters of the compass; but the birds that are banded east or west of this meridian rarely cross it (see map, page 344).

the Oregon-California line, and in the Sacramento Valley of California, though a few birds push on to the San Joaquin Valley.

The route taken by the white-winged scoters that winter on the Atlantic coast already has been indicated (page 335). Some birds of this species, however, winter on the Pacific coast from Puget Sound south to southern California. Their passage by thousands up and down the coast has been noted as far north as northwestern British Columbia. The species is known to nest in Alaska, which may be the home of some of the scoters that winter on the Pacific coast.

If such be the case, however, a part of the route taken by the birds when on migration is unknown. Very few observations are available from the interior of northern British Columbia, across which the route may lie.

The southward route of those migratory land birds of the Pacific coast that in winter leave the United States extends chiefly through the interior of California to the mouth of the Colorado River and on to winter quarters in western Mexico.

The western tanager breeds in the mountains from the northern part of Baja California and western Texas north to northeastern British Columbia and southwestern Mackenzie. Its winter range is in two discontinuous areas—southern Baja California and eastern Mexico south to Guatemala (map, page 336).

On the spring migration the birds enter the United States about April 20, appearing first in western Texas and the southern parts of New Mexico and Arizona. By April 30 the van has advanced evenly to an approximate east-and-west line across central New Mexico, Arizona, and southern California. But by May 10 the easternmost birds have advanced only to southern Colorado, while those in the Far West have reached northern Washington.

THE ROUTE OF THE PACIFIC GOLDEN PLOVER IS AS REMARKABLE AS THAT OF ITS EASTERN COUSIN

Ten days later the northward advance of the species is shown as a wide curve, extending northeastward from Vancouver Island to central Alberta and thence southeastward to northern Colorado. Since these tanagers do not reach northern Colorado until May 20, it is evident that those present in Alberta on that date, instead of traveling northward through the Rocky Mountains, reached there by the Pacific coast route to southern British Columbia, and thence across the mountains, still partly snow covered.

The route of the Pacific golden plover *(Pluvialis dominica fulva)* is fully as remarkable as the elliptical course followed by its eastern cousin *(P. d. dominica)* (page 327).

The breeding range of the eastern golden plover extends through Arctic America west to the northern coast of Alaska, where, in the vicinity of Point Barrow, it meets the nesting grounds of the Pacific form, really an Asiatic subspecies. It breeds chiefly in the Arctic coast region of Siberia and merely overflows upon the Alaskan coast, some of the birds probably migrating south along the coast of Asia to winter quarters in Japan, China, India, Australia, New Zealand, and Oceania, including the Hawaiian and Marquesas Islands, and the Low Archipelago, or Tuamotus.

Golden plovers in migration have been observed at sea on a line that apparently extends from these islands to the Aleutians, and it therefore appears certain that at least some of the Alaskan birds make a nonstop flight of 2,000 miles across a landless sea from Alaska to Hawaii.

While it seems incredible that any birds could lay a course so straight as to attain these mid-Pacific islands, the evidence proves that year after year this transoceanic round-trip journey between Alaska and Hawaii is made by considerable numbers of golden plovers.

The Pacific oceanic route probably is used also by the Arctic terns that breed in Alaska, and possibly by those from the more western tern colonies of Canada. This species occurs regularly on the western coasts of the United States and South America, indicating that the western representatives travel southward to the Antarctic winter quarters without the spectacular migration features that appear to characterize the flight of those from the eastern continent (map, page 315).

It seems likely that there are other species than the Arctic tern (page 329), including the parasitic jaeger, that regularly breed in the northern part of the Western Hemisphere but migrate back to the Old World for their winter sojourn. Others, such as the red-legged kittiwake and Ross's gull, remain near the Arctic region through-

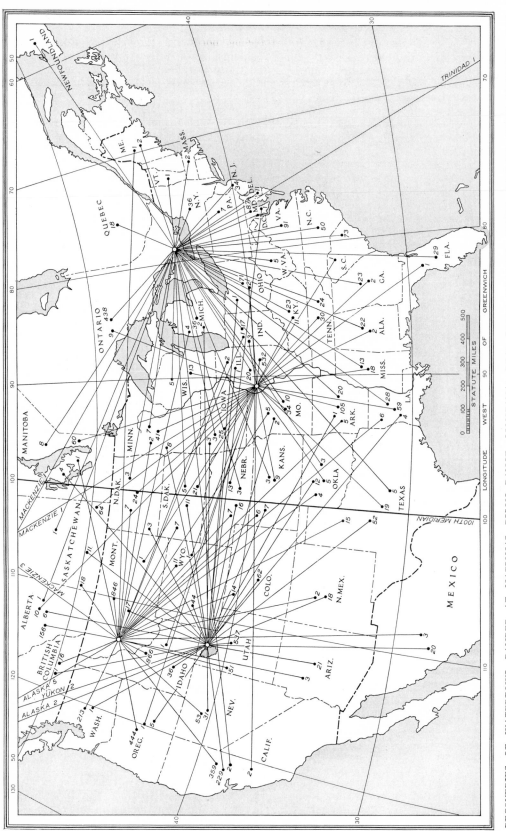

RECOVERIES OF WATERFOWL BANDED AT NATIONAL BISON RANGE, MONTANA; BEAR RIVER MARSHES, UTAH; ILLINOIS RIVER MARSHES, AND KINGSVILLE, ONTARIO, SHOW DIVISION OF THE FLYWAYS

During the migratory season there is little interchange of waterfowl between the East and West. On the breeding grounds in central Canada the eastern and western ducks intermingle freely, but when the time comes for migration they separate and each group adheres to its ancient course. The proof of this lies in the fact that very few ducks banded in the United States east of the 100th meridian are killed west of this line while in the United States, and vice versa (page 349).

out the year, retreating southward in winter only a few hundred miles.

The emperor goose in winter is found only a relatively short distance south of its breeding grounds, and eider ducks, although wintering in latitudes well south of the breeding gounds, nevertheless remain farther north than do the majority of other species of ducks. The routes followed by these birds are chiefly coastwise.

EASTERN BIRDS ARE EVER PUSHING THEIR COLONIES WESTWARD

The tendency is for eastern species to extend their ranges by pushing westward, particularly in the north. For example in the Stikine River Valley of northern British Columbia and southwestern Alaska the eastern nighthawk, eastern chipping sparrow, rusty blackbird, eastern yellow warbler, redstart, and others have established breeding stations at points 20 to 100 miles from the Pacific Ocean.

The robin, flicker, slate-colored junco, black-poll warbler, myrtle warbler, and oven-bird, all common eastern species, also are established as breeding birds in western Alaska, the oven-bird having been detected on the lower Yukon River.

These birds, however, do not migrate in fall by any of the Pacific routes, but retrace their journey across the mountains and move southward along the broad flyways of the interior.

The red-eyed vireo, a striking example of an abundant woodland bird, is essentially an inhabitant of States east of the Great Plains, but an arm of its breeding range extends northwest to the Pacific coast in British Columbia. It seems evident that this range extension has taken place comparatively recently by a westward movement from the upper Missouri Valley, and that the invaders retrace in spring and fall the general route by which they originally entered the country.

A new extension of the bobolink's breeding range, and a consequent change in the migration of the species, has taken place since the spread of settlement in this country. A bird of damp meadows, it was originally cut off from the Western States by the intervening arid regions. But with the advent of irrigation and the bringing of large areas under cultivation, small colonies of nesting bobolinks have appeared at several western points, and now the species is established as a regular breeder in the mountain parks and irrigated valleys of Colorado and elsewhere almost to the Pacific coast.

In retracing their course to reach the western edge of the southward route followed by the bulk of the bobolinks that breed in the northern United States and southern Canada, these western pioneers must fly long distances along a line that runs almost due east and west.

SOME BIRDS MIGRATE VERTICALLY

To find winter quarters many North American birds merely move down the sides of a mountain. In such cases a few hundred feet of altitude correspond to hundreds of miles of latitude. Such "vertical migrations" are found wherever there are large mountain ranges.

In the Rocky Mountain region chickadees, rosy finches, juncos, pine grosbeaks, and other species that nest in the Alpine Zone move down to the lower levels to pass the winter.

Such species as Williamson's sapsucker and the western wood pewee, which nest in the higher mountains, move down to the lower regions in August following the breeding season. At this time there is a distinct tendency also among the young of mountain-breeding birds to work down to the lower levels as soon as the nesting season is over. The sudden increases among birds in the edges of the foothills are particularly noticeable when cold spells with snow or frost occur at the higher altitudes.

Some species that normally breed in the Hudsonian or Arctic Zones find suitable breeding areas on the higher levels of the mountains. An example is the pipit, or titlark, which breeds on the tundras of Alaska and northern Canada and also south as far as Colorado on the summits of many peaks in the Rocky Mountains.

A few species, like the Clark's crow, or nutcracker, nest at relatively low altitudes in the mountains and as the summer advances move higher up, thus performing a vertical migration that in a sense is comparable with the post-breeding movements of herons on the Atlantic coast (page 339).

LONG WANDERINGS FOLLOW NESTING SEASON

The most striking feature of the migrations of some of the herons is a northward movement after the nesting season. These species commonly wander late in summer and in fall, sometimes traveling several hundred miles north of the district in which they were hatched.

The little blue heron usually breeds north to South Carolina, and by the last of July the young birds begin to appear along the Potomac, Patuxent, and Susquehanna Rivers, tributary to Chesapeake Bay. Although almost all are immature individuals, as shown by their white plumage, an occasional adult may be noted.

With them come American and snowy egrets, and on occasion all three species will travel in the east as far north as New England and the Maritime Provinces of Canada, and in the Mississippi Valley to southeastern Kansas and Illinois. In September most of them disappear, probably returning south by the same route.

The black-crowned night heron has similar wandering habits, and young birds banded in a large colony at Barnstable, Massachusetts, have been recaptured the same season north to Maine and Quebec and west to New York. This habit seems to be shared by some of the gulls. Herring gulls banded as chicks at colonies in the Great Lakes have scattered in all directions after the breeding season, some having been recovered well north in Canada.

These movements may be considered as migration governed only by the availability of food.

Snowy owls are noted for occasional invasions that probably are caused by a shortage of the lemmings and rabbits that constitute their normal food in the north. At least nine notable flights of these birds occurred from 1876 to 1927. In the flight of 1926-27 they were noted as far south as Iowa, Ohio, West Virginia, and North Carolina.

In the Rocky Mountain region flights of the beautiful Bohemian waxwing are occasionally recorded. The greatest invasion in the history of Colorado ornithology occurred in February, 1917, at which time I estimated that at least 10,000 were within the corporate limits of the city of Denver. The last previous occurrence of the species in large numbers in that section was in 1908.

Evening grosbeaks likewise are given to performing more or less wandering journeys, and curiously enough, in addition to occasional trips south of their regular range, they travel east and west, sometimes

for long distances. For example, grosbeaks banded at Sault Ste. Marie, Michigan, have been recaptured on Cape Cod, Massachusetts, and in the following season have been retrapped at the banding station. This east-and-west trip across the northeastern part of the country is sometimes made also by purple finches.

MANY VICTIMS OF STORMS

The period of migration is a season full of peril for birds. Untold thousands of the smaller migrants are destroyed each year by storms, in unfamiliar habitats, and through attacks of predatory birds, mammals, and reptiles. If each pair of adult birds should succeed in raising two fledglings to maturity, the population of migratory birds would have a potential annual increase of 100 per cent and the world would soon be heavily overpopulated with them. The annual mortality from natural causes is heavy enough to keep them in check.

Storms are the most potent factor in limiting the abundance of birds. Special sufferers are those birds that, crossing broad stretches of water, are forced by a storm down within reach of the waves. Such a catastrophe was once seen from the deck of a vessel in the Gulf of Mexico, 30 miles off the mouth of the Mississippi River. Large numbers of migrating birds, chiefly warblers, had accomplished nearly 95 per cent of their long flight and were nearing land when, caught by a norther, hundreds were drowned in the waters of the Gulf.

On Lake Michigan, a severe storm, coming up at a time when large numbers of migratory birds were crossing, forced numerous victims into the waves. In the fall migration of 1906, when thousands of birds were crossing Lake Huron, a sudden drop in temperature, accompanied by a heavy snowfall, killed incredible numbers. Literally thousands were forced into the water and subsequently cast up along the beaches, where in places their bodies were piled in windrows.

Most of them were species that rank among our most desirable birds as destroyers of insects and weed seeds. There were slate-colored juncos, tree sparrows, white-throated sparrows, swamp sparrows, winter wrens, and golden-crowned kinglets, together with many brown creepers, hermit thrushes, warblers, vireos, and others.

Of all species of North American birds,

A DECEIVER, THOUGH NOT A GAY ONE, IS THE KILLDEER

This bird near Ithaca, New York, is simulating decrepitude to lure Professor Allen away from its nest.

the Lapland longspur seems to be the most frequent victim of storms. These birds sometimes congregate in enormous numbers where grass or weed seed is abundant. Almost every winter brings in reports of their death by thousands somewhere in the Middle West. While migrating northward at night they have encountered blinding storms of wet, clinging snow, which have so bewildered them that they have flown into various obstructions, or have sunk to the ground and perished of exposure and exhaustion.

In 1907 an experienced ornithologist estimated that 750,000 longspurs were lying dead on the ice of two lakes in Minnesota, each about one square mile in extent, and dead birds were reported in greater or less abundance on this occasion over an area of more than 1,500 square miles.

The heaviest mortality occurred in towns, where, bewildered by the darkness and the heavy falling snow, some of the birds, congregating in great numbers, flew against obstacles and were killed or stunned, while many others fell to the ground exhausted.

During the early part of June, 1927, a hailstorm of exceptional severity around Denver, Colorado, killed large numbers of robins, meadowlarks, sparrows, and others. The lawns of parks were strewn with their bodies, and many lay dead in their nests where they had been covering their eggs or young when the storm broke.

HUMAN LIFESAVERS SOMETIMES ARE BIRD DESTROYERS

The destruction of migratory birds by their striking lighthouses, light ships, tall bridge piers, monuments, and other obstructions has been tremendous. Beams of lanterns at light stations have a powerful attraction for aerial travelers.

Especially when the atmosphere is moisture laden, as in a heavy fog, the rays have a dazzling effect that lures the birds to their death. They may fly straight up the beam and dash themselves headlong against the glass, or they may keep fluttering around the source of the light until exhausted, and then drop to the rocks or waves below.

The fixed, white, stationary light 180 feet above sea level at Ponce de Leon Inlet (formerly Mosquito Inlet), Florida, has caused heavy destruction of bird life even though the lens is shielded by wire netting. Once an observer gathered up a bushel-basketful of warblers, sparrows, and other small passerine birds that had struck during the night. The birds apparently beat themselves to death against the wire or fell exhausted to the pavement, frequently to be destroyed there by cats or skunks.

Two other lighthouses at the southern end of Florida, Sombrero Key and Fowey Rocks, have been the cause of many bird tragedies, and heavy mortality has been noted also at some of the lights on the Great Lakes and on the coast of Quebec.

It is the fixed white lights that cause such disasters to birds; the stations equipped with flashing or red lights do not present such strong attractions.

At some light stations in England and elsewhere, shelves and perches have been placed below the lanterns to afford places where birds can rest until they have overcome their bewilderment.

For many years at the National Capital, the Washington Monument, although unilluminated, caused the destruction of large numbers of small birds. One morning in the spring of 1902 the bodies of nearly 150 warblers, sparrows, and other birds were found about its base. Then, as the illumination of the city was improved and the Monument became more visible at night, the loss became steadily less, until by 1920 only a few birds would be killed during the entire migration.

On November 11, 1931, however, as part of the Armistice Day celebration, batteries of brilliant floodlights, grouped on all four sides about the base of the 555-foot shaft, were added to the two searchlights already trained on the apex, so that the lighted shaft probably corresponded in brilliancy to a very low-magnitude lighthouse lantern. Airplane pilots say that on a clear night it may be seen for 40 miles.

On clear, dark nights when the nocturnal travelers seem to fly at lower altitudes, many are attracted to the Monument as to a lighthouse beacon, and wind currents prevent a last-minute avoidance.

During the fall migration of 1932 more than 500 warblers, vireos, thrushes, kinglets, sparrows, and others were killed. In 1933 the mortality was less, but the Monument at times still remains a serious menace to birds during migration.

When the torch on the Statue of Liberty in New York Harbor was kept lighted, it caused a heavy toll of bird life, tabulations showing as many as 700 birds in a single month.

Although it would seem that the exertion from long flights of many migratory birds would result in exhaustion, this is not the case. Both in soaring and in sailing birds are proficient in the use of factors only recently understood and imitated by aeronautical engineers. Ascending currents of air, utilized by all soaring birds, and easily demonstrated by observing the gulls that glide hour after hour along the windward side of a ship, are now considered by man in his operation of gliders.

WHY BIRDS ARE PERFECT FLYING MACHINES

The structure of a bird renders it the perfect machine for extensive flight. Hollow, air-filled bones, making an ideal combination of strength and lightness, and the lightest and toughest material possible for flight in the form of feathers, combine to produce a perfect flying machine.

Consideration of a bird's economy of fuel or energy also is enlightening. The golden plover, traveling over the oceanic route, makes the entire distance of 2,400 miles from Nova Scotia to South America without stop, probably requiring about 48 hours of continuous flight. This is accomplished with the consumption of less than two ounces of fuel in the form of body fat.

To be as economical in operation, a 1,000-pound airplane would consume in a 20-mile flight not the gallon of fuel usually required, but only a pint.

The sora, or Carolina rail, which is such a notoriously weak flyer that at least one writer was led to infer that most of its migration was made on foot, has one of the longest migration routes of all members of its family, and easily crosses the wide reaches of the Caribbean Sea. The tiny ruby-throated hummingbird crosses the Gulf of Mexico in a single flight of more than 500 miles.

While birds that have recently arrived from a protracted flight over land or sea sometimes show evidences of being tired, their condition is far from a state of exhaustion, unless they have encountered unusual conditions, and with a few hours' rest and a crop well filled with proper food they exhibit eagerness to resume their journey.

Under favorable conditions birds can fly when, where, and how they please. Consequently, the distance covered in a single flight is governed chiefly by the food supply. Exhaustion, except as the result of unusual

Photograph by George Shiras, 3rd

FLORIDA QUAIL TAKE THEIR OWN PICTURES BY PULLING A BAITED STRING

A flock discovers seeds put out for smaller birds. In the group are three cocks and two females. The tugging of the cock, which is attempting to detach a seed on the string, releases the camera shutter. The fascinating story of how the Honorable George Shiras, 3rd, obtained his remarkable action pictures of birds and animals is told in *Hunting Wild Life with Camera and Flashlight—A Record of Sixty-five Years' Visits to the Woods and Waters of America,* with 950 illustrations, published by the National Geographic Society as a contribution to knowledge.

circumstances, cannot be said to be an important peril of migration.

BANDING STUDIES ARE SOLVING MANY MYSTERIES

The study of living birds by the banding method, whereby many individuals are marked with numbered aluminum leg rings, is recognized as an accurate means of bird study. Since 1920, banding work in North America has been under the direction of the Bureau of Biological Survey, in cooperation with the National Parks Branch of Canada.

Every year volunteer cooperators, now numbering 2,000, working under permit, place bands on thousands of birds, game and nongame, large and small, migratory and nonmigratory, each band carrying a serial number and the legend, "NOTIFY BIOLOGICAL SURVEY, WASHINGTON, D. C.," or, on the smaller sizes, "NOTIFY BIOL. SURV., WASH., D. C."

When a banded bird is reported from a second locality, a definite fact relative to its movements becomes known, and a study of many cases of this nature develops increasing knowledge of the details of migration.

From the study of recovery records of banded ducks and geese has come the "flyway concept" that is proving of such importance in the administration and conservation of these important game species.

In the United States the 100th meridian, to a remarkable extent, separates the Atlantic and Mississippi flyways from the Central and Pacific systems (map, page 344). In the southern regions of the flyways it is a relatively rare occurrence when a banded duck is recovered that was banded on the opposite side of this meridian, even though that particular species has a coast-to-coast distribution.

MOVEMENTS OF RESIDENTS

Ducks banded in Kansas, however, through which State the 100th meridian passes, have scattered to all points of the compass, the dispersal from banding stations in this State being greater than from those in any other State or Province of Canada (map, page 342).

There are several species that are customarily grouped under the heading "permanent residents." Among these are the cardinal, tufted titmouse, wren-tit, Carolina wren, house finch, bobwhite, California quail, screech owl, mockingbird, and ruffed grouse.

Each species may be present constantly throughout the year, although in the northern part of the range there is probably a slight withdrawal of the breeding birds in winter. The individuals to be seen at that season, therefore, may not always be the same as those observed during the summer. It is certain, however, that these species do not regularly perform extensive journeys.

While the blue jay is disposed to be secretive, it is such a showy and noisy bird that it is not likely to escape notice. In the vicinity of Washington, D. C., as in many other places, it is present the year round, but at the end of September or early in October when the weather is becoming cooler, troops of jays are sometimes seen working southward through the trees. A corresponding northward movement occurs again in May.

This is unquestionably a migration to and from some winter range, but its extent or significance is not now known.

One jay, banded on September 14, 1923, at Waukegan, Illinois, was killed at Peruque, Missouri, on November 15 of the same year; another, banded at Winnetka, Illinois, on June 16, 1925, was retaken at Sulphur Rock, Arkansas, the following December 10; a third, banded on May 6, 1925, at Whitten, Iowa, was recaptured at Decatur, Arkansas, on January 22, 1926. These three birds unquestionably had made a flight that had every appearance of being a true migration to winter quarters in Missouri and Arkansas (see page 357).

A screech owl banded at Glenwood, Minnesota, in March, was recovered the following December at Emmetsburg, Iowa, 180 miles south. Such flights, however, are probably more in the nature of a search for new feeding areas, or to escape from a winged enemy, than a true migratory journey.

The white-throated sparrow, one of the most abundant members of its family, breeds from northern Mackenzie and the southern part of the Ungava Peninsula south to southern Montana, northern Pennsylvania, and Massachusetts. The winter range extends from the southern part of the breeding range south to the Gulf coast and northeastern Mexico. It is therefore a common migrant in many sections.

THE WHITE-THROATED SPARROW MYSTERY

Since it is a ground-feeding bird and is readily attracted to the vicinity of dwellings, it has been banded in large numbers, the total to January 1, 1937, being nearly 125,000. It would be expected that these birds would yield a comparable number of return records, and that the facts would furnish basic data relative to the migrations of the species. Such, however, is not the case.

Operators of stations in the winter area, such as Thomasville, Georgia, and Summerville, South Carolina, have obtained return records showing that these birds come back to the exact winter quarters occupied in previous seasons, but stations located at points between the wintering and nesting grounds rarely recapture banded birds of this species.

The fact that they do not return to the banding stations on their migration routes indicates some unusual aspects of their travels, which it is hoped will eventually be discovered by banding studies. Problems of this type constitute definite challenges to the student of bird migration.

The Federal Government has recognized its responsibility to the migratory birds under changing conditions brought about by man, and by enabling acts for carrying out treaty obligations it is now giving many important species legal protection under regulations administered by the Bureau of Biological Survey.

Much is being done by legislation for the welfare of the birds. The effectiveness of these conservation laws, however, is increased in the same measure that the people of the country become acquainted with the facts in the life histories of the migrants and interest themselves personally in the well-being of the several species.

INTERESTING RECOVERIES OF
BANDED BIRDS

By Frederick C. Lincoln

IN THE chapter on "Our Greatest Travelers" (page 301), frequent reference was made to facts that have been learned from the recapture of banded birds.

Analysis of hundreds of recoveries reported by hunters and students gives us precise knowledge of the movements of some species of migratory waterfowl. But for many other species the records accumulate much more slowly. Nevertheless, even for these, the files of the U. S. Biological Survey already contain many remarkable cases of recovery which permit a glimpse behind the curtain of mystery that covers the travels of our feathered friends.

From this wealth of information a few cases have been selected that are of outstanding interest because of the distance covered, or the indicated direction of the flight, or the age of the bird as shown by the elapsed time between banding and recovery.

Bald Eagle.

299451, banded at Ephraim, Wisconsin, June 29, 1928, caught in trap at South Boardman, Michigan, December 15, 1933.

303351, banded at Delaware City, Delaware, May 5, 1928, captured alive in trap at Olivet, Maryland, February 4, 1931.

322057, banded at Grand Rapids, Michigan, May 20, 1928, found wounded (later released and able to fly) at Roscommon, Michigan, October 22, 1934.

Blackbird, Red-Winged.

B216373, banded at Antwerp, Ohio, June 6, 1933, killed at Castleberry, Alabama, December 27, 1933.

B231515, banded at Branchport, New York, August 11, 1933, killed at Four Oaks, North Carolina, December 15, 1933.

B252553, banded 7 miles east of Bashaw, Alberta, Canada, July 9, 1933, killed at Weleetka, Oklahoma, about January 1, 1935.

Blackbird, Yellow-Headed.

A-292940, banded at Great Falls, Montana, June 7, 1932, found dead at Camargo, Chihuahua, Mexico, March 1, 1935.

Bluebird.

C122773, banded at Manchester, New Hampshire, July 26, 1932, shot at Sharpsburg, North Carolina, February 14, 1933.

34-117023, banded at Truro, Cape Cod, Massachusetts, May 17, 1934, caught at Soperton, Georgia, December 1, 1934.

Bobwhite.

A408428, banded at Fairhope, Alabama, July 23, 1932, killed at Atmore, Alabama, about February 16, 1933. This quail traveled 40 miles.

A429771, banded at Madison, Wisconsin, December 28, 1931, killed by locomotive at Wauzeka, Wisconsin, December 24, 1934. This quail traveled 76 miles.

Bunting, Snow.

C98323, banded at McMillan, Michigan, February 17, 1931, shot at Igdlarpait, Julianehaab District, Greenland, April 30, 1931. This bird was killed by an Eskimo who took it to a missionary. A part of the skin was saved and sent to the Zoological Museum at Copenhagen, Denmark, which reported the capture and returned the specimen to the author.

Catbird.

392781, banded at Schoharie, New York, May 14, 1927, flew into house at Tela, Honduras, October 25, 1929.

36-135855, banded at Northville, South Dakota, September 20, 1936, killed at Tuxpam, Vera Cruz, Mexico, about January 1, 1937.

A222905, banded at Norristown, Pennsylvania, July 5, 1929, retaken same place, May 18, 1930; September 29, 1931; May 12, 1932; found dead July 3, 1933.

Coot.

A692718, banded at Lake Merritt, Oakland, California, January 23, 1934, caught in muskrat trap at Poplar Island Creek, Mackenzie, Canada, spring of 1934.

34-550090, banded at Avery Island, Louisiana, December 20, 1934, caught in muskrat trap at Little Playgreen Lake, Norway House, Manitoba, Canada, about May 20, 1935.

Cormorant, Double-Crested.

A720445, banded at Fog Island, Saguenay County, Quebec, August 8, 1932, killed at Register, Georgia, about July 26, 1933.

Cowbird.

A cowbird banded at Brunswick, Maine, May 8, 1926, was retaken in King William County, Virginia, August 31, 1926.

Another, banded at Rochester, New York, April 25, 1925, was retaken at Dayton, Texas, August 15, 1926.

A288157, banded at Gates Mills, Ohio, July 4, 1933, shot at Mayflower, Texas, October 14, 1933.

B136471, banded at Mont Belvieu, Texas, February 4, 1932, found dead at East Oxford, Ontario, Canada, about July 1, 1933.

B253310, banded at Winnipeg, Manitoba, Canada, May 22, 1933, killed by hunters at Guadalajara, Jalisco, Mexico, about November 23, 1933.

34-243531, banded at Waukesha, Wisconsin, August 2, 1934, shot at Flake, 12 miles from Galveston, Texas, November 25, 1934.

34-216529, banded at Avery Island, Louisiana, November 16, 1935, killed at Athens, Ohio, April 26, 1936.

Crossbill, Red.

B168051, banded at Milton, Massachusetts, May 12, 1932, found dead at Bemidji, Minnesota, April 9, 1934.

Crow.

225931, banded March 19, 1926, at Kansas, Illinois, shot June 22, 1936, at Traverse City, Michigan.

Curlew, Long-billed.

531112, banded at Bear River Bay, 20 miles west of Brigham, Utah, June 11, 1929, shot at Ensenada de Todos Santos, Baja California, Mexico, September 18, 1930.

Dove, Mourning.

212300, banded at Indianapolis, Indiana, June 30, 1924, shot at Tampa, Florida, September 10, 1930.

365529, banded at San Diego, California, January 3, 1929, killed at Boise, Idaho, September 7, 1929.

520964, banded at East Lansing, Michigan, May 24, 1928, shot 20 miles south of Blountstown, Calhoun County, Florida, December 8, 1930.

A426443, banded at North Eastham, Cape Cod, Massachusetts, June 13, 1931, killed at Dandridge, Tennessee, November 21, 1931.

B330872, banded at Key West, Florida, January 4, 1932, shot 3 miles south of Decatur, Illinois, September 12, 1932.

B342726, banded at Fairmount, North Dakota, June 7, 1932, killed at Cartazar, Guanajuato, Mexico, October 19, 1932.

B381158, banded at Key West, Florida, October 19, 1932, killed at Walton, Texas, November 20, 1933.

34-307922, banded at Key West, Florida, December 7, 1934, killed at Mérida, Yucatán, Mexico, January 12, 1935.

B392928, banded at Lakin, Kansas, May 28, 1934, shot at Morelos, Mexico, November 29, 1936.

A460926, banded at Fargo, North Dakota, July 14, 1934, killed at Silacayoapan, Oaxaca, Mexico, November 18, 1934.

A451773, banded at Paoli, Pennsylvania, June 15, 1933, found dead at Bayview, Prince Edward Island, December 1, 1933.

A452651, banded at North Eastham, Massachusetts, August 21, 1934, shot at Garfield, Georgia, September 28, 1934.

A452531, banded at North Eastham, Massachusetts, July 31, 1934, shot at Gallatin, Texas, January 15, 1935, 1,500 miles distant from place of banding.

Dowitcher.

34-258359, banded at North Eastham, Cape Cod, Massachusetts, August 24, 1935, shot at Fox River, near Fort Randolph

Reservation, Canal Zone, September 12, 1935. This bird traveled 2,100 miles at the rate of at least 117 miles a day.

34-258536, banded at North Eastham, Cape Cod, Massachusetts, July 31, 1935, captured at Pointe-à-Pitre, Guadeloupe, West Indies, August 26, 1935. This bird traveled 1,800 miles at the rate of at least 70 miles a day.

DUCKS

Baldpate.

A558500, banded at Voltage, Oregon, April 10, 1933, killed by Indian near Allakaket, Koyukuk River, Alaska, in 1935.

35-513264, banded at Lake Merritt, Oakland, California, February 6, 1935, killed by an Indian near Allakaket, Koyukuk River, Alaska, in spring of 1936.

Black.

496164, banded at Oakdale, Long Island, New York, March 10, 1927, caught in a muskrat trap near Starks, Maine, spring of 1936.

C631908, banded at Munuskong State Park, Chippewa County, Michigan, September 9, 1936, killed at Willards, Maryland, November 26, 1936.

34-644113, banded at Phoenixville, Pennsylvania, October 24, 1935, shot at Mount Stewart, Prince Edward Island, Canada, November 13, 1936.

Canvasback.

A626090, banded at Abbeville, Louisiana, February 4, 1929, shot at Barrett Lake, San Diego County, California, November 13, 1929.

A697135, banded at Tillamook Bay, Oregon, April 8, 1931, was killed by Indian at Delta of Athabaska River, Alberta, Canada, September, 1931.

C600368, banded at Abbeville, Louisiana, January 29, 1933, shot at Huaniqueo de Morales, Michoacán, Mexico, January 2, 1934.

Mallard.

237653, banded Union Springs, New York, February 23, 1924, killed at Attawapiskat Lake, Ontario, Canada, November 1, 1935.

C611722, banded at Vasseux Lake, British Columbia, November 6, 1933, shot at Aklavik, in Mackenzie River Delta, Mackenzie, Canada, fall of 1935.

36-600119, banded at Thief Lake, Marshall County, Minnesota, September 24, 1935, shot at St. Andrews, near Winnipeg, Manitoba, Canada, November 1, 1935. *This duck traveled north in the autumn.*

36-629027, banded at Squaw Creek Refuge, Mound City, Missouri, April 11, 1936, shot at Women Lake, 100 miles north of Sioux Lookout, Ontario, Canada, about October 9, 1936.

Pintail.

The pintails and blue-winged teals among the ducks have made the longest flights. A pintail, 367451, banded at Ellinwood,

Kansas, flew northwest more than 3,300 miles to the mouth of the Kobuk River, Alaska; another, 227609, banded at Keno, Oregon, in September, was killed 2,800 miles to the southeast, near Belize, British Honduras; two others, A638860 and A647295, both banded on the same day, one at the Bear River Marshes in Utah, the other at Dawson, North Dakota, were killed on the same day by the same man at Toluca, near Mexico City, Mexico.

A584480, banded at Avery Island, Louisiana, December 22, 1933, killed at Pitt Point, between Dease Inlet and Cape Halkett, on north Arctic coast, Alaska, July 29, 1934.

C607524, banded at Avery Island, Louisiana, shipped to Berkeley, California, and released March 4, 1933, shot at Steep Rock, Manitoba, Canada, in fall of 1936.

34-515257, banded at Ellinwood, Kansas, April 11, 1934, shot at Laguna de Garrobas, 15 miles southeast of Puerto Cortés, Honduras, January 29, 1935.

34-541216, banded at Midwest, Wyoming, April 6, 1936, shot at Copándaro, Michoacán, Mexico, in December, 1936.

35-519649, banded at Irvington, California, March 6, 1935, shipped to Molokai, Hawaii, and released. It *found its way back to California* and was killed at Los Banos, California, December 4, 1935, a short distance from Irvington.

Redhead.

A607348, banded at Bear River Marshes, Utah, July 23, 1929, killed in Baja California, Mexico, 35 miles below border, January 15, 1930.

B639195, banded at Lake Malheur Migratory Waterfowl Refuge, Burns, Oregon, April 1, 1932, shot at Tijuana, Baja California, Mexico, January 5, 1935.

B691733, banded at Thief Lake, Marshall County, Minnesota, May 10, 1934, shot at Currituck Sound, North Carolina, January 12, 1935.

36-628245, banded at Lake Malheur Migratory Waterfowl Refuge, Burns, Oregon, October 14, 1936, killed at Todos Santos, Baja California, Mexico, December 4, 1936.

Shoveller.

A569557, banded at Lakin, Kansas, April 7, 1935, found dead at Los Angeles, California, May 11, 1935.

Teal, Blue-Winged.

A510183, banded at Ellinwood, Kansas, flew 1,800 miles southeast to Corocito, Honduras, while another, 531961, banded at the same place, traveled more to the eastward and was recaptured near Elia, Camagüey, Cuba.

One of these little ducks, 363850, banded April 13, 1927, at Kearney, Nebraska, flew southeast about 2,600 miles to Santa Marta, Colombia, where it was shot October 15, 1927. Another, 4576, banded at Lake Scugog in southern Ontario, was recovered after a flight of about the same length, on the island of Trinidad, off the north coast of South America.

237861, banded at La Batture aux Loups, Marins, near L'Islet, Quebec, September 5, 1930, shot at Plantation Enmore, Georgetown, British Guiana, October 2, 1930. It had traveled 2,875 miles in 27 days.

A500231, banded at Ellinwood, Kansas, April 12, 1930, shot at Caroni Swamps, Trinidad, British West Indies, March 24, 1932.

A544414, banded at Munuskong State Park, Chippewa County, Michigan, August 17, 1932, captured at Loiza, Puerto Rico, April 11, 1935.

Teal, Cinnamon.

526899, banded at Modesto Properties, 15 miles west of Merced, California, July 16, 1933, shot at Hacienda La Casita, Sonora, Mexico, August 25, 1934.

Teal, Green-Winged.

35-401788, banded at Ellinwood, Kansas, April 1, 1936, shot by native at Kaltag, Alaska, in the spring of 1936.

Egret, American.

34-661891, banded at Good Hope, Mississippi, June 16, 1935, shot near Belize, British Honduras, December 1, 1935.

Egret, Snowy.

B611997, banded at Vingt'une Island, off Smith Point, Galveston Bay, Chambers County, Texas, May 29, 1932, shot at Banana River, Costa Rica, July 8, 1933.

Finch, House.

180327, banded at Pomona, California, April 17, 1926, found dead at same place, April 24, 1935.

Finch, Purple.

The number of small birds recovered after long flights is not large, but, considering the size of the birds, some of the distances traveled are remarkable. A purple finch, A127258, banded at Hyde Park, Massachusetts, was recaptured more than 1,400 miles to the southwest, at Nacogdoches, Texas, and another individual of this same species, 77230, banded at Peterboro, New Hampshire, flew nearly 1,500 miles to Thornton, Texas.

37929, banded at Groton, Massachusetts, April 30, 1929, retrapped at same place, May 2, 1934, and April 27, 1935.

135603, banded at Northeast Harbor, Maine, June 21, 1924, retrapped at same place, April 10, 1931, and April 28, 1933.

A128605, banded at West Hartford, Connecticut, February 14, 1929, killed at Strawberry, Arkansas, January 28, 1933.

A141578, banded at Sault Ste. Marie, Michigan, August 5, 1929, returned to same banding station, May 10, 1930; April 24, 1931; May 1, 1932; May 18, 1933; May 6, 1934, and May 2, 1935.

B29770, banded at Westfield, Massachusetts, April 26, 1928, found dead at Columbus, Ohio, July 23, 1933.

Photograph from Harold E. Edgerton, Massachusetts Institute of Technology

AN INCREDIBLY FAST LENS REVEALS THE INVISIBLE

With an exposure of about 1/100,000th of a second, by means of a very short flash of light result-ing when an electrical condenser charged to about 1,500 volts was suddenly discharged into an argon-filled stroboscopic lamp, Dr. Edgerton obtained this marvelous photograph of hummingbirds in flight. The picture was taken on the porch of the home of Mr. and Mrs. Laurence J. Webster at Holderness, New Hampshire. By making available sweetened water, Mrs. Webster has attracted a colony of from 30 to 50 ruby-throated hummingbirds that almost continually drink from these vials located at various places on the estate and kept filled. The camera and light source were placed in the house and the pictures taken through a window. The brilliant flash of light momentarily dis-turbed the birds, but not sufficiently to interrupt their feeding. This tiny bird crosses the Gulf of Mexico in a 500-mile flight over water.

C191932, banded at Washington, D. C., Jan-uary 3, 1934, trapped and released at Athol, Massachusetts, April 27, 1934.

C199849, banded at Milford, New Hampshire, April 30, 1933, caught at Gros-Louis, San-ford Station, Lake St. John, Quebec, Canada, about July 1, 1935.

L4209, banded at Athol, Massachusetts, May 10, 1933, trapped and released at Great Head, Bar Harbor, Maine, May 13, 1933. This bird traveled 230 miles in three days.

L62402, banded at Groton, Massachusetts, August 31, 1934, shot at Warren, Arkan-sas, February 8, 1936.

34-176155, banded at Belchertown, Massachu-setts, April 6, 1935, killed at Bishopville, South Carolina, February 1, 1936.

Flicker, Northern.

B259302, banded at Rosyth, Alberta, Canada, June 27, 1933, found dead at Ennis, Texas, about January 8, 1934.

C304820, banded at East Westmoreland, New Hampshire, June 13, 1934, killed at Tren-ton, Florida, in November, 1934.

C311727, banded at Bashaw, Alberta, Canada, June 16, 1934, shot at Jasper, Texas, about January 20, 1935.

C332523, banded at Wilton, North Dakota, July 20, 1934, killed at Marietta, Okla-homa, September 28, 1934.

Flycatcher, Crested.

B272230, banded at Lisle, Illinois, May 30, 1934, captured and released at same place, June 13, 1936. This bird was rescued

Photograph courtesy Massachusetts Institute of Technology

THE MAGIC EYE OF THE CAMERA CATCHES A MOURNING DOVE JUST LAUNCHED
IN LIGHTNING FLIGHT

This photograph, made in 1/50,000th of a second, was taken by Dr. Harold E. Edgerton and Kenneth J. Germeshausen of the Department of Electrical Engineering of the Massachusetts Institute of Technology. It reveals in detail the position of the primary feathers of the wing on an up stroke, indicating that the individual feathers are rotated slightly to open slots through which the air passes to reduce resistance as the wing moves upward. On a down stroke the feathers overlap to increase resistance. The photograph was taken at the birdbanding station of Dr. Oliver L. Austin on Cape Cod, Massachusetts, by means of Professor Edgerton's unique electrical circuit, which produces a flash of extremely short duration. (See page 352 for instances of its migration.)

from a garter snake at the time of banding, an ordeal it survived, as witness its return to the same point two years later.

A-147214, banded June 30, 1929, at Norristown, Pennsylvania, was recaptured June 22, 1933; July 8, 1934; May 23, 1935; June 27, 1936. It mated for three successive years with same bird and was at least eight years old, 1936.

Goose, Blue.

A723544, banded at Avery Island, Louisiana, November 12, 1933, killed by Indian at Albany, via Moosonee, Ontario, Canada, May, 1936.

Goose, Canada.

A726253, banded at Earleville, Maryland, March 7, 1935, shot by an Eskimo on the Inmuksuak River, Ungava Peninsula, near Port Harrison, Quebec, summer of 1936.

A726266, banded at Earleville, Maryland, March 7, 1935, trapped, banded with a Miner band, and released, at Kingsville, Ontario, Canada, April 10, 1935.

A726539, banded at Earleville, Maryland, March 24, 1936, shot by Eskimo on Inmuksuak River, Ungava Peninsula, near Port Harrison, Quebec, summer of 1936.

Grosbeak, Evening.

462165, banded on March 9, 1927, at Sault Ste. Marie, Michigan, retrapped at banding station at Sandwich, Massachusetts, March 22, 1930. The following year, March 14, 1931, it was again captured at the Michigan station.

Grosbeak, Rose-Breasted.

> 117473, banded at Peterboro, New Hampshire, June 20, 1926, trapped at same place, May 23, 1932.
>
> 117477, banded at Peterboro, New Hampshire, June 5, 1926, trapped at same place, June 1, 1931.

GULLS

California Gull.

> 544378, banded at Bittern Lake, 12 miles West of Camrose, Alberta, June 22, 1927, killed in valley of Yaqui River, Sonora, Mexico, about June 16, 1934.
>
> A571947, banded at Woody Island, Lake Bowdoin, Malta, Montana, June 17, 1934, found at Río Yaqui, Sonora, Mexico, about April 22, 1936.
>
> 36-511802, banded at Redberry Lake, Saskatchewan, Canada, July 8, 1936, killed at Chihuahua, Mexico, October 29, 1936.

Herring Gull.

> C624020, banded at Sister Islands, Wisconsin, June 28, 1933, killed at Makkovik, Labrador, about September 15, 1933.
>
> 35-542860, banded at Little Sister Island, Green Bay, Wisconsin, June 25, 1935, found dead at the island of Triángulo, Campeche, Mexico, February 11, 1936.
>
> 385626, banded Mire Island, 8 miles east of St. James, Michigan, July 2, 1925, caught on a fish hook, South Manitou, Michigan, about July 15, 1936.
>
> A herring gull in adult plumage was wing-tipped in 1889 and kept as a pet by Dr. Ben Royal, Morehead City, North Carolina, until its death apparently of old age in July, 1935, at an age of at least 49 years. Even more surprising than its long life in confinement is the record of its mate as given to Dr. T. Gilbert Pearson by Dr. Royal. "Kaiser's mate laid eggs every year from 1893 until and including 1934, 42 years; in 1935-6 she has built a nest but has not laid."

Laughing Gull.

> A547404, banded at Muskeget Island, Massachusetts, August 7, 1933, found sick and exhausted on April 30, 1936, cared for and released in good condition, May 5, 1936, at Balboa, Canal Zone.

Ring-Billed Gull.

> C612629, banded at Kehoe Lake, near Barons, Alberta, Canada, July 11, 1933, killed near Poza, Sonora, Mexico, May 11, 1934.

HAWKS

Broad-Winged Hawk.

> 660558, banded at Huntington, Massachusetts, July 10, 1932, killed eight miles west of Winchester, Virginia, September 8, 1932.
>
> A675276, banded at Huntington, Massachusetts, July 5, 1930, caught at Atkins, Michigan, August 28, 1930.

Duck Hawk.

> 310753, banded at King's Point, Yukon Territory, killed at Duchesne, Utah, more than 2,000 miles south.

> A701032, banded at Mohonk Lake, New York, June 18, 1929, shot at Grand Island, Nebraska, September 26, 1929.
>
> B661961, banded at Scout Camp, Treasure Island, New Jersey, September 3, 1932, caught at McClure, Illinois, September 22, 1932.

Ferruginous Rough-Legged Hawk.

> A709881, banded at Rosebud, Alberta, killed 1,700 miles south at Alpine, Texas.
>
> A717523, banded at Rosebud, Alberta, Canada, June 19, 1934, caught in coyote trap at Brea, California, about November 15, 1934.
>
> A717541, banded at Rosebud, Alberta, Canada, June 23, 1935, shot eight miles south of Whiteface, Texas, November 28, 1935.

Marsh Hawk.

> 542479, banded at Andover, New York, June 18, 1932, killed at Waco, Texas, September 17, 1932.
>
> 656129, banded at Dayton, Ohio, June 15, 1930, wounded four miles from Harlingen, Texas, January 12, 1931.
>
> A697063, banded at Argusville, North Dakota, July 13, 1931, retaken 1,100 miles distant, at Guantánamo, Cuba, about January 16, 1932.
>
> B646388, banded at Rosebud, Alberta, Canada, July 8, 1933, found dead at Casa Grande, Arizona, about November 18, 1933.

Osprey.

> ABBA-26584, banded as a nestling at Gardiners Island, New York, June 19, 1914, found dead at Gardiners Island, New York, June 1, 1935. *Its recovery makes the greatest longevity record thus far reported for any bird not captive.*
>
> ABBA-26591, banded as a nestling at Gardiners Island, New York, June 15, 1914, killed at West Durham, North Carolina, April 4, 1930.
>
> A719002, banded at Slaughter Beach, Delaware, April 25, 1932, shot at Milk River, Jamaica, British West Indies, March 10, 1933.
>
> A719077, banded at Slaughter Beach, Delaware, April 26, 1934, killed at El Mojan-Estado, Zulia, Venezuela, South America, June 28, 1935.
>
> A727056, banded at Orient Point, Long Island, New York, July 23, 1933, shot attempting to alight on mast of ship 73 miles east of Cape Hatteras, North Carolina, October 9, 1933.

Pigeon Hawk.

> A420558, banded at Rosebud, Alberta, Canada, July 6, 1931, killed at Tucson, Arizona, January 28, 1933.

Prairie Falcon.

> A557904, banded at Carmangay, Alberta, Canada, June 4, 1933, caught in muskrat trap at Moscow, Kansas, about January 17, 1936.
>
> B671641, banded at Jackson, Wyoming, June 28, 1932, killed 2½ miles west of Morris, Illinois, January 26, 1933.

Red-Shouldered Hawk.

210898, banded at H. Beadel Plantation, Leon County, Florida, May 7, 1924, killed at Tallahassee, Florida, April 18, 1930. This bird was banded as a fledgling and was killed on its nest.

660552, banded at Huntington, Massachusetts, June 14, 1931, killed at Freeman, North Carolina, January 4, 1934.

C616793, banded at Leverett, Massachusetts, June 11, 1935, shot at Roberta, Georgia, October 28, 1935.

Red-Tailed Hawk.

655444, banded at Hepburn, Saskatchewan, flew south about 1,800 miles to Flatonia, Texas.

302126, banded at Jackson, Wyoming, June 22, 1931, found wounded at Coalcomán, Michoacán, Mexico, January 11, 1932.

309018, banded at Muscow, Saskatchewan, Canada, July 3, 1927, shot at Iota, Louisiana, about February 1, 1934.

B661937, banded at Williamston, Michigan, May 13, 1933, killed at Greensboro, Alabama, December 26, 1933.

Rough-Legged Hawk.

324943, banded at Kamouraska, Quebec, Canada, May 5, 1931, shot at Kempton, Illinois, November 11, 1931.

Sparrow Hawk.

368572, banded at Babson Park, Massachusetts, June 14, 1929, killed at Allsbrook, South Carolina, February 19, 1931.

A462120, banded at Rosebud, Alberta, Canada, July 5, 1933, found dead at Proctor, Texas, March 27, 1934.

35-312052, banded at Saskatoon, Saskatchewan, Canada, July 12, 1935, shot at Flatonia, Texas, about February 5, 1936.

Swainson's Hawk.

A605212, banded at Dollard, Saskatchewan, Canada, August 12, 1934, shot at Clinton, Oklahoma, October 12, 1934.

B646421, banded at Rosebud, Alberta, Canada, July 15, 1934, shot at Chillicothe, Texas, October 20, 1934.

HERONS

Black-Crowned Night Heron.

B604768, banded at Los Banos, Merced County, California, June 26, 1932, killed at Coalcomán, Michoacán, Mexico, March 17, 1936.

B664630, banded at East Springfield, Massachusetts, June 18, 1932, killed at Los Hermanos, Cuba, about February 15, 1935.

B670084, banded at Duck Creek, Brown County, Wisconsin, July 10, 1932, shot at Lake Ariguanabo, near Habana, Cuba, December 21, 1932.

34-519494, banded at Lakin, Kansas, on June 12, 1934, killed in March, 1935, at Toluca, Mexico.

Great Blue Heron.

This bird makes long flights. Two banded at Waseca, southeastern Minnesota, were re- captured almost due south in Central America. The first (334487) was taken 1,900 miles distant at El Hule, State of Oaxaca, southern Mexico; the other (334402) was killed after a flight of 2,600 miles to Gatun Lake, Panama. Still a third (204206), banded at Hat Island, in Green Bay, Wisconsin, flew southeast nearly 1,700 miles to the southern coast of Cuba, its capture forming the first record for the race in that country.

A717307, banded at Spider Island, Door County, Wisconsin, June 30, 1933, killed at Mendoza, Pinar del Rio, Cuba, about July 1, 1934. The second record of the eastern form of this species in Cuba.

C622169, banded at Woody Island, Lake Bowdoin, Malta, Montana, June 20, 1933, found wounded at San Pedro, Tamaulipas, Mexico, April 12, 1935.

34-632334, banded at Depue, Illinois, June 21, 1936, shot on Monkey River, British Honduras, November 30, 1936.

Little Blue Heron.

A540044, banded at Heron Island, Charleston County, South Carolina, June 12, 1932, shot near St. Thomas, Jamaica, British West Indies, October 30, 1934.

34-523162, banded at Heron Island, Charleston County, South Carolina, June 6, 1934, killed at Cumaná, Venezuela, South America, October 21, 1934.

Jay, Blue.

A270924, banded at Madison, Wisconsin, June 27, 1931, caught at Armuchee, Georgia, about November 15, 1933.

A445664, banded at Minneapolis, Minnesota, July 12, 1932, caught in trap at Claremore, Oklahoma, December 17, 1932.

9612, banded at Ann Arbor, Michigan, January 2, 1922, retrapped at same place, November 17, 1933.

212532, banded at Ann Arbor, Michigan, July 26, 1925, retrapped at same place, February 6, 1936.

Junco, Slate-Colored.

C88327, banded at Barkerville, British Columbia, Canada, August 2, 1934, trapped and released at Grand Canyon National Park, South Rim, Village Area, Arizona, February 4, 1935.

F26935, banded at Elmhurst, Long Island, New York, November 2, 1932, captured and released at Shelbyville, Indiana, November 6, 1933.

H49053, banded at Mohonk Lake, New York, April 9, 1933, killed at Kellyton, Alabama, about December 25, 1933.

35-43839, banded at Fairfield, Iowa, April 19, 1935, found dead at Martin, North Dakota, May 3, 1935.

Killdeer.

B270449, banded at Black River, South Reef, Michigan, July 6, 1935, killed at Tuscumbia, Alabama, October 20, 1935.

A281957, banded at East Durham, New York, June 7, 1932, killed at Milledgeville, Georgia, January 10, 1933.

A373979, banded at Regina, Saskatchewan, Canada, June 27, 1933, killed at Annaudville, Louisiana, January 5, 1936.

A222471, banded at Notre Dame, Indiana, July 12, 1929, caught at Gaffney, South Carolina, February 27, 1930.

Martin, Purple.

240552, banded at Winnipeg, Manitoba, July 31, 1924, trapped in martin house and released unharmed, June 27, 1930, at Fertile, Garfield Township, Polk County, Minnesota.

B221369, banded at McMillan, Michigan, May 10, 1933, killed at Clayton, Alabama, April 16, 1936.

Mockingbird.

B226502, banded at Haddonfield, New Jersey, November 25, 1932, found dead at Shadyside, Maryland, May 25, 1935.

34-224540, banded at Nashville, Tennessee, May 26, 1934, killed at Fulton, Mississippi, January 29, 1936.

Nuthatch, White-Breasted.

A23071, banded at North Middleboro, Massachusetts, February 22, 1926, caught by cat at St. George, New Brunswick, April 23, 1926.

Oriole, Baltimore.

486720, banded at Lancaster, Wisconsin, June 8, 1927, caught in trap at Platteville, Wisconsin, July 16, 1931.

OWLS

Barn Owl.

223277, banded at Oconomowoc, Wisconsin, July 22, 1929, caught in steel trap at Tuckerman, Arkansas, May 23, 1932.

232151, banded at Horsham, Pennsylvania, June 25, 1929, captured at Boston, Georgia, January 8, 1931.

B664405, banded at Leetonia, Ohio, May 22, 1933, killed at Naples, Florida, January 30, 1934.

Barred Owl.

662512, banded at Prairie du Sac, Wisconsin, May 24, 1931, captured at Galena, Illinois, November 28, 1931. Distance covered: about 70 miles.

Burrowing Owl.

A544093, banded at Northville, South Dakota, June 21, 1933, killed during hailstorm at Snyder, Texas, April 3, 1935.

Great Horned Owl.

301328, banded at Indian Head, Saskatchewan, Canada, May 5, 1928, shot five miles north of Qu'Appelle, Saskatchewan, Canada, June 19, 1935.

661183, banded at Muscow, Saskatchewan, Canada, May 22, 1932, shot at Moose Mountain Indian Reserve, near Manor, Saskatchewan, Canada, about November 3, 1933 Distance covered: about 115 miles.

Long-Eared Owl.

B661927, banded at Williamston, Michigan, April 27, 1932, caught in trap at Gladstone, Virginia, about February 15, 1936.

B661987, banded at Escondido, California, April 22, 1934, shot at Corbeil, Ontario, Canada, October 9, 1934. One of the most remarkable recoveries reported and all details have been fully verified.

Saw-Whet Owl.

439545, banded at Sound Beach, Connecticut, January 15, 1929, found dead at Kittery, Maine, about February 16, 1930.

Screech Owl.

209911, banded at Ashton, Iowa, December 16, 1928, caught and died of cold at Tabor, South Dakota, January, 1930. Distance between points of banding and recovery is nearly 100 miles.

A510850, banded at Glenwood, Minnesota, March 25, 1932, found dead in Palo Alto County, near Emmetsburg, Iowa, December 20, 1932. Distance covered: nearly 200 miles.

Short-Eared Owl.

A685603, banded at Tregarva, Saskatchewan, Canada, July 18, 1931, shot at Rice Lake, Minnesota, October 23, 1931.

Snowy Owl.

237336, banded at Fairdale, North Dakota, March 9, 1930, retaken at Crooked Gutway, Fort George, Quebec, Canada, about September 10, 1932.

Pelican, Brown.

36-800315, banded at Pelican Island, Mosquito Lagoon, Florida, October 20, 1935, captured and released at Nuevitas, Cuba, February 25, 1936. Fourteen others, banded at same time and place, also reported from Cuba.

Pelican, White.

A714413, banded at Big Quill Lake, near Dafoe, Saskatchewan, July 6, 1932, killed at Laguna de Yesca, north of Panuco, Vera Cruz, Mexico, January 22, 1935.

A727470, banded at Clear Lake, Modoc County, California, June 26, 1934, killed at Pajacuaran, Michoacán, Mexico, February 24, 1935.

34-701825, banded at Chase Lake, Stutsman County, North Dakota, July 26, 1934, brought in by Mexican hunter at Matamoros, Tamaulipas, Mexico, June 1, 1935.

Phoebe.

One banded at East Westmoreland, New Hampshire, June 11, 1931, by Lewis O. Shelley, was retaken at same station, 1932, 1934, 1935.

B74327, banded at Holderness, New Hampshire, June 21, 1929, retaken at Headline, Alabama, November 1, 1929.

C144541, banded at Westfield, Wisconsin, June 4, 1935, retaken at Hallettsville, Texas, about December 25, 1935.

Plover, Wilson's.

A226261, banded at Bird Bank, Charleston County, South Carolina, July 6, 1931, shot at Rose Hall Village, Carentyne Coast, Berbice, British Guiana, September 22, 1932.

Photograph by Myra Keen

A FEMALE WESTERN HOUSE WREN MANEUVERS A TWIG INTO HER HOUSE

She accomplished the feat by rapidly vibrating her beak until she obtained a hold near enough the end to permit her to enter and then to drag the stick in after her.

Redstart.

B86035, banded at Groton, Massachusetts, May 18, 1929, retrapped at same place, May 11, 1932, and May 17, 1933.

Robin.

273933, banded at Crystal Bay, Minnesota, July 7, 1924, killed at Pachuca, Hidalgo, Mexico, December 17, 1925.

507494, banded at Germantown, Philadelphia, Pennsylvania, March 25, 1928, killed at Torquay, near Selby's Cove, Trinity South, Newfoundland, August 31, 1928.

A227267, banded at Wolfville, Nova Scotia, July 13, 1933, shot near Summerville, South Carolina, December 15, 1933.

A354325, banded at Duncan, British Columbia, Canada, April 30, 1931, caught in steel trap in Marin County, near Point Reyes, California, January 15, 1932.

A364355, banded at Midnapore, Alberta, Canada, June 18, 1933, found dead at Spring Valley, California, March 8, 1934.

B138516, banded at Ah-gwah-ching, Minnesota, June 22, 1932, killed at Wauchula, Florida, about March 15, 1935.

B223642, banded at Pasadena, California, February 23, 1933, killed by automobile at West Jordan, Utah, about June 22, 1934.

B272192, banded at Summerville, South Carolina, March 23, 1934, killed by cat at Fond du Lac, Wisconsin, May 26, 1934.

B339318, banded at Minneapolis, Minnesota, May 28, 1932, recaptured and released at St. Paul, Minnesota, May 9, 1934.

Returning to that city, it was killed by a dog about April 15, 1935.

C331282, banded at Kingston, Ontario, July 22, 1934, caught in steel trap at Lake Pontchartrain, Louisiana, December 21. 1934.

34-315331, banded at Nicolet, Quebec, Canada, June 7, 1936, captured 12 miles north of Waycross, Georgia, about November 3, 1936.

34-340316, banded at Elmhurst, Long Island, New York, July 27, 1935, killed at Cottonport, Louisiana, January 19, 1936.

Sandpiper, Least.

H03763, banded at North Eastham, Cape Cod, Massachusetts, August 20, 1932, captured and released at same place August 2, 1934.

Sandpiper, Red-Backed.

169170, banded at Shell Point, Wakulla County, Florida, October 31, 1926, found dead at Monroe Marshes, Michigan, May 25, 1927.

Sandpiper, Semipalmated.

L1986, banded at North Eastham, Cape Cod, Massachusetts, August 29, 1933, caught by boys at Carúpano, Venezuela, September 24, 1933.

L19823, banded at North Eastham, Cape Cod, Massachusetts, September 9, 1933, captured and released at same place August 25, 1934, and August 14, 1935.

Sandpiper, Spotted.

63244, banded at Boxford, Massachusetts, July 1, 1923, found dead under telephone wires at Babson Park, Needham, Massachusetts, July 5, 1927.

F117228, banded at Wantagh, New York, August 19, 1933, killed at Fort-de-France, Martinique, French West Indies, September 13, 1933. It had traveled 1,930 miles in 24 days.

Sapsucker, Yellow-Bellied.

34-316506, banded at Neebish, Michigan, June 28, 1934, killed in Floyd County, near Rome, Georgia, December 14, 1934.

Shrike, Loggerhead.

A280215, banded at Amenia, North Dakota, April 7, 1932, killed at Chriesman, Texas, November 8, 1932.

B166224, banded at Carmangay, Alberta, Canada, June 25, 1933, killed at The Grove, Texas, December 22, 1933.

Shrike, Northern.

A214218, banded at Hepburn, Saskatchewan, July 4, 1931, found dead at Cross Timbers, Missouri, September 23, 1931.

B271756, banded at Harwich, Massachusetts, November 8, 1934, found dead at Clarenceville, Quebec, Canada, about April 1, 1936.

Snipe, Wilson's.

241721, banded at Colquitz, Vancouver Island, British Columbia, December 23, 1924, killed at Sumas Lake, British Columbia, October 20, 1927.

B319966, banded at North Eastham, Cape Cod, Massachusetts, September 4, 1932, shot at Buck Island, four miles south of Coinjock, Currituck County, North Carolina, January 12, 1933.

SPARROWS

Chipping Sparrow.

C79688, banded at North Eastham, Massachusetts, recaptured at Grand Crossing, Florida.

Eastern Chipping Sparrow.

B37036, banded March 27, 1928, at Summerville, South Carolina, taken as a return for the fourth time on March 3, 1936.

Fox Sparrow.

643516, banded at Rhinebeck, New York, March 18, 1929, killed by cat at Port au Port, Newfoundland, April 30, 1929.

132677, banded at Newton Center, Massachusetts, March 15, 1930, caught at Little St. Lawrence, Newfoundland, April 20, 1930.

Golden-Crowned Sparrow.

124102, banded at Stanford University, California, November 18, 1924, found dead at Berkeley Park, California, March 15, 1931.

150330, banded at Stanford University, California, March 2, 1925, trapped and released at same place, October 27, 1928, and February 10, 1931.

Lincoln's Sparrow.

B95144, banded at Jamestown, North Dakota, May 12, 1929, found dead at Mildmay Park, Saskatchewan, Canada, May 24, 1929. In twelve days this bird traveled 420 miles.

Savannah Sparrow.

F91198, banded at McMillan, Michigan, August 10, 1932, killed at Beatrice, Alabama, January 24, 1933.

Song Sparrow.

Male and female song sparrows, carried by Syracuse University naturalists in closed containers, and in several instances liberated at dusk, were nevertheless able to find their way back to the point of original capture. Three birds (34-140217, 34-140253, 34-140275) were liberated at a point nine miles east of the city and were recaptured two, three, and twenty-one days later, respectively, at the point where they were originally taken. 34-140217 was subsequently caught and taken to Chittenango, a village about fifteen miles east of Syracuse. After liberation there, it returned and was caught again at the original point of capture thirty-six hours later. It was then taken to Cortland, about thirty-five miles south of Syracuse, and released. It was again recaught six days later at the original point, 1936.

Tree Sparrow.

38765, banded at Berlin, Massachusetts, recovered at Hardin, Texas.

White-Crowned Sparrow.

A196315, banded at Woodland, New York, retaken at Moody, Texas.

34-112582, banded at Jamestown, North Dakota, May 8, 1934, recovered at Rancho Nuevo, Coahuila, March 25, 1935.

White-Throated Sparrow.

36-139123, banded at Northeast Harbor, Maine, August 25, 1936, killed at Black Creek, North Carolina, December 13, 1936.

A bird banded at Waynesville, North Carolina, April 21, 1929, returned October 26, 1929, October 27, 1930, and November 8, 1935, when it was found dead under a porch.

Starling.

632443, banded at Washington, D. C., March 23, 1928, caught in pigeon coop at Mount Vernon, New York, July 8, 1936.

C335705, banded at Elmhurst, Long Island, New York, March 16, 1934, caught in chicken coop and released unharmed at Grand Cascapedia, Bonaventure County, Quebec, January 27, 1935.

34-223118, banded at Columbus, Ohio, March 26, 1934, found dead at St. Pascal de Kamouraska, Quebec, Canada, August 5, 1934.

34-360187, banded at Glen Olden, Pennsylvania, January 28, 1936, found dead at Augusta, Maine, April 3, 1936.

Swallow, Bank.

C30270, banded at Clear Lake, Indiana, (4 miles southwest of Camden, Michigan), June 12, 1932, found in house on Río Marañon, near Iquitos, Peru, June, 1936.

Swallow, Barn.

158141, banded at Juneau, Alaska, July 23, 1927, recaptured same place, May 4, 1930.

F35418, banded at North Eastham, Cape Cod, Massachusetts, June 28, 1931, found dead, August 26, 1931, caught in asphalt on roof of building at Panama City, Florida.

Swallow, Tree.

L1436, banded at North Eastham, Cape Cod, Massachusetts, June 28, 1933, killed at Tegucigalpa, Honduras, Central America, December 18, 1936.

Swift, Chimney.

A84145, banded at Clayton, Illinois, September 23, 1928, captured at Toledo, Iowa, about August 2, 1935.

F8906, banded at Soddy, Tennessee, September 28, 1930, captured alive and released at Chatham, Michigan, about July 7, 1936. When recaptured, this bird had a nest with two young birds.

F127958, banded at Quincy, Illinois, September 23, 1934, captured in chimney at Loreauville, Louisiana, about October 6, 1934.

36-101183, banded at Hattiesburg, Mississippi, October 5, 1935, came down a chimney into a house at West Townsend, Massachusetts, July 15, 1936.

35-118074, banded at Beloit, Wisconsin, May 11, 1935, came down a chimney into a stove at Drayden, Maryland, about May 26, 1935. The surprising date of recapture has been fully verified.

A73881, banded at Daytona Beach, Florida, August 26, 1927, found dead in a fireplace at Ormond Beach, Florida, about July 17, 1936.

Harold S. Peters of the Biological Survey station at Auburn, Alabama, reports in *Bird-Banding* how he and his fellows in six Alabama towns and Atlanta, Georgia, during an eight-weeks period, August 16 to October 11, 1936, banded 21,503 swifts captured in flues of ten buildings. The largest number, 6,025, taken in Atlanta, required seven hours of continuous effort by eight persons. Because of lack of bands, 6,500 specimens were released unmarked after examination to determine whether any had been banded previously. Among the total handled, 24 wore bands from other stations and 553 bore the investigators' own bands from earlier trappings. Of the latter 248 were recoveries more than 10 miles from the first catching, and 305 repeats retaken inside that radius.

Four birds had moved northeast from Opelika to Atlanta, 105 miles in five days, proof that the species does considerable random flying for food during its leisurely southward migration.

Eleven of 24 recoveries from other stations were from Kingston, Ontario; and others were from New Brunswick, New York, Pennsylvania,

Virginia, West Virginia, South Carolina, Tennessee, and Alabama, the original localities of their first bandings making an almost direct northeast-southwest line, indicating migration down the eastern slope of the Appalachians.

A swift was captured (1936) in England where it had been ringed as full-grown 13 years before.

TERNS

Caspian Tern.

A565352, banded at Gull Island, Georgian Bay, 33 miles east of Little Current, Ontario, July 9, 1933, shot at Barranquilla, Colombia, May 31, 1934.

34-415749, banded at Shoe Island, Lake Michigan, Michigan, July 2, 1935, found dead at Nipe Bay, Oriente, Cuba, November 5, 1935.

Common Tern.

From groups of this bird banded in the O. L. Austin Ornithological Station at North Eastham, Cape Cod, Massachusetts, four, banded June 24-27, 1934, were recaptured December, 1934, and April, 1935, near Cayenne, French Guiana.

Six, banded June 24-26, 1934, were recaptured November 15 and December 9, 1934, near Cumaná, Venezuela.

Four, banded June 26-July 1, 1934, were recaptured September 15 and October 20, 1934, in the Dominican Republic.

Nine, banded June 24-July 15, 1934, were recaptured September 13 and December 28, 1934, near Puerto Rico.

478068, banded at Brant Beach, New Jersey, July 13, 1927, found exhausted at Upper Pomeroon, British Guiana, January 7, 1933.

A330171, banded at Penikese Island, Massachusetts, July 5, 1929, killed at El Guamache, Venezuela, January, 1934.

C316881, banded at Penikese Island, Massachusetts, July 2, 1933, flew aboard ship 15 miles northeast entrance to San Juan River, Venezuela, April 3, 1934.

B348371, banded at Weepecket Island, Gosnold, Massachusetts, July 6, 1933, killed at Fort-de-France, Martinique, August 30, 1933.

B378353, banded at Brant Beach, New Jersey, June 25, 1933, captured alive at Port Royal, Jamaica, British West Indies, September 2, 1933.

C305260, banded at Ram Island, Mattapoisett, Massachusetts, June 27, 1934, flew aboard boat, exhausted, died in an hour near Georgetown (Demerara), British Guiana, November 28, 1934.

35-302133, banded at Billingsgate Island, Massachusetts, June 25, 1935, killed at Golden Fleece, Essequibo Coast, British Guiana, about April 5, 1936.

34-337361, banded at Lower Wedgeport, Nova Scotia, June 30, 1934, found dead at Chavon River near La Romana, Dominican Republic, about October 10, 1934.

34-343410, banded at Penikese Island, Massachusetts, July 5, 1935, captured alive at São Salvador (Bahia), Brazil, April 23, 1936, and is being cared for in captivity.

Roseate Tern.

34-304635, banded at Weepecket Island, Gosnold, Massachusetts, July 6, 1934, captured alive at "Corozo," Cabo Rojo,
Puerto Rico, about September 10, 1934.

B397832, banded at Tern Island, Chatham,
Massachusetts, June 24, 1934, found sick
at Buxton, east coast of Demerara, British
Guiana, June 3, 1935.

35-314924, banded at Tern Island, Cape Cod,
Massachusetts, July 6, 1935, found on
shore near Lawn, Newfoundland, about
October 5, 1935.

Royal Tern.

A531082, banded at Cape Romain, Charleston
County, South Carolina, July 18, 1931,
found exhausted and died on board ship,
west part of the Gulf of Mexico, June
16, 1934.

A578141, banded at Cape Romain, Charleston
County, South Carolina, July 11, 1933,
killed at Turbo, Gulf of Uraba, Department of Antioquia, Colombia, South
America, October 3, 1934.

Thrasher, Brown.

B308048, banded at Shakopee, Minnesota,
May 6, 1932, killed at Vick, Louisiana,
about March 20, 1934.

B382142, banded at Aberdeen, South Dakota,
June 25, 1934, caught in steel trap at
Glen Allen, Mississippi, about December
30, 1934.

A322167, banded at Norristown, Pennsylvania, August 27, 1929, retaken same
place May 8, 1930; July 3, 1934.

Towhee, Red-Eyed.

252040, banded at Demarest, New Jersey,
September 28, 1932, caught by cat at
Andrews, South Carolina, October 17,
1932.

A262921, banded at Mohonk Lake, New York,
July 22, 1931, caught at Ambrose,
Georgia, November 26, 1931.

A270281, banded at Summerville, South Carolina, January 14, 1931, caught by cat at
Palmer, Massachusetts, May 8, 1931.

Turnstone, Ruddy.

A217098, banded at Zion, Illinois, September
4, 1929, shot at Lat. 89° Long. 30°,
Bayou Scofield, Louisiana, October 10,
1929.

WARBLERS

Black-Throated Green Warbler.

C92, banded at Hanover, New Hampshire,
September 16, 1930, found dead at Milledgeville, Georgia, February 25, 1935.

H91583, banded at Groton, Massachusetts,
May 24, 1933, caught at West Memphis,
Arkansas, October 22, 1933.

34-75026, banded at Overbrook, Philadelphia,
Pennsylvania, October 4, 1934, killed at
Tetela, Oaxaca, Mexico, December 17,
1935. This recovery was reported by the
Honorable Josephus Daniels, United
States Ambassador to Mexico.

Chestnut-Sided Warbler.

A65059, banded at Holderness, New Hampshire, June 25, 1926, retrapped at same
place, July 3, 1927.

Kirtland Warbler.

F30387, banded at South Branch Township,
Crawford County, Michigan, June 30,
1932, captured at same place May 21,
1933. This is one of the rarest of the
warblers and this particular bird, an adult
male at the time of banding, was killed
by a sharp-shinned hawk the following
year in the identical jack pine thicket
where it was banded. Fortunately, the
specimen was recovered and is preserved
in the collections of the Zoological Museum at the University of Michigan.

Myrtle Warbler.

F80373, banded at Fargo, North Dakota, October 2, 1932, found dead at Clarence,
Louisiana, December 5, 1932.

H03040, banded at North Eastham, Cape
Cod, Massachusetts, April 30, 1932, caught
by cat at North Harpswell, Maine, October 19, 1932.

Palm Warbler.

H44302, banded at North Eastham, Cape Cod,
Massachusetts, October 9, 1932, caught
in house at Point Verde, Placentia, Newfoundland, November 28, 1932. Both
these dates have been verified, showing
that this bird went *north* instead of south
in the autumn.

Pine Warbler.

F35800, banded at North Eastham, Cape Cod,
Massachusetts, August 4, 1931, retrapped
at the same place, April 16, 1934.

Yellow Warbler.

A36074, banded at Sault Ste. Marie, Michigan,
May 30, 1926, retrapped at the station of
banding, May 29, 1929.

B8834, banded at Sault Ste. Marie, Michigan,
May 20, 1928, killed by automobile at
Sault Ste. Marie, Michigan, June 28,
1934.

C7329, banded at Wolfville, Nova Scotia, June
25, 1929, found evidently run over by
automobile at Wickwire Hill, Kentville,
Nova Scotia, July 5, 1933.

Water Turkey.

34-661814, banded at Holly Bluff, Mississippi,
June 15, 1935, killed near Palizada, Campeche, Mexico, December 8, 1935. The
anhinga, snakebird, or water turkey, is
generally supposed to be nonmigratory.

Waxwing, Bohemian.

C119645, banded at Summerland, British
Columbia, Canada, February 15, 1933,
killed in line of fire while shooting
squirrels at Silver City, South Dakota,
March 20, 1934.

Waxwing, Cedar.

B148030, banded at North Eastham, Cape
Cod, Massachusetts, May 12, 1931, killed
at Girard, Alabama, January 3, 1933.

Photograph courtesy U. S. Biological Survey

"AHA," SAYS A MIGRATING RED-BREASTED NUTHATCH, "A GOOD
PLACE TO REST"

C177657, banded at Shirley, Massachusetts, July 11, 1933, found dead at Houma, Louisiana, February 25, 1934.

C190051, banded at Groton, Massachusetts, August 31, 1933, captured at Watson, Louisiana, February 16, 1934.

35-101358, banded at Modesto, California, March 10, 1935, found dead enmeshed in a poultry netting, at Olympia, Washington, June 10, 1935.

Willet.

A435411, banded 30 miles southeast of Brooks, Alberta, July 6, 1932, found dead at Hamilton, Missouri, September 3, 1932.

Woodcock.

244598, banded May 8, 1932, at Fort Snelling Reservation, Minnesota, killed at Ocean Springs, Mississippi, January 7, 1933.

287099, banded July 9, 1926, at La Crosse, Wisconsin, killed at Baton Rouge, Louisiana, in December, 1928.

A408449, banded at Fairhope, Alabama, December 16, 1932, shot at Sydney, Nova Scotia, October 31, 1933.

Wren, House.

C8008, banded at Youngstown, Ohio, July 15, 1931, found dead at West Newton, Massachusetts, about October 10, 1933.

C14530, banded at South Bend, Indiana, June 20, 1930, caught by cat at Atmore, Alabama, January 18, 1931.

Yellow-Legs, Lesser.

B234496, banded at North Eastham, Cape Cod, Massachusetts, August 14, 1933, shot at Barbados, British West Indies, August 23, 1934.

34-258391, banded at North Eastham, Cape Cod, Massachusetts, August 28, 1935, killed at Lamentin, Martinique, French West Indies, September 3, 1935. It had traveled 1,930 miles in five days.

34-258574, banded at North Eastham, Cape Cod, Massachusetts, August 3, 1935, killed at São Paulo, Brazil, November, 1935.

Yellow-Throat, Maryland.

C2085, banded at Oliverea, New York, May 15, 1929, retrapped at same place August 15, 1930, May 16, 1931, and May 10, 1932.

INDEX TO VOLUME II

A

Page

Acanthis hornemanni exilipes (hoary redpoll) 255
   linaria linaria (common redpoll) 255
Aegothelidae (owlet frog-mouths) 40
Aëronautes saxatilis saxatilis (white-throated swift) ... 43
Agelaius phoeniceus phoeniceus (eastern redwing) 233
   tricolor (tricolored redwing) 233
Aimophila aestivalis aestivalis (pine-woods sparrow) .. 276
   aestivalis bachmani (Bachman's sparrow) 276
   botterii botterii (Botteri's sparrow) 276
   carpalis (rufous-winged sparrow) 274
   cassini (Cassin's sparrow) 276
   ruficeps scotti (Scott's sparrow) 274
Alaudidae (larks) 177
Alcedinidae (kingfishers) 79
Alcedo atthis (kingfisher) 79
Allen, Arthur A. 65, 179, 211, 235, 248
   Killdeer on cap photographed by ....ill. 334
Amazilia tzacatl tzacatl (Rieffer's hummingbird) 38
   yucatanensis chalconota (buff-bellied hummingbird) 38
Ammodramus bairdi (Baird's sparrow) 270
   savannarum australis (eastern grasshopper sparrow) 270
   savannarum bimaculatus (western grasshopper
   sparrow) 270
   savannarum floridanus (Florida grasshopper sparrow) 270
Ammospiza caudacuta caudacuta (sharp-tailed sparrow) 272
   caudacuta nelsoni (Nelson's sparrow) 272
   caudacuta subvirgata (Acadian sparrow) 272
   maritima maritima (northern seaside sparrow) ... 272
   mirabilis (Cape Sable seaside sparrow) 272
   nigrescens (dusky seaside sparrow) 272
Amphispiza belli belli (Bell's sparrow) 278
   belli cinerea (gray sage sparrow) 278
   bilineata deserticola (desert sparrow) 276
   nevadensis canescens (California sage sparrow) .. 278
   nevadensis nevadensis (northern sage sparrow) .. 278
Anderson, (Dr.) W. W., Virginia's warbler discovered
   by 205
Ani 77
   Groove-billed ....82; color plate 83
   San Lucas 82
   Smooth-billed ....82; color plate 83
Anthony, A. W. 127, 291
Anthus spinoletta rubescens (American pipit) 177
   spraguei (Sprague's pipit) 177
Antrostomus carolinensis (chuck-will's-widow) 45
   vociferus arizonae (Stephens's whippoorwill) 45
   vociferus vociferus (whippoorwill) 41
Aphelocoma californica californica (California jay) .. 129
   californica hypoleuca (Xantus's jay) 118
   californica immanis (long-tailed jay) 118
   californica obscura (Belding's jay) 118
   californica oocleptica (Nicasio jay) 118
   californica texana (Texas jay) 118
   californica woodhousei (Woodhouse's jay) 118
   coerulescens (Florida jay) 118
   insularis (Santa Cruz jay) 129
   sieberi arizonae (Arizona jay) 123
   sieberi couchi (Couch's jay) 123
Archilochus alexandri (black-chinned hummingbird) .. 32
   colubris (ruby-throated hummingbird) 32
Arctic birds 329
Armfield, Joseph 64
Arremonops rufivirgatus rufivirgatus (Texas sparrow) .. 264
Asio flammeus flammeus (short-eared owl) 10
   wilsonianus (long-eared owl) 10
Asyndesmus lewis (Lewis's woodpecker) 67
Audubon, John James 62, 80, 209, 270, 276
Audubon Association 155, 298
Auriparus flaviceps (verdin) 140
   flaviceps flaviceps (common verdin) 140

B

Bachman, (Rev.) John 205, 276
Baeolophus atricristatus (black-crested titmouse) 136
   atricristatus atricristatus (black-crested titmouse) 136
   atricristatus sennetti (Sennett's titmouse) 136
   bicolor (tufted titmouse) 136
   inornatus (plain titmouse) 136
   wollweberi annexus (bridled titmouse) 136
Bailey, (Mrs.) Florence Merriam 114, 125
Baird, (Prof.) Spencer Fullerton 36, 270
   Virginia's warbler named by 205
Baker, E. C. Stuart, flight of swifts recorded by 31

Page

Balanosphyra formicivora bairdi (California wood-
   pecker) 67
Baldwin, S. Prentiss
   Driving birds into "gathering cage," ill. 321;
   Records of house wren kept by, 149
Banded birds, Recovery of 301, 330, 341,
   349, 350, 351; ill. 304, 313, 319; maps 342, 344
Banded robin. See *Thrush, Varied*
Beaks adapted for crushing seeds 260
Beal, (Prof.) F. E. L. 64
Beecher, Henry Ward 107
Bendire, (Maj.) C. E. 69, 86, 127
"Billy owl." See *Owl, Burrowing*
Bird boxes 130-131
Bird-Lore 64, 255, 298
"Bird of paradise." See *Flycatcher, Scissor-tailed*
Birdbanding 301, 330, 338, 341,
   342, 344, 349, 350, 351; ill. 304, 313, 319, 321
   Crows 120
   Hummingbirds 99
Birds of Massachusetts and Other New England States
   (Forbush) 41
Birds of Passage (Longfellow) 180-181
Blackbird
   Brewer's ....218; color plate 219
   Crow. See *Grackle, Purple*
   Rusty ....218; color plate 219
   "Thrush." See *Grackle, Boat-tailed*
   Yellow-headed ....214, 215, 233; color plate 232
Blackbirds 211-215
   Feeding and brooding of young, 215; Fine song-
   sters, 213-214; Migration, 213; Nest building
   and egg laying, 214; New World origin, 211, 212
"Blue crow." See *Jay, Piñon*
"Blue robin," found by English colonists in America .. 156
Bluebird
   Azure 164
   Chestnut-backed 164
   Common. See *Bluebird, Eastern*
   Eastern ....156, 164; ill. 157; color plate 165
     Woodpecker's hole utilized as nest ....ill. 157
   Mountain ....156, 164; color plate 165
   Western ....156, 164; color plate 165
Bluebirds 156-157, 164
   Nesting habits 157
Bobolinks ....218; ill. 215; color plate 219
   Extension of breeding range, 345; map 329;
   Migration and route followed, 213, 337; map 329;
   Mother with meal for young, ill. 215; Nesting
   habits, 214, 215
Bodine, Margaret L. 98
Bombycilla cedrorum (cedar waxwing) 220
   garrula pallidiceps (Bohemian waxwing) 220
Bowles, J. H., chickadee described by 138
Breeding grounds, Some birds linger briefly on 305
Brewster, William 175, 270
Brooks, (Maj.) Allan 183, 235
Bubo virginianus (great horned owl) 8
"Buffalo birds." See *Cowbirds*
"Bull-bat." See *Nighthawk*
Bunting
   "Bay-winged." See *Sparrow, Eastern vesper*
   Beautiful ....237, 246; color plate 247
   Eastern snow ....297; color plate 296
   Indigo ....237, 246; color plate 247
     Color caused by light, 235; Nesting habits,
     238-239
   Lark ....260, 268; color plate 269
   Lazuli ....237, 246; color plate 247
   McKay's snow ....297; color plate 296
   Painted ....251; color plate 250
   Varied 246
Buntings 260, 268-269, 296-297
Bureau of Biological Survey 349, 350
   Stomachs of birds examined by 88, 130
Burroughs, John 41, 274
"Bush bird." See *Towhee, Brown*
Bush-tit ....140; color plate 141
   Lloyd's ....140; color plate 141
Butcher birds. See *Shrikes*
"Butter-birds." See *Bobolinks*
Butterfly, Mourning cloak, stupefied by sap 53-54

C

Calamospiza melanocorys (lark bunting) 268
Calcarius lapponicus lapponicus (Lapland longspur) .. 297
   ornatus (chestnut-collared longspur) 295
   pictus (Smith's longspur) 297
Calothorax lucifer (Lucifer hummingbird) 36

Page

Calypte anna (Anna's hummingbird)................ 32
  costae (Costa's hummingbird)................ 32
  helenae (Helena's hummingbird)............ 28
Camera, Desert sparrow perched on............ill. 262
"Camp robbers." See *Crow, Clark's; Jay, Canada;
  and Jay, Oregon*
Campephilus principalis (ivory-billed woodpecker).... 73
Camptostoma imberbe (beardless flycatcher)........ 97
"Canaries, Wild" 199, 257
"Canary, Mexican." See *Bunting, Painted*
Canvasback: Migratory route..................... 335
Caprimulgidae (goatsuckers).................. 40
Cardellina rubrifrons (red-faced warbler)............ 184
Cardinal.........236-237, 239, 244, 248; color plate 245
  Crumbs invite to window ledge, ill. 131; Rigid in
  palm of hand, ill. 331
"Cardinal, Gray." See *Pyrrhuloxia, Arizona*
Carpodacus cassini (Cassin's purple finch).......... 253
  mexicanus frontalis (house finch)............. 253
  purpureus (purple finch)................... 253
Carraway, J. C................................ 78
Cassidix mexicanus major (boat-tailed grackle)..... 231
  mexicanus mexicanus (great-tailed grackle)..... 231
Cassin, John 60
Cat, Possession of, keeps birds away............. 300
Catbird.......................164; color plate 165
Catherpes mexicanus (cañon wren)............. 147
Centurus aurifrons (golden-fronted woodpecker)... 71
  carolinus (red-bellied woodpecker)............ 71
  uropygialis (Gila woodpecker)................ 71
  uropygialis brewsteri (Brewster's woodpecker)... 71
  uropygialis cardonensis (Cardón woodpecker)... 71
Ceophloeus pileatus (pileated woodpecker)........ 73
  pileatus abieticola (northern pileated woodpecker). 73
  pileatus floridanus (Florida pileated woodpecker). 73
  pileatus picinus (western pileated woodpecker).. 73
  pileatus pileatus (southern pileated woodpecker). 73
Certhia familiaris (brown creeper)................ 140
Certhiidae (creepers).......................... 140
"Chad." See *Woodpecker, Red-bellied*
Chaetura pelagica (chimney swift)............43, 301
  vauxi (Vaux's swift) 43
Chamaea fasciata (wren-tit)................... 140
Chamaeidae 140
Chapman, (Dr.) Frank M. 80, 192, 207, 240, 299
Chat, Yellow-breasted............184; color plate 185
Cherry bird. See *Waxwing, Cedar*
"Chewink." See *Towhee, Red-eyed*
Chickadee
  Acadian 138
  Black-capped..................138; color plate 139
  Carolina 138
  Chestnut-backed ....138; color plate 139
  Hudsonian ....138; color plate 139
  Mexican 138
  Mountain ....138; color plate 139
Chickadees 51, 135, 138
  Feeding young .... ill. 134
Chloroceryle americana septentrionalis (Texas king-
  fisher) 86
Chondestes grammacus grammacus (eastern lark spar-
  row) 274
  grammacus strigatus (western lark sparrow)..... 274
Chordeiles acutipennis (Texas nighthawk)........ 47
  acutipennis inferior (San Lucas nighthawk)..... 47
  acutipennis texensis (Texas nighthawk)....... 47
  minor (nighthawk)...................... 47
Chuck-will's-widow..................45; color plate 44
Cinclidae (dippers) 151
Cinclus mexicanus unicolor (dipper) 151
Cistothorus stellaris (short-billed marsh wren)..... 151
Cleaning nest, Redwing.....................ill. 212
Coccyzus americanus (yellow-billed cuckoo)....... 84
  americanus americanus (yellow-billed cuckoo).... 84
  americanus occidentalis (California cuckoo)..... 84
  erythropthalmus (black-billed cuckoo).......... 84
Cockatoo
  Black 76
  Sulphur-crested 77
Cockatoos 75, 76, 77
Colaptes auratus auratus (southern yellow-shafted
  flicker) 69
  auratus luteus (northern yellow-shafted flicker).. 69
  cafer (red-shafted flicker).................. 69
  chrysoides (gilded flicker)................. 71
  chrysoides brunnescens (San Fernando flicker)... 71
  chrysoides chrysoides (Cape gilded flicker)..... 71
  chrysoides mearnsi (Mearns's gilded flicker).... 71
Collocalia (swiftlets) 31
Color in feathers...................27-28, 235-237
Compsothlypidae (wood warblers).............. 179
Compsothlypis americana (parula warbler)........ 194
Conuropsis carolinensis (Carolina parakeet)....... 80
  carolinensis carolinensis (Carolina parakeet).. 80
  carolinensis ludovicianus (Louisiana parakeet)... 80

Page

Cooke, (Dr.) Wells W. 298
Coot ....ill. 326
  Nest and eggs............................ill. 326
Corthylio calendula (ruby-crowned kinglet)........ 153
Corvidae 104, 109
Corvus brachyrhynchos brachyrhynchos (eastern crow) 112
  brachyrhynchos caurinus (northwestern crow).... 112
  brachyrhynchos hesperis (western crow)....... 112
  brachyrhynchos pascuus (Florida crow)........ 112
  brachyrhynchos paulus (southern crow)........ 112
  corax principalis (northern raven)............ 112
  corax sinuatus (American raven)............. 112
  cornix cornix (hooded crow)................ 104
  cryptoleucus (white-necked raven)........... 112
  frugilegus frugilegus (rook)................ 104
  ossifragus (fish crow)..................... 112
Coues, (Dr.) Elliott.............203, 249, 264, 301
Cowbird
  Bronzed 209
  Eastern ....216; color plate 217
  Red-eyed ....209; color plate 208
Cowbirds 214-215, 216
  Male display of plumage, 214; Parasitism of, ill.
  340, 341; Young in redstart's nest, ill. 341
Craighead brothers take up falconry.............ill. 4
Creeper, Brown................51, 140; color plate 141
Crops saved by birds.......................... 89
Crossbill
  Red ....257; color plate 256
  White-winged ....257; color plate 256
Crossbills ....237, 249, 257; ill. 304
Crotophaga ani (smooth-billed ani)............. 82
  sulcirostris (groove-billed ani).............. 82
  sulcirostris pallidula (San Lucas ani).......... 82
Crow
  "Blue." See *Jay, Piñon*
  Carrion 104
  Clark's. See *Nutcracker, Clark's*
  Common. See *Crow, Eastern*
  Eastern ....112; color plate 113
  Fish ....112; color plate 113
  Hooded 104
  Northwestern 112
  "Rain." See *Cuckoo, Yellow-billed*
  Southern 112
  Western 112
Crows 6, 13, 14, 89, 104-109, 112, 120-121
  At water hole, Ithaca, New York, ill. 107; Food
  items of a young crow, ill. 103; Make amusing
  pets, 107; ill. 105; Roosts, 107, 120-121; War
  on, 105, 121; Young in nest, ill. 102
Cryptoglaux acadica (saw-whet owl)............. 19
  acadica acadica (saw-whet owl)............. 19
  acadica brooksi (Queen Charlotte owl)........ 19
  funerea magna (Tengmalm's owl)............ 19
  funerea richardsoni (Richardson's owl)........ 19
Cuckoo
  Black-billed.................79, 84; color plate 85
  California 84
  Common 79
  European 77, 78, 85
  Yellow-billed.................79, 84; color plate 85
Cuckoos 77-79, 82-84
  Parasitism, 78-79; Relatives of parrots, 77
Cuculidae (cuckoos) 77
Cyanocephalus cyanocephalus (piñon jay)........ 125
Cyanocitta cristata cristata (northern blue jay)...... 116
  cristata florincola (Florida blue jay)......... 116
  cristata semplei (Semple's blue jay)......... 116
  stelleri (Steller's jay)..................... 116
  stelleri annectens (black-headed jay)......... 116
  stelleri carbonacea (coast jay)............. 116
  stelleri carlottae (Queen Charlotte jay)....... 116
  stelleri diademata (long-crested jay)......... 116
  stelleri frontalis (blue-fronted jay).......... 116
Cynanthus latirostris (broad-billed hummingbird).... 36

D

Davis, E. R.................................. 255
Dawson, W. L., quoted on Santa Cruz jay........ 129
Dendroica (North American warblers)............ 179
Dendroica æstiva (yellow warbler)............. 199
  auduboni (Audubon's warbler)............. 199
  caerulescens (black-throated blue warbler)...... 194
  caerulescens cairnsi (Cairns's warbler)....... 194
  castanea (bay-breasted warbler)............ 190
  cerulea (cerulean warbler)................ 203
  chrysoparia (golden-cheeked warbler)........ 207
  coronata (myrtle warbler)................. 203
  discolor (prairie warbler)................. 188
  dominica (yellow-throated warbler)......... 203
  dominica albilora (sycamore warbler)........ 203
  fusca (Blackburnian warbler)............... 192
  graciae (Grace's warbler)................. 203
  kirtlandi (Kirtland's warbler).............. 203

Page

Dendroica magnolia (magnolia warbler)............ 192
　nigrescens (black-throated gray warbler)........ 190
　occidentalis (hermit warbler).................... 207
　palmarum (palm warbler)....................... 188
　pensylvanica (chestnut-sided warbler).......... 192
　pinus (pine warbler)........................... 190
　pinus florida (Florida pine warbler)............ 190
　striata (black-poll warbler)................... 192
　tigrina (Cape May warbler).................... 194
　townsendi (Townsend's warbler)................ 207
　virens (black-throated green warbler)........... 190
　virens waynei (Wayne's warbler)............... 190
Depth of water to which belted kingfisher dives for
　food 76
"Dick" (cockatoo) 77
Dickcissel.......................251; color plate 250
Dickey, Donald 14
Dipper....................151; ill. 144; color plate 150
Display of plumage by male cowbird................ 214
Docimastes ensifera (sword-bearer hummer)........ 28
Dolichonyx oryzivorus (bobolink).................. 218
Dove, Mourning
　Flight of, ill. 355; Rigid in palm of hand, ill.
　331
Dryobates albolarvatus (white-headed woodpecker).. 62
　albolarvatus albolarvatus (white-headed wood-
　　pecker) 62
　albolarvatus gravirostris (southern white-headed
　　woodpecker) 62
　arizonae arizonae (Arizona woodpecker)........ 58
　borealis (red-cockaded woodpecker)............. 58
　nuttalli (Nuttall's woodpecker)................. 58
　pubescens (downy woodpecker)................. 56
　pubescens gairdneri (Gairdner's woodpecker)..... 56
　pubescens medianus (northern downy woodpecker) 56
　scalaris symplectus (Texas woodpecker)........ 58
　villosus (hairy woodpecker)................... 56
　villosus harrisi (Harris's woodpecker)........... 56
Ducks, Migration routes of...... 335, 337; maps 342, 344
Dumetella carolinensis (catbird)................. 164
Dwight, (Dr.) Jonathan, quoted on Ipswich sparrow.. 268

E

Eastern birds are pushing their colonies westward.... 345
Economic value of birds....................88-89, 130
Edgerton, (Dr.) Harold E.....................354, 355
Emberizinae 260
Empidonax difficilis (western flycatcher)........ 95
　flaviventris (yellow-bellied flycatcher)........... 95
　fulvifrons pygmaeus (buff-breasted flycatcher).... 95
　minimus (least flycatcher).................... 95
　trailli (alder flycatcher).................... 95
　viriscens (Acadian flycatcher).................. 95
Eugenes fulgens (Rivoli hummingbird).............. 38
Euphagus carolinus (rusty blackbird)............. 218
　cyanocephalus (Brewer's blackbird)............ 218

F

Fable of the king of birds...................... 145
Fables concerning owls......................... 5
Falco peregrinus (peregrine falcon)............... 313
Falconry, Owls trained for.....................ill. 4
Fastest flight yet recorded...................... 314
Feeding of young blackbirds..................... 215
Fifty-nine pairs of birds nest on one acre, "Wild
　Acres," Maryland............................ 298
Finch
　California purple 253
　Cassin's purple ....253; color plate 252
　Gray-crowned rosy............. 255; color plate 254
　"Grass." See *Sparrow, Eastern vesper*
　"Green." See *Sparrow, Texas*
　House.................237, 239, 253; color plate 252
　Purple........98, 237, 239, 253; color plate 252
　Rosy................237, 255; color plate 254
Finches 236-258
　Coloring, 236-237; Favorite songsters, 239; Feed-
　ing habits, 239; Nesting habits, 238-239; Spe-
　cies, 238; Where found, 238
Finches, Weaver 238, 280
Firecrest 153
Fisher, (Dr.) A. K. 36
Flashlight picture of an owl.....................ill. 74
Flicker
　Cape gilded 71
　Gilded ....71; color plate 70
　Mearns's gilded 71
　Red-shafted ....69; color plate 68
　San Fernando 71
　Yellow-shafted..........69; ill. 55; color plate 68
Flickers
　Borings made by, 64-65; Feeding habits, 64;
　Stomach contents, 88; Tongue, 64; Young, ill. 55

Page

Flocking of small birds during migration........181-182
Flycatcher
　Acadian 95
　Alder ....95; color plate 94
　Ash-throated ....93; color plate 92
　Beardless ....97; color plate 96
　Buff-breasted ....95; color plate 94
　Coues's ....97; color plate 96
　Derby ....93; color plate 92
　Great crested ....93; color plate 92
　Least ....95; color plate 94
　Northern crested 93
　Olivaceous ....93; color plate 92
　Olive-sided ....97; color plate 96
　Royal 79
　San Lucas 95
　Scissor-tailed ....91; color plate 90
　Silky. See *Phainopepla*
　Southern crested 93
　Sulphur-bellied ....93; color plate 92
　Vermilion ....97; color plate 96
　Western 95
　Yellow-bellied ....95; color plate 94
Flycatchers 79, 91-97
Flyways of North America: Map Showing Bird Migra-
　tion Routes...................map on lining-papers
Fog, Birds fly through densest 319-320
Folklore, Raven in............................. 101
Food log, Nuthatch and house sparrow on.......ill. 262
Food supply cause of migration............303, 304, 346
Forbush, E. H. 41
Forests preserved by birds....................179, 183
Fringillidae (finch family)................238, 260, 280
Frog-mouths 40
　Owlet 40
Fuertes, Louis Agassiz.....................183, 240

G

Geococcyx californianus (road-runner)............ 82
Geographical distribution of birds..............211-213
Geothlypis trichas (Maryland yellow-throat)........ 184
Germeshausen, Kenneth J...................... 355
Giraud, J. P., Audubon's oriole discovered by...... 209
Glaucidium brasilianum ridgwayi (ferruginous pygmy
　owl) 23
　gnoma (pygmy owl) 23
Gnatcatcher
　Black-tailed ....153; color plate 152
　Blue-gray ....153; color plate 152
　Plumbeous ....153; color plate 152
Goatsuckers 40-41, 45-49
　Active only at night, 40; Legends concerning,
　41; Notes, 41
Goldcrest 153
Goldfinch
　Eastern ....color plate 254
　Green-backed ....237, 257; color plate 256
　Lawrence's ....237, 257; color plate 256
　Pale 255
　Willow 255, 257
Goldfinches.....................159, 237, 255, 257
　Feeding of young, 239; Nesting habits, 238, 248-
　249; ill. 239; Winter coloring, 248
Goose
　Blue
　　Flock in flight, ill. 312; Late migration of,
　　314, 340
　Canada ....ill. 313
　　Eggs in nest, ill. 313; Migratory route of,
　　335; map 305
　Ross's: Breeding range and migration route..map 333
Gourds utilized as nests by purple martins........ill. 158
Grackle
　Boat-tailed ....231; color plate 230
　　Stomach contents 88
　Bronzed 231
　Florida 231
　　Nesting habits 169
　Great-tailed 231
　Purple ....231; color plate 230
Grackles: Nesting habits....................214, 215
"Grass finch." See *Sparrow, Eastern vesper*
"Green finch." See *Sparrow, Texas*
Grinnell, (Dr.) George......................... 242
Griscom, Ludlow, quoted on green jay............. 123
Grosbeak
　Black-headed.........237, 239, 246; color plate 247
　Blue.................237, 244; color plate 245
　Evening............237, 238, 251; color plate 250
　Pine ....237, 253; color plate 252
　Rose-breasted....237, 239, 244; ill. 258; color
　　plate 245
　　Breeding range and migratory path, 332; map
　　322; Nest and eggs, ill. 258

Page

Grosbeaks..........................238, 239, 248
Grosvenor, Gilbert, birds around home of........298-299
Guatemala, National bird of.................. 79
Guiraca caerulea (blue grosbeak)................. 244

H

Haunts of wood warblers....................... 179
Havens, Essentials in bird....................130-133
Hawk
  Duck 313
  Sharp-shinned 51
  Swainson's: Stomach contents............... 88
Hawks, Insects and rodents destroyed by......... 89
Hedymeles ludovicianus (rose-breasted grosbeak)..... 244
  melanocephalus (black-headed grosbeak)........ 246
Height at which birds fly....................317-319
Heleodytes brunneicapillus (cactus wren).......... 147
Helmitheros vermivorus (worm-eating warbler)....... 201
Hemiprocnidae (tree swifts) 30
Henshaw, Henry W..........36, 60, 114, 129, 179, 298
Herons, Migration of 345-346
Hesperiphona vespertina (evening grosbeak)......... 251
Hirundinidae (swallows) 168
Hirundo erythrogaster (barn swallow)............. 173
Holt, Ernest G............................. 65
Homing instinct of birds....................320-321
Hosking, Eric J., flashlight picture by...........ill. 74
Hummer
  Fairy 28
  Giant 28
Hummingbird
  Allen's ....34; color plate 35
  Anna's ....32; color plate 33
  Arizona blue-throat 38
  Black-chinned ....32; color plate 33
  Blue-throated ....38; color plate 39
  Broad-billed ....36; color plate 37
  Broad-tailed ....34; color plate 35
  Buff-bellied ....38; color plate 39
  Calliope ....34; color plate 35
  Costa's ....32; color plate 33
  Emerald 27
  Giant 28
  Helena's 28
  Long-tailed Sappho 27
  Lucifer ....36; color plate 37
  Racket-tailed 28
  Rieffer's ....38; color plate 39
  Rivoli ....38; color plate 39
  Ruby-throated.......27, 32, 98, 99; ill. 26, 28;
                                       color plate 33
  Rufous ....34; color plate 35
  Sword-bearer 28
  Texas blue-throat 38
  Vervain 29
  White-eared ....36; color plate 37
  Xantus's ....36; color plate 37
Hummingbirds..................27-29, 32-39, 98-99
  Absence from English landscape, 211; Crests, 29;
  Drinking sweetened water, ill. 354; Feeding habits,
  29; ill. 26; Habitat, 27; Nesting habits, 29;
  Plumage under a microscope, 27-28; Powers of
  vision, 98; Pugnacity of, 29, 98-99; Sickle-
  shaped bills, 28; Size and form, 28; Species num-
  bers decrease as climate becomes colder, 27; Tail
  feathers, 28-29; Young, 99; ill. 26, 28
Hunting Wild Life with Camera and Flashlight
  (Shiras) 349
Hylocharis leucotis leucotis (white-eared hummingbird) 36
  xantusi (Xantus's hummingbird)............ 36
Hylocichla fuscescens fuscescens (veery)........... 162
  fuscescens salicicola (willow thrush)........... 162
  guttata (hermit thrush) 162
  minima aliciae (gray-cheeked thrush)........ 162
  minima minima (Bicknell's thrush)......... 162
  mustelina (wood thrush) 162
  ustulata swainsoni (olive-backed thrush)....... 162
  ustulata ustulata (russet-backed thrush)........ 162

I

Icteria virens (yellow-breasted chat)............. 184
Icteridae (oriole family)...................... 211
Icterus bullocki (Bullock's oriole)............... 229
  cucullatus (hooded oriole)................. 229
  galbula (Baltimore oriole)................. 227
  melanocephalus auduboni (Audubon's oriole).... 209
  parisorum (Scott's oriole).................. 229
  spurius (orchard oriole).................... 227
Increase of crows, Reasons for..............120, 121
Incubation period of parasitic birds...........214-215
Indians, North American...................... 5
Indians, South American...................... 29
Insects and rodents devoured by birds....88-89, 179, 183

Page

Iridoprocne bicolor (tree swallow).................. 175
Ixoreus naevius (varied thrush).................. 160

J

Jack Miner's Bird Sanctuary, Ontario...........ill. 313
"Jackdaw." See *Grackle, Boat-tailed*
Jacklight, Hunting birds with aid of.............. 40
Jay
  Alaska 127
  Arizona...................123; color plate 122
  Belding's 118
  Black-headed 116
  Blue ....ill. 106
    Cries and shouts of, 110; Nest, ill. 106; Rigid
    in palm of hand, ill. 331
  Blue-fronted 116
  California........118, 129; ill. 106; color plate 128
  Canada...................127; color plate 126
    Eating venison ....ill. 104
  Coast 116
  Couch's 123
  Florida............118; ill. 100; color plate 119
  Florida blue................116; ill. 100, 108
  Green.....................123; color plate 122
  Long-crested 116
  Long-tailed 118
  Nicasio 118
  Northern blue ....116; color plate 117
  Oregon...................127; color plate 126
  Piñon....................125; color plate 124
  Queen Charlotte 116
  Rocky Mountain 127
  Santa Cruz...............129; color plate 128
  Semple's blue 116
  Steller's ....116; color plate 117
  Texas 118
  Woodhouse's ....118; color plate 119
  Xantus's 118
Jays.....................93, 110, 116-118, 123-129
  Migration of 350
"Jenny wren." See *Wren, House*
Junco
  Arizona..................283; color plate 282
  Carolina 280
  Gray-headed..............283; color plate 282
  Montana 283
  Oregon...................283; color plate 282
  Pink-sided...............283; color plate 282
  Red-backed 283
  Shufeldt's 283
  Slate-colored.........278, 280, 281; color plate 279
  White-winged.............278; color plate 279
Junco aikeni (white-winged junco).............. 278
  caniceps (gray-headed junco)............... 283
  hyemalis hyemalis (slate-colored junco)....... 278
  mearnsi (pink-sided junco)................ 283
  oreganus (Oregon junco)................... 283
  oreganus montanus (Montana junco).......... 283
  oreganus oreganus (Oregon junco).......... 283
  oreganus shufeldti (Shufeldt's junco)......... 283
  phaeonotus dorsalis (red-backed junco)........ 283
  phaeonotus palliatus (Arizona junco)......... 283
Juncos......................280-281; ill. 263
  Association with white-throat sparrows, 280; Coloring, 280; Distances traveled by, 281

K

Kalmbach, E. R. 120
Killdeer 88
  Photographed on man's cap, ill. 334; Simulates
  decrepitude to lure people from nest, ill. 347
Kingbird
  Arkansas ....91; color plate 90
  Cassin's ....91; color plate 90
  Couch's ....91; color plate 90
  Eastern ....91; color plate 90
  Gray 91
  Western. See *Kingbird, Arkansas*
Kingfisher
  Belted..........79, 86; ill. 76; color plate 87
  Eastern belted 86
  Green-backed 79
  Texas...................86; color plate 87
  Western belted 86
Kingfishers 79, 86
  Dive from 50-foot height, 76; Young, ill. 77
Kinglet
  Eastern golden-crown 153
  Golden-crowned ....153; color plate 152
  Ruby-crowned ....153; color plate 152
  Western golden-crown 153
Kleberg, Richard 242
Kookaburra 79

L

Page

Lampornis clemenciae (blue-throated hummer) 38
   clemenciae bessophilus (Arizona blue-throated
     hummer) 38
   clemenciae clemenciae (Texas blue-throated hum-
     mer) 38
Lanius borealis (northern shrike) 220
   borealis invictus (northwestern shrike) 220
   ludovicianus (logger-head shrike) 220
Large birds serve as aerial transports for smaller
   species 302
Lark
   Arctic horned ....color plate 176
   Horned ....177; color plate 176
   Pallid horned. See Lark, Arctic horned
   Prairie horned...............177; color plate 176
Laughing jackass 79
Leucosticte tephrocotis tephrocotis (gray-crowned rosy
   finch) 255
Light, Hunting birds with aid of 40
Light stations cause of bird tragedies..............347-348
Limnothlypis swainsoni (Swainson's warbler) 205
Lincoln, Frederick C. 301, 351
"Linnet, California." See Finch, House
Locust, Red-legged 26
Loggerhead. See Shrike, Loggerhead
Longevity of parrots 76, 77
Longfellow, Henry W., Birds of Passage, quoted.. 180-181
Longspur
   Chestnut-collared ....295; color plate 294
   Lapland ....297; color plate 296
   McCown's ....295; color plate 294
   Smith's ....297; color plate 296
Longspurs 260, 294-297
   Frequent victims of storms 347
"Lord Baltimore." See Oriole, Baltimore
Lories 75, 76
Louisiana harbors last of ivory-billed woodpeckers.... 65
Louisiana State Conservation Commission.......... 65
Loxia curvirostra (red crossbill) 257
   leucoptera (white-winged crossbill) 257

M

Macaw, Hyacinthine 76
Macaws 75
McCown, (Capt.) John P. 295
Magpie
   American...............109, 114; color plate 115
   Black-billed. See Magpie, American
   Yellow-billed..................114; color plate 115
Magpies 109, 114
   Nests raided by..........................109-110
Mailliard, Joseph, quoted on California jay........ 129
Mallards
   In wire-mesh trap, ill. 318; Migratory route,
   335
Map: Flyways of North America: Map Showing Bird
   Migration Routes................map on lining-papers
Maps of migratory routes...........305, 306, 307
       308, 309, 315, 320, 322, 323, 324, 327,
       329, 333, 336, 342, 344
Martin, Purple............168-169, 173; color plate 172
   Nesting in gourds...........................ill. 158
Martins
   Nesting habits, 168-169; ill. 158; Roosts, 169
Maynard, C. J. 268
Meadowlark 177
   Eastern...................213, 216; color plate 217
   Rio Grande 216
   Southern 216
   Western ....209, 214, 216; color plate 208
Meadowlarks ....ill. 224
   Nesting habits 214, 215
Meat, Canada jay eating....................ill. 104
Megaceryle alcyon (belted kingfisher).......... 86
   alcyon alcyon (eastern belted kingfisher)........ 86
   alcyon caurina (western belted kingfisher)...... 86
Melanerpes erythrocephalus (red-headed woodpecker) 67
Melospiza georgiana (swamp sparrow)............. 295
   lincolni lincolni (Lincoln's sparrow).......... 295
   melodia (song sparrows)...................... 293
   melodia melodia (eastern song sparrow)........ 293
   melodia rufina (sooty song sparrow).......... 293
   melodia saltonis (desert song sparrow)........ 293
   melodia sanaka (Aleutian song sparrow)........ 293
Merriam, (Dr.) C. Hart......................... 19
Merrill, (Dr.) James C. 38
Micropallas whitneyi (elf owl) 23
   whitneyi idoneus (Texas elf owl) 23
   whitneyi sanfordi (Sanford's elf owl) 23
   whitneyi whitneyi (Whitney's elf owl) 23
Micropodidae (swifts) 30
Migration
   Blackbirds and vireos, 213; Maps of migratory
   routes, 305, 306, 307, 308, 309, 315, 320, 322,

Page

Migration—Continued
   323, 324, 327, 329, 333, 336, 342, 344; Range of
   migration, 326, 328-330, 332-333; Recovery of
   banded birds, 301, 330, 341, 349, 350, 351; ill.
   304, 313, 319; maps 342, 344; Tanagers and
   finches, 237; Wood warblers, Spectacular migration
   of, 180-181
Mimidae (thrashers and mockingbirds)............. 168
Mimus polyglottos (mockingbird)..............166, 168
   polyglottos leucopterus (western mockingbird).... 166
Mniotilta varia (black and white warbler)........ 199
"Mocking" wren. See Wren, Carolina
Mockingbird........................166; color plate 167
   Western 166
Mockingbirds 166, 168
Molothrus ater (cowbird) 216
Motacillidae (wagtails and pipits).............. 177
Muscivora forficata (scissor-tailed flycatcher)........ 91
Myadestes townsendi (Townsend's solitaire)....... 160
Myiarchus cinerascens (ash-throated flycatcher)...... 93
   crinitus (great crested flycatcher)............ 93
   crinitus boreus (northern crested flycatcher)...... 93
   crinitus crinitus (southern crested flycatcher).... 93
   tuberculifer olivascens (olivaceous flycatcher).... 93
Myiochanes pertinax pallidiventris (Coues's flycatcher) 97
   richardsoni (western wood pewee)............. 97
   richardsoni richardsoni (western wood pewee).... 97
   virens (eastern wood pewee)................. 97
Myiodynastes luteiventris swarthi (sulphur-bellied flycatcher) 93

N

Nannus hiemalis (winter wren) 149
National Museum, Washington, D. C. 16, 31, 36, 40
National Zoological Park, Washington, D. C.......12, 77
Nelson, (Dr.) E. W. ....19, 38, 201; ill. 100
Nephoecetes niger borealis (black swift)........ 43
Nest building 238-239
   Blackbirds, 214; Chipping and white-throat spar-
   rows, 260, 261; ill. 263; Time when birds start,
   159
Nets for catching birds..........................ill. 338
Nice, (Mrs.) Margaret Morse.................... 293
Night flying of migratory birds.............310-312
Nighthawk....................47; color plate 46
   San Lucas 47
   Texas ....47; color plate 46
Nighthawks
   Nest and eggs, ill. 50; Stomach contents, 88
Nightingale, European 157
Nightjar 40
Nightjars, Wood 40
"None so Small" (picture of sparrow)..........ill. 281
"Nonpareil." See Bunting, Painted
Nucifraga columbiana (Clark's nutcracker)......... 125
Nutcracker, Clark's................111, 125; ill. 111;
       color plate 124
   Cleaning surplus flesh from pelts, ill. 339; Verti-
   cal migration, 339, 345
Nuthatch
   Brown-headed ....142; color plate 143
   Gray-headed 142
   Pygmy ....142; color plate 143
   Red-breasted ....142; color plate 143
      Resting on fishing rod...............ill. 363
   White-breasted.........51, 135, 142; color plate 143
Nuthatches 51, 135, 142
   Nuthatch and house sparrow on food log......ill. 262
Nuttallornis mesoleucus (olive-sided flycatcher)...... 97
Nyctea nyctea (snowy owl) 12
Nyctibiidae (wood nightjars).................... 40
Nyctidromus albicollis merrilli (Merrill's pauraque).. 49

O

Oak trees brought jays to Florida, Cultivation of.... 110
Oberholseria chlorura (green-tailed towhee).......... 266
Oporornis agilis (Connecticut warbler)........... 186
   formosus (Kentucky warbler)................. 188
   philadelphia (mourning warbler)............. 186
   tolmiei (Macgillivray's warbler)............. 186
Oreoscoptes montanus (sage thrasher)............ 166
Origin of North American bird life......211-212, 237-238
Oriole
   Audubon's ....209; color plate 208
   Baltimore ....214, 227; color plate 226
      Uses string in nest building.............ill. 210
   Bullock's ....229; color plate 228
   Hooded ....229; color plate 228
   Orchard ....214, 227; color plate 226
      Spends only 2½ months on breeding grounds 305
   Scott's ....229; color plate 228
Orioles 214, 215, 227-229
   Nesting habits, 214, 215; New World origin, 211,
   212

Page

Orthotomus (tailor-birds)......................... 153
Otocoris alpestris (horned lark).................... 177
Otus asio (screech owl).......................... 25
  asio kennicotti (Kennicott's screech owl)........ 25
  asio naevius (eastern screech owl).............. 25
  flammeolus (flammulated screech owl).......... 19
  trichopsis (spotted screech owl)............... 19
Ouzel, Water...............151; ill. 144; color plate 150
Oven-bird............184, 302; ill. 303; color plate 185
  Nest ....ill. 303
Owl
  American hawk ....21; color plate 20
  Arctic horned ....color plate 9
  Barn ....5, 10, 16, 88; ill. 7, 74
  Barred 14
  "Billy." See *Owl, Burrowing*
  Burrowing 6, 7, 17, 21
  California spotted 14
  Eastern screech...............25; color plate 24
  Elf ....23; ill. 74
  European barn: Entering nest............ill. 74
  Ferruginous pygmy..............23; color plate 22
  Flammulated screech.............19; color plate 18
  Florida barred 14
  Florida burrowing 21
  Great barred 5
  Great gray ....12, 14; color plate 13
  Great horned ...6, 7, 8, 121, 159; color plate 9
    Trained for falconry....................ill. 4
  Kennicott's screech ....25; color plate 24
  Long-eared ....10, 16; ill. 17; color plate 11
  Mexican spotted 14
  "Monkey-faced." See *Owl, Barn*
  Northern barred ....14; color plate 15
  Northern spotted ....14; color plate 15
  Pygmy 23
  Queen Charlotte 19
  Richardson's ....19; color plate 18
  Rocky Mountain pygmy...............color plate 22
  Sanford's elf owl....................... 23
  Saw-whet ....19; color plate 18
  Screech ....25; color plate 24
  Short-eared ....10; color plate 11
  Siberian gray 12
  Siberian hawk 21
  Snowy........6, 7, 12, 16-17, 21; color plate 13
    Invasions caused by shortage of food...... 346
  Spotted 14
  Spotted screech 19
  Tengmalm's 19
  Texas barred 14
  Texas elf 23
  Western burrowing ....21; color plate 20
  Whitney's elf ....23; color plate 22
Owls   5-25
  Aggressiveness of, 6; Fables concerning, 5; Feed-
  ing habits, 6, 7, 16; ill. 74; Habitat, 16; Insects
  and rodents destroyed by, 88, 89; Nesting habits,
  6; ill. 7, 17; Pellets regurgitated by, 6-7, 11;
  Plumage, 6, 16; Range, 11; Size, 5, 16; Stuffed
  owl provides fun, 299; ill. 100; Young, 16

P

Panama, Birds found in........................ 211
Parakeet
  Carolina...............75, 80; color plate 81
  Louisiana 80
Parakeets 75, 80
Parasitism of cuckoos........................78-79
Paridae (titmice) 135
Parrot
  African gray 76
  Amazon 75, 76
  Thick-billed...............75, 80; color plate 81
"Parrot-bill." See *Pyrrhuloxia, Arizona*
Parrots 75-77, 80
  Longevity of, 76, 77; Mimicry, 76-77; Not native
  to Europe, 75; Size, 76; Tongue, 75-76
Passer domesticus (house sparrow)............. 280
  domesticus domesticus (house sparrow)........ 240
Passerculus beldingi (Belding's sparrow)......... 268
  princeps (Ipswich sparrow).................. 268
  rostratus rostratus (large-billed sparrow)...... 268
  sandwichensis savanna (eastern Savannah sparrow) 268
Passerella iliaca fuliginosa (sooty fox sparrow)... 291
  iliaca iliaca (eastern fox sparrow)............ 291
  iliaca stephensi (Stephens's fox sparrow)...... 291
Passerherbulus caudacutus (Leconte's sparrow) ... 270
  henslowi henslowi (western Henslow's sparrow).. 270
  henslowi susurrans (eastern Henslow's sparrow).. 270
Passerina amoena (lazuli bunting).............. 246
  ciris (painted bunting)..................... 251
  cyanea (indigo bunting).................... 246
  versicolor pulchra (beautiful bunting)........ 246
  versicolor versicolor (varied bunting).......... 246

Page

Pauraque, Merrill's...............49; color plate 48
"Peabody bird." See *Sparrow, White-throated*
Pearson, T. Gilbert.........51, 64, 101, 155, 168,
                                  259, 280, 300
Pellets regurgitated by owls.................... 6
Penthestes atricapillus (black-capped chickadee)..... 138
  carolinensis (Carolina chickadee).............. 138
  gambeli (mountain chickadee)................ 138
  hudsonicus (Hudsonian chickadee)............ 138
  hudsonicus hudsonicus (Hudsonian chickadee).... 138
  hudsonicus littoralis (Acadian chickadee)....... 138
  rufescens (chestnut-backed chickadee)......... 138
  sclateri eidos (Mexican chickadee)............ 138
Perisoreus canadensis (Canada jay)............. 127
  canadensis canadensis 127
  canadensis capitalis (Rocky Mountain jay)..... 127
  canadensis fumifrons (Alaska jay)............ 127
  obscurus (Oregon jay)...................... 127
  obscurus griseus (gray jay)................. 127
Petrochelidon albifrons albifrons (northern cliff swal-
  low) 173
Pets, Crows as..................107; ill. 105
Peucedramus olivaceus (olive warbler)........... 207
Pewee
  Eastern wood ....97; color plate 96
  Western wood ....97; color plate 96
Phainopepla................220; color plate 221
  New World origin.....................211, 212
Phainopepla nitens lepida (phainopepla)......... 220
Phalaenoptilus nuttalli (poorwill)............... 49
  nuttalli californicus (dusky poorwill).......... 49
  nuttalli hueyi (desert poorwill).............. 49
  nuttalli nuttalli (Nuttall's poorwill).......... 49
Pharomacrus mocinno (quetzal)................ 79
Pheasant, Ring-necked: Contents of crop......... 88
Phillips, Charles L.......................... 64
Phoebe
  Black ....95; color plate 94
  Eastern ....95; color plate 94
  Say's ....95; color plate 94
Phoebes, Nest building of..................... 298
Photographing birds 248
Pica nuttalli (yellow-billed magpie)............ 114
  pica hudsonia (American magpie)............ 114
Picidae (woodpeckers) 51
Picoides arcticus (Arctic three-toed woodpecker)..... 62
  tridactylus bacatus (American three-toed wood-
    pecker) 62
  tridactylus dorsalis (Alpine three-toed woodpecker) 62
  tridactylus fasciatus (Alaska three-toed wood-
    pecker) 62
Pigments in feathers..............27-28, 235-237
Pike, Nicolas 240
Pilgrims warred on raven..................... 101
Pine, Yellow, storehouse for woodpeckers.......ill. 178
Pinicola enucleator (pine grosbeak)............ 253
Pintails in wire-mesh trap....................ill. 318
Pipilo 259
  aberti (Abert's towhee).................... 266
  erythrophthalmus alleni (white-eyed towhee).... 264
  erythrophthalmus canaster (Alabama towhee).... 264
  erythrophthalmus erythrophthalmus (red-eyed
    towhee) 264
  fuscus crissalis (California towhee)........... 266
  fuscus mesoleucus (cañon towhee)........... 266
  maculatus montanus (spurred towhee)......... 264
Pipit
  American ....177; color plate 176
  Sprague's ....177; color plate 176
Piranga erythromelas (scarlet tanager)........... 240
  flava hepatica (hepatic tanager)............. 242
  ludoviciana (western tanager)............... 242
  rubra cooperi (Cooper's tanager)............ 240
  rubra rubra (summer tanager)............... 240
Pitangus sulphuratus derbianus (Derby flycatcher)... 93
Plectrophenax hyperboreus (McKay's snow bunting).. 297
  nivalis nivalis (eastern snow bunting).......... 297
Ploceidae (weaver finches).................... 238
Plover
  Golden: Migratory flight of ..334, 343, 348; map 327
  Pacific golden: Migratory route of............. 343
Plumage
  Display of male cowbird, 214; Pigments in
  feathers, 27-28, 235-237; Plumage of hummer
  under microscope, 27-28; Wearing out of feathers,
  237, 240
Pluvialis dominica dominica (eastern golden plover)... 343
  dominica fulva (Pacific golden plover).......... 343
Podargidae (frog-mouths)..................... 40
Policeman giving drink to sparrow..............ill. 281
Policemen of the air, Birds are............89, 225
Polioptila caerulea (blue-gray gnatcatcher)......... 153
  melanura californica (black-tailed gnatcatcher)... 153
  melanura melanura (plumbeous gnatcatcher) 153

Page

Pooecetes gramineus confinis (western vesper sparrow). 274
    gramineus gramineus (eastern vesper sparrow)... 274
Poorwill 49
    Desert 49
    Dusky 49
    Nuttall's ....49; color plate 48
    San Ignacio 49
"Preacher-bird." See Vireo, Red-eyed
Predatory pets, Restraint of, protects warblers....... 183
Progne subis (purple martin)........................ 173
Protonotaria citrea (prothonotary warbler).......... 205
Psaltriparus minimus (bush-tit).................... 140
    minimus lloydi (Lloyd's bush-tit).............. 140
Psittacidae (parrots) 75
Ptilogonatidae (phainopeplas) 220
Pugnacity of female hummingbirds................. 29
Pyrocephalus rubinus mexicanus (vermilion flycatcher) 97
Pyrrhuloxia 237, 242
    Arizona ....242; color plate 243
    San Lucas 242
    Texas 242
Pyrrhuloxia sinuata (pyrrhuloxia)................... 242
    sinuata peninsulae (San Lucas pyrrhuloxia)...... 242
    sinuata sinuata (Arizona pyrrhuloxia)........... 242
    sinuata texana (Texas pyrrhuloxia)............. 242

Q

Quail, Florida: Pulling bait releasing camera shutter ill. 349
Quetzal 79
Quiscalus quiscula aeneus (bronzed grackle).......... 231
    quiscula aglaeus (Florida grackle)............... 231
    quiscula quiscula (purple grackle).............. 231

R

Railroads, Beautifying of stations and roadways by... 132
"Rain crow." See Cuckoo, Yellow-billed
Ramphomicron microrhynchum (hummingbird)....... 28
Raven
    American 112
    Northern ....112; color plate 113
    White-necked 112
Ravens
    Feeding habits, 101-102; ill. 109; Folklore con-
    cerning, 101; Mate for life, 104; Nesting habits,
    102-104; ill. 109; Young, ill. 109
Recovery of banded birds ...301, 330, 341, 349, 350,
    351; ill. 304, 313, 319; maps 342, 344
"Redbird." See Cardinal
Redhead, Migratory route of....................... 335
Redpoll
    Common ....255; color plate 254
    Hoary ....255; color plate 254
Redpolls 237, 248, 249, 255
Redstart 199
    American ....color plate 198
    Painted ....207; color plate 206
Redstarts
    Migration route, 332; map 323; Victimized by
    cowbird, ill. 340, 341
Redwing
    Eastern ....233; color plate 232
    Tricolored ....233; color plate 232
Redwings
    Nesting habits, 214, 215; ill. 212, 213; Young,
    ill. 212, 224
Refraction of light in birds' feathers.......27-28, 235-237
Regulus ignicapillus (firecrest)...................... 153
    regulus (goldcrest) 153
    satrapa (golden-crowned kinglet)............... 153
    satrapa olivaceus (western golden-crown kinglet). 153
    satrapa satrapa (eastern golden-crown kinglet).... 153
Regurgitation
    Goldfinch young fed by, 239; Young humming-
    birds fed by, 99; Young of flickers fed by, 65
Rhynchophanes mccowni (McCown's longspur)..... 295
Rhynchopsitta pachyrhyncha (thick-billed parrot).... 80
Riccordia swainsonii (emerald hummingbird)......... 27
"Rice-birds." See Bobolinks
Richmondena cardinalis (cardinal)................... 244
Ridgway, Robert 123
Riparia riparia riparia (bank swallow).............. 175
Road-runner......................78, 82; ill. 78; color plate 83
Roberts, (Dr.) T. S., investigation of longspur catas-
    trophe 297
Robin
    Banded. See Thrush, Varied
    Eastern 160
    Northwestern 160
    San Lucas 160
    Southern 160
    "Swamp." See Thrush, Wood
    Western 160
Robins........155-156, 157, 159, 160; color plate 161
    Protective laws 155

Page

Rook 104
Roosts
    Crow 120-121
    Martin 169
Routes Migratory..333-337, 340-343, 345; maps 305,
    307, 308, 309, 315, 320, 322, 323, 324,
    327, 329, 333, 336, 342, 344
Rowan, (Prof.) William 306
Royal Photographic Society......................... 74

S

Salpinctes obsoletus (rock wren).................... 147
    obsoletus obsoletus (rock wren).................. 147
Sanctuary, Jack Miner's, Kingsville, Ontario......ill. 313
Sappho sapho (long-tailed Sappho hummer)........ 27
Sapsucker 60
    Natalie's 60
    Northern red-breasted ....60; color plate 61
    Red-breasted ....60; color plate 61
    Red-naped 60
    Southern red-breasted 60
    Williamson's ....60; color plate 61
    Yellow-bellied ....60; color plate 61
    Trees tapped by...............................54-55
Sayornis nigricans (black phoebe).................... 95
    phoebe (eastern phoebe)......................... 95
    saya (Say's phoebe).............................. 95
Scoter, White-winged: Migratory route.............. 343
Scotiaptex nebulosa (great gray owl)................ 12
    nebulosa barbata (Siberian gray owl)............ 12
    nebulosa nebulosa (great gray owl).............. 12
Seasonal differences in male plumage................ 237
Seedeater, Sharpe's..................237, 251; color plate 250
Seiurus aurocapillus (oven-bird).................... 184
    motacilla (Louisiana water-thrush).............. 188
    noveboracensis (northern water-thrush)......... 188
Selasphorus alleni (Allen's hummingbird)........... 34
    platycercus platycercus (broad-tailed hummingbird) 34
    rufus (rufous hummingbird)..................... 34
Setopagis parvulus (goatsucker).................... 40
Setophaga picta (painted redstart).................. 207
    ruticilla (redstart) 199
Several species migrate together....................321-324
Sheaths for feathers, Chimney swift's............ill. 30
Sherman, Althea 32
Shiras, George, 3d...............................45, 349
Shrike
    Loggerhead ....220; color plate 221
    Northern ....220; color plate 221
    Northwestern 220
Shrikes: Old World origin..............211, 212-213
Sialia currucoides (mountain bluebird)............. 164
    mexicana (western bluebird)..................... 164
    mexicana bairdi (chestnut-backed bluebird)...... 164
    mexicana occidentalis (western bluebird)........ 164
    sialis sialis (eastern bluebird)................... 164
Siskin
    European 249
    Pine ....249, 255; color plate 254
    Stomach contents 88
Siskins 248, 249
Sitta canadensis (red-breasted nuthatch)........... 142
    carolinensis (white-breasted nuthatch).......... 142
    pusilla (brown-headed nuthatch)................ 142
    pygmaea (pygmy nuthatch).................... 142
Skylark: Attempts to introduce into North America... 212
Smith, (Capt.) John................................ 80
Smithsonian Institution, Washington, D. C.........7, 16
Snake devoured by a road-runner................ill. 78
"Snowbird." See Junco, Slate-colored
"Snowflake." See Bunting, Eastern snow
Solitaire, Townsend's..................160; color plate 161
Songs and calls
    Grosbeaks and finches............................ 239
    Hermit thrush........................158-159, 168
    Mockingbird 168
    Sparrows 260-261, 280
    Wrens 145
Spain, Bird lover's paradise found in................ 135
Sparrow
    Acadian 272
    Aleutian song ....293; color plate 292
    Bachman's ....276; color plate 277
    Baird's ....270; color plate 271
    Belding's ....268; color plate 269
    Bell's ....278; color plate 279
    Botteri's ....276; color plate 277
    Brewer's ....287; color plate 286
    California black-chinned.........287; color plate 286
    California sage..................................... 278
    Cape Sable seaside..............272; color plate 273
    Cassin's ....276; color plate 277
    Chipping 260
    Nesting habits.................................... 260

Page

Sparrow—Continued

Clay-colored ....287; color plate 286
Desert ....276; ill. 262; color plate 277
Desert song................293; color plate 292
Dusky seaside................272; color plate 273
Eastern chipping...........285; color plate 284
Eastern field................285; color plate 284
Eastern fox................291; color plate 290
Eastern grasshopper...........270; color plate 271
Eastern Henslow's............270; color plate 271
Eastern lark.............................274
Eastern Savannah........268; color plate 269
Eastern song................293; color plate 292
Eastern tree...............285; color plate 284
Eastern vesper............274; color plate 275
English. See *Sparrow, House*
Field 261, 285
Florida grasshopper.......................270
Fox ....ill. 263
Gambel's ....289; color plate 288
Golden-crowned ....287; color plate 286
Harris's ....289; color plate 288
  Migration of..........................332
House..........237, 240, 280; ill. 238, 262, 263;
  color plate 241
Ipswich ....268; color plate 269
Large-billed ....268; color plate 269
Leconte's ....270; color plate 271
Lincoln's ....295; color plate 294
Nelson's 272
Northern sage.............278; color plate 279
Northern seaside..........272; color plate 273
Pine-woods 276
Rufous-winged ....274; color plate 275
Scott's ....274; color plate 275
Sharp-tailed ....272; color plate 273
Song ....260-261, 293; ill. 263
  Range and subspecies, 261; Singing of, 260-261
Sooty fox.................291; color plate 290
Sooty song................293; color plate 292
Stephens's fox............291; color plate 290
Swamp ....295; color plate 294
Texas ....264; color plate 265
Tree ....280, 285; ill. 263
  Song of...............................280
Western chipping..........................285
Western field............................285
Western grasshopper.......................270
Western Henslow's.........................270
Western lark...............274; color plate 275
Western vesper............................274
White-crowned ....289; color plate 288
  Nest and eggs........................ill. 263
White-throated ...261, 291; ill. 263; color plate 290
  Nesting habits and migration, 261; Range of, 350; Song of, 261
Worthen's ....285; color plate 284
Sparrows ......260-265, 268-281, 284-295; ill. 263, 281
  Nesting habits, 261; ill. 263; Rectrices in tail, 280; Size, 280; Sparrow overcome by heat, ill. 281; Variety in North America, 280; Weeds destroyed by, 89
Spathura (racket-tailed hummers)..................28
Speed champions of bird world, Swifts are..........30-31
Speed of flight and migration...........313-314, 316-317
Speotyto cunicularia (burrowing owl)...............21
  cunicularia floridana (Florida burrowing owl)....21
  cunicularia hypugaea (western burrowing owl)....21
Sphyrapicus thyroideus (Williamson's sapsucker)....60
  thyroideus nataliae (Natalie's sapsucker)........60
  varius (sapsucker)..............................60
  varius daggetti (southern red-breasted sapsucker)..60
  varius nuchalis (rep-naped sapsucker)...........60
  varius ruber (northern red-breasted sapsucker)...60
  varius varius (yellow-bellied sapsucker).........60
Spinus lawrencei (Lawrence's goldfinch)...........257
  pinus (pine siskin).............................255
  psaltria (green-backed goldfinch)...............257
  tristis (goldfinch).............................255
  tristis pallidus (pale goldfinch)...............255
  tristis salicamans (willow goldfinch)...........255
Spiza americana (dickcissel).....................251
Spizella arborea arborea (eastern tree sparrow)....285
  arborea ochracea (western tree sparrow)........285
  atrogularis atrogularis (black-chinned sparrow)..287
  atrogularis cana (California black-chinned sparrow) 287
  breweri breweri (Brewer's sparrow)..............287
  pallida (clay-colored sparrow)..................287
  passerina arizonae (western chipping sparrow)...285
  passerina passerina (eastern chipping sparrow)..285
  pusilla arenacea (western field sparrow)........285
  pusilla pusilla (eastern field sparrow).........285
  wortheni (Worthen's sparrow)....................285
Sporophila morelleti sharpei (Sharpe's seedeater)....251

Page

Starling ....209; color plate 208
  Raided by barn owls, 16; Spread of, in United States, 212
State birds 225
Steele, E. S..............................14
Stellula calliope (Calliope hummingbird)............34
Stomachs, Capacity of birds'...................88-89
Storehouses for woodpeckers, Fence posts and trees are ....ill. 53, 178
Storms, Birds victims of................346-347
Strange habits of kingfishers.....................79
Strigidae (owls) 5
Strigiformes (owls) 5
Strix occidentalis (spotted owl)..................14
  occidentalis caurina (northern spotted owl)......14
  occidentalis lucida (Mexican spotted owl)........14
  occidentalis occidentalis (California spotted owl)..14
  varia (barred owl)..............................14
  varia alleni (Florida barred owl)...............14
  varia helveola (Texas barred owl)...............14
  varia varia (northern barred owl)...............14
Sturnella magna argutula (southern meadowlark).....216
  magna hoopesi (Rio Grande meadowlark)..........216
  magna magna (eastern meadowlark)..............216
  neglecta (western meadowlark)............209, 216
Sturnus vulgaris vulgaris (starling)..............209
Surnia ulula caparoch (American hawk owl)........21
Swallow
  Bank ....169, 175; color plate 174
    Flight of, ill. 159; Stomach contents, 88
  Barn ....173; color plate 172
    Nesting habits, 169; Silhouette of, ill. 156
  Cliff ....color plate 172
    Colony of nests, 169; ill. 154; Migratory route, 317; map 308; Stomach contents, 88
  Eave. See *Swallow, Cliff*
  Northern cliff 173
  Rough-winged ....color plate 174
  Tree ....175; color plate 174
    Nesting habits, 169; Stomach contents, 88
  Violet-green ....175; color plate 174
Swallows 168-169, 173-175
"Swamp robin." See *Thrush, Wood*
Swift
  Black ....43; color plate 42
  Chimney ....43; ill. 30, 31; color plate 42
    Screen trap for capture of, ill. 302; Winter home of, 301
  Cloud 30
  Tree 30
  Vaux's ....43; color plate 42
  White-throated ....43; color plate 42
Swiftlets 31
Swifts 29-31, 43
  Bill, 29-30; Feeding habits, 31; Nearest relatives of hummingbirds, 29; Nesting habits, 31; ill. 31; Sheaths for feathers, ill. 30; Speed champions of bird world, 30; Young, ill. 31
Sylviidae (warblers) 153, 179

T

Table showing fruit-bearing shrubs and trees that attract birds......................132-133
Tachycineta thalassina lepida (violet-green swallow)..175
Tailor-birds 153
Tanager
  Cooper's 240
  Hepatic ....237, 242; color plate 243
  Scarlet ..236-237, 240, 249; ill. 236; color plate 241
    Feeding young, ill. 236; Migration range, 332; map 320
  Summer ....237, 239, 240, 249; color plate 241
  Swallow 236
  Western ....237, 242; color plate 243
    Migration and range of............343; map 336
Tanagers 235-238, 240-243, 249
  Coloring, 236-237; East and west species, 237; Nesting habits, 238, 249
Tangavius aeneus (red-eyed cowbird)..............209
  aeneus involucratus (bronzed cowbird)..........209
Tarin. See *Siskin, European*
Telmatodytes palustris (long-billed marsh wren)......151
Tern
  Arctic ....ill. 317
    Eggs, ill. 317; Long migratory route, 329-330, 343; map 315
  Black: Removing egg shell from nest.........ill. 316
  Caspian: Corralled for banding.............ill. 319
Theories of migration....................303-310
"Thistle bird." See *Goldfinch, Eastern*

Page

Thrasher
Bendire's ....171; color plate 170
Brown ....166; color plate 167
Rigid in palm of hand, ill. 331; Song of, 168
Brownsville 166
California ....171; color plate 170
Crissal ....171; color plate 170
Curve-billed ....166; color plate 167
Desert 171
Leconte's ....171; color plate 170
Palmer's 166
Sage ....166; color plate 167
Thrashers 166-168, 171
Song of 180
Thrush
Bicknell's 162
On kitchen table.................ill. 182
Gray-cheeked ....162; color plate 163
Rapid migration of............314; map 306
Hermit ....157, 162; color plate 163
Song of 158
Olive-backed ....162; color plate 163
Russet-backed 162
Varied ....160; color plate 161
Willow 162
Wood ....162; color plate 163
Song of 158-159
See also Water-thrush
Thrushes 155-162
Songs of 158-159, 180
Thryomanes bewicki (Bewick's wren) 149
Thryothorus ludovicianus (Carolina wren).......... 147
ludovicianus miamensis (Florida wren).......... 147
"Tip-up, Yellow." See Warbler, Palm
Titmice 135, 136
Absence from Panama..................... 211
Titmouse
Black-crested ....136; color plate 137
Blue 135
Bridled ....136; color plate 137
Greater 135
Marsh 135
Plain ....136; color plate 137
Sennett's 136
Tufted ....136; color plate 137
"Tomtit." See Titmouse, Tufted
Tongue of flicker...................... 64
Towhee
Abert's ....266; color plate 267
Alabama 264
Arctic 264
Brown 259-260, 266
Varieties 260
California ....266; color plate 267
Cañon ....266; color plate 267
Cape Colnett 264
Green 259
Green-tailed ....266; color plate 267
Large-billed 264
Nevada 264
Oregon 264
Red-eyed ....259, 264; color plate 265
Sacramento 264
San Clemente 264
San Diego 264
San Francisco 264
Spurred ....264; color plate 265
White-eyed 264
Towhees 259-260, 264-267
Feeding habits, 259, 260; Size, 280; Species in
North America, 259
Toxostoma bendirei (Bendire's thrasher)............ 171
curvirostre (curve-billed thrasher)........... 166
curvirostre oberholseri (Brownsville thrasher).... 166
curvirostre palmeri (Palmer's thrasher)........ 166
dorsale dorsale (crissal thrasher)............... 171
lecontei arenicola (desert thrasher)........... 171
lecontei lecontei (Leconte's thrasher)........ 171
redivivum redivivum (California thrasher)....... 171
rufum (brown thrasher)...................... 166
Traps
"Gathering cage," ill. 321; Hunters operating clap
net, ill. 338; Mallards and pintails in wire-mesh
trap, ill. 318; Raided by owls, 16; Scientific trap
for catching chimney swifts, ill. 302
Tree, woodpecker's storehouse.............. ill. 178
Trees injured by sapsuckers.................. 54-55
Trees preserved by insect-eating birds.......... 179, 183
Trochilidae (hummingbirds) 27
Troglodytes aëdon (house wren) 149
aëdon aëdon (eastern house wren)............. 149
aëdon parkmani (western house wren).......... 149
Troglodytidae (wren family)................. 145
Trogon, Coppery-tailed ....84; color plate 85
Trogon ambiguus ambiguus (coppery-tailed trogon)... 84

Page

Trogonidae (trogons) 79
Trogons 79, 84
Tropics, Birds found in..................... 211
Turdidae (thrushes) 157
Turdus migratorius (robin).................. 160
migratorius achrusterus (southern robin)........ 160
migratorius caurinus (northwestern robin)....... 160
migratorius confinis (San Lucas robin)........ 160
migratorius migratorius (eastern robin) 160
migratorius propinquus (western robin)....... 160
Tyrannidae (flycatchers) 79
Tyrannus dominicensis dominicensis (gray kingbird).. 91
melancholicus couchi (Couch's kingbird)........ 91
tyrannus (eastern kingbird).................. 91
verticalis (Arkansas kingbird)................ 91
vociferans (Cassin's kingbird)................ 91
Tyto alba pratincola (barn owl)............... 10
Tytonidae (barn owls)...................... 5

V

Veery ....162; color plate 163
Verdin ....140; color plate 141
Feeding young, ill. 134; Nest, ill. 134
Vermivora bachmani (Bachman's warbler)........... 205
celata celata (orange-crowned warbler)......... 201
chrysoptera (golden-winged warbler).......... 201
luciae (Lucy's warbler)................... 205
peregrina (Tennessee warbler)............... 194
pinus (blue-winged warbler)................. 201
ruficapilla ridgwayi (Calaveras warbler)........ 194
ruficapilla ruficapilla (Nashville warbler)....... 194
virginiae (Virginia's warbler)................ 205
Vertical migration of birds....................339, 345
Vireo
Blue-headed ....222; color plate 223
Hutton's ....222; color plate 223
Least ....222; color plate 223
Red-eyed ....222; ill. 210; color plate 223
Warbling ....222; color plate 223
White-eyed ....222; color plate 223
Yellow-throated ....222; ill. 258; color plate 223
Nest and eggs.................ill. 258
Vireo belli (least vireo)................... 222
flavifrons (yellow-throated vireo)............. 222
gilvus (warbling vireo).................... 222
griseus griseus (white-eyed vireo)............. 222
huttoni huttoni (Hutton's vireo)............. 222
olivaceus (red-eyed vireo)................. 222
solitarius (blue-headed vireo)................ 222
Vireos 222
Migration, 213; New World origin, 211, 212

W

Wallace, (Mr. and Mrs.) George J., Bicknell's thrush
kept by ....ill. 182
Warbler
Audubon's ....199; color plate 198
Bachman's ....205; color plate 204
Bay-breasted ....190; color plate 191
Black and white........199; color plate 198
Breeding range, 310; Pictured on a shoe,
ill. 181; Speed of migration, 310; map 307
Black and yellow. See Warbler, Magnolia
Black-capped. See Warbler, Wilson's
Black-poll ....192; ill. 311; color plate 193
Nest, ill. 311; Speed of migratory flight, 316;
map 309
Black-throated blue ...194; ill. 196; color plate 195
Black-throated gray .....190; color plate 191
Black-throated green ....190; color plate 191
Blackburnian ....192; color plate 193
Blue-winged ....201; color plate 200
Cairns's 194
Calaveras 194
Canada ....186; color plate 187
Cape May ....194; color plate 195
Cerulean ....203; color plate 202
Chestnut-sided ....192; color plate 193
Connecticut ....186; color plate 187
Florida pine 190
Golden-cheeked ....207; color plate 206
Golden-winged ....201; color plate 200
Grace's ....203; color plate 202
Hermit ....207; color plate 206
Hooded ....186; color plate 187
Kentucky ....188; color plate 189
Kirtland's ....203; color plate 202
Lucy's ....205; color plate 204
Macgillivray's ....186; color plate 187
Magnolia ....192; color plate 193
Mourning ....186; color plate 187
Myrtle ....199, 203; color plate 202
Migrating warbler aboard ship..........ill. 325

Page

Warbler—*Continued*
Nashville ....194; color plate 195
Olive ....207; color plate 206
Orange-crowned ....201; color plate 200
Palm ....188; color plate 189
Parula ....194; color plate 195
Pine ....190; color plate 191
Prairie ....188; color plate 189
Prothonotary ....205; color plate 204
Red-faced ....184; color plate 185
Swainson's ....205; color plate 204
Sycamore 203
Tennessee ....194; color plate 195
Townsend's ....207; color plate 206
Virginia's ....205; color plate 204
Wayne's 190
Wilson's ....186; color plate 187
Worm-eating ....201; color plate 200
Yellow ....199; color plate 198
   Gathering wool for nest, ill. 197; Reflection
   in mirror, ill. 197
Yellow palm.................188; color plate 189
Yellow-rumped. See *Warbler, Myrtle*
Yellow-throated ....203; color plate 202
Warblers 53, 179-207
   Insects destroyed by, 179, 183; Migration of, 180-
   181; Song of, 179-180
Water hole, Crows at, Ithaca, New York..........ill. 107
Water-thrush
Louisiana ....188; color plate 189
Northern ....188; color plate 189
   Habitat of ....ill. 196
Waxwing
Bohemian ....220; color plate 221
   Invasions of 346
Cedar ....220; ill. 234; color plate 221
Japanese 220
Waxwings
   Feeding young, ill. 234; Old World origin, 211,
   212-213
Wearing out of feathers.....................237, 240
Weaver birds. See *Finches, Weaver*
Webster, (Mr. and Mrs.) Laurence J. 354
Wetmore, Alexander..........5, 16, 27, 40, 75, 135, 145
Wheelock, Irene Grosvenor, quoted on California jay.. 129
Whippoorwill 41, 45
Eastern ....45; color plate 44
Stephens's 45
Whippoorwills 41
"Whiskey Jack." See *Jay, Canada*
"Wild Acres," Maryland, birds observed at......298-299
Wild parrots in United States.................... 75
Wilsonia canadensis (Canada warbler).............. 186
   citrina (hooded warbler) 186
   pusilla chryseola (western Wilson's warbler).... 186
   pusilla pusilla (Wilson's warbler).............. 186
Winter coloring of plumage...........237, 248; ill. 238
Woodpecker
Alaska three-toed 62
Alpine three-toed 62
American three-toed ....62; color plate 63
Arctic three-toed ....62; color plate 63
Arizona ....58; color plate 59
Brewster's 71
California ....67; color plate 66
   Storehouses of ....ill. 53
Cardón 71
Downy ....51, 56; ill. 53
Florida pileated 73
Gairdner's ....56; color plate 57

Woodpecker—*Continued*
Gila ....71; color plate 70
Golden-fronted ....71; color plate 70
Hairy ....56; ill. 50, 52; color plate 57
Harris's ....56; color plate 57
Ivory-billed ....54, 65, 73; color plate 72
Ladder-backed 58
Lewis's ....67; color plate 66
Northern downy ....56; color plate 57
Northern pileated ....73; color plate 72
Northern white-headed ....62; color plate 63
Nuttall's ....58; color plate 59
Pileated ....65, 73; ill. 54
   Borings made by ....ill. 52
Red-bellied ....71; color plate 70
Red-cockaded ....58; color plate 59
Red-headed ....64, 67; color plate 66
Southern pileated 73
Texas ....58; color plate 59
Three-toed: Foot of.......................ill. 52
Western pileated 73
White-headed ....62; color plate 63
"Zebra." See *Woodpecker, Red-bellied*
Woodpeckers 51-73
   Barbed tongue, ill. 50; Borings made by, 52-53;
   ill. 52, 54; Eggs in nest laid on chips, 157;
   Family easily recognized, 51; Feet, 53; ill. 52;
   Nesting habits, 51, 53; Species and subspecies, 52
Wren
Bewick's ....149; color plate 148
Cactus ....145, 147; color plate 146
Cañon ....145, 147; color plate 146
Carolina ....145, 147; color plate 146
Eastern house ....149; color plate 148
Florida 147
House ....145, 149; color plate 148
"Jenny." See *Wren, House*
Long-billed marsh ....151; color plate 150
Marsh 145
"Mocking." See *Wren, Carolina*
Rock ....145, 147; color plate 146
Short-billed marsh ....151; color plate 150
Western house ....149; color plate 148
   Entering house with twig...............ill. 359
Winter ....145, 149; color plate 148
Wren-tit ....140; color plate 141
Wrens ....145-151; ill. 144
Songs of 145

X

Xanthocephalus xanthocephalus (yellow-headed black-
   bird) 233
Xanthoura luxuosa glaucescens (green jay).......... 123
Xantus, John 36

Y

"Yellow bird." See *Warbler, Yellow*
Yellow-hammer. See *Flicker, Yellow-shafted*
Yellow-rump. See *Warbler, Myrtle*
Yellow-throat, Maryland............184; color plate 185

Z

Zonotrichia albicollis (white-throated sparrow)...... 291
   coronata (golden-crowned sparrow)............. 287
   leucophrys gambeli (Gambel's sparrow)......... 289
   leucophrys leucophrys (white-crowned sparrow).. 289
   querula (Harris's sparrow)................... 289

OTHER AUTHORITATIVE PUBLICATIONS OF THE SOCIETY

These maps and pictures—as well as the books listed in back of Vol. I—may be obtained only from the National Geographic Society. *Prices below include postage in United States and Possessions; for mailing to other countries, add 25c per item. Shipment abroad of framed pictures is not advised. To minimize expense and reduce costs, it is requested that remittance accompany order.*

MAPS

NOTED FOR READABILITY—ACCURACY—REFERENCE VALUE

British Isles: 29 x 35 inches; decorative design; ten colors; drawings of illustrious Britons, famous places, armorial ensigns; directing symbols to cathedral towns, charming villages, castles, churches, abbeys, battlefields, monuments, etc. *Paper, 50c; linen, $1.*

Pacific Ocean: 38 x 31 inches; ten colors; includes 73 large-scale insets of the multitudinous islands and harbors. Shows reef formations, time zones, and principal airway and steamship routes, distances. *Paper, 50c; linen, 75c. Index, 25c additional.*

Canada: 40 x 27 inches; ten colors; shows important highways, railroads, main routes of exploration, general elevation, topography of former blind spot areas, time zones, etc. *Paper, 50c; linen, 75c. Index, 25c additional.*

The World: 23 x 44 inches; ten colors; drawn in two hemispheres; shows railways and airlines of importance, official spellings, recent boundary readjustments, and new discoveries. *Paper, 50c.*

Africa: 29 x 31½ inches; ten colors; 7,162 place names; shows changed political boundaries, new railway routes, highways, other important data. *Paper, 50c; linen, 75c. Index, 25c additional.*

Mexico, Central America, West Indies: 24 x 41 inches; ten colors; 5,460 place names; large-scale insets of Cuba, Canal Zone, Bermuda Islands, Jamaica, Puerto Rico and Virgin Islands. *Paper, 50c; linen, 75c. Index, 25c additional.*

United States: 40¾ x 26¾ inches; ten colors; includes adjoining portions of Canada and Mexico; shows States, towns, highways, railways, national parks, rivers, etc.; 8,686 place names. *Paper, 50c. Index, 25c additional.*

Asia: 38¼ x 31 inches; ten colors; 6,500 place names. *Paper, 50c; linen, 75c. Index, 25c additional.*

Europe and the Near East: Of timely importance; 39 x 34¼ inches; ten colors; 9,000 hand-lettered place names; local official names and English equivalents. *Paper, 50c. Index, 25c additional.*

The Antarctic Regions: 26½ x 19¾ inches; four colors. *Paper, 50c.*

The Arctic Regions: 20⅛ x 18⅞ inches; seven colors. *Paper, 50c.*

North America: 28 x 38¼ inches; ten colors; large-scale showing of Canada and Arctic. *Paper, 50c.*

South America: 28 x 38¾ inches; six colors; insets show products, climate, etc. *Paper, 50c.*

PICTURES

LARGE-SCALE PRINTS IDEAL FOR WALL DISPLAY

Curvature of the Earth: Photograph taken from *Explorer II* at the highest altitude ever reached by man; shows for the first time the division between the troposphere and stratosphere and also the actual curvature of the earth; black gravure. *Unframed print, 23 x 14¼ inches, 50c.*

The Discoverer: N. C. Wyeth depicts the Explorer as he contemplates the goal of his dreams; in full color. *Unframed print, 30 x 8 inches, $1.00; framed, 34⅞ x 13, $5.00.*

Columbus Finds a New World: Tiny caravels sailing into a radiant dawn; N. C. Wyeth's painting reproduced in colors. *Unframed print, 11⅞ x 7⅞ inches, 50c; framed, 16½ x 12¾, $3.00.*

Western and Eastern Hemispheres: N. C. Wyeth's two maps of Discovery, superbly illuminated in color, giving 15th-century chart effect, show the routes of great explorers from Marco Polo (1271) to Peary (1909). *Unframed print, 18 x 15⅞ inches, each Hemisphere, 50c; framed, 19½ x 17½, each Hemisphere, $4.00.*

Byrd at the North Pole: N. C. Wyeth's brilliant painting embodies the spirit of Admiral Byrd's Arctic flight; in full color. *Unframed print, 11⅞ x 8 inches, 50c; framed, 16½ x 12¾, $3.00.*

Majesty of the Matterhorn: In black and white. *Unframed print, 23 x 17⅜ inches, 50c; framed, 26½ x 20⅞, $4.00.*

The Argosy of Geography: A "square-rigger" with full sail spreading; marine-blue graphotint. *Unframed print, 20⅞ x 15 inches, $1.00; framed, 24¼ x 18¾, $5.00.*

Greater New York: An aërial photograph encompassing 3,000 square miles; dark green gravure. *Unframed print, 22 x 17¼ inches, 50c.*

"The Oldest Living Thing": General Sherman Tree in Sequoia National Park; green photogravure. *Unframed print, 9⅜ x 23 inches, 50c; framed, 11¾ x 25½, $4.00.*

Hark!: George Shiras 3d's prize photograph of a wild buck; woodland sepia. *Unframed print, 11¾ x 8⅛ inches, 50c; framed, 14⅝ x 10⅞, $3.00.*

Doe and Twin Fawns: Mr. Shiras' prize-winning companion picture to "Hark!"; woodland sepia. *Unframed print, 11¾ x 8⅛ inches, 50c; framed, 14⅝ x 10⅞, $3.00.*

The Palms: On the banks of the ancient Nile; sepia photogravure. *Unframed print, 8⅜ x 22⅛ inches, 50c; framed, 11⅛ x 24¼, $3.00.*

NATIONAL GEOGRAPHIC SOCIETY, WASHINGTON, D. C.

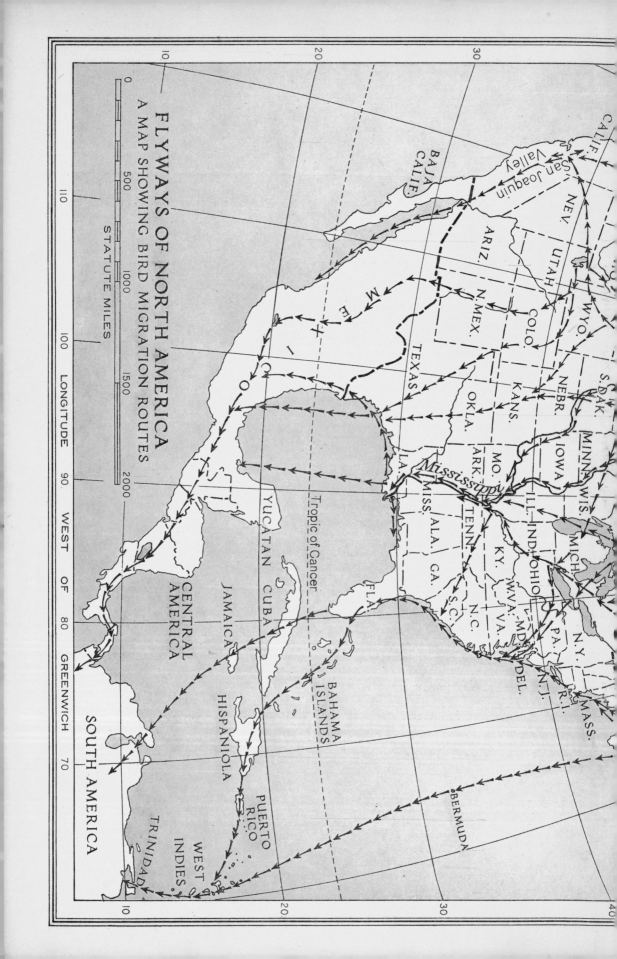

FLYWAYS OF NORTH AMERICA
A MAP SHOWING BIRD MIGRATION ROUTES

STATUTE MILES

0   500   1000   1500   2000

110   LONGITUDE   100   WEST   90   OF   80   GREENWICH   70

10   20   30   40

BAJA CALIF.

CALIF.

NEV.

UTAH

San Joaquin Valley

ARIZ.

N. MEX.

COLO.

WYO.

S. DAK.

NEBR.

IOWA

MINN.

WIS.

MICH.

KANS.

OKLA.

TEXAS

MO.

ARK.

LA.

MISS.

ALA.

GA.

TENN.

KY.

ILL.

IND.

OHIO

W. VA.

VA.

MD.

DEL.

PA.

N.Y.

N.J.

R.I.

MASS.

N.C.

S.C.

FLA.

Mississippi

MEXICO

Tropic of Cancer

YUCATAN

CENTRAL AMERICA

CUBA

JAMAICA

HISPANIOLA

BAHAMA ISLANDS

BERMUDA

PUERTO RICO

WEST INDIES

TRINIDAD

SOUTH AMERICA